MUSIC IN AMERICA

MUSIC IN AMERICA

An Anthology from the Landing of the Pilgrims to the Close of the Civil War. 1620-1865

Compiled and Edited, with Historical and Analytical Notes, by

W. THOMAS MARROCCO

PROFESSOR OF MUSIC, UNIVERSITY OF CALIFORNIA AT LOS ANGELES

and

HAROLD GLEASON

FORMER DIRECTOR OF GRADUATE STUDIES,
EASTMAN SCHOOL OF MUSIC OF THE UNIVERSITY OF ROCHESTER

W · W · NORTON & COMPANY · INC · NEW YORK

Library of Congress Catalog Card No. 62-8635

Published simultaneously in Canada by
George J. McLeod Limited, Toronto

PRINTED IN THE UNITED STATES OF AMERICA

3 4 5 6 7 8 9 0

Contents

Illustrations

Between pages 246–247

Preface

THIS *Anthology* is designed for the use of all who are interested in the growth of music in America, the teacher, student, layman, scholar, and above all the performer. Between its covers are presented musical compositions spanning nearly 250 years, attesting to a surprising amount of activity in all media, and conceived within a periphery extending from Massachusetts to Georgia, Louisiana, and Ohio. Drawing from an extensive body of metrical psalms, psalm-settings, sacred and secular choral works, solo songs, keyboard pieces, opera, and music for small instrumental groups, the editors have endeavored to present a panorama of musical landmarks which have played an important part in the religious, social, and cultural life of our country.

The music, presented in an approximate chronology, has been selected on the basis of its artistic significance and musico-historical importance in American history from 1620 until the close of the Civil War in 1865. Special emphasis has been placed on music by native American composers. The problem of selection has been a thorny one. Some will question the absence of a piece particularly favored, and others will note that many compositions of undoubted merit and historical value have been omitted. No attempt has been made to include the music of "New Spain," folk music, tribal music of the American Indian, music of the Negro, Gospel songs, ragtime, blues, jazz, or the music of many religious sects, including the Quakers, Mennonites, Pietists, Dunkards, and others.

All the music in the *Anthology*, with the exception of the chapter devoted to the music of the Moravians, has been taken from the original edition or manuscripts, or from photocopies of these sources. Most of the music is from the first editions, in which it appears with the *words* and *music* as given in the *Anthology*. Variants are indicated in the footnotes.

The editors have endeavored to present the music as closely to the original as possible, retaining the original keys, dynamic indications, time signatures, note values, barring, and the order of the voices in part-music.

The original spelling and capitalization of the texts have been preserved, except for spelling out abbreviated words and substituting the modern "s" for "f." The often haphazard punctuation of the texts in the early music has been retained as far as practical, with additions and revisions provided when necessary to clarify the thought and phrasing. We use the Kings James numbering of the psalms.

To facilitate reading, the C-clef, frequently used in the early psalters and tunebooks, has been changed to the G-clef. The diamond-shaped notes of the early psalters and tunebooks, and the shape-notes used in Southern folk hymnody have been transcribed into conventional notation. Most of the homophonic part-music, which was originally written in open score, has been transcribed into close score, with the original voices carefully identified. When the voice parts are printed in score, a piano reduction with conventional time signatures has been provided.

Accidentals found in the original are placed before the note affected, and the few accidentals which were missing in the original have been placed above the notes. All corrections of misprints and doubtful notes have been indicated in footnotes. Slurs have been added in the vocal parts when omitted in the original version.

Two or more stanzas of the text have been included occasionally in order to give a better idea of the quality of the poetry, for purposes of comparison, or to complete the thought of the poem. The name of the composer is placed at the right of the title; the name of the author or source of the text is placed at the end of the composition. The source of the music is placed at the left of the title.

Finally, only complete compositions have been presented except in multi-movement works when, because of limitations of space, only one or two movements appear in the *Anthology*.

The commentaries are in no way intended to be a history of music in America or a detailed analysis of the music. It is the hope of the editors, however, that they will furnish sufficient background to stimulate extensive supplementary study. Biographical notes on the composers are included in the Appendix.

Those who wish to increase their knowledge and appreciation of early music in America will find available many books and periodicals with important scholarly contributions by leading authorities in the field. Books with general bibliographies include *America's Music* by Gilbert Chase (McGraw-Hill Book Co., New York); *American Music from 1620–1920* (Music Literature Outlines, Series III) by Harold Gleason (Levis Music Store, Rochester, New York); *The History of American Church Music* by Leonard Ellinwood (Morehouse-Gorham Co., New York); and *Our American Music* by John Tasker Howard (Thomas Y. Crowell, New York).

There remains the pleasant duty of acknowledging the aid of the many persons and institutions without whose co-operation this *Anthology* would never have become a reality.

We are especially grateful to Mr. Irving Lowens of the Music Division of the Library of Congress, who has followed the progress of this *Anthology* from the beginning and has been most generous with his help and advice, and to Dr. Donald M. McCorkle, Director of the Moravian Music Foundation, and Boosey and Hawkes, Inc. for making available the music of the Moravians.

Our sincere thanks also go to Dr. Leonard Ellinwood and the late Rev. Dr. Maurice Frost; to Dr. Harold Spivacke, Mr. Edward N. Waters, and Dr. Donald W. Krummel of the Music Division of the Library of Congress; Mr. Frank C. Campbell and Mr. Harold Merkleen of the New York Public Library; Dr. Ruth Watanabe and Miss Elizabeth Smith of the Sibley Music Library, University of Rochester; Dr. Wayne Barlow of the Eastman School of Music, University of Rochester; Dr. Zoltán Haraszti and Miss Ellen M. Oldham of the Boston Public Library; The Henry E. Huntington Library, San Marino, California; Mr. Stephen T. Riley, Massachusetts Historical Society, Boston; Dr. Brooks Shepard, Jr., Mr. George Nally, and Miss Reva B. Schwartz of the Yale University Library, New Haven, Connecticut; The Library Company of Philadelphia; Mrs. Marian Clarke and Mr. Donald B. Engley of the Watkinson Library, Trinity College, Hartford, Connecticut; Dr. Howard H. Peckham of the William L. Clements Library of American History and Dr. Allen P. Britton of the University of Michigan, Ann Arbor; The American Antiquarian Society, Worcester, Massachusetts; Mr. S. Foster Damon and Mr. David A. Jonah of the John Hay Library, Brown University, Providence, R.I.; The Johns Hopkins University Library, Baltimore, Maryland; The Rollins College Library, Winter Park, Florida; The Provost and Fellows of King's College, Cambridge, England; The Trustees of the British Museum; Mr. Walter Hinrichsen, President of the C. F. Peters Corporation; Mr. Wilbur Smith of the University of California, Special Collections Library, Los Angeles; and the Worcester Historical Society,

Worcester, Massachusetts.

We wish here to express our appreciation to Sig. Arturo Monzardo of Milan, Italy, for his painstaking work in copying the music.

Finally our sincere thanks go to Dr. Paul Henry Lang, and to Mr. Nathan Broder and other members of the staff of W. W. Norton & Company, and especially to Mr. Robert E. Farlow who realized the need for this *Anthology* and has followed its progress with patience and understanding.

W. Thomas Marrocco
Harold Gleason

June, 1963

MUSIC IN AMERICA

Chapter One

METRICAL PSALMODY IN NEW ENGLAND

1620-1720

The Ainsworth Psalter

> Open wide in her lap lay the well-worn psalm-book of Ainsworth,
> Printed in Amsterdam, the words and music together,
> Rough-hewn, angular notes, like stones in the wall of a churchyard,
> Darkened and overhung by the running vine of the verses.
>
> *The Courtship of Miles Standish* by Henry Wadsworth Longfellow

DURING the first hundred years, the church music of the Puritans in America was confined to the unaccompanied unison singing of the metrical versions of the psalms as found in the various editions of the Ainsworth Psalter, the Sternhold and Hopkins Psalter, and the *Bay Psalm Book*. The more musically inclined Puritans doubtless sang psalm-tunes in harmony at home and possibly used some instrumental accompaniments. This is evinced by the fact that they knew, among others, Thomas Ravenscroft's psalter (1621), with the tunes "composed into 4. parts," and Richard Allison's psalter (1599) with the tune "to be sung and plaide vpon the Lute, Orpharyon, Citterne or Base Violl, seuerally or altogether, the singing part to be either Tenor or Treble to the Instrument, according to the nature of the voyce, or for fowre voyces."

When the Pilgrims left Delfthaven in 1620, on the first part of their journey to the New World, they brought with them a psalter prepared by the Biblical scholar, Henry Ainsworth (c. 1570–1623), for the use of the Puritan "Separatists" who had fled to Holland to escape religious intolerance. The title page of the Ainsworth Psalter reads as follows:

THE BOOK OF PSALMES: Englished both in Prose and Metre. *With Annotations, opening the words and sentences, by conference with other scriptures.* By *H. A.*
Ephe. 5.18.19.
Be ye filled with the Spirit: speaking to your selves in Psalms, and hymnes, and spiritual Songs: singing & making melodie in your hart to the Lord. Imprinted at Amsterdam, By GILES THORP. A°. D^{i}. 1612.

The psalter contained 39 different melodies for the 150 psalms which Ainsworth set in meter. Ainsworth took the tunes from 16th-century English (Sternhold and Hopkins) and Dutch psalters, the latter being musically identical with the French.[1] The tunes selected for the *Anthology* were originally French (*Psalms 7, 8, 100*—Nos. 1, 2, 5), English (*Psalm 15*, No. 3), or German (*Psalm 34*, No. 4).

The tune used for *Psalm* 7 (No. 1) originally appeared in Calvin's first Psalter (Strasbourg, 1539), set to Clément Marot's French versification of *Psalm 130* (No. 1a). This psalter contained eighteen psalms, six with texts translated by Calvin, the remaining twelve by Marot. Ainsworth based his version of the tune on Sternhold and Hopkins, but divided the penultimate note in alternate lines in order to provide for the eight syllables in his text.

The famous tune for *Psalm 100*, known to all English-speaking people as "Old 100th," has been preserved intact from its first appearance in 1551 to the present time. It will, however, be noticed that the rhythmic pattern of the original tune, as set to *Psalm 134* (No. 5a), varies slightly from each of the other tunes. Other versions of *Psalm 100* may be found later in this chapter and in Chapter Two. The four-part setting of *Psalm 100* by William Parsons (No. 5b) is the first harmonization of the tune by an English composer. Parsons set William Kethe's well-known text which Kethe made in 1561 for the Anglo-Genevan Psalter by "Thomas Sterneholde and others." Of special interest regarding the use of instruments is the title of Parsons's psalter, which reads in part: "The whole Psalmes in foure partes, whiche may be song [*sic*] to al Musical instrumentes, set forth for the encrease of vertue: and aboleshyng of other vayne and triflyng ballades."

The versified texts of the psalms are almost invariably set with one note to a syllable, and the rhythm is binary. All the stanzas have the same meter and are sung to the same music, the psalm thus taking on the form of a hymn.

Fifteen different meters were employed by Ainsworth, stanzas with more than four lines and unusual meters predominating. Only one of his tunes is in short meter, and only two are in the four-line common meter in which most of the texts in the Sternhold and Hopkins Psalter and the *Bay Psalm Book* were set. The meter indicates the number of syllables in each line of the text. A table of the most usual meters is given below:

Short Meter	S.M. (6.6.8.6.)
Common Meter	C.M. (8.6.8.6.), also known as Ballad Meter
Common Meter Double	C.M.D. (8.6.8.6.8.6. 8.6.) or (8.6.8.6. D.)
Long Meter	L.M. (8.8.8.8.)
Long Meter Double	L.M.D. (8.8.8.8.8.8. 8.8.) or (8.8.8.8. D.)
Hallelujah Meter	H.M. (6.6.6.6.4.4.4. 4.)

Six-line stanzas and irregular meters (sometimes called Particular or Peculiar Meter, P.M.) are usually designated by the number of syllables in each line, i.e. 6–8s (8.8.8.8.8.8.), 5–10s(10.10.10.10.), 10.10.11.11.

Most of the tunes in the Ainsworth Psalter are modal or quasi-modal. A few have definite major (Ionian) characteristics (*Psalm 8* and *Psalm 100*). *Psalm* 7 and *Psalm 34* are in the Dorian mode with a lowered sixth near the end of the tune. *Psalm 15*, with its narrow range,

[1] For detailed information on the early history of psalm-tunes consult *English & Scottish Psalm & Hymn Tunes, c. 1543–1677* (London, 1953) by Maurice Frost, *The Music of the French Psalter of 1562* (New York, 1939) by Waldo Selden Pratt, and *Grove's Dictionary of Music and Musicians*, article *Psalter* (5th edition, London and New York, 1954).

could be considered as being in either the Dorian or Aeolian mode.

A wide variety of rhythmic patterns is found throughout the psalter and in the tunes selected for the *Anthology*, and none of the melodies has the same note values throughout. Each line of the tunes in the *Anthology*, except *Psalm 15*, begins and ends with a long note. The tune for *Psalm* 7 has the same rhythmic pattern in lines 1, 3, 6, and 7 and in lines 2, 4, and 8, while line 5 is irregular. In *Psalm 8*, lines 1 and 4 and 2 and 5 are alike, while line 3 is irregular. *Psalm 15* is one of the two tunes in common meter and is unique in that it has a different rhythmic pattern for each line, and all lines but the first begin with a short note followed by a long note. Ainsworth has altered the equal-value notes of the original version of *Psalm 34* to an unusual pattern in which the second and third notes of each line are short (compare with *Psalm 85*, No. 10).

The Pilgrims at Plymouth are said to have been able to sing the long and sometimes complicated tunes from the music, without resorting to the practice of "lining-out" (singing by rote) which was used in the other Colonies. The melodies were all written in the C-clef in the range of men's voices, and Ainsworth suggested "that each people is to use the most grave, decent and comfortable manner of singing that they know."

The Ainsworth Psalter went through a number of editions, the last in 1690. It was used for a time in Salem and by the Pilgrims at Plymouth until they merged with the Massachusetts Bay Colony in 1692. The Pilgrims then adopted the *Bay Psalm Book* (1651), which was used by the Puritans of the Massachusetts Bay Colony. Thereafter the influence of the Ainsworth Psalter virtually disappeared, resulting in the loss of many fine tunes with longer stanzas and more melodic, rhythmic, and metrical variety than those found in the English Psalter (Sternhold and Hopkins), which favored four-line stanzas and common meter.

A number of the melodies chosen by Ainsworth for his versifications have, however, withstood the test of time and are found in many modern hymnals. The *Anthology* includes the tunes known today as *Old 124th* (*Psalm 8*), *Windsor* (*Psalm 15*), *Old 112th* (*Psalm 34*), and *Old 100th* (*Psalm 100*).

The *Bay Psalm Book* of 1640

> That soe wee may sing in Sion the Lords songs of prayse according to his owne will; untill hee take us from hence, and wipe away all our teares, & bid us enter into our masters ioye to sing eternall Halleluiahs.
>
> From John Cotton's Preface to the *Bay Psalm Book*, 1640

The Puritans who established the Massachusetts Bay Colony in 1628–1630 brought from England the Ravenscroft Psalter (London, 1621) and one of the many editions of the Sternhold and Hopkins Psalter (the first complete English edition was published in 1562). There was, however, in America as well as in England, a growing dissatisfaction with Sternhold and Hopkins's translations of the psalms, which many divines regarded as too far removed from the original Hebrew. As a result, a new and "faithful" metrical translation of the psalms was undertaken by thirty "pious and learned Ministers." Their efforts culminated in the *Bay Psalm Book* (as it came to be called), printed in Cambridge, Massachusetts, in 1640—the first book to be printed in British North America. It was soon adopted by most of the congregations in the Massachusetts Bay Colony, and exerted a strong influence on New England psalmody for the next hundred years. The title page of the *Bay Psalm Book* reads in part:

> THE WHOLE BOOKE OF PSALMES *Faithfully* TRANSLATED *into* ENGLISH *Metre.* Whereunto is prefixed a discourse declaring not only the lawfullnes, but also the necessity of the heavenly Ordinance of singing Scripture Psalmes in the Churches of God. *Imprinted,* 1640.

At the end of the book, "An admonition to the Reader" names the tunes, drawn from the Ravenscroft and the Sternhold and Hopkins Psalters, that could be sung to the six meters of the psalms as follows:

> The verses of these psalmes may be reduced to six kindes [meters], the first whereof may be sung in very neere fourty common tunes; as they are collected, out of our chief musicians, by *Tho. Ravenscroft.*
> The second kinde may be sung in three tunes as *Ps.* 25. 50. & 67. in our english psalm books. [Sternhold and Hopkins]
> The third. may be sung indifferently, as *ps.* the 51. 100. & ten commandements, in our english psalme books. which three tunes [meters] aforesaid, comprehend almost all this whole book of psalmes, as being tunes [meters] most familiar to us.
> The fourth. as *ps.* 148. of which there are but about five.
> The fift. as *ps.* 112. or the *Pater noster,* of which there are but two. *viz.* 85. & 138.
> The sixt. as *ps.* 113, of which but one, *viz.* 115.

The use of only six meters in the metrical psalms of the *Bay Psalm Book* (1640), with the heavy emphasis on common meter, resulted, as has been pointed out, in the loss of the wide variety of tunes found in the Ainsworth Psalter. There were also single examples of eleven other meters in the Sternhold and Hopkins Psalter which were not retained. One hundred and twelve of the psalms in the *Bay Psalm Book* are in common meter, fourteen in short meter, fifteen in long meter, six in Hallelujah meter, two in 6–8s, and one in 12–8s. Examples of tunes in each of these six meters are given in the *Anthology*, following the order of the above "Admonition."

Yorke (*York*) is one of the 39 harmonized tunes in common meter included in the Ravenscroft Psalter (London, 1621), the first source mentioned in the "Admonition." As was customary in part-music, the tunes were placed in the tenor. They were named (many for the first time by Ravenscroft) after English cathedral and university towns or after various localities with which the tunes were especially identified. The Ravenscroft Psalter contained 105 four-part settings by some of England's most accomplished musicians. Among them were Allison (Alison), Dowland (Douland), Farnaby, Morley, Tallis, Tomkins, John Milton, Sr. (father of the poet), and Ravenscroft himself. The use of the mensural notation sign for Imperfect Time and Perfect Prolation in Milton's setting of *York* (No. 6) is characteristic of Ravenscroft's effort to preserve an already obsolete practice. Milton's harmonization is characterized by three cadences on the dominant, a striking modal progression at the beginning of the third line, and an effective final cadence. The text of the versification of *Psalm 73*, taken from the *Bay Psalm Book* (1640), is set beneath Milton's text as it might have been sung by the Puritans. The original version of *York* is also given (No. 6a) as it is found in the Scottish Psalter (1615), where it is called *The Stilt*, obviously because of the alternating skips in the melody. The tune, with the B-natural in the second line, appears in a two-part setting in the *Bay Psalm Book* (1698), and it has maintained its popularity up to the present time.

The simple, chant-like melody of *Psalm 7* (No. 7) moves above the key-note within a range of a fifth. It will be noted that the first and third lines have an unusual rhythmic pattern. The tune first appeared in the Ravenscroft Psalter, where it is called *Canterbury*.

Sternhold and Hopkins's version of the tune for *Psalm 100* (No. 8) follows the rhythmic pattern used in the Parsons Psalter (1563) and varies only in the last line from the French-Genevan Psalter (1551; *Anthology*, Nos. 5b and 5a).

The versifications of the six psalms in Hallelujah meter in the *Bay Psalm Book* were all sung to the tune for *Psalm 148* (No. 9) as found in the Sternhold and Hopkins Psalter —the only psalm in that meter. The last five lines in *Psalm 148* have varied rhythmic patterns, and the use of a B-flat in the fourth and sixth lines is also of special interest.

Psalm 85 (No. 10) is set to the tune that Sternhold and Hopkins used for the metrical version of the *Lord's Prayer*. The melody also appeared in the Ainsworth Psalter (*Psalm 34*) in the Dorian mode (*Anthology*, No. 4). The use of accidentals in lines 3 and 4 in the Sternhold and Hopkins version, however, has given the tune a tonal character. It will also be noticed that the rhythmic pattern varies from Ainsworth's version.

The sixth meter (12–8s) is represented by only one psalm in Sternhold and Hopkins (*Psalm 113*) and one in the *Bay Psalm Book* (*Psalm 115;* No. 11). This striking tune, known in Germany as early as 1526, was used by Calvin in his first psalter of 1539 and entered the repertory of German chorales as *O Mensch, bewein' dein' Sünde gross*. The tune was also a famous battle-song of the French Huguenots and became known as the "Huguenot Marseillaise." Ainsworth set his version of *Psalm 84* and *Psalm 136* to this tune; the latter psalm, however, required a change in meter from 8.8.8.8.8.8.D. to 8.8.7.8.8.7.D.

The title page of the *Bay Psalm Book* (1640) includes a quotation from James 5: "*If any be afflicted, let him pray, and if any be merry let him sing psalmes.*" The Puritans followed this admonition with enthusiasm and sang their psalms with "a lively voyce." There were some, however, who objected to the melodies made by "sinful men" and called the tunes "Genevah Gigs."

"Lining-out" of the psalms, already practiced in England, was recommended in 1647 by John Cotton "as a necessary helpe," except "where all have books and can reade, or else can say the *Psalme* by heart." "Lining-out" was also applied to psalm-singing, and a deacon or elder would "set the tune" at the proper pitch (if he could) and sing the psalm one line at a time, the congregation repeating what he had just sung. The lack of deacons with a good sense of pitch and an ear for music was one of the contributing factors in the gradual deterioration of congregational singing.

The *Bay Psalm Book* of 1698

> Let the word of God dwell in you richly in all wisdom, teaching and admonishing one another in Psalms, Hymns and spiritual Songs, singing to the Lord with grace in your hearts. Colossians 3:16
>
> From the title page of the *Bay Psalm Book*, ninth edition, 1698.

In spite of the popular acceptance of the *Bay Psalm Book* of 1640 and the reprint of 1647, "persons of culture" thoroughly disapproved of the many crude and awkward "close-fitting" metrical translations made by pious men who they felt had little, if any, ability as poets. The demand for metrical psalms that would be more singable and of greater literary value led to the publication of a third edition of the *Bay Psalm Book* in 1651.

This "revised and refined" edition was largely the work of the Rev. Henry Dunster, first president of Harvard College. The poetry was improved, new versifications were made, and alternate versions of some psalms were added. A new title page was given the book, and a number of hymns and spiritual songs (found in English psalters) were included for the first time in the *Bay Psalm Book*.

The 1651 edition of the *Bay Psalm Book* (known also as the *New England Psalm Book*) was enthusiastically received. It became the definitive version for over one hundred years and went through many editions here as well as in England and Scotland. Only the metrical versions of Sternhold and Hopkins, Tate and Brady, Isaac Watts, and the Scottish Psalter exceeded it in the number of editions, or in long-continued use.

The first known edition of the *Bay Psalm Book* to include music was the ninth, published in Boston in 1698. Its title, identical in text with the 1651 edition, reads:

THE PSALMS HYMNS, AND SPIRITUAL SONGS, OF THE Old & New Testament: Faithfully Translated into *English Meetre*. For the use, Edification and Comfort of the Saints in publick and private, especially in *New-England* . . . . *Boston*, Printed by *B. Green*, and *J. Allen*, for *Michael Perry*, under the West-End of the Town house. 1698.

The thirteen tunes at the back of the book were selected by an unknown compiler from one of the identical versions in the 1674 and 1679 editions of *An Introduction to the Skill of Musick* by the London publisher, John Playford (1623–1686).[2] The tunes appear in the following order: *Oxford* (C.M.), *Lichfield* [sic] (C.M.), *Low Dutch* (C.M.), *York* (C.M.), *Windsor* (C.M.), *Cambridge Short* (S.M.), *St. Davids* (C.M.), *Martyrs* (C.M.), *Hackney* (C.M.), *Psalm 115* (12–8s), *Psalm 148* (H.M.).

A note preceding the music states that *Oxford*, *Litchfield*, and *Low Dutch* may be sung to "Psalms Consolatory"; *York* and *Windsor* to "Psalms of Prayer, Confession and Funerals"; *St. Davids* and *Martyrs* to "Psalms of Praise and Thanksgiving."

The large proportion of common meter versifications in the *Bay Psalm Book* (there were 125 in the 1651 edition) is reflected in the fact that nine of the thirteen tunes in the 1698 edition are in common meter (one of these is C.M.D.). It will also be noticed that short meter, long meter, 12–8s, and Hallelujah meter are represented by one tune each and that there is no tune given for 6–8s, although one is provided for in the 1640 edition (*Anthology*, No. 10).

The tunes are all set in two parts, treble and bass, without a text but with the number of a psalm in appropriate meter indicated. The letters F[a], S[ol], L[a], M[i], known as "fasola" notation, are placed under the diamond-shaped notes. This notation is identical with that used by Playford in his *Introduction to the Skill of Music* (London, 1672).

Six of the tunes from the *Bay Psalm Book*, 1698, are included in this section of the *Anthology*. Four of the seven remaining tunes may be found in the present volume—*Windsor* (*Psalm 15* in Ainsworth; No. 3); *Yorke* [*sic*] and *Psalm 115* (Nos. 6, 11); and *Litchfield* (*London Tune* in Walter; No. 24). The melodies of *London Tune* (*Litchfield*) and *Yorke* are identical with those in the *Bay Psalm Book* of 1698; *Windsor* and *Psalm 115* have been slightly altered. The tunes must have been well known to the Puritans, since they could all be found in the Sternhold and Hopkins or the Ravenscroft Psalters, and their quality and durability are attested to by the fact that at least nine of the thirteen tunes are to be found in modern hymnals.

The rhythmic patterns show considerable variety. All six tunes, except *Psalm 100* (No. 15), have one or more lines that begin with a short note. A few tunes have regular patterns for the first half of the tune and irregular patterns for the second half. All have common-time signatures, except *Martyrs*, which is in triple time.

Four of the six tunes given in the *Anthology* lie within the range of an octave (*Martyrs*, *Psalm 100*) or ninth (*Psalm 119*, No. 16; *Psalm 148*, No. 17), while the remaining two tunes have a compass of a fourth (*Low Dutch*, No. 13), or fifth (*Oxford*, No. 12). Most of

[2] Irving Lowens, "The Bay Psalm Book in 17th-Century New England," *Journal of the American Musicological Society*, VIII (1955), 28.

the six tunes are modal. These are *Psalm 119* (Aeolian), *Martyrs* (Dorian), and *Psalm 148* (Mixolydian). The B-naturals in the latter psalm are *musica ficta*. *Oxford* (with the D and E missing) and *Low Dutch* (with the D missing) are incomplete hexatonic melodies. *Oxford* is interesting in the use of F-sharp in the tune in place of F-natural. *Psalm 100* is one of two out of the thirteen tunes in the *Bay Psalm Book* that are in the pure Ionian (major) mode. Modulations occur in *Psalm 119* and *Psalm 148*.

The section in the *Bay Psalm Book* that contains the music begins with "some few directions for ordering the Voice in Setting these following Tunes of the Psalms." The Preface, borrowed from Playford's *Brief Introduction to the Skill of Musick* (London, 1667) continues with the following often-quoted passage intended as an aid to the deacon in selecting the initial pitch:

> First observe of how many *Notes* compass the *Tune* is. Next, the place of your first *Note;* and how many *Notes* above & below that: so as you may begin the *Tune* of your first *Note* as the rest may be sung in the compass of your and the peoples voices, without *Squeaking* above, or *Grumbling* below. . . .

The Preface names *Oxford*, *Litchfield* (also known as *London*), *Low Dutch*, *York*, *Windsor*, and *Cambridge Short* as tunes in which "the first note will bear a cheerful high pitch"; for *St. Davids*, *Martyrs*, *Hackney* (also known as *St. Mary's*), *Psalm 119*, *Psalm 115*, and *Psalm 148* "begin your first note low"; for *Psalm 100*, with the first note about in the middle of the compass, "begin your first note indifferently high," that is, not too low.

The New Version

> The Lord Bishop of London, in 1698, "persuaded that it [the *New Version*] may take off that unhappy objection which has hitherto lain against the Singing Psalms . . . heartily recommended the Use of this Version to all his Brethren within his Diocess."
>
> A maid in the household of Tate's brother refused, however, to sing the new psalms saying: "If you must know the plain truth, sir, as long as you sung Jesus Christ's psalms I sung along with ye; but now that you sing psalms of your own invention, ye may sing by yourselves."
>
> *Three Centuries of American Hymnody* by Henry Wilder Foote

During the 17th century there was a growing desire in England, and to some extent in America, for more fluent and poetic metrical translations of the psalms, and many freer versions began to appear. These culminated in 1696 with the publication in London of the *New Version of the Psalms of David, fitted to the tunes used in churches* by Nahum Tate (1652–1715), Poet Laureate and librettist for Henry Purcell's opera *Dido and Aeneas*, and Nicholas Brady (1659–1726), an Anglican divine. The Sternhold and Hopkins Psalter soon became known as the "Old Version" and the Tate and Brady as the "New Version." The two existed in the English church side by side, until eventually they were lost in the hymn-like psalmody and hymnody of the non-conformist divine, Isaac Watts (1674–1748), and later writers. Music was not included in the first edition of the *New Version* of 1696, but in 1700 *A Supplement to the New Version* was issued which included six hymns and a number of tunes set in two- and three-part harmony.

The congregations in New England were partial to the *Bay Psalm Book,* which had 27 editions there before 1762; and the *New Version* had little influence in America until the middle of the 18th century. However, King's Chapel in Boston, an Episcopal church, adopted the *New Version* as early as 1713, and in the same year an edition including nine tunes was published there. In 1720 Samuel Sewall noted in his *Diary* that, at a meeting in the school-house, they "sang four times out of Tate and Brady." The Baptists in Boston changed to the *New Version* in 1740, and gradually it was accepted in other localities, particularly in the Episcopal churches.

The *Supplement to the New Version* introduced to America some of our finest hymn tunes, among them *St. Anne's* (No. 18) and *Winchester* (*Winchester Old*). The former, known today by Watts's text "O God, our help in ages past," is ascribed to William Croft, organist of St. Anne's in Soho, London. It first appeared anonymously in the *Supplement* (1708), where it is set to Nahum Tate's well-known versification of *Psalm 42*. The tune for the *Song of the Angels* (No. 19) had its origin in Thomas East's *Whole Booke of Psalmes* (1592) and was named *Winchester* by Ravenscroft in his psalter of 1621. Nahum Tate's paraphrase of the Biblical text from Luke 2 is one of our best-known Christmas hymns.

In 1755 Thomas Johnston published in Boston a *Tune Supplement to the New Version* containing, possibly for the first time in America, a three-part setting of the famous tune *Mear*. This tune made its initial appearance (under the title *Middlesex*) in Simon Browne's *A Sett of Tunes in 3 Parts* (London, 1720). It will be noted that Johnston's version of the tune (No. 20) varies from Browne's (No. 20a) only in the last two measures of the first line, and that the tune is in the treble in Browne's setting. A distinguishing characteristic of the melody is the sudden shift in the rhythmic pattern in the penultimate measure of the second and fourth lines. *Mear* was not only a favorite 18th-century tune, but it became one of the popular tunes in 19th-century Southern folk hymnody and may also be found in many modern hymnals.

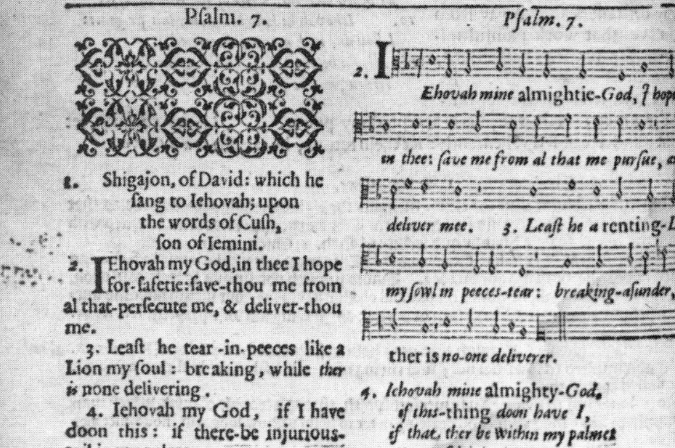

16 Psalm. VI. VII.

V. 6. for in the death &c.] This doctrine, King Hezekiah explayneth thus; for hel[l] not confess thee, death shal not prayse thee; they that goe down the pit, shal not hope for truth: the living the living, he shal confess thee as I doo this day: thee father to the children make-knowne thy truth. Isa. 38. 18. 19. So after, in Psal. 115. 17. 18. hel] or the gr[ave] deadlyshed; the place or state of the dead. See the note on Psal. 16, 10. confess] or, g[ive] thanks, celebrate, divulge or freely publish with praise and comendation. This same wo[rd] also used for confessing of synns; Psal. 32. 5.

V. 7. I fayne.] or am over-yawed with my sighing; the like speech Baruch useth, Ier. 45. The original word iagaghn, signifieth yawing, toyl, turmoil and sore labour, of body or m[ind] and consequently, fainting, through wearynes: and is opposed to rest or quietnes: Lam. every night] or, the whole night. I water] that is, baeth, or dissolve into wat[er] I melt my bedsted. These ar excessive figurative speeches, to expres the greatnes of his [sor]row. In the Hebrue they ar also in the future time, I shal melt; I shal make swim; that is usually melt and baeth; noting the continuance of his affliction.

V. 8. myne eye] This may be taken for the whole face or visage; as in Num. 11. 7. th[e eye] is used for the colour or appearance. gnawen] The Hebrue Ghnashash is to gnaw, fret, and so to make deformed and ugly, and to consume. Herof Ghnash is a moth-worm, [Psal.] 39. 12. that fretteth garments. A like speech Iob useth, myne eye is dimmed with indig[nation] Iob. 17. 7. but gnawen, here is a word more vehement. So after in Psal. 31. 10, 11. indignation] for greif that I take being provoked by the enemies.

V. 11. let be abasht] or, shal be abasht; The Hebrue Bosh, signifieth to be abasht, wey and wann; as when the colour fadeth and withereth; and noteth both disappointment of expectation, Iob. 6. 20. and confusion or destruction. Ier. 48. 1, 20. let them retu[rn] or, recoyl: a signe also of discomfiture and shame. so Psal. 56. 10. in a moment] or minute: that is, a short space, or suddaynly.

Psalm. 7.

1. Shigajon, of David: which he sang to Iehovah; upon the words of Cush, son of Iemini.

2. IEhovah my God, in thee I hope for-safetie: save-thou me from al that-persecute me, & deliver-thou me.

3. Least he tear-in-peeces like a Lion my soul: breaking, while ther is none delivering.

4. Iehovah my God, if I have doon this: if there-be injurious-evil in my palms,

Psalm. 7.

2. IEhovah mine almightie-God, I hope in thee: save me from al that me pursue, and deliver mee. 3. Least he a renting-Lion my soul in peeces-tear: breaking-asunder, ther is no-one deliverer.

4. Iehovah mine almighty-God, if this-thing doon have I, if that, ther be within my palmes wrongful-iniquitie,

Psalm. VII. 17

5. If I have rewarded, evil to him-that-had-peace-with-me: (yea I have-released, my distresser without cause.)

6. Let the enemy pursue my sowl, and take it; and tread-down my life on the earth: and my glorie, let him make-it-dwel, in the dust Selah.

7. Rise-up, Iehovah, in thy anger; be thou lifted-up, for the rages of my distressers: & wake-thou-up-unto me, judgement thou-hast-commanded.

8. And the congregation of peoples, shall compasse-thee-about: and for it, return thou to the high-place.

9. Iehovah, wil judge the peoples: judge-thou me Iehovah; according-to my justice, and according-to my perfection in me.

10. Oh let the malice of the wicked, be at-an-end, and stablish thou the just: for thou triest the harts, and reins, just God.

11. My sheild is in God: the saviour, of the right in hart.

12. God is a just judge: and God angerly-threatneth, every day.

13. If he-turn not, he wil whet his sword: he hath bent his bow, and made it ready.

14. And for him, he-hath made-ready the instruments of death: his arrowes, he-worketh for the hot-persecutors.

15. Loe he shalbe-in-travel of painful-iniquitie: for he hath conceived molestation, and shal bring-forth a lye.

16. He hath digged a pit, and delved it: and is-fallen, into the corrupting-ditch he wrought.

5. If I have him rewarded yll,
that with mee was at-peace:
(yea him that my distresser was
causless, I did release.)

6. Let foe pursue my sowl, and take
and tread my life on clay:
my glorie also let him make-
dwel, in the dust Selah.

7. Rise-up, Iehovah, in thy wrath;
for rages of my foes,
be thou lift-up: and wake to me,
judgement thou-diddst propose.

8. And round-about thee compass shal,
the peoples assembly:
and for the same, doo thou return
unto the place-on-hye.

9. Iehovah, wil the peoples judge:
Iehovah judge thou me;
even-as my justice is, and as
my perfectnes in me.

10. Oh let the wickeds malice, end,
and stablish-thou-firmly
the iust-man: for, ô iust God, thou
the harts and reins doost-try.

11. My sheild in God; the saviour,
of the upright in hart.

12. God, is a iust judge: and ech day,
God, angry-threatneth smart.

13. For if that he doo not return,
his sword he sharp wil whett;
his bow he bended hath; and he
the same hath ready-sett.

14. And for him, he hath ready-made
the instruments of death:
for them that hotly-persecute,
his arrowes he worketh.

15. Loe he shalbe in travel of
painful-iniquitie:
for molestation he conceivd,
and shal bring forth a lye.

16. A hollow-pit he digged hath,
and delved-deep the same:
and falln he is, into the ditch
that he did working-frame.

17 C 17

Psalme 7 from the Ainsworth Psalter (Amsterdam, 1612).
By courtesy of the Trustees of the Boston Public Library.
See No. 1, p. 24.

1. PSALME 7 (C.M.D.)

1539

The Book of Psalmes
Henry Ainsworth
(*Amsterdam, 1612*)

Henry Ainsworth
(c. 1570–1623)

1a. PSALME 130 (7.6.7.6.D.)

1539

Aulcuns pseaulmes et cantiques
Calvin's First Psalter
(*Strasbourg, 1539*)

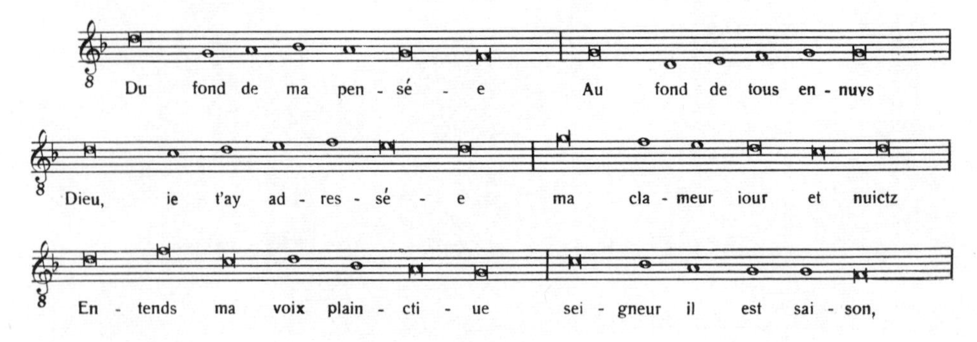

Note: The dates given for the music in Nos. 1–17 are dates when the tunes were first published. The two-part settings, Nos. 12–17, first appeared in John Playford's *Introduction*, 1674.

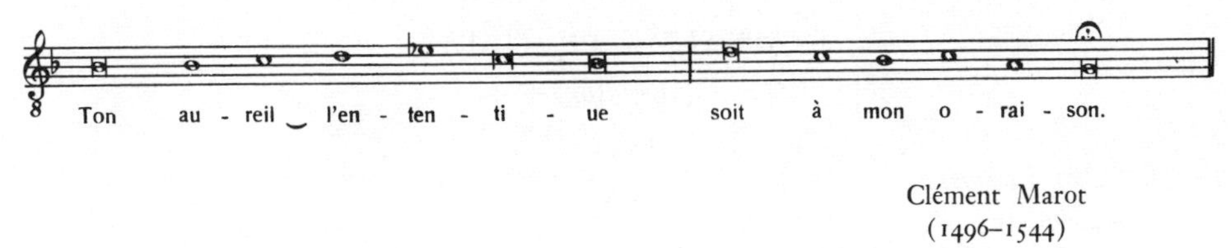

Clément Marot
(1496–1544)

Note: This is *Psalm 129* in the Catholic system of numbering.

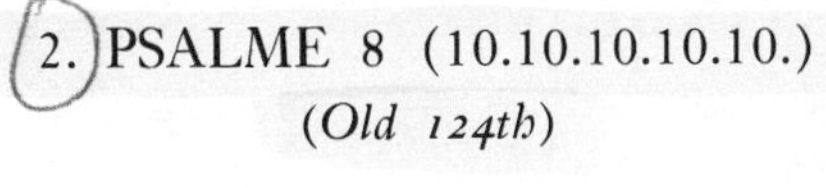

2. PSALME 8 (10.10.10.10.10.)
(Old 124th)

1551

The Book of Psalmes
Henry Ainsworth
(Amsterdam, 1612)

Louis Bourgeois
(c. 1510–c. 1561)

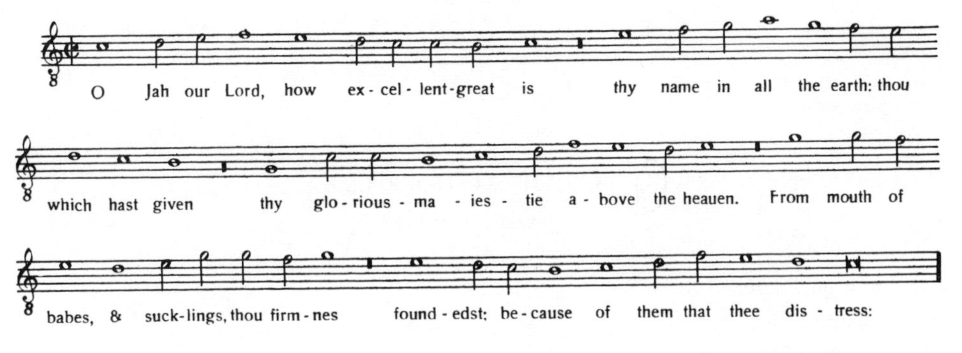

2
To make the foe, and self-avenger cease:
When I behold thy heav'ns, thy fingers deed:
the moon and starrs, which thou hast stablished.
What is frayl-man that him thou remembrest?
and Adams son, that him thou visitest?

3
For thou a little lesser hast made him,
than be the Gods: and crownd him with glorie
and-eke with honourable-decencie.
Of thy hand-works, thou gavest him ruling:
under his feet, thou set didst every-thing.

4
Sheep & beeves all: and feild beasts with the same.
Fowl of the heav'ns, fish of the sea also:
that through the path-wayes of the seas dooth go.
O Jah our Lord: how excellent-great-fame
in all the earth hath thy renouned-name.

Henry Ainsworth
(c. 1570–1623)

3. PSALME 15 (C.M.)

(Windsor)

1591

The Book of Psalmes
Henry Ainsworth
(Amsterdam, 1612)

Henry Ainsworth
(c. 1570–1623)

4. PSALME 34 (8.8.8.8.8.8.)

(Old 112th)

1539

The Book of Psalmes
Henry Ainsworth
(Amsterdam, 1612)

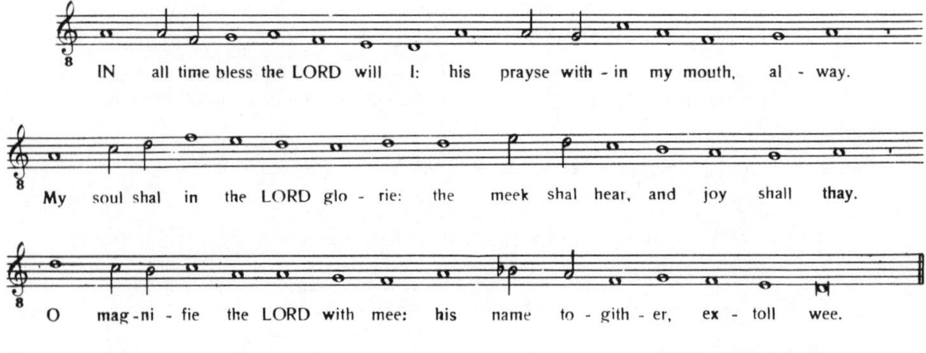

Henry Ainsworth
(c. 1570–1623)

5. PSALME OLD 100TH (L.M.)

1551

The Book of Psalmes
Henry Ainsworth
(*Amsterdam, 1612*)

Louis Bourgeois
(c. 1510–c. 1561)

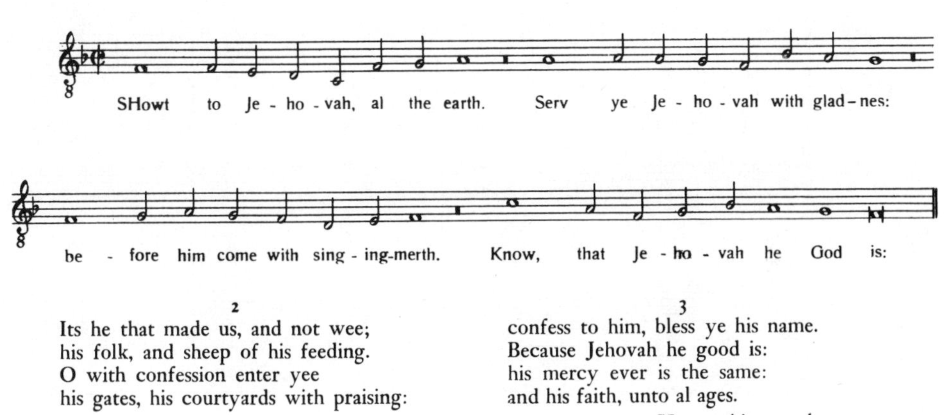

2
Its he that made us, and not wee;
his folk, and sheep of his feeding.
O with confession enter yee
his gates, his courtyards with praising:

3
confess to him, bless ye his name.
Because Jehovah he good is:
his mercy ever is the same:
and his faith, unto al ages.

Henry Ainsworth
(c. 1570–1623)

5a. PSEAUME CXXXIV (L.M.)

1551

Trente quatre pseaumes
French-Genevan Psalter
(*Geneva, 1551*)

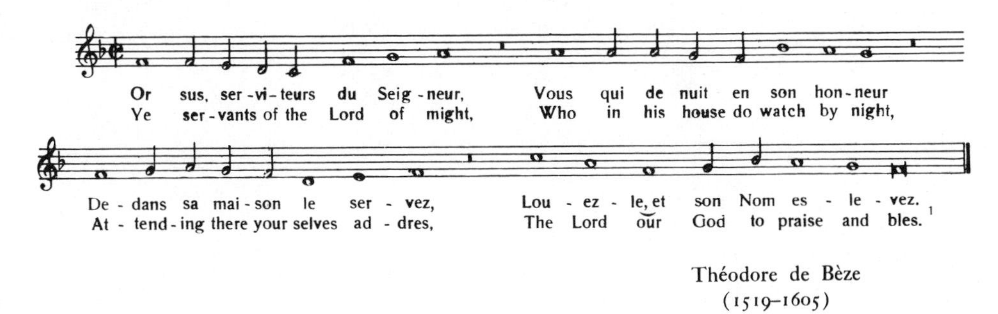

Théodore de Bèze
(1519–1605)

[1] The English words, dating from 1632, are quoted by Gustave Reese in *Music in the Renaissance* (New York, 1959), p. 361.

5b PSALME C (L.M.)

1551

The Whole Psalmes in Foure Partes, Parsons's Psalter (*London, 1563*)

William Parsons (16th century)

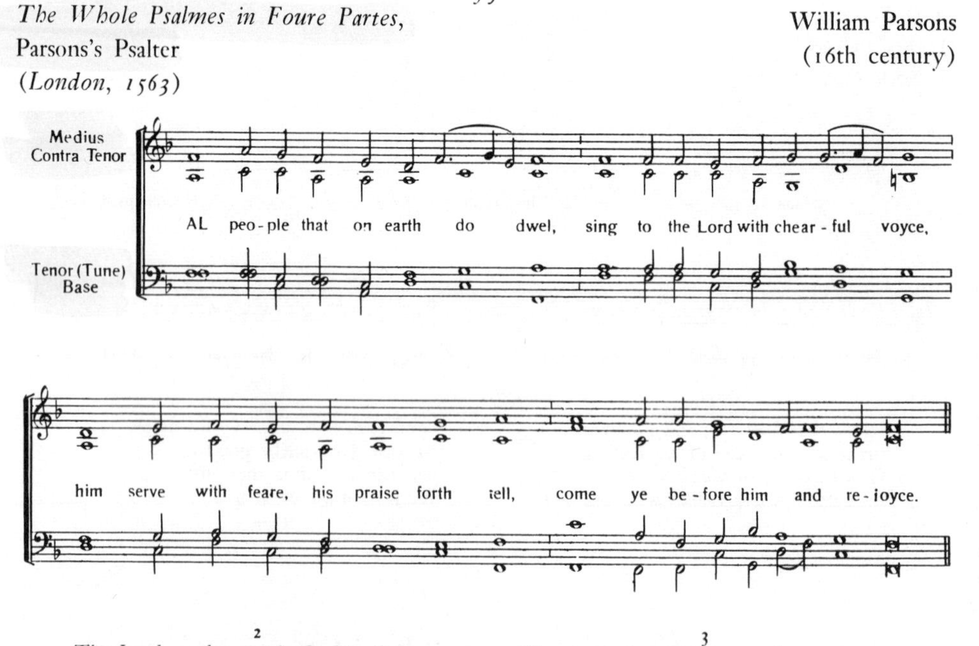

2

The Lord, ye knowe, is God in dede:
Without our aide, he did us make:
We are his folke: he doeth us fede.
And for his shepe, he doeth us take.

3

Oh, entre then his gates with praise:
Approche with ioye, his courtes unto
Praise, laude, and blesse his name alwayes
For it is semely so to do.

4

For why? the Lord our God is good:
His mercie is for euer sure:
His trueth at all times firmely stoode
And shal from age to age indure.

William Kethe
(16th century)

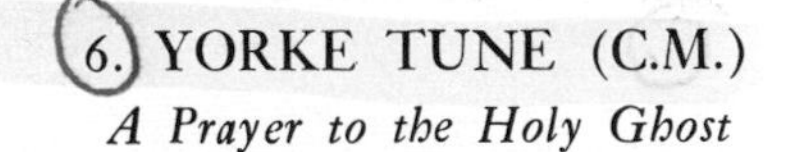

6. YORKE TUNE (C.M.)

A Prayer to the Holy Ghost

1621

The Whole Booke of Psalmes
Thomas Ravenscroft
(*London, 1621*)

John Milton, Sr.
(c. 1563–1647)

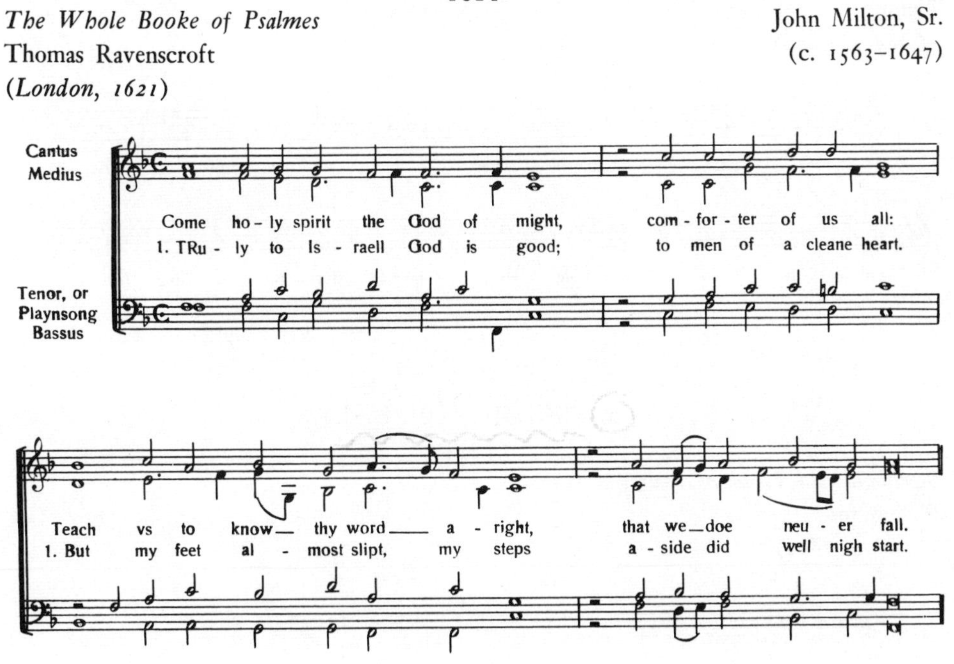

The alternate stanza (1.) is taken from Ps. 73: *Bay Psalm Book*, 1640.

6a. THE STILT (C.M.)

1615

The CL. Psalmes of David
Scottish Psalter
(*Edinburgh, 1615*)

7. PSALME 7 (S.M.)

1621

Sternhold and Hopkins Psalter
Psalme 25
(*London, 1624*)

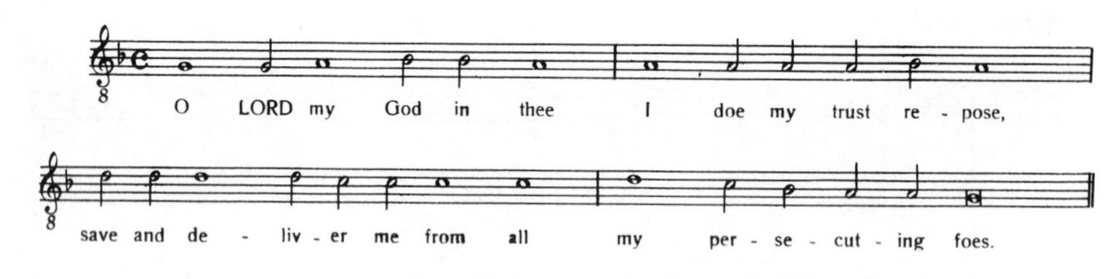

Ps. 7: *Bay Psalm Book*, 1640

8. PSALME 100 (L.M.)

1551

Sternhold and Hopkins Psalter
Psalme 100
(*London, 1624*)

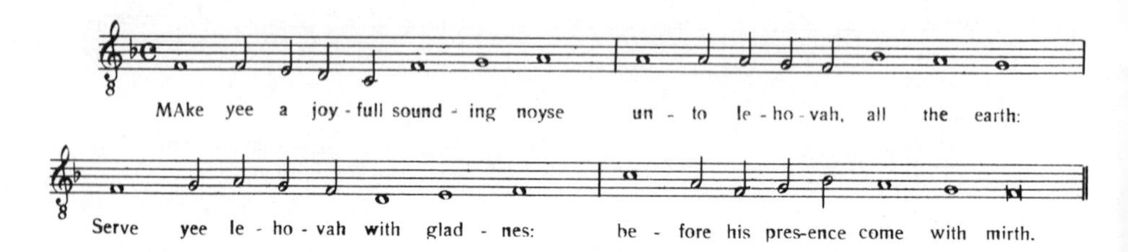

2
Know, that Iehovah he is God,
who hath us formed it is hee,
& not our selves: his owne people
& sheepe of his pasture are wee.

3
Enter into his gates with prayse,
into his Courts with thankfullness:
make yee confession unto him,
& his name reverently blesse.

4
Because Iehovah he is good,
for evermore is his mercy:
& unto generations all
continue doth his verity.

Ps. 100: *Bay Psalm Book*, 1640

9. PSALME 148 (H.M.)

Hallelujah

1558

Sternhold and Hopkins Psalter
Psalme 148
(*London, 1624*)

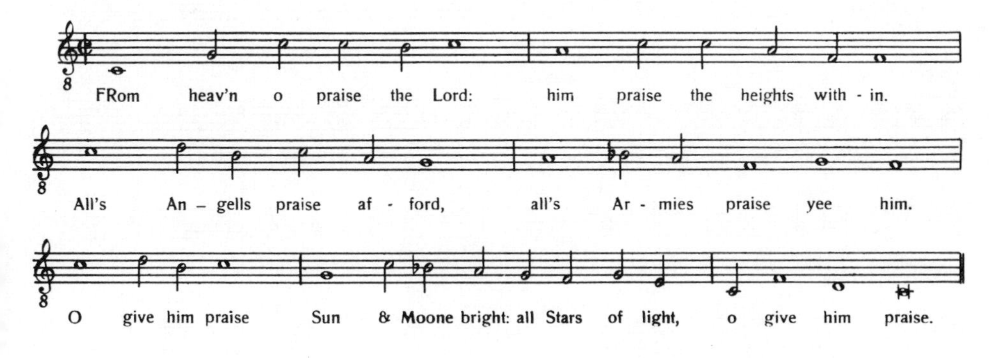

Ps. 148: *Bay Psalm Book*, 1640

10. PSALME 85 (6-8s)

1539

Sternhold and Hopkins Psalter
Pater noster
(*London, 1624*)

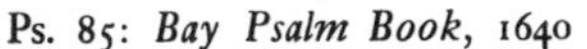
Ps. 85: *Bay Psalm Book*, 1640

11. PSALME 115 (12-8s)

1556

Sternhold and Hopkins Psalter
Psalme 113
(*London, 1624*)

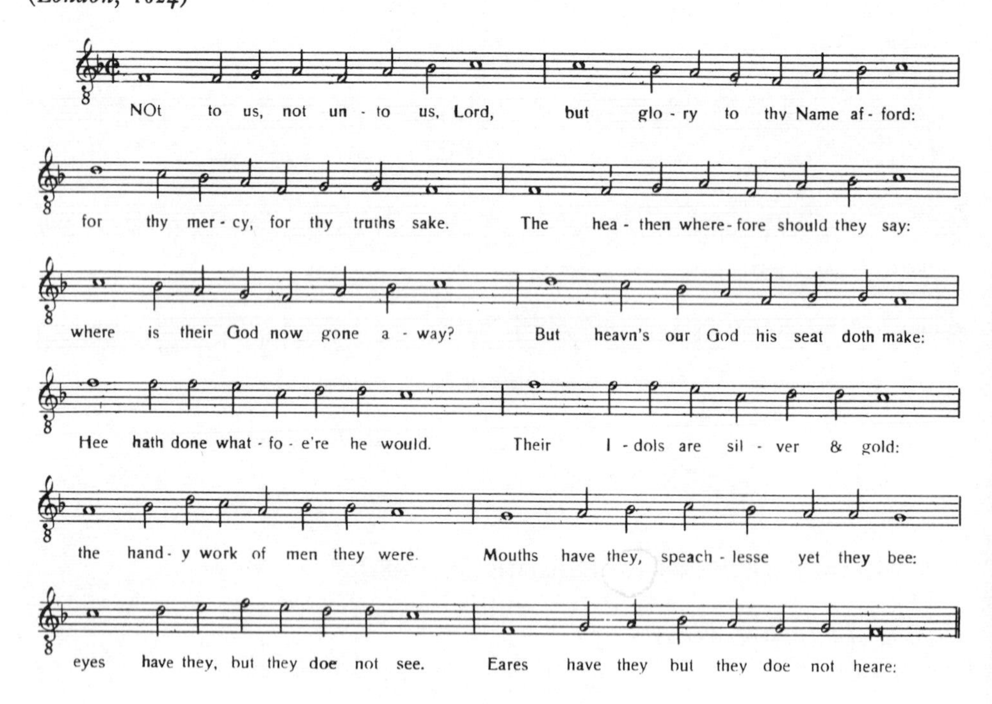

2

Noses have they, but doe not smell.
Hands have they, but cannot handell,
  feet have they but doe not go:
And through their throat they never spake.
Like them are they, that doe them make:
  & all that trust in them are so.
Trust to the Lord O Israell,
He is their help, their shield as well.
  O Arons house the Lord trust yee:
Hee is their help, & hee their shield.
Who fear the Lord, trust to him yield:
  their help also their shield is hee.

Ps. 115: *Bay Psalm Book*, 1640

12. OXFORD TUNE (C.M.)

1564

Bay Psalm Book
(Boston, 1698)

2
Ye sons of men my glory turn
to shame how long will you?
How long will yee love vanitie
and still deceit pursue?

3
But know the LORD hath set apart
for him his gracious saint;
The LORD will hear when unto him
I pour out my complaint.

4
Be stirred up; but do not sinn
consider seriously
Within your heart, with silence deep
when on your bed you lie.

5
The sacrifice of righteousness
let sacrificed bee;
And confidently put your trust
upon the LORD do yee.

Ps. 4: *Bay Psalm Book*, 1698

13. LOW DUTCH TUNE (C.M.)

1592

Bay Psalm Book
(Boston, 1698)

2

Hee leads mee to the waters still.
Restore my soul doth hee:
In paths of righteousness, he will
for his names sake lead mee.

3

In valley of deaths shade although
I walk I'le fear none ill:
For thou with me thy rod, also
thy staff me comfort will.

4

Thou hast 'fore me a table spread,
in presence of my foes:
Thou dost anoint with oyle my head,
my cup it ouer-flowes.

5

Goodness and mercy my dayes all
shall surely follow mee:
And in the LORDs house dwell I shall
so long as dayes shall bee.

Ps. 23: *Bay Psalm Book*, 1698

Note: The above version of *Psalm 23* is identical with that in the 1651 edition of the *Bay Psalm Book*.

1

The Lord to mee a shepheard is,
want therefore shall not I.
Hee in the folds of tender-grasse,
doth cause mee downe to lie:

2

To waters calme me gently leads
Restore my soule doth hee:
he doth in paths of righteousnes:
for his names sake leade mee.

3

Yea through in valley of death's shade
I walk, none ill I'le feare:
because thou art with mee, thy rod,
and staffe my comfort are.

4

For mee a table thou hast spread,
in presence of my foes:
thou dost annoynt my head with oyle,
my cup it over-flowes.

5

Goodnes & mercy surely shall
all my dayes follow mee:
and in the Lords house I shall dwell
so long as dayes shall bee.

Ps. 23: *Bay Psalm Book*, 1640

14. MARTYRS TUNE (C.M.)

1615

Bay Psalm Book
(Boston, 1698)

Ps. 39: *Bay Psalm Book*, 1698

15. PSALM 100 (L.M.)

1551

Bay Psalm Book
(Boston, 1698)

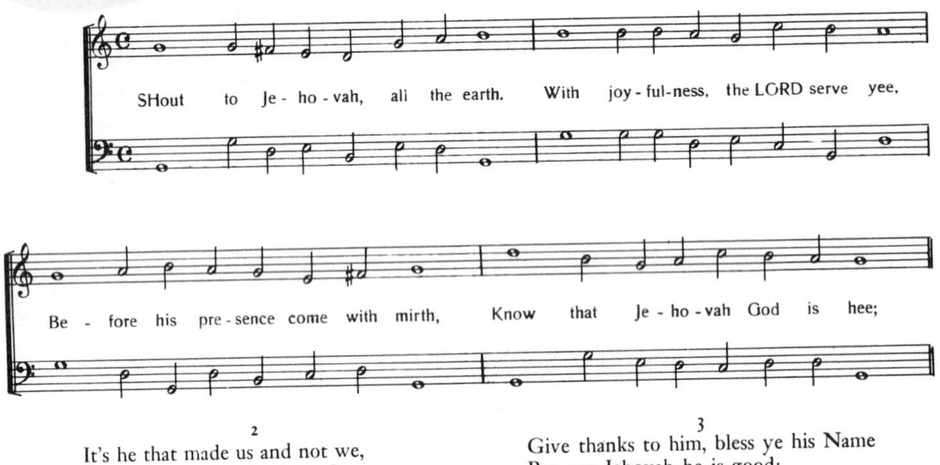

2

It's he that made us and not we,
His folk his pastures sheep also.
Into his gates with thanks come ye
With praises to his Court-yards go.

3

Give thanks to him, bless ye his Name
Because Jehovah he is good:
His mercy ever is the same:
His truth throughout all ages stood.

Ps. 100: *Bay Psalm Book*, 1698

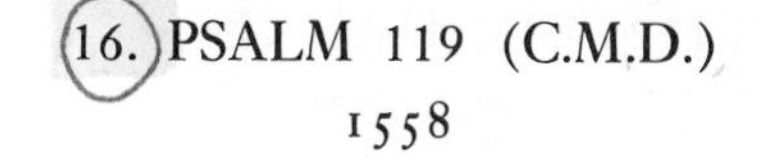

16. PSALM 119 (C.M.D.)

1558

Bay Psalm Book
(Boston, 1698)

Ps. 119: *Bay Psalm Book*, 1698

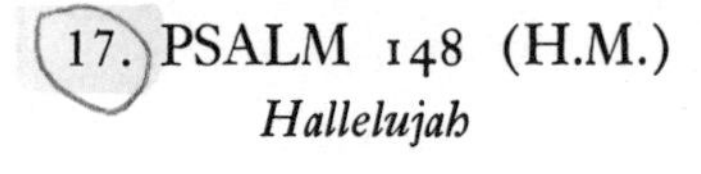

17. PSALM 148 (H.M.)

Hallelujah

1558

Bay Psalm Book
(Boston, 1698)

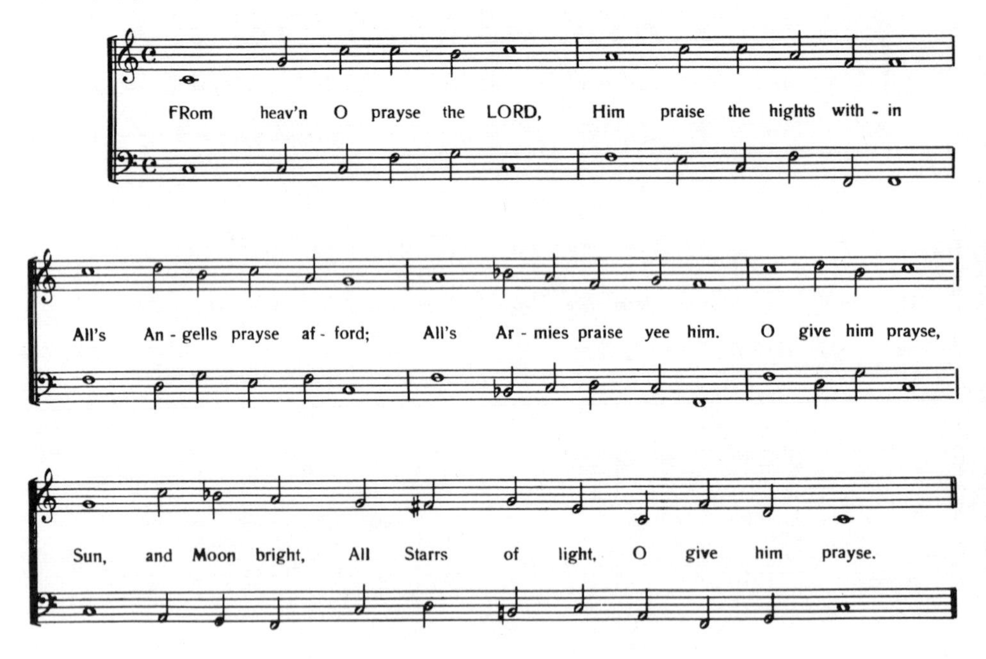

2

Yee heav'ns of heav'ns him prayse.
'Bove heav'ns yee waters clear,
The LORDs Name let them prayse.
For he spake made they were
  Them stablisht hee
For ever and ay:
Nor pass away
  Shall his decree.

Ps. 148: *Bay Psalm Book*, 1698

18. ST. ANNE'S TUNE (C.M.)

1708

A Supplement to the New Version
Tate and Brady
(*London, 1708*)

William Croft
(1678–1727)

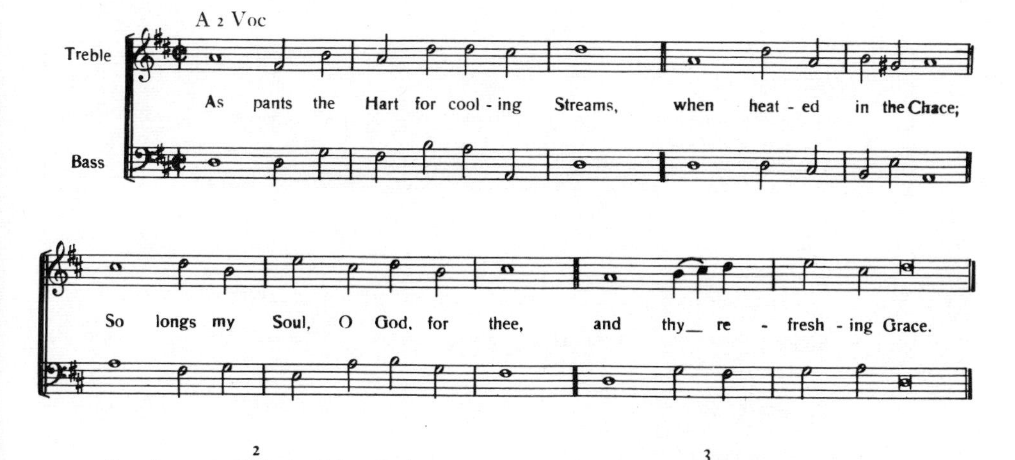

2

For thee, my God, the living God,
my thirsty Soul doth pine;
O when shall I behold thy Face,
thou Majesty Divine!

3

Tears are my constant Food, while thus
insulting Foes upbraid,
"Deluded Wretch, where's now thy God?
and where his promis'd Aid?"

Ps. 42: Nahum Tate (1698)
(1652–1715)

19. SONG OF THE ANGELS (C.M.)

(Winchester Tune)

1700

A Supplement to the New Version
Tate and Brady
(London, 1708)

2

"Fear not, said he, (for mighty Dread
"had seiz'd their troubled Mind);
"Glad Tidings of great Joy I bring
"to you, and all Mankind:

3

"To you, in David's Town, this Day
"is born, of David's Line,
"The Saviour, who is Christ the Lord;
"and This shall be the Sign:

4

"The heav'nly Babe you there shall find
"to humane View display'd,
"All meanly wrapt in swathing Bands,
"and in a Manger laid.

5

Thus spake the Seraph, and forthwith
appear'd a shining Throng
Of Angels praising God, and thus
address'd their joyful Song:

6

"All Glory be to God on high,
"and to the Earth be Peace:
"Good Will, henceforth, from Heav'n to Men,
"begin and never cease.

Luke 2: Nahum Tate (1700)
(1652–1715)

20. MEAR (C.M.)

1720

From a tune supplement for the *New Version*
Engraved, printed, and sold by Thomas Johnston
(*Boston, 1755*)

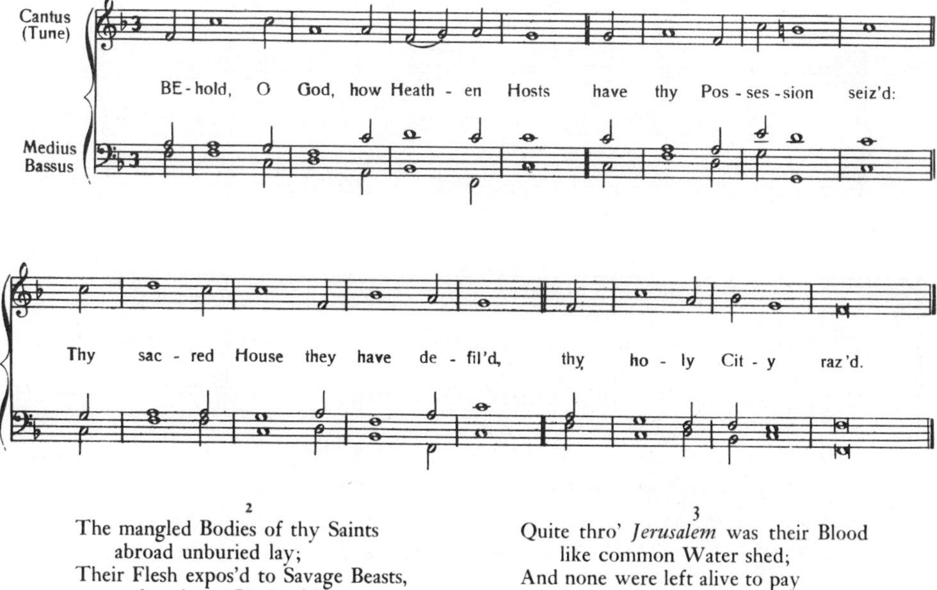

2

The mangled Bodies of thy Saints
abroad unburied lay;
Their Flesh expos'd to Savage Beasts,
and rav'nous Birds of Prey.

3

Quite thro' *Jerusalem* was their Blood
like common Water shed;
And none were left alive to pay
last Duties to the Dead.

Ps. 79: Nahum Tate (1698)
(1652–1715)

20a. MIDDLESEX (C.M.)

[*Mear*]

1720

A Sett of Tunes in 3 Parts
Simon Browne
(*London, 1720*)

Simon Browne?

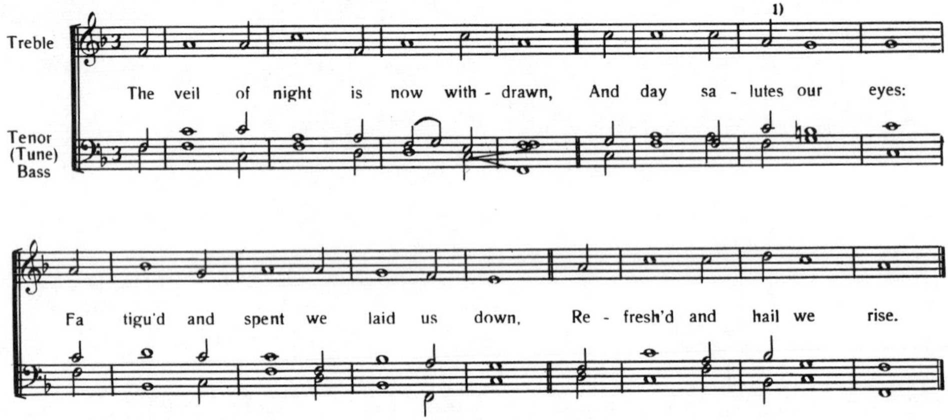
Treble
Tenor (Tune) Bass
1)
The veil of night is now with - drawn, And day sa - lutes our eyes:
Fa tigu'd and spent we laid us down, Re - fresh'd and hail we rise.

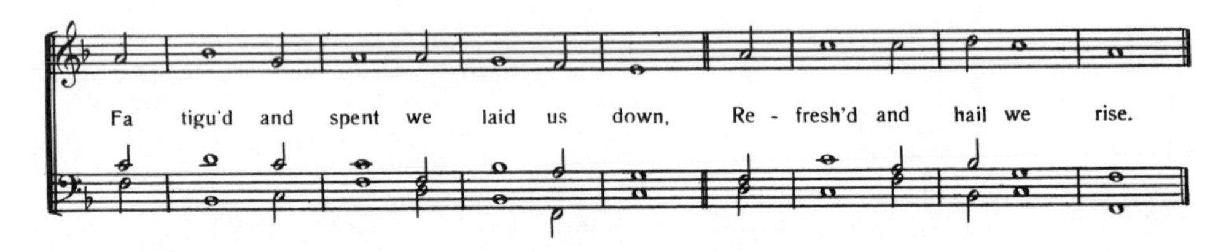

[1] The A is a whole note, and the G is a half note in the original.

Hymns and Spiritual Songs, Simon Browne, 1720

Chapter Two

THE FIRST INSTRUCTION BOOKS AND SINGING SCHOOLS

1721-1764

Just Publish'd, & to be Sold by Samuel Gerrish, A Small Singing Book of 18 Psalm Tunes (both Trible and Bass) in the easy Method of Singing by Letters instead of Notes, first contrived by the Reverend Mr. TUFTS. Neatly engraven on Copper, with suitable directions, very Useful for People even of the meanest capacities, and for Children. Price 1s.

Boston News-Letter, January 21/28, 1723

THE SINGING of hymns and psalms in New England churches gradually deteriorated until at the beginning of the 18th century many congregations were unable to sing more than a few tunes and no two sang them alike. The dearth of printed music in America, and the lack of any means of music education, afforded little if any opportunity for learning to read music. Music was learned by rote, without the help of professional musicians, by a people who were for the most part musically illiterate. The practice of "lining-out" the psalm-tunes had gradually changed the lively singing of the early Puritans into a slow and often highly embellished type of psalm-singing, later called the "Common" or "Usual Way" of singing.

As the need for reform became increasingly apparent, leading ministers, among whom were the Rev. Thomas Symmes of Bradford, Massachusetts, the Rev. John Tufts of Newburyport, and the Rev. Thomas Walter of Roxbury (all contemporaries of J. S. Bach), took steps to improve the situation. Symmes wrote pamphlets and preached sermons on "The Reasonableness of Regular Singing or Singing by Note" (1720) and urged the people to return to the ways of the early New England settlers who could sing correctly by note, and to give up the "many turnings and flourishings with the voice." It remained for the Rev. John Tufts and the Rev. Thomas Walter to publish the first instruction books with music and to lay the foundation for music education in the United States.

The new "Correct" or "Regular Way" of singing by note was not immediately acceptable to all congregations, and many arguments ensued between the older conservatives who preferred the old "Common" or "Usual Way" and the more progressive groups who favored the new "Correct" or "Regular Way." It was not long, however, before the pleasure of meeting together and learning to sing by note in the "Correct Way" led to the establishment of the singing school. The need for music books eventually resulted in a flow of instruction books with music, and in the last decades of the 18th century the singing school became the principal source of music pedagogy, an important part of the social life, and a stimulus to native composers which lasted throughout the 19th century.

John Tufts's *An Introduction to the Singing of Psalm-Tunes*

The complete title page of the Rev. John Tufts's instruction book reads:

AN INTRODUCTION To the Singing OF *Psalm-Tunes*, In a plain & easy Method. With A COLLECTION of Tunes In Three Parts. By the Rev. Mr. TUFTS. The FIFTH EDITION. Printed from *Copper-Plates*, Neatly Engraven. BOSTON, in N.E. Printed for *Samuel Gerrish*, at the Lower End of Cornhill. 1726.

No copies of the first edition of 1721 (which contained twenty tunes in one part) nor of the subsequent three editions are known to exist. The first known edition, the fifth, was published in 1726 with 37 tunes set in three parts. Tufts borrowed 31 of his tunes from Thomas Walter's *Grounds and Rules of Musick Explained* (Boston, 1721, 1723) or John Playford's *Whole Book of Psalms* (London, 1677 and later); the six remaining tunes were taken from other sources.[1] Tufts included all thirteen tunes found in the *Bay Psalm Book*, 1698.

In search of a system that would enable "People even of the meanest capacities and Children" to sing a tune at sight, Tufts used a letter notation that was well known in England and had already appeared underneath the notes in the *Bay Psalm Book* of 1698. Tufts, however, placed the letters F[a], S[ol], L[a], and M[i] on the staff in lieu of the notes. In his "Short Introduction To the Singing of PSALM-TUNES," he explains the notation, clefs, intervals, scales, keys, and time signatures. Tunes in triple time, he states, "are sung about One Third swifter than Common Time." Significantly, he mentions that the ability to sing intervals correctly is "not to be attained ordinarily, without the help of some skilful Person, or of an Instrument." The use of the cello ("the Lord's fiddle") and pitch-pipe in singing schools eventually led to their use in church.

Three tunes from Tufts's *Introduction* are included in the *Anthology*. The tune *Northhampton* is one of three that Tufts evidently took from Simon Browne's *A Sett of Tunes in 3 Parts* (London, 1720). It had also appeared earlier in John Bishop's *A Set of New Psalm Tunes in Four Parts*, advertised in London in 1710. *Northhampton* (No. 21) is unique in being moderately florid, while almost all other

[1] Irving Lowens, "John Tufts' *Introduction to the Singing of Psalm-Tunes* (1721–1744): The First American Music Textbook," *Journal of Research in Music Education*, II (1954), 89–102.

previous settings of psalm-tunes are syllabic.

Tufts's acquaintance with Tate and Brady's *A Supplement to the New Version* (London, 1708) is apparent by his inclusion of *149 Psalm Tune* (No. 22), which first appeared anonymously in that collection. The strong melody, known since 1730 as *Hanover*, is attributed to William Croft and is included in a three-part setting for the first time in Tufts's *Introduction*. It is quite possible that Tufts himself supplied the Medius part.

The *100 Psalm Tune New* (No. 23) is perhaps the most interesting tune in Tufts's publication, not because of any esthetic considerations but because it may possibly be the first complete composition by a native American composer.[2] In the natural minor (Aeolian) mode, the piece is a rare example of a setting of *Psalm 100* in triple time.

Thomas Walter's *The Grounds and Rules of Musick Explained*

The subtitle of this instruction book with music, published in Boston in 1721, reads:

An *Introduction* to the Art of Singing by *Note*. Fitted to the meanest Capacities.

The "Recommendatory Preface" to the Rev. Thomas Walter's book was signed by fifteen ministers, including Walter's grandfather, Increase Mather (1639–1723), and his uncle, Cotton Mather (1663–1728). In the preamble to the *Grounds and Rules* Walter gives a clear picture of the sad state of music as he saw it. It reads in part:

[Once the tunes] were sung according to the Rules of the *Scale of Musick*, but are now miserably tortured, and twisted, and quavered, [ornamented] in some Churches, into a horrid Medly of confused and disorderly Noises . . . and there are no two Churches that sing alike. Yea, I have my self heard (for Instance) *Oxford* Tune sung in *three* Churches (which I purposely forbear to mention) with as much Difference as there can possibly be between *York* and *Oxford* or any two other different Tunes. . . . I have observed in many Places one Man is upon this Note, while another is a Note before him, which produces something so hideous and disorderly, as is beyond Expression bad.

Walter also complains about the "tedious Protraction of the Notes beyond the Compass of a Man's Breath" and says, "I my self have twice in one Note paused to take Breath." In regard to the "Old Way" of singing, Walter affirms that "the Notes sung according to the *Scale and Rules of Musick* are the true "*Old Way*," that is, the way of the early New England settlers.

The 24 tunes in Walter's *Grounds and Rules* were set in three parts without a text, and neatly engraved with regular bar-lines (for the first time in the Colonies). They include all thirteen tunes in the *Bay Psalm Book* of 1698, and 23 of Walter's tunes are also found in Tufts's *Introduction* (1726). Playford's *Whole Book of Psalms . . . Composed in Three Parts* (1677) was the principal source for Walter's settings. The Introduction to his *Grounds and Rules*, although lacking the conciseness and clarity of Tufts's, includes "Some brief and very plain Instructions for Singing by Note."

London Tune (No. 24, not to be confused with *London New*) was named *Litchfield* by Playford (1671), and his two-part setting of the tune called *Lichfield* [*sic*] is one of the thirteen in the *Bay Psalm Book* (1698). The hexatonic melody, with the seventh omitted, is of special interest, for it begins in dominant harmony. Walter retained Playford's lowered sixth degree of the scale in the first edition (1721), but not in the second edition (1723).

The tune *Southwel New* (No. 25) has not been located in earlier sources and may have been composed entirely by Walter. If so, it

[2] *Ibid.*, pp. 97–99.

would antedate Tufts's *100 Psalm Tune New* by several years and would be the first composition by a native-born American.

The rhythmic pattern of the familiar *100 Psalm Tune* (No. 26), typical of Playford's settings, is found in the *Bay Psalm Book* (1698) but varies from the patterns of most earlier versions. This is the first three-part setting of the *100 Psalm Tune* to be published in America.

The Collections of William Tans'ur and Aaron Williams

One of the strong influences on the composers of early sacred music in America was the popular *The Royal Melody Compleat: or, The New Harmony of Sion* (London, 1755) by William Tans'ur (Tanzer), an English composer-compiler and theoretician. His "new and correct introduction to the grounds of musick" in *The Royal Melody* was extensively copied by William Billings and other early New England composers. Daniel Bayley (c. 1725–1799) published the first American edition of *The Royal Melody* in Boston in 1767, and by 1774 the work had gone through seven editions.[3]

Selections of music from the *Universal Psalmodist* (London, 1763) by another English psalmodist, Aaron Williams, were included in Bayley's early editions of *The Royal Melody*. In 1769, Bailey [*sic*] brought out the fifth edition with a new title, *The American Harmony: or, Royal Melody Complete* and incorporated Williams's *Universal Psalmodist* as the second part of the book.

Following the trend toward a livelier type of church music, partly the result of the evangelical revival in England, Tans'ur added "fuging" choruses to some of his psalm-tunes, suggesting, however, that they "may be omitted, where *Voices* can't be had to perform them according to *Art*."

Tans'ur's *Westerham* (No. 27) is an 18th-century example of an added fuging chorus, a form of imitative writing that had been in use in England since the late 16th century. This type of English psalmody was also well known in New England and was imitated by Billings in his comparatively few fuging tunes.

St. Martin's tune by Tans'ur (No. 28), with Tate and Brady's version of *Psalm 78*, is still sung today by the alumni at Harvard commencements.

Aaron Williams's *St. Thomas's* (No. 29) is another tune that has stood the test of time, and except for the melody being in the soprano it is found in modern hymnals in almost the identical form of the original.

Josiah Flagg's *A Collection of the Best Psalm Tunes*

Josiah Flagg took an active part in the concert life of Boston and introduced many foreign musicians there, among them William Selby. His collection of psalm-tunes, engraved on copper plates by Paul Revere, included 116 psalm-tunes in two, three, and four parts and two anthems ("the greater part of them never before printed in America") and was published in Boston in 1764. *Hallelujah* (No. 30), taken from Flagg's collection, is an interesting example of five-part writing and the use of imitation, the trumpet-like theme even ap-

[3] A bibliographical study of Daniel Bayley's *The American Harmony* by Irving Lowens and Allen P. Britton appeared in the *Papers* of the Bibliographical Society of America, Vol. 49, Fourth Quarter, 1955.

pearing in stretto and augmentation. Flagg published a second collection in 1766 which contained upwards of twenty anthems by English composers. The anthems in his two collections and Daniel Bayley's edition of Tans'ur's *Royal Melody* (1767) served as models for American composers, particularly in New England.[4]

[4] Ralph T. Daniel, "English Models for the First American Anthems," *Journal of the American Musicological Society*, XII (1959), 49–58.

21. NORTHAMPTON (C.M.)

c. 1710

An Introduction to the Singing of Psalm-Tunes
John Tufts
(*Boston, 1726*)

[1] This note is A in Tufts's *Introduction* and in Browne's *Sett of Tunes*, 1720. Bishop (c. 1710) has G.

2
But he upon Jehovah's law
doth set his whole delight,
And in his law doth meditate
both in the day and night.

3
He shall be like a planted tree
by water-brooks which shall
In his due season use his fruit,
whose leaf shall never fail.

4
And all he doth, shall prosper well,
the wicked are not so:
But they are like unto the chaff
which wind drives to and fro.

5
For of the righteous men, the Lord
acknowledgeth the way:
Where as the way of wicked men
shall utterly decay.

Ps. 1: *Bay (New England) Psalm Book*, 1651

22. 149 PSALM TUNE (10.10.11.11.)

(*Hanover*)

1708

An Introduction to the Singing of Psalm-Tunes
John Tufts
(*Boston, 1726*)

William Croft
(1678–1727)

Cantus (Tune)

Medius
Bassus

O Praise ye the Lord, pre - pare your glad Voice,

His Praise in the great As - sem - bly — to — sing,

In our great Cre - a - tor let Is - r'el re - joice;

And the Chil - dren of Sion be glad in their King.

[1] F in the original.
[2] B-flat in the original.
[3] E-flat in the original.

2

Let them his great Name extol in the Dance;
With Timbrel and Harp his praises express;
Who always takes pleasure his Saints to ad-
vance,
And with his Salvation the Humble to bless.
Ps. 149: *New Version*, Tate and Brady, 1698

23. 100 PSALM TUNE NEW (L.M.)

1726

An Introduction to the Singing of Psalm-Tunes
John Tufts
(*Boston, 1726*)

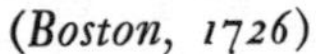

John Tufts?
(1689–1750)

2

Convinc'd that he is God alone,
From whom both we and all proceed;
We, whom he chuses for his own,
The Flock that he vouchsafes to feed.

3

O enter then his Temple-Gate
Thence to his Courts devoutly press,
And still your grateful Hymns repeat,
And still his Name with Praises bless.

Ps. 100: *New Version*, Tate and Brady, 1698

24. LONDON TUNE (C.M.)

(Litchfield)

1677

The Grounds and Rules of Musick Explained
Thomas Walter
(Boston, 1721)

2
Into deep waters I am come,
where floods me overflow.
I of my crying weary am;
my throat is dried so.

3
Mine eyes fail, for my God I wayt.
They that have hated mee
Without a cause, then mine heads hairs,
they more in number bee:

4
Also mine enemies wrongfully
they are that would me slay,
They mighty are, then I restor'd
what I took not away.

5
O God thou know'st my foolishness,
my sin's not hid from thee.
Who wayt on thee, Lord GOD of hoasts,
let not be sham'd for mee:

Ps. 69: *Bay (New England) Psalm Book*, 1651

25. SOUTHWEL NEW (S.M.)

1721

The Grounds and Rules of Musick Explained
Thomas Walter
(*Boston, 1721*)

Thomas Walter?
(1696–1725)

2
In safety keep my soul,
for gracious am I.
My God save thou thy servant now,
that doth on thee rely.

3
Jehovah gracious
O be thou unto mee:
Because that I aloud do cry
Through all the day to thee.

4
O make thy servants soul
that it may joyfull bee:
Because that I O LORD, on high
do lift my soul to thee.

5
For thou O LORD art good,
to pardon prone also;
And to them all on thee that call
in mercy rich art thou.

Ps. 86: *Bay (New England) Psalm Book*, 1651

26. 100 PSALM TUNE (L.M.)

1677

The Grounds and Rules of Musick Explained
Thomas Walter
(*Boston, 1721*)

[1]B in the original.

2

It's he that made us, and not wee,
His folk, his pasture sheep also.
Into his gates with thanks come yee:
With prayses to his Court-yards go.

3

Give thanks to him, bless ye his name,
Because Jehovah he is good:
His mercy ever is the same,
His trueth throughout all ages stood.

Ps. 100: *Bay (New England) Psalm Book*, 1651

27. WESTERHAM TUNE (C.M.)

Psalm 81

1755

The Royal Melody Complete: or, The New Harmony of Zion
William Tans'ur, Sr.
(*Boston, 1767*)

William Tans'ur, Sr.
(1706–1783)

Lift up your Voice, To Ja - cob's God al - way.
and lift up your Voice, To Ja - cob's God al - way.
and lift up your Voice, To Ja - cob's God al - way.
Lift up your Voice, To Ja - cob's God al - way.
Chorus
Be
Be joy - - full. and lift

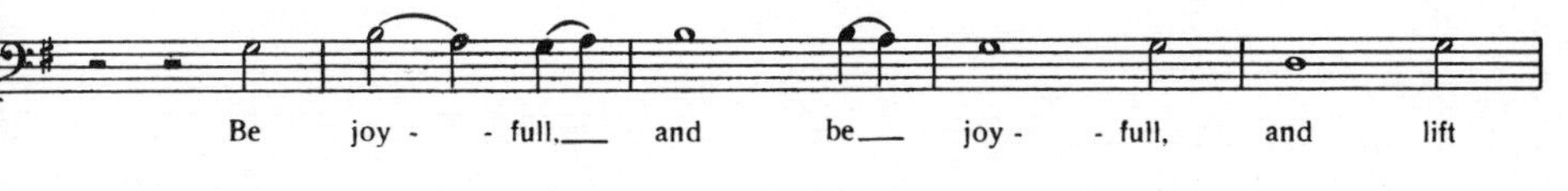
Be joy - - full, and be joy - - full, and lift

Be joy - full, and lift up your Voice, To
joy - full, and be joy - full, and lift up your Voice, To
up your Voice, be joy - full, and lift up your Voice, To
up your Voice, be joy - full, and lift up your Voice, To
Ja - - - - cob's God al - way.
Ja - - - - cob's God al - way.
Ja - - - - cob's God al - way.
Ja - - - - cob's God al - way.

28. ST. MARTIN'S (C.M.)

1755

The American Harmony: or, Royal Melody Complete
William Tans'ur, Sr.
(*Newbury-Port, 1769*)

William Tans'ur, Sr.
(1706–1783)

Ps. 78: *New Version*, Tate and Brady, 1717

29. ST. THOMAS'S (S.M.)

1770

The Universal Psalmodist
Aaron Williams
(*London, 1770*)

Aaron Williams
(1731–1776)

2
These Temples of his Grace,
How beautifull they Stand,
The honours of our Native place,
And Bulwarks of our Land.

3
In Sion God is Known
A refuge in Distress,
How Bright has his Salvations shown,
Through all her Palaces.

5
When Navies tall and Proud
Attempt to spoil our Peace,
He sends his Tempests roaring loud,
And sinks them in the Seas.

7
In every new Distress,
We'll to his House repair,
We'll Think upon his Wondrous Grace,
And Seek Deliv'rance there.

Ps. 48: Isaac Watts (1719)
(1674–1748)

30. HALLELUJAH

A Chorus for 5 Voices

1764

A Collection of the Best Psalm-Tunes
Josiah Flagg
(*Boston, 1764*)

Josiah Flagg?
(1738–1794)

Hal - le - lu - jah, Hal - le - lu - jah, Hal - le - lu -
Hal - le - lu - jah, Hal - le - lu - jah, Hal - le - lu - jah, Hal - le - lu -
- lu - jah, Hal - le - lu - jah, Hal - le - lu - jah, Hal - le -
Hal - le - lu - jah, Hal - le - lu - jah,
Hal - le - lu - jah, Hal - le - lu - jah, Hal - le - lu -

jah.
jah, Hal - le - lu - jah.
lu - jah, Hal - le - lu - jah.
Hal - le - lu - jah, Hal - le - lu - jah, Hal - le - lu - jah.
jah, Hal - le - lu - jah.

Chapter Three

THE MUSIC OF THE EPHRATA CLOISTER AND THE MORAVIANS

"While at Bethlehem, I inquir'd a little into the practice of the Moravians: some of them had accompanied me, and all were very kind to me. . . . I was at their church, where I was entertain'd with good musick, the organ being accompanied with violins, hautboys, flutes, clarinets, etc."

The Autobiography of Benjamin Franklin

The Ephrata Cloister

FOR THE first hundred years the mainstream of musical activity in America centered in New England. Early in the 18th century, however, a strong musical current was felt in Philadelphia, Charleston, and New York. Pennsylvania, a Quaker province, became a refuge for many religious sects from Central Europe, particularly from Germany. One of these groups, a semi-monastic community of Seventh-Day Baptists, was established in 1732 by Conrad Beissel at Ephrata ("the beautiful") in Lancaster County.[1]

[1] Hans David has made a comparison of Ephrata and Bethlehem in Pennsylvania, published in the *Papers of the American Musicological Society*, 1941.

Music played an important part in the religious services at the Ephrata Cloister, and Beissel organized and trained a chorus capable of singing in as many as eight parts, with antiphonal singing an important feature. Music of European composers was not drawn on, however, and in addition to managing all the affairs of the Cloister the indefatigable Beissel composed over a thousand hymns and even settings of whole chapters from the Old Testament. Instrumental accompaniments were not indicated, but the lower part was often played by an instrument, with instruments possibly doubling the other voices.

Virtually a self-taught composer, Beissel

developed his own unorthodox and highly original theories of composition, which are demonstrated in his setting of the text, *Gott ein Herrscher aller Heyden* (No. 31). Chords in root position are interchanged indiscriminately with second inversions, and hymns may even begin with a second inversion. Parallel fifths and octaves are a common occurrence. There is little if any use of modulation or suspensions, and dissonances appear only as passing notes. An occasional brief imitation between two parts is as far as Beissel was able to go in counterpoint. The music was sung rather freely, the rhythm following the text. Stressed syllables were held longer, the length depending on the amount of stress the syllable received.

The activities of the Ephrata Cloister were known to many Pennsylvania families whose children attended their schools and to such leaders as Francis Hopkinson, George Washington, and Benjamin Franklin (who printed one of the Ephrata hymnals as early as 1730). However, the music composed by Beissel and his successor, Peter Miller, although interesting as an example of primitive art, lacked the ingredients necessary for it to have any lasting significance.

Music of the Moravians

In 1732 a small band of members of the *Unitas Fratrem* (Unity of Brethren), spiritual descendants of the Bohemian reformer, John Hus, sought refuge in Georgia; they later moved to Nazareth, Pennsylvania, and in 1741 founded Bethlehem. The missionary zeal of the Moravians, as they came to be known, also led to the establishment of other communities, notably in Lititz, Pennsylvania, and Salem, North Carolina.

The activities at the communities were numerous and varied, especially at Bethlehem, where an intensively active musical life developed. A *Collegium musicum* was formed in 1744 and performed throughout the years choral, chamber, and symphonic works by Karl F. Abel, Johann Christoph Friedrich Bach, Johann Stamitz, Handel, Graun, Haydn, Mozart, and many other composers, often for the first time in America.

Trombone choirs were organized; they have remained an integral part of Moravian life up to the present time. The concerts by the *Collegium musicum* attracted music lovers from Philadelphia and New York as well as other communities. The work of the Moravians became known to many prominent men, including the Marquis de Lafayette, George Washington, and Benjamin Franklin.

In 1766 a Moravian composer, Jeremiah Dencke, wrote the first sacred music in America with an instrumental accompaniment. Other professionally trained Moravian musicians, who modelled their style after the pre-Classical Central Europeans, composed the first chamber music in America and wrote elaborate arias and choruses with instrumental accompaniment for use in church. The art of organ building was developed, especially by David Tannenberg (1728–1804) of Lititz, who constructed organs along the lines of those by the famous German builders Arp Schnitger (1648–1720) and Gottfried Silbermann (1683–1753). Woodwinds, strings, and brasses were imported, since comparatively few of these instruments were made here until the early 19th century.

The period of the Moravians' greatest musical activity and accomplishment began about 1770, the date of William Billings's first publication, *The New-England Psalm-Singer*. By 1850 the Moravian force was spent, but the musical tradition was handed down by Johann C. Till (1762–1844) and Peter Wolle (1792–1871), both pupils of Johann Friedrich Peter (1746–1813). Today Bethlehem is known by the annual performances of the Bach Choir, and music by the Moravians is heard in church and concert with increasing frequency.

Three outstanding Moravian composers, John Antes, Johann Friedrich Peter, and David Moritz Michael, are represented in the *Anthology*. The music was chosen by Dr. Donald M. McCorkle,[2] Director of The Moravian Music Foundation, and represents a cross section of the finest Moravian compositions.

John Antes's preferred medium was the anthem, 25 of which have been found. Some are solo anthems, while others call for a four-part chorus, but in all cases they are supplied with an instrumental accompaniment, usually strings and only rarely with the addition of two horns and continuo. According to Dr. McCorkle, *Go, congregation, go!* (No. 32) and *Surely He has borne our griefs* (No. 33) were intended to be performed as a unit, the resulting form being what the English often loosely termed an Ode. These two outstanding compositions were originally scored for strings, and their poignancy and melodic beauty point to Antes as one of the most able American-born composers of his time.

The first chamber works by a native-born American composer were three trios for two violins and cello, also by John Antes. They were composed, probably between 1779–1781, while he was a missionary in Cairo, and were published in London. At a time when compositions for small string groups often focused the melodic interest on the first violin, Antes expertly distributed the melody and accompaniment figures among all three instruments. The influence of Haydn is apparent in these works, and there is some evidence that he knew Haydn and his string trios. The first movement, Allegro, of the Trio II in D minor, Opus 3, is in the conventional sonata-allegro form (No. 34). The other two movements of the Trio are Andante un poco Adagio and Presto.

Johann Friedrich (John Frederik) Peter, who went to Salem in 1780, composed six quintets for two violins, two violas, and one cello, which have survived in a holograph score and parts dated January 9, 1789. The thoroughness of his study of the music of pre-Classical European composers, as well as Haydn, is reflected in the form and the harmonic and melodic styles of the quintets. The second movement (Adagio) of Quintet V (No. 35) is in binary form, and it reveals Peter's progressive harmonic style and freedom of modulation. The two violins and two violas are handled in pairs, while the cello, assigned to its principal function as bass, occasionally joins the violin or viola in short passages in thirds or sixths.

I will make an everlasting covenant (No. 36), originally scored for strings, is one of Peter's finest sacred songs. He achieves unity in this through-composed solo through repetitions of the 16th-note motif, the frequent use of appoggiaturas at the ends of phrases, and the simple rhythmic pattern of the voice part. Of special interest are the uneven lengths of the phrases.

Although David Moritz Michael composed anthems and sacred ariettas, his most unusual contributions were fourteen *Parthien*, or Suites, for two clarinets, two horns, one or two bassoons, and an additional flute or trumpet. It is not fanciful to imagine these compositions as works intended for "al fresco" performances, for two of these wind sextets were actually composed as "water music" and were played on a barge excursion on the Lehigh River. In the first movement of *Parthia No. 1*, which is in binary form, Michael demonstrates a thorough knowledge of wind instruments (No. 37).

Dr. McCorkle[3] has pointed out that very little of the music of the Moravians became a part of musical life in America. The Moravians did, however, contribute to the musical culture through their instruments, their *Collegia musica*, their first performances of major European oratorios and symphonies, and the quantity and quality of their various musical activities.

[2] Dr. McCorkle's many articles on Moravian music and musicians are available from The Moravian Music Foundation, Winston-Salem, North Carolina.

[3] Donald M. McCorkle, "The Moravian Contribution to American Music," Music Library Association *Notes*, XIII (Dec. 1956).

31. GOTT EIN HERRSCHER ALLER HEYDEN

1754

Wunder-Spiel
(*Ephrata*, 1754)

Johann Conrad Beissel
(1690–1768)

und ihr recht las - sen hoch her-gehn an sei - nem Ei - gen-thum, dass nun giebt Preiss und Ruhm.
so wird man Freud und Won - ne sehen
und ihr recht las - sen hoch her-gehn an sei - nem Ei - gen-thum, dass nun giebt Preiss und Ruhm.
so wird man Freud und Won - ne sehen
und ihr recht las - sen hoch her-gehn an sei - nem Ei - gen-thum, dass nun giebt Preiss und Ruhm.
so wird man Freud und Won - ne sehen

Gott — dem Kö - nig, der sie er- höht, ihr Völ - ker seht! wie — Got -tes Braut — nun ein- her - geht.
Gott — dem Kö - nig, der sie er- höht ihr Völ - ker seht! wie — Got -tes Braut — nun ein- her-geht.
Gott — dem Kö - nig, der sie er- höht, ihr Völ - ker seht! wie — Got -tes Braut — nun ein - her-geht.

32. GO, CONGREGATION, GO!

Aria for Soprano

c. 1795

Manuscript

John Antes
(1740–1811)
Edited and arranged by
Donald M. McCorkle

Note: *tr* indicates the points at which double trills (in the top voices simultaneously) are used in the original accompaniment. Since it is impossible to transcribe this device for keyboard, it may be more satisfactory to omit all such trills.

iour, thy Sav - iour in Geth - se - ma - ne;
tr
rinf.
(ten.)
tr
B
Go, con - gre - ga - tion, go! go and see, go and see thy Sav - iour, thy Sav - iour
(9)
p

Christian Gregor
(1723–1801)

33. SURELY HE HAS BORNE OUR GRIEFS

Anthem for Mixed Voices

c. 1795

Manuscript
(*Fullneck, England, c. 1795*)

John Antes
(1740–1811)
Edited and arranged by
Donald M. McCorkle

griefs and car - - ried our sor - - rows.
griefs and car - - ried our sor - - rows.
griefs and car - - ried our sor - - rows.
griefs and car - - ried our sor - - rows.
A
He was wound - - ed for our trans -
He was wound - - ed for our trans -
He was wound - - ed for our trans -
He was wound - - ed for our trans -

gress - - ions, He was bruis - ed for
gress - - ions, He was bruis - ed for
gress - - ions, He was bruis - ed for
gress - - ions, He was bruis - ed for
our in - i - qui - ties;
our in - i - qui - ties;
our in - i - qui - ties;
our in - i - qui - ties;

B
The chas - tise - ment of our peace lay up -
The chas - tise - ment of our peace lay up -
The chas - tise - ment of our peace lay up -
The chas - tise - ment of our peace lay up -
on Him: And with His stripes we are heal - -
on Him; And with His stripes we are heal - -
on Him; And with His stripes we are heal - -
on Him: And with His stripes we are heal - -
tr

Isaiah 53: 4, 5

34. TRIO II
from
Tre Trii, per due Violini and Violoncello, Obligato
c. 1779/81
First Movement

J. Bland
(*London, c. 1780*)

John Antes
(1740–1811)
Edited and arranged by
Thor Johnson and Donald M. McCorkle

10
(dolce)

20
f
(f)
f

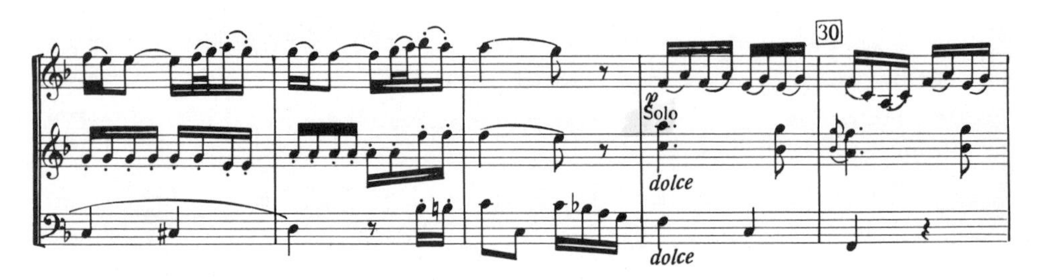
30
p
Solo
dolce
dolce

40

p
ff
p
ff
p
ff

50
dolce
Solo
dolce
dolce

f
f
f

60
rinf.
rinf.
rinf.

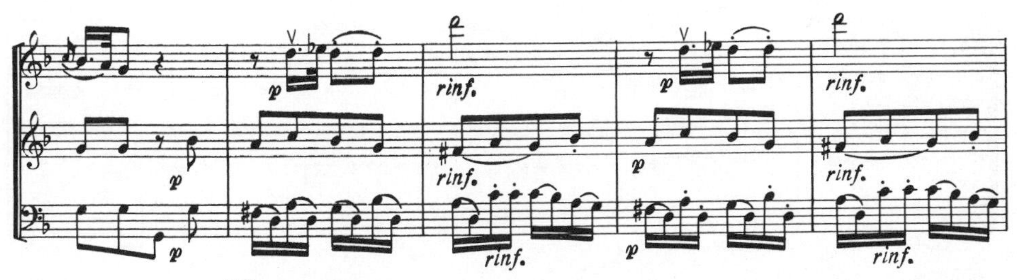
p
rinf.
p
rinf.
p
p
rinf.
p
rinf.
rinf.
p
rinf.

70
p
dolce
p
p
p
p

80
f
Solo
p

f
p
rinf.
(rinf.)

90
dolce

rinf.

100
p

110
Solo
f
f
f

pp tutti(a) una corda
pp
p(p)

120
Solo

(dolce)
(dolce)

130
f
ff
(f)
ff
(f)
ff

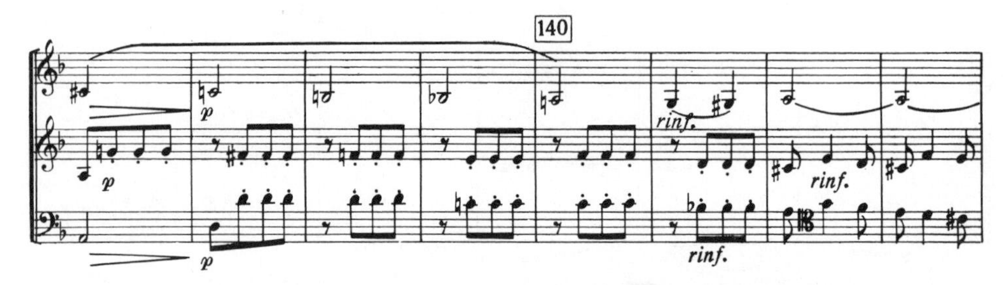
140
p
rinf.
p
rinf.
p
rinf.

(Solo)
p
Solo
dolce

150
rinf.
rinf.

160

p
ff
p
ff
p
ff

35. QUINTET V

from

Quintetti a Due Violini, Due Viole, e Violoncello

1789

Second Movement

Manuscript
(*Salem, N.C., 1789*)

Johann Friedrich Peter
(1746–1813)
Edited by Hans T. David

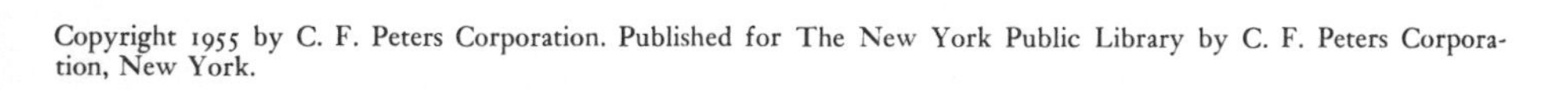

tr
tr
cresc.
f
p
pp
cresc.
f
p
pp
cresc.
f
p
pp
cresc.
f
p
pp
cresc.
f
p
pp

tr
tr
mf
tr
tr
mf
mf
mf
mf

cresc.
f
cresc.
f
cresc.
f
cresc.
f
cresc.
f

tr
ff
cresc.

p
mf
cresc.
tr

tr
f
p
pp

36. I WILL MAKE AN EVERLASTING COVENANT

Ich will mit euch einen ewigen Bund machen

1782

Manuscript
(*Salem, N.C., 1782*)

Johann Friedrich Peter
(1746–1813)
Edited and arranged by
Thor Johnson and Donald M. McCorkle

Original in D major.
Note: *tr* indicates the points at which double trills (in the top voices simultaneously) are used in the original accompaniment. Since it is impossible to transcribe this device for keyboard, it will be more satisfactory to omit all such trills.

(p)
an ev - er - last - ing
Ich will mit euch, mit
p

cov - e - nant, I will make, I will make, will
euch ei- nen e - - wi - gen Bund, ei- nen e - wi- gen

(p)
make with you, an
Bund ma- chen, Ich
3
3
f
p

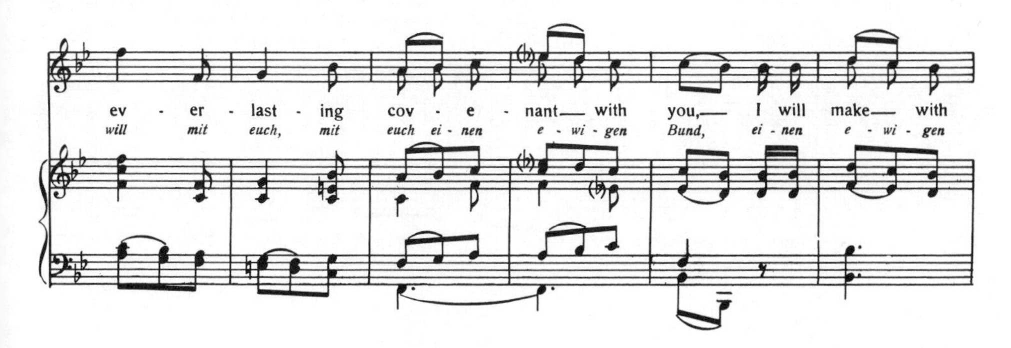
ev - er - last - ing cov - e - nant with you, I will make with
will mit euch, mit euch ei- nen e - wi - gen Bund, ei - nen e - wi - gen

Isaiah 55: 3
(Original in German)

37. PARTHIA NO. 1

First Movement

c. 1807

Manuscript
(*Bethlehem, c. 1807*)

David Moritz Michael
(1751–1827)
Edited by Donald M. McCorkle

Cl.
Trpt.
Hn.
Bsn.
(p)
p
(p)
(p)
p
p

B
Cl.
Trpt.
Hn.
Bsn.
f
p
(f)
(p)
f

C
Cl.
Trpt.
Hn.
Bsn.
Cl.
Trpt.
Hn.
Bsn.

D
Cl.
Trpt.
Hn.
Bsn.

Cl.
Trpt.
Hn.
Bsn.

E
Cl.
Trpt.
Hn.
Bsn.
(p)
(p)
(p)
(p)
(p)
(p)

Cl.
Trpt.
Hn.
Bsn.
f
p
f
p
f
p
f
f
p
f
f
p
f
f
(p)
(f)

F
Cl.
Trpt.
Hn.
Bsn.

Cl.
Trpt.
Hn.
Bsn.

G

H
Cl.
Trpt.
Hn.
Bsn.

Cl.
Trpt.
Hn.
Bsn.

J
Cl.
rpt.
In.
Bsn.
K

Cl.
p
f
(p)
p
f
p
Trpt.
(f)
(p)
Hn.
(f)
(p)
(f)
(p)
Bsn.
(f)
(p)

L
Cl.
(p)
(f)
(p)
(f)
Trpt.
(p)
(f)
Hn.
(p)
(f)
(p)
(f)
Bsn.
(p)
(f)

Chapter Four

NATIVE AMERICAN COMPOSERS

1759-1810

Enlisted in the cause of sin,
Why should a good be evil?
Music, alas, too long has been
Press'd to obey the devil.
Jeremiah Ingalls

KNOWN AS our first native American composers, Francis Hopkinson and James Lyon stand apart from the sturdy, self-made New England composers of the last three decades of the 18th century.

Hopkinson, one of America's most versatile men, belonged to a circle of gentlemen amateurs who were active in the musical life of Philadelphia. He began to compose while still a student; and in 1759, at the age of twenty-two, he wrote his art-song, *My days have been so wondrous free* (No. 38), the first known secular composition by a native American composer.

Hopkinson's songs were modelled after those of popular contemporary English composers, particularly Thomas Arne (1710–1778). The songs were written in two parts, treble and bass, and the harpsichordist was expected to fill in the harmonies according to his own discretion or ability. Although not without charm, the lack of originality and limited circulation prevented the songs from having any real influence on the development of music in America.

George Washington, emerging as the military and political leader of our new nation, became the subject for many songs, among them *A Toast* written by his friend, Francis Hopkinson (No. 39). The music is stylistically akin to the English national anthem, and several measures were apparently freely borrowed.

The Rev. James Lyon published in Philadelphia, 1761, a collection with the following title:

Urania, or a Choice Collection of Psalm-Tunes, Anthems, and Hymns, From the most approved Authors, with some Entirely New, in Two, Three and Four Parts. The whole Peculiarly adapted to the Use of CHURCHES and PRIVATE FAMILIES. To which are Prefixed The Plainest & most Necessary Rules of Psalmody.

The music was entirely by English composers except for six original compositions by Lyon. The tune *God Save the King* appeared for the first time in America in Lyon's *Urania*, where it was called *Whitefield's* (No. 40) and set to the hymn *Come Thou Almighty King*, taken from the hymn collection of the great English Methodist revivalist, George Whitefield (1714–1770).

Lyon's *Friendship* (No. 41), one of his most important compositions, was first published anonymously in 1774 in John Stickney's extensive collection *Gentleman and Lady's Musical Companion*. The somewhat florid anthem or ode is in three sections, all integrated through the use of a group of 16th notes which appears in the various voices at different times. The effective middle section, in the tonic minor key of G, reflects the sentiment of the text, "in floods our sorrows roll."

By 1770 the singing school, which had its beginnings in New England in the first decades of the 18th century, had developed into a flourishing institution. The demand for music and instruction was met by a talented group of self-taught composer-compilers who published over 370 tunebooks before 1811.

The typical New England musician of the period 1770–1810 was a hardy and enthusiastic individual steeped in the heritage of psalm-singing, a man of modest circumstances and humble occupation. He was a composer, a compiler of tunebooks, and a singing master who traveled through the countryside holding classes in taverns, schools, and churches. Most of these men had a limited education, a few were college graduates. Some were prominent in politics and became leading citizens; others fought in the Revolution.

The music in the tunebooks included psalm-tunes, hymns, fuging tunes, anthems, and set pieces, and it was "designed for the use of singing-schools, musical societies, and churches." Thus, the same music served the secular as well as the religious needs of the people and was a part of their everyday life.

The theoretical part of the tunebooks varied from elementary explanations to extensive treatises covering music theory, tone production, and interpretative suggestions. A detailed explanation of the balance of voices in the chorus was often included. In general the bass was heavily emphasized. William Billings, whose lively introductions are of special interest, recommended that in a chorus of 40 voices, twenty should sing the bass, with the other twenty divided among the upper parts. He also preferred two or three voices on the parts marked "solo" and suggested that these be sung softly until all the parts join in the chorus as strong as possible.

Jacob Kimball (*Rural Harmony*, 1793) gives some suggestions for interpretation and states:

In a company of singers it would have a good effect for some of the performers on each part to be silent when passages marked *piano* occur; the additional strength of their voices in the *forte*, which generally precedes or succeeds the *piano* would mark the contrast more distinctly and give peculiar force and energy to the performance. In fuguing music, the strength of the voices should increase as the parts fall in.

With reference to double or "choosing" notes in one part, Kimball advised that the singers should divide the notes equally between them. Other writers suggested that one or the other note be chosen.

As for tone production, Simeon Jocelin (*Chorister's Companion*, 1782) wrote:

Let the voice be clear and smooth as possible neither forcing the sound through the nose, nor blowing through the teeth with the mouth shut. . . . a trembling of the voice is also carefully to be avoided. . . . the notes should not be struck abruptly like the report of a smith's hammer, but should be begun and ended soft, swelling greatly as the air of the tune requires. Notes of 2 beats admit of a double swell, the first fullest, the second soft like an echo. High notes should be sung soft, but not faint; low notes full but not harsh. Let the bass be sung bold and majestic, the tenor firm and manly, the counter clear and lofty, and the treble soft and delicate.

All vocal music of this period was written in open score, and the principal melody (air or tune) was invariably placed in the tenor voice in all part-music for four voices; only in the early 19th century did it find its way up to the treble voice. It was the usual practice for a few treble voices to sing the tenor part an octave higher than the men and for a few tenors to sing the treble part an octave lower than the women. Billings enthusiastically wrote that "a tune so sung (although it has but four parts) is in effect the same as six. Such a conjunction of masculine and feminine voices is beyond expression sweet and ravishing." The doubling of voices may not have been followed strictly, however, since it was customary to sing the tunes with any combination of singers that was available. The fuging sections were often sung without doubling the voices, some tunes were sung throughout in four-part harmony, and on occasion the sopranos and tenors may have exchanged parts. Another possibility is the doubling of the tenor by a few sopranos, but not the doubling of the sopranos by the tenors. Pitches were set by the singing master with a pitch-pipe and were probably lower than the present-day pitch.

The tempos were often indicated by the time signatures, and for this reason the latter have been retained in the *Anthology*. The piano reductions of the part-music have, however, been given conventional time signatures. It must be kept in mind that the deciding factor in the choice of a tempo should, of course, rest in the character of the text and the music. Jacob Kimball gave the following good advice: "A performer should endeavor to form a proper idea of the author's design in a piece of music, and his own judgment and taste must be his principal directors in doing justice to it." The table below summarizes the time signatures as given by Billings in his *Continental Harmony* (Boston, 1794), with their approximate metronomic equivalents.

C	Adagio	quarter note equals	60
¢	Largo	quarter note equals	80
Ↄ̸	Allegro	half note equals	60
2/4		quarter note equals	120
6/4		dotted half note equals	80
6/8		dotted quarter note equals	80
3/2		half note equals	60
3/4		quarter note equals	80
3/8		dotted quarter note equals	53

Twenty-eight compositions by eighteen New England composers are included in this chapter of the *Anthology*. The composers were all born before 1780, and the music was published between 1770 and 1810.

At first the composers were strongly influenced by the English church music found in the collections of William Tans'ur, Aaron Williams, Josiah Flagg, and James Lyon. Towards the close of the Revolutionary War, however, a characteristically American music began to appear in the psalm-tunes and fuging tunes of Daniel Read, Simeon Jocelin, Lewis Edson, Timothy Swan, and many others. This new idiom, with its elements of folk music and harmonic vitality, spread rapidly and dominated the tunebooks until the early 19th century, when public taste began to demand imported European music.

The stylistic traits in this strong and highly original American music include folk-like tunes, irregular phrase-lengths, natural minor (Aeolian) and gapped scales, and virile rhythms. Unconventional harmonic progressions, parallel fifths and octaves, triadic and dyadic harmonies, occasional rhythmic independence of voices (fuging), sudden dissonances derived from contrapuntal part-writing, and the lack of suspensions are among some of the other important characteristics of this music.[1] The

[1] Allen P. Britton has summarized "The Musical Idiom in Early American Tunebooks" in an abstract

personality, environment, and musical independence of these composers are reflected in their music, and they composed, as Billings said, without being "confin'd to any Rules for Composition."

Among the basically homophonic compositions represented here are Billings's *Chester* (No. 43) and *Conquest* (No. 46), Swan's *China* (No. 53, named for a town in Maine), Belknap's *Summer* and *Autumn* (Nos. 63, 64), Holyoke's *Arnheim* (No. 66, written when he was sixteen),[2] and Read's *Windham* (No. 50). Billings's *Jargon* (No. 44), composed as a sarcastic answer to some of his critics, consists of an unbroken succession of discords. Most of the music of this period is in four parts. The occasional use of two-part writing may be found in *Bunker Hill* (No. 47), Ingalls's *Innocent Sounds* (No. 67), Wood's *Worcester* (No. 52), and Jenks's *Evening Shade* (a three-part fuging tune, No. 61).

The melodic lines are the result of horizontal part-writing, and they are usually completely singable in spite of the dissonant clashes resulting from the meeting of independent melodic strands. The principal melody or tune is in the tenor, except in fuging sections, where all voices share the tune. The other voice parts often vary in their melodic interest, the counter (alto) sometimes serving only to complete the harmony. The treble and sometimes the counter may take on the character of a descant with the tenor, and the bass, while serving its harmonic function, not infrequently provides an agreeable melodic line. The bass part was sometimes doubled in octaves, particularly by Billings, and it is quite possible that a cello ("bass viol") was used to play the lower notes.

In the late 18th century, stringed and woodwind instruments were used to accompany the singing in churches as well as performances of secular music. There were however, few organs in the churches in Boston during this time, and most of these were in the Episcopal churches.

Voice ranges vary considerably. Whereas the treble voice rarely exceeds an octave and does not go higher than g^2, the counter has the smallest range—usually a fourth or fifth. The tenor and bass have the widest range, not infrequently an eleventh or twelfth.

A considerable number of the compositions are in major keys, with G, D, and F major the most common. The natural minor is used in Law's *Bunker Hill*, Read's *Windham*, and Doolittle's *Exhortation* (No. 60). The last-named is also one of the few pieces to use the rhythmic device of two against three. Modulations to closely related keys are frequent (see the third relationship in Kimball's *Woburn*, No. 56, second section), but chromaticism is rarely encountered. The last chord often lacks the third and sometimes the fifth, and cadences may be unprepared.

Dotted rhythms are fairly common. Sometimes these are dictated by the rhythm of the text, or they may be a part of a melismatic figure, as in Kimball's *Invitation* (No. 55).

Tone-painting is frequently used to reflect the meaning of the text, or for single words. It is used appropriately in Kimball's *Invitation* on the word "fly," on the word "peace" in Kimball's *Woburn*, for "Blow ye trumpets" in Belcher's *Jubilant* (No. 59), and in many other instances.

Expression marks are rarely indicated in the music and were probably given to the singers by the leader or singing-master. *Forte* and *piano* signs are used in Belknap's *Winter* (No. 65) and Holden's *Coronation* (No. 54); *forte* and *fortissimo* in Billings's *Jargon*.

By far the most popular texts for psalm-tune and hymn settings were the paraphrases by Isaac Watts (1674–1748), who is known as the father of English hymnody. The religious poetry of John and Charles Wesley, Nahum Tate, James Relly, and many others was also set to music by the New England composers. A few compositions with secular texts are found in most tunebooks, but there is no essential difference in musical style between those

in *The Journal of the American Musicological Society*, III (1950), 286.

[2] Louis Pichierri, *Music in New Hampshire, 1623–1800*. New York: Columbia University Press, 1960.

pieces and the ones with sacred texts.

English fuging tunes, as well as psalm-tunes, hymns, and anthems, were known in New England some years before Billings published his first collection, *The New-England Psalm-Singer*, in Boston in 1770.

Irving Lowens has described the fuging tune as follows:

> The typical American fuging tune usually begins with a homophonic section in the course of which a definite cadence is reached, frequently but not always on the tonic of the key. A fresh start is then made, in which each individual voice makes its entrance in succession, the order varying according to the inclination of the composer. In this second section—which was customarily referred to as the "fuge"—some form of imitation, in most cases quite free, was utilized for a measure or two. Normally, the fuge was then repeated, thus making the whole a small, rather tightly organized ABB form.[4]

Typical fuging tunes in the *Anthology* are Morgan's *Montgomery* (No. 58), with two fuging sections, French's *Harmony* (No. 57), Kimball's *Invitation*, Jocelin's *Psalm 146* (No. 48), Belknap's *Spring* (No. 62), Edson's *Lenox* (No. 49), and Ingalls's *Northfield* (No. 68). Atypical fuging tunes are Wood's *Worcester* and Kimball's *Woburn*. *Worcester* begins with fuging, and then proceeds into homophony, with the sequence repeated in the second section. *Woburn* makes special use of fuging in which each part resolves on a pedal point immediately after announcing its one-measure subject. Many of the fuging tunes use a typical repeated-note figure which may be seen in Edson's vigorous *Lenox*, Jocelin's *Psalm 146*, and others. Jenks's *Evening Shade*, a modified form of fuging tune, was one of those that found their way into Southern folk hymnody.

The writing of canons was a popular diversion, and Billings wrote several, of which the serious *When Jesus Wept* (No. 42), composed when he was twenty-two, is extraordinarily successful.

[4] Irving Lowens, "The Origins of the American Fuging Tune," *Journal of the American Musicological Society*, VI (1953), 46.

The anthem differs from the psalm-tune and hymn in length and form and may have either a religious or a secular text, although Billings defines it as "a divine song, generally in prose." Secular anthems by Lyon, Billings, Read, and Shaw are included in this chapter of the *Anthology*. They are all extended compositions, consisting of several sections that are unrelated thematically. Written for mixed voices, they include two-, three-, and four-part writing, occasional "solo" parts (sung by several voices), and chordal and imitative fuging textures. Tone-painting, including quickly changing moods and irregular meters, is often employed. William Billings's entertaining anthem *Modern Music* (No. 45) has a variety of time signatures, with the half note approximately equal to 60 MM, the quarter note equal to 120 MM, and in the final $\frac{6}{4}$ the dotted half note equal to about 80 MM. This amusing piece is in Billings's best homophonic style with almost no fuging. It clearly reflects the meaning and spirit of the text and must indeed have been a popular number at singing schools and concerts.

Down steers the Bass (1785), an anthem in praise of music by Daniel Read (No. 51), is composed to a text that had been set by Billings in 1781 under the title of *Consonance*. Read, like Billings, portrays in music the sense of the words ("Down steers the bass"; "up the treble mounts"; "mix in close embrace"). Separate words such as "warbling" and "rolls" are also imitated in the music. The first part of Read's setting is in two-, three-, and four-part writing; the last section, beginning "And sympathetic strains," makes considerable use of fuging.

Oliver Shaw's *Thanksgiving Anthem* (No. 69) was "composed and arranged for a choir of Singers, with symphonies and interludes for instruments, *ad libertum* [*sic*], and for the piano forte or organ." Although independent parts are not indicated, it may be assumed that the four instruments (clarinet and three strings) would support the voices throughout. The contrast of *forte* and *piano* is achieved not only through the usual use of "P" and "F" symbols, but also by lightening the texture through pairing the voices. The indications "dolce" and "expressivo [*sic*]," rare in music of this period, are also used. This English-influenced anthem includes a short bass solo and a "Hallelujah" ending, characteristic of many compositions of the time and later.

The term "set piece" was generally applied to music that was composed especially for a particular text and that, in contrast to psalm-tunes and hymns, could not be properly sung with another text. The texts of set pieces might be sacred or secular, and irregular meters were often employed. Among the set pieces in this chapter, although not identified as such, is *Bunker Hill* (No. 47).

The fuging tunes had for many years been under criticism in England, and even at the height of their popularity in America toward the end of the 18th century the seeds of dissatisfaction were being sown. Ministers contended that "fuging tunes pall the senses and cease to excite admiration,"[5] and Samuel Holyoke, who included only a few fuging tunes in his *Harmonia Americana* (Boston, 1791), wrote:

> The principal reason why few fuging tunes were inserted was the trifling effect produced by that sort of music; for the parts falling in, one after another each conveying a different idea, confound the sense, and render the performance a mere jargon of words.

Professionally trained European musicians were coming to America in increasing numbers and soon there seemed no longer to be any place for the rough-hewn New England school of composers. After flourishing for three decades, their music went out of fashion and gave way to a new era led by Lowell Mason and the European professional musicians. The music of the New Englanders, however, was not lost. It found its way to the West and South; much of it was preserved in Southern folk hymnody, and it is being heard again today.

[5] Ezra Weld, *A Sermon Preached at a Singing Lecture*, Springfield, 1789, as quoted by Allen P. Britton, *Theoretical Introductions in American Tune-Books to 1800* . . . Unpublished Ph.D. dissertation, University of Michigan, 1949, p. 113.

38. MY DAYS HAVE BEEN SO WONDROUS FREE

1759

Songs (MS, 1759)
Francis Hopkinson

Francis Hopkinson
(1737–1791)

Thomas Parnell
(1679–1718)

39. A TOAST

1778

Benjamin Carr
(*Philadelphia*, [*1799*])

Francis Hopkinson
(1737–1791)

1.'Tis WASH-ING-TON'S Health fill a bump - er a - round, For— he is our
2.'Tis WASH-ING-TON'S Health loud— can - nons should roar, And— trum-pets the
3.'Tis WASH-ING-TON'S Health our— He - ro to bless, May— heav-en look

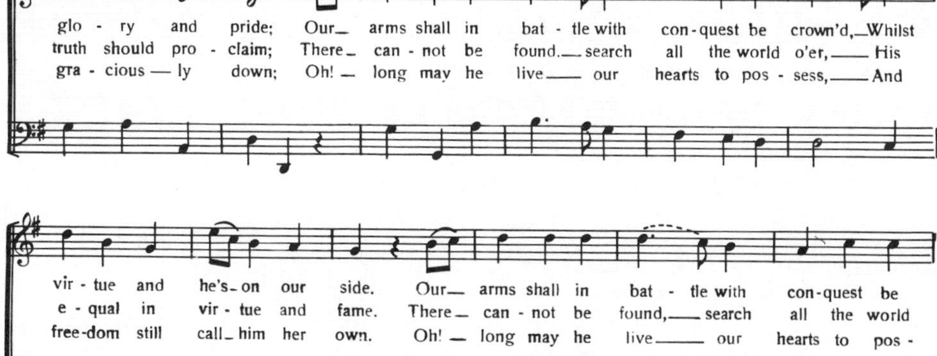

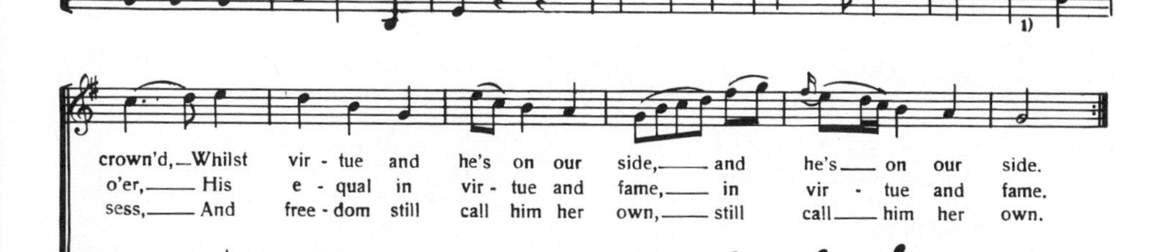

[1] D in the original.

Francis Hopkinson (1778)

The Pennsylvania Packet, April 8, 1778, carried the text only with no reference to its author. When published by Benjamin Carr, Francis Hopkinson, Esq. is named as the composer.

40. WHITEFIELD'S

1761

Urania
James Lyon
(*Philadelphia, 1761*)

Tune: *God Save the King* (1744)

2

Jesus our Lord, arise,
Scatter our enemies,
And make them fall:
Let thine almighty aid,
Our sure defence be made,
Our souls on thee be staid:
Lord, hear our call.

3

Come holy comforter,
Thy sacred witness bear,
In this glad hour:
Thou, who almighty art,
Descend in every heart,
And ne'er from us depart,
Spirit of power.

From George Whitefield's Hymn Collection (1757)

41. FRIENDSHIP

An Ode

1774

Gentleman and Lady's Musical Companion
John Stickney
(*Newburyport, 1774*)

James Lyon
(1735–1794)

Treble
Counter

Tenor
Bass

Friend - ship, thou Char - mer__ of the__ Mind, Thou sweet__ de - lud - ing__ ill,____ The

bright - est__ min - utes Mor - tals find, And sharp - est Hours we feel. Fate has di -

vi - ded__ all__ our__ Shares Of Pleas - ure__ and__ of Pain, Of Pleas - ure, Pleas - ure,

Pleas - ure, Pleas - ure, Pleas - ure__ and__ of__ Pain, Fate has di - vi - ded all our Shares

[1] In later editions.

[2] "Mourn" in later editions.
[3] In later editions.

Horae Lyricae: Isaac Watts (1706)
(1674–1748)

42. A CANON OF 4 IN 1

When Jesus Wept

1770

The New-England Psalm-Singer
William Billings
(Boston, 1770)

William Billings
(1746–1800)

This canon may be sung by four men's voices, four women's voices, or by mixed voices. It should conclude when each voice has sung the four lines of the melody through twice, the voices dropping out in turn.

43. CHESTER

1770

The Singing-Master's Assistant
William Billings
(Boston, 1778)

William Billings
(1746–1800)

2

Howe and Burgoyne and Clinton too,
With Prescot and Cornwallis join'd,
Together plot our Overthrow
In one Infernal league combin'd.

3

When God inspir'd us for the fight,
Their ranks were broke, their lines were forc'd,
Their Ships were Shatter'd in our sight,
Or swiftly driven from our Coast.

4

The Foe comes on with haughty Stride,
Our troops advance with martial noise,
Their Vet'runs flee before our Youth,
And Gen'rals yield to beardless Boys.

5

What grateful Off'ring shall we bring,
What shall we render to the Lord?
Loud Hallelujahs let us Sing,
And praise his name on ev'ry Chord.

William Billings

44. JARGON

1778

The Singing-Master's Assistant
William Billings
(*Boston, 1778*)

William Billings
(1746–1800)

[1] C may have been intended here.

William Billings

45. MODERN MUSIC

1781

The Psalm-Singer's Amusement
William Billings
(Boston, 1781)

William Billings
(1746–1800)

And since we all a - gree to set the tune on E, the
Au - thor's dar - ling Key he pre - fers to the rest,
Let the Treb - le in the
Let the Coun - ter in - spire the
Let the Ten - or suc - ceed and fol - low the
Let the Bass take the Lead and firm - ly pro - ceed, till the
rear no long - - er for - bear, but ex - press - ly de -
rest of the Choir, in - flam'd with de - sire
Lead till the parts are a - - greed
parts are a - greed to fuge a - - way,

clare for a fuge a - way.
to fuge a - way.
Then change to brisk - er
to fuge a - way.
to fuge a - way.
time, and up the Lad - der climb, and down a - -
gain, Then mount the sec - ond time and end the strain.
Then change the Key to pen - - sive tones, and
slow in Treb - le time the Notes. Ex - ceed - - ing

low keep down a - while, then rise by slow de - grees; The
pro - cess sure - ly will not fail to please.
Thro Com-mon and Treb - le we joint - ly have run, We'el
give you their Es - sence com - pound - ed in one: All - tho we are strong-ly at -
tach'd to the rest, Six four is the move-ment that pleas-es us best, that

pleas - es us best, six four is the move-ment that pleas - es us best.
And now we ad - dress you as Friends to the cause (Per_
form - ers are_ mod - est_ and_ write their own laws) Al - tho we are san-guine and_
clap at the Bars, 'tis the part of the Hear - ers to clap their Ap - plause, to_
clap their Ap - plause, 'tis the part of the Hear - ers to clap their Ap - plause.

46. CONQUEST

1786

The Suffolk Harmony
William Billings
(*Boston, 1786*)

William Billings
(1746–1800)

James Relly
(c. 1722–1778)

47. BUNKER HILL

A Sapphick Ode

1775

From a Broadside Version
(*Norwich, Connecticut, 1775*)

Andrew Law?
(1748–1821)

2

Death will invade us by the Means appointed,
And we must all bow to the King of Terrors;
Nor am I anxious, if I am prepared,
What shape he comes in.

8

Now, *Mars,* I dare thee, clad in smoky Pillars
Bursting from Bomb-Shells, roaring from the Cannon,
Rattling in Grape Shot, like a Storm of Hailstones,
Torturing AEther!

14

Fame and dear Freedom, *lure* me on to Battle,
While a fell Despot, grimer than a Death's-Head,
Stings me with Serpents, fiercer than Medusa's:
To the Encounter.

15

Life, for my Country and the Cause of Freedom,
Is but a Trifle for a Worm to part with;
And if preserved in so great a Contest,
Life is redoubled.

From *The American Hero* by Nathaniel Niles

48. PSALM 146

1788

The Chorister's Companion
Simeon Jocelin & Amos Doolittle
(New Haven, 1788)

Simeon Jocelin
(1746–1823)

death, ___ Praise shall em - ploy my no - - bler powers:
death, ___ Praise shall em - ploy my no - - bler powers:
My days of praise
My
My days of praise shall ne'er be
My days of praise shall ne'er be past, ___

4

The Lord hath eyes to give the blind;
The Lord supports the sinking mind;
He sends the labouring conscience peace:
He helps the stranger in distress,
The widow and the fatherless,
And grants the prisoner sweet release.

5

He loves his saints; he knows them well,
But turns the wicked down to hell;
Thy God, O Zion! ever reigns:
Let every tongue, let every age;
In this exalted work engage;
Praise him in everlasting strains.

Ps. 146: Isaac Watts (1719)
(1674–1748)

49. LENOX

1782

The Chorister's Companion
Simeon Jocelin & Amos Doolittle
(*New Haven, 1782*)

Lewis Edson, Sr.
(1748–1820)

[1] The customary repeat signs appear in later editions.

[2] This note is E in the original.
[3] The note D is found in later editions.

2

Thou sun, with dazzling rays,
And moon that rules the night,
Shine to your Maker's praise,
With stars of twinkling light:
His power declare,
Ye floods on high,
And clouds that fly
In empty air.

10

Let all the nations fear
The God that rules above:
He brings his people near,
And makes them taste his love:
While earth and sky
Attempt his praise,
His saints shall raise
His honours high.

Ps. 148: Isaac Watts (1719)
(1674–1748)

50. WINDHAM

1785

The American Singing Book
Daniel Read
(*New Haven, 1785*)

Daniel Read
(1757–1836)

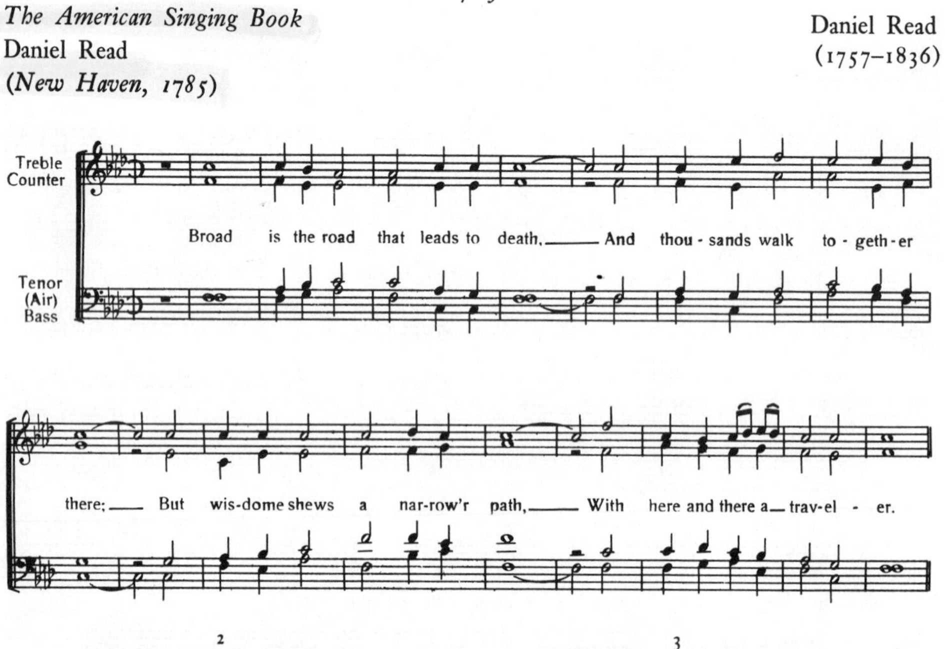

2

"Deny thyself, and take thy cross,"
Is the Redeemer's great command:
Nature must count her gold but dross,
If she would gain the heavenly land.

3

The fearful soul that tires and faints,
And walks the ways of God no more,
Is but esteem'd almost a saint,
And makes his own destruction sure.

4

Lord, let not all my hopes be vain;
Create my heart entirely new;
Which hypocrites could ne'er attain
Which false apostates never knew.

Hymn: Isaac Watts (1707)
(1674–1748)

51. AN ANTHEM

Down Steers the Bass

1785

The American Singing Book
Daniel Read
(*New Haven, 1785*)

Daniel Read
(1757–1836)

Treble
Altus
Tenor
Bass

Down steers the Bass with grave Ma - jes - tic Air,

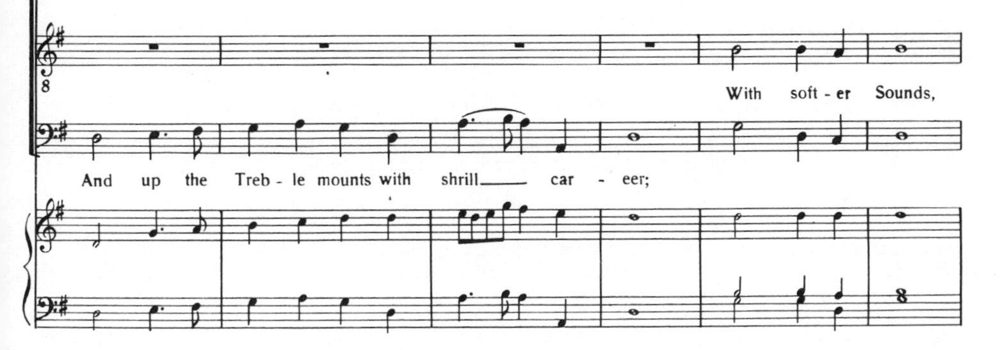

in mild Mel - o - dious Maze, Warbl - - ing be-tween the
8
in mild Mel - o - dious Maze, Warbl - ing be-tween, warbl -
Ten - or_ gent - ly Plays, the Ten - or gent - ly Plays, warbl - ing be -
8
ing be - tween the_ Ten - or gent-ly Plays, warbl - ing_ be -

tween the Ten - or gent - ly Plays:
But if th'a - spir - ing
tween the Ten - or gent - ly Plays:
But if th'a - spir - ing
Al - tus joins its Force,
See! like the Lark, it
Al - tus joins its Force,
See! like the Lark, it

Wings its tow'r - ing Course: Through Har-mo - ny's sub - lim - est Sphere it
Wings its tow'r - ing Course; Through Har-mo - ny's sub - lim - est Sphere it
flies, And to An - gel - ic Ac - cents seems to rise;
flies, And to An - gel - ic Ac - cents seems to rise;

[1] The dynamic indications are in the original.

to meet, and mix in close Em - brace,
8
to meet, and mix in close Em - brace,

Through dif - f'rent Sys - tems all the Parts di - vide, With
8
Through dif - f'rent Sys - tems all the Parts di - vide. With

Mu - sick's Chords the dis - tant Notes are ty'd;
Mu - sick's Chords the dis - tant Notes are ty'd;
And
And Sym - pa-thet - ic
And Sym - pa - thet - ic Strains en - chant - - ing winde
And Sym - pa-thet - ic Strains en - chant - -
Sym - pa - thet - ic Strains en - chant - - ing winde Their rest - less

Strains en - chant - - ing winde Their rest - - less Race,
Their rest - - less Race, their rest - less Race,
- ing winde Their rest - - less Race,
Race, their rest - less Race, till all the Parts are join'd,

their rest - - less Race, till all the Parts are join'd, till
their rest-less Race, till all the Parts are join'd, till
their rest - less Race, till all the Parts are join'd, till
their rest - less Race, till all the Parts are join'd, till

all the Parts are join'd
all the Parts are join'd.
all the Parts are join'd
all the Parts are join'd. Then rolls
Then rolls the Rap - ture
Then rolls
Then rolls the Rap - ture thro' the Air a - round,
the Rap - ture thro' the Air a - round, then rolls

thro' the Air a - round, then rolls the
the Rap - ture thro' the Air a - round, In
then rolls the Rap - ture thro the
the Rap - ture thro' the Air a - round, In sweet En - chant - ing
Rap - ture, then rolls the Rap - ture thro' the Air a -
sweet En - chant - ing Mel - o - dy of Sound, In sweet En - chant - ing
Air a - - round, then rolls the
Mel - o - dy of Sound, then rolls the

From a *Miscellany* of the Rev. Dr. Byles
(1706–1788)

52. WORCESTER

1778

The Worcester Collection of Sacred Harmony
Isaiah Thomas
(*Worcester, 1786*)

Abraham Wood
(1752–1804)

[1] B-flat in the original.
[2] E in the original.

This composition was first included in Andrew Law's *Select Harmony* (Philadelphia, 1778).

veal, Who bring Sal - va - tion on their Tongues, And
Who bring Sal - va - tion on their Tongues, And
Who bring Sal - va - tion on their Tongues, And
veal, Who bring Sal - va - tion on their Tongues, And
Words of Peace re - veal! How charm - ing, charm - ing,
Words of Peace re - veal! How charm - ing, charm - ing,
Words of Peace re - veal! How charm - ing, charm - ing,
Words of Peace re - veal! How charm - ing, charm - ing,

is their Voice! How sweet the Tid - ings are!
is their Voice! How sweet the Tid - ings are!
is their Voice! How sweet the — Tid - ings are!
is — their Voice! How sweet the Tid - ings are!
Zi - on, be - hold thy Sav - iour
Zi - on, be - hold thy Sav - iour King, He reigns and
Zi - on, be - hold thy Sav - iour King, He reigns and tri - umphs here,
Zi - on, be - hold thy Sav - iour King, He reigns and — tri-umphs here, Zi - on, behold thy

Hymn: Isaac Watts (1707)
(1674–1748)

CHINA

1793

The New England Harmony
Timothy Swan
(*Northampton, 1801*)

Timothy Swan
(1758–1842)

2
Are we not tending upward too,
As fast as time can move?
Nor would we wish the hours more slow
To keep us from our love.

6
Then let the last loud trumpet sound,
And bid our kindred rise;
Awake, ye nations, under ground;
Ye saints, ascend the skies.

Hymn: Isaac Watts (1707)
(1674–1748)

This composition was first included in Oliver Holden's *Union Harmony*, Vol. II (Boston, 1793); text and music identical.

54. CORONATION

1793

The Union Harmony
Oliver Holden
(*Boston, 1793*)

Oliver Holden
(1765–1844)

2

Crown him, ye martyrs of our God,
Who from his altar call;
Extol the stem of Jesse's rod,
And crown him Lord of all.

5

Let every kindred, every tribe,
On this terrestrial ball,
To him all majesty ascribe,
And crown him Lord of all.
Edward Perronet (1779)
(1726–1792)

55. INVITATION

1784

The Rural Harmony
Jacob Kimball
(*Boston, 1793*)

Jacob Kimball
(1761–1826)

This tune, Kimball's first composition, first appeared in Daniel Bayley's *Select Harmony* (Newbury-Port, [1784]). Later, Kimball reharmonized the melody and included it in his *Rural Harmony*, 1793.

Roe, O - ver the hills where spic - es grow.
Roe, O - ver the hills where spic - es grow.
Fly like a
Fly like a youth - ful Hart
Fly like a
Fly like a youth - ful Hart or Roe, O - ver the
youth - ful Hart or Roe, O - ver the hills where spic - -

or Roe, O - - ver the hills where spic - es
youth - ful Hart or Roe, O - - ver the hills where spic - es
hills where spic - es grow, Fly like a youth - ful Hart or Roe,
- es grow, Fly like a youth - ful Hart or Roe,
grow, O - ver the hills where spic - es grow.
grow, O - ver the hills where spic - es grow.
O - ver the hills where spic - es grow.
O - ver the hills where spic - es grow.

56. WOBURN

1793

The Rural Harmony
Jacob Kimball
(*Boston, 1793*)

Jacob Kimball
(1761–1826)

Ps. 30: Isaac Watts (1719)
(1674–1748)

57. HARMONY

1793

The Psalmodist's Companion
Jacob French
(*Worcester, 1793*)

Jacob French
(1754–1817)

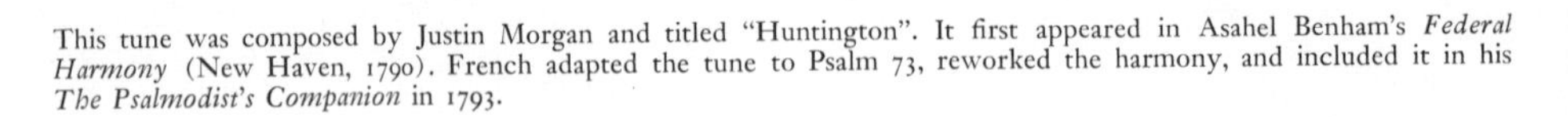
This tune was composed by Justin Morgan and titled "Huntington". It first appeared in Asahel Benham's *Federal Harmony* (New Haven, 1790). French adapted the tune to Psalm 73, reworked the harmony, and included it in his *The Psalmodist's Companion* in 1793.

word, And sound it dread - - ful down to hell.
word, And sound it dread - - ful down to hell. The
The Lord, how ab - so -
p
p
The Lord, how ab - so - lute he reigns! Let every angel
The Lord, how ab - so - lute he reigns! Let
Lord, how ab - so - lute he reigns! Let ev - ery an - gel bend the knee, bend,
- lute he reigns! Let ev - ery an - gel bend the knee, bend, bend the knee:

11

Jehovah! 'tis a glorious word;
O may it dwell on every tongue!
But saints, who best have known the Lord,
Are bound to raise the noblest song.

12

Speak of the wonders of that love
Which Gabriel plays on every chord;
From all below, and all above,
Loud hallelujahs to the Lord!

Ps. 148: Isaac Watts (1719)
(1674–1748)

58. MONTGOMERY

1790

Union Harmony
Oliver Holden
(*Boston, 1793*)

Justin Morgan
(1747–1798)

First published in Benham's 1790 *Federal Harmony*.

[1] A in the original.

[2] D in the original.

Ps. 63: Isaac Watts (1719) (1674–1748)

59. JUBILANT

1794

The Harmony of Maine
Supply Belcher
(*Boston, 1794*)

Supply Belcher
(1751–1836)

[1] E in the original.

60. EXHORTATION

1800

The Easy Instructor
Wm. Little & Wm. Smith
(*Albany, c. 1809*)

Eliakim Doolittle
(1772–1850)

[1] These two eighth notes are A and B in the original.

This composition was first published in Stephen Jenk's *Musical Harmonist*, New Haven, 1800. Only the first line of the text was given.

2

Behold the aged sinner goes,
Laden with guilt and heavy woes,
Down to the regions of the dead,
With endless curses on his head.

4

Eternal King! I fear thy name;
Teach me to know how frail I am:
And when my soul must hence remove,
Give me a mansion in thy love.

Hymn: Isaac Watts (1707)
(1674–1748)

61. EVENING SHADE

1800

The Delights of Harmony; or Norfolk Compiler
Stephen Jenks
(Dedham, 1805)

Stephen Jenks
(1772–1856)

3
Lord keep us safe this night,
Secure from all our fears;
May angels guard us while we sleep,
Till morning light appears.

5
And when our days are past,
And we from time remove;
O may we in thy bosom rest,
The bosom of thy love.

John Leland
(1754–1841)

First published by Jenks under the title *Mount Vernon* in his 1800 *New-England Harmonist.*

62. SPRING

1797

Harmonist's Companion
Daniel Belknap
(*Boston, 1797*)

Daniel Belknap
(1771–1815)

63. SUMMER

1797

Harmonist's Companion
Daniel Belknap
(*Boston, 1797*)

Daniel Belknap
(1771–1815)

a - way! The spi - cy shrub, and flow'r with
head in - clin'd, Must per - ish leav - ing not a
wreck be - hind! Thus the rich growth of the most friend - ly
clime, Must fall a vic - tim to de - vour - ing time.

64. AUTUMN

1800

Evangelical Harmony
Daniel Belknap
(*Boston, 1800*)

Daniel Belknap
(1771–1815)

na - ked and de - form'd are seen, The mea - dows late - ly
drest in green: The groves and fields are
dis - ar - ray'd, The song - sters of the wood are fled.

65. WINTER

1800

Evangelical Harmony
Daniel Belknap
(*Boston, 1800*)

Daniel Belknap
(1771–1815)

Note: The "Piano" and "Forte" are in the original.

66. ARNHEIM

1799

The Columbian Repository
Samuel Holyoke
(*Exeter, 1799*)

Samuel Holyoke
(1762–1820)

2

Sing, how he left the worlds of light,
And the bright robes he wore above;
How swift and joyful was his flight,
On wings of everlasting love.

7

Among a thousand harps and songs,
Jesus, the God, exalted reigns;
His sacred name fills all their tongues,
And echoes through the heav'nly plains!

Hymn: Isaac Watts (1707)
(1674–1748)

67. INNOCENT SOUNDS

1805

The Christian Harmony
Jeremiah Ingalls
(Exeter, 1805)

Jeremiah Ingalls
(1764–1828)

2

Who, on the part of God, will rise,
  Innocent sounds recover;
Fly on the prey, and seize the prize,
  Plunder the carnal lover:
Strip him of every moving strain,
  Of every melting measure;
Music in virtue's cause retain,
  Risk the holy pleasure.

5

Then let us in his praises join,
  Triumph in his salvation,
Glory ascribe to love divine,
  Worship and adoration.
Heaven already is begun,
  Open'd to each believer,
Only believe, and still sing on,
  Heaven is ours for ever.

68. NORTHFIELD

1800

The Village Harmony
Henry Ranlet
(*Exeter, N.H., 5th ed., 1800*)

Jeremiah Ingalls
(1764–1828)

Fly swif - ter round the wheel of time, And
swif - ter round the wheel of time, And
wheel of time, And bring the wel - come day, And
swif - ter round the wheel of time, And
bring the wel - come day. day.
bring the wel - come day. day.
bring the wel - come day. day.
bring the wel - come day. day
1.
2.

69. THANKSGIVING ANTHEM

1809

Printed and sold by H. Mann,
for the Author (*Dedham, 1809*)

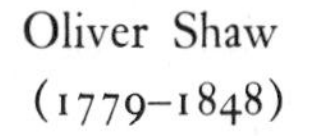

Tell the people, what things — he hath done, — Tell the people,
Tell the people, what things — he hath done, — Tell the people,
Tell the people, what things he hath done, Tell the people,
Tell the people, what things — he hath done, Tell the people,
Tell the people what things he hath done.
SYM.
Tell the people what things he hath done.
Tell — the people what things he hath done.
Tell — the people what things he hath done.

p
O let your songs be of him and praise him,
p
O let your songs be of him and praise him,
p
f
O let your songs be of him and praise him,
dolce
And let your talk-ing
f
O let your songs be of him and praise him, And let your talk-ing
f
O let your songs be of him and praise him,
f
O let your songs be of him and praise him,
dolce
f

be — of all his won'drous works, — re - joice, re - joice in his ho - ly name, — re -
be — of all his won'drous works, — re - joice, re - joice in his ho - ly name, — re -
re - joice, re - joice in his ho - ly name, — re -
re - joice, re - joice in his ho - ly name, — re -
joice — in his ho - ly — name.
SYM.
joice — in his ho - ly — name.
joice — in his ho - ly name.
joice — in his ho - ly name.

Allegretto
Let the heart of them re - joice that seek, that seek, the Lord;
Let the heart of them re - joice that seek, that seek, the Lord;
Let the heart of them re - joice that seek, that seek, the Lord;
Let the heart of them re - joice that seek, that seek, the Lord;
SOLO
Seek the Lord and his strength, seek his face for - e - ver more.

f
Seek the Lord, and his strength, seek his face for e - ver more. He
f
Seek the Lord, and his strength, seek his face for e - ver more. He
f
Seek the Lord, and his strength, seek his face for e - ver more. He
f
Seek the Lord, and his strength, seek his face for - e - ver more. He
f
espress.
is the Lord our God, his judg - ments are in all the world, his judg - ments are in
espress.
is the Lord our God, his judg - ments are in all the world, his judg - ments are in
espress.
is the Lord our God, his judg - ments are in all the world, his judg - ments are in
espress.
is the Lord our God, his judg - ments are in all the world, his judg - ments are in
espress.

all the world, he hath been always mind-ful of his co - ve - nant and prom - ise that he
all the world, he hath been always mind-ful of his co - ve - nant and prom - ise that he
all the world, he hath been always mind-ful of his co - ve - nant and prom - ise that he
all the world, he hath been always mind-ful of his co - ve - nant and prom - ise that he
made to a thou - sand ge - ne - ra - tions. that he made to a thou - sand, a
made to a thou - sand ge - ne - ra - tions. that he made to a thou - sand, a
made to a thou - sand ge - ne - ra - tions, that he made to a thou - sand, a
made to a thou - sand ge - ne - ra - tions, that he made to a thou - sand, a

thou - sand,— thou-sand, thou - sand—— ge - ne - ra-tions Hal-le-lu-jah.
thou - sand,— thou-sand, thou - sand—— ge - ne - ra-tions Hal-le-lu jah.
thou - sand, thou-sand, thou - sand ge - ne - ra-tions Hal-le-lu-jah.
thou - sand, thou-sand, thou - sand ge - ne - ra-tions Hal-le-lu-jah.

Hal - le - lu - jah.—— A - men. Hal-le-lu-jah. Hal - le - lu - - jah. A - men.
Hal - le - lu - jah. A - men. Hal-le-lu-jah. Hal - le - lu - - jah. A - men.
Hal - le - lu - jah.—— A - men. Hal - le - lu - - jah. A - men.
Hal - le - lu - jah. A - men. Hal - le - lu - - jah. A - men.

Chapter Five

EUROPEAN MUSICIANS IN CHARLESTON, PHILADELPHIA, NEW YORK, AND BOSTON

Mr. and Mrs. Van Hagen, Messrs. Moller and Rausch, most respectfully solicit the patronage of their friends and the public, to Three Concerts, as follows, viz.

	Dols.	Cts.
A subscriber for a ticket to admit 2 ladies and a gentleman to the concerts, to pay	6	
Do. for do. one lady and a gentleman	4	50
Do. for do. one person	3	
Non-subscribers for each concert	1	25

After each Concert, a Ball

Advertisement in *The Daily Advertiser* New York, Thursday, December 24, 1795

DURING the pre-Revolutionary period, professionally trained European musicians, in addition to those in the religious communities, began to arrive in America to seek their fortune. Charleston, South Carolina was the main center of attraction at first, but after the Revolution many settled in Philadelphia, New York, and Boston.

Public concerts were held in Boston and Charleston as early as 1731 and 1732.[1] Charles-

[1] O. G. Sonneck, *Early Concert Life in America (1731–1800)*, Leipzig: Breitkopf & Härtel, 1907.

ton saw the first performance of a ballad opera in 1735, and the St. Cecilia Society was formed there in 1762. Williamsburg was dominated by the British, and the inhabitants "behaved themselves exactly as the Gentry in London."

In 1736 the first concert in New York was given as a benefit for Charles Theodore Pachelbel (Pachelbell) before his departure for Charleston. Pachelbel, a son of the famous German organist Johann Pachelbel, arrived in Boston about 1732 and was one of the first of the European musicians who were to come to America in large numbers after the Revolutionary War. These musicians carried on their activities as composers, performers, conductors, impresarios, teachers, publishers, and sellers of music and musical instruments, and they virtually took over the musical life from Virginia to Massachusetts.

The self-taught, native-born composers of late 18th-century New England were soon totally eclipsed, and their music was replaced by that of Handel, Haydn, Stamitz, and their professional rivals from Europe. The New England composers had concentrated their efforts on psalm-tunes, fuging tunes, hymns, set pieces, and anthems, mostly with religious texts, while the foreign-born professionals were particularly interested in music for public entertainment—compositions for keyboard, small instrumental groups, ballad operas, and secular songs. Oscar Sonneck's *Bibliography of Early Secular American Music of the 18th Century*, revised by William Treat Upton in 1945, lists over 3500 items. Most of this music was by foreign composers, and it was published principally between 1790 and 1800. Among the more influential musicians who came to America in pre-Revolutionary days, in addition to Pachelbel, were William Tuckey, Peter A. van Hagen, Sr., Jacob Eckhard, and William Selby.

William Tuckey, one of the early arrivals from England, came to New York in 1753. Simeon Jocelin might have had Tuckey's *Knighton* (No. 70) in mind when he stated in the Preface to his *Chorister's Companion* (1782) that "the tunes formerly in common use are now laid aside, instead of which those of a more lively and airy tune are substituted."

One of Charleston's leading musicians from 1786 until his death in 1833 was the German composer Jacob Eckhard, who first settled in Richmond in 1776. *The Pillar of Glory*, for solo voice and unison chorus (No. 71), was written to celebrate the American victories at sea over Albion (England) in the War of 1812. Eckhard, whose acquaintance with *To Anacreon in Heaven* is obvious, "gained a prize" for his piece in a national competition held in 1813.

William Selby, a London organist and composer, settled in Boston in 1771 and for many years played an active part in the development of the musical life there. His *Voluntary VIII* (No. 72) was written so that it could be played on the organ or harpsichord, a characteristic of much keyboard music of the period. The short prelude in Handelian style is unified by a recurring 32nd-note figure and comes to an unusual cadence on C-sharp. The free fugue that follows returns to the original key of A major. Alberti-bass figures (in the upper part also) and long episodes of sequences are characteristic of this music. Selby's *Ode for the New Year* (No. 73) is for two solo voices in simple duple time with a three-part chorus in compound duple time. This fine composition was written as a tribute to George Washington, who was then, 1790, beginning his second year as President of the United States.

Following the Revolutionary War, Philadelphia replaced Charleston as a musical center, and the English musicians Alexander Reinagle, Raynor Taylor, and Benjamin Carr were active there for many years.

Reinagle's Sonata in E major, composed after 1786, is the second of four sonatas he wrote for the pianoforte. The *Anthology* includes the second and third movements of this three-movement work (No. 74), taken from the original manuscript. In binary form, the Adagio opens in E minor with an eight-measure introduction followed by the principal theme, the lyricism of which bears a close affinity to the style of Carl Philipp Emanuel

Bach's sonatas. The subordinate theme in G major (measure 17) brings the first part to a close at the double bar. The second part, in G major, presents the theme in a highly embellished form. This culminates in a short cadenza, followed by the return of the principal theme in its original key (m. 53). Marked Allegro, the gay third movement is in a modified second rondo form with a coda. A short cadenza precedes the final appearance of the first theme.

The title of Raynor Taylor's *Sonata for the Piano Forte with an Accompaniment for A Violin* would seem to imply a subordinate role for the violin, but a glance at the score shows that the violin is not treated as an *ad libitum* instrument and that both instruments are about equally active, even though the violin part is contained within the first position. The accompanied sonata represents an important stage in the transition from the Baroque solo sonata with continuo accompaniment to the Classic sonata for piano and violin. The present Sonata (No. 75) is in two movements; the first, marked Andante, is in binary form with the first section repeated, and the second is a Tempo di Menuetto with the usual Minuet–Trio–Minuet (varied).

Benjamin Carr, one of the most influential foreign musicians of his time in this country, wrote the music for the ballad opera *The Archers; or, the Mountaineers of Switzerland.* The opera, adapted by William Dunlap from the story of William Tell, was first performed by the Old American Company of New York on April 18, 1796. The song *Why, Huntress, why?* (No. 76) was published in Carr's *Musical Journal*, and it is one of the two numbers from the opera that have survived.

Among the prominent foreign-born musicians in New York during the post-Revolutionary period were the Englishman James Hewitt (an exact contemporary of Beethoven), the Frenchman Victor Pelissier, and John Christopher Moller, who came from England.

Alknomook (No. 77), subtitled *The Death Song of the Cherokee Indians*, is the sole surviving excerpt from the ballad opera *Tammany*, by James Hewitt. It is a musical trifle but is included here because *Tammany* is perhaps the first ballad opera composed in the United States and because of its political connotation. The opera takes its name from the Tammany Society, founded by William Mooney in New York in 1789, who called it Tammany in honor of a Cherokee chieftain. Produced in 1794 under the auspices of the Tammany Society, the opera deals with the struggle against the aristocratic theories of the Anti-Federalists by allegorically portraying the stoicism of the Cherokees. Tammany laments the fate of his tribe in this short strophic air, completely devoid of Indian flavor, which Hewitt borrowed for inclusion in his work. The tune enjoyed wide favor in Scotland, England, and the Colonies, and it eventually found its way into Southern folk hymnody (compare with *Morality*, No. 92).

Few are the joys (No. 78) is one of two surviving pieces from Pelissier's ballad opera *Edwin and Angelina,* whose libretto was adapted from a novel by Oliver Goldsmith. The opera had its first and last performance on December 19, 1796 in New York.

John C. Moller's *Sinfonia* (No. 79), of which only the piano reduction has survived, was printed and sold by Moller and Capron in 1793. An unusual feature of this composition is the second movement, a Menuetto with an interpolated Rondo having the form: minuet–rondo–minuet.

European musicians had taken an increasingly active part in the musical life of Boston from the time of William Selby's arrival in 1771. Among those who settled there after the Revolution were Hans Gram from Denmark, Peter A. van Hagen, Sr. and his musical family from Holland, and the Englishman George K. Jackson.

Gram, although an influential composer of anthems, is known today principally through his solo song *The Death Song of an Indian Chief* (1791, No. 80). This song is accompanied by a small ensemble and is the first orchestral score to be published in the United States. The title page reads:

The Death Song of an Indian Chief. Taken from OUABI, an Indian Tale, in Four Cantos, by PHILENIA, a Lady of Boston. Set to Musick by Mr. Hans Gram, of Boston.

Many songs and poems were written in honor of George Washington while he was alive. Following his death in 1799, an unparalleled number of "sacred dirges" were published of which Peter van Hagen's simple, through-composed song (No. 81) is typical.

George K. Jackson was one of the more able musicians who came to America just before the turn of the century. His *Verses for the Fourth of July* (No. 82) is a festive piece composed during his residence in New York and before he settled in Boston in 1812. Only the keyboard score, with some instruments cued in, has survived. The anthem is for solo voice and chorus, with a violin part that occasionally doubles the vocal line. The title page states that the composition was sung at the Presbyterian Church in New York. Jackson exerted a considerable influence on American composers of the next generation, particularly through his association with the Handel and Haydn Society and Lowell Mason.

70. KNIGHTON

1782

The Chorister's Companion
Simeon Jocelin
(*New Haven, 1782*)

William Tuckey
(1708–1781)

Ps. 108: Nahum Tate
(1652–1715)

71. NAVAL SONG
The Pillar of Glory
1813

The Port Folio
(Philadelphia, 1813)

Jacob Eckhard, Sr.
(1757–1833)

[1] F-sharp in the original.

4

Already the storm of contention has hurl'd,
From the grasp of Old England the TRIDENT of WAR,
The beams of our STARS have illumin'd the world,
Unfurl'd our Standard beats proud in the air:
Wild glares the Eagle's eye,
Swift as he cuts the sky,
Marking the wake where our heroes advance;
Compass'd with rays of light,
Hovers he o'er the fight;
Albion is heartless—and stoops to his glance.

Edwin C. Holland

72. VOLUNTARY VIII

c. 1767

Ten Voluntarys for the Organ or Harpsichord
(*C. & S. Thompson, London, c. 1767*)

William Selby
(1738–1798)

tr
tr

73. ODE FOR THE NEW YEAR

January 1, 1790

The Massachusetts Magazine (*Vol. II, January, 1790*)

William Selby (1738–1798)

2

"And as the golden car of light,
Refulgent beams on mortal sight;
As fiery steeds (which oft times lave
Their winged feet in ocean's wave)
Ascend above the mantling deep,
And rapid gain th' empyrean steep,
Let slumb'ring nations rise, and loud prolong,
To Day's celestial Prince, the choral song."

3

Columbia heard the high behest,
Her free born millions smote the breast!
And silent slept the heav'n strung lyre,
Till Freedom breath'd impassion'd fire;
Till Virtue form'd the hallow'd sound,
And Fame enraptur'd roll'd it round.
"All hail to Freedom's, Virtue's, Glory's Sun!
Ye worlds repeat, repeat! 'Tis WASHINGTON"!

74. SONATA IN E FOR THE PIANO FORTE

Adagio—Allegro

From an original manuscript (*Philadelphia*, c. 1790)

Alexander Reinagle (1756–1809)

[1] The two dots indicate a sharp.

tr
R
L
p
f
p
f
R

tr
p
f
p
tr
f

tr
f

tr
f
p

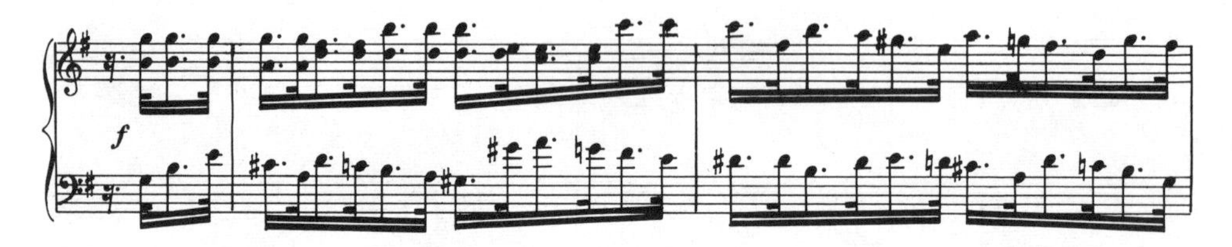

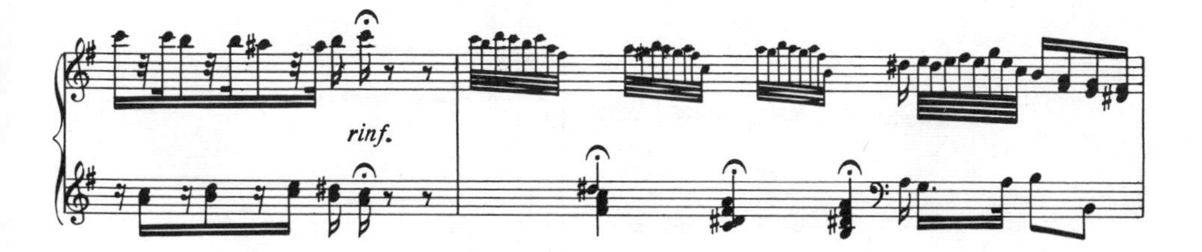
rinf.

cresc.
f
p

rinf.

tr
R

tr
p
f
tr
p
f

tr

f

Allegro
cresc.
f

tr

tr

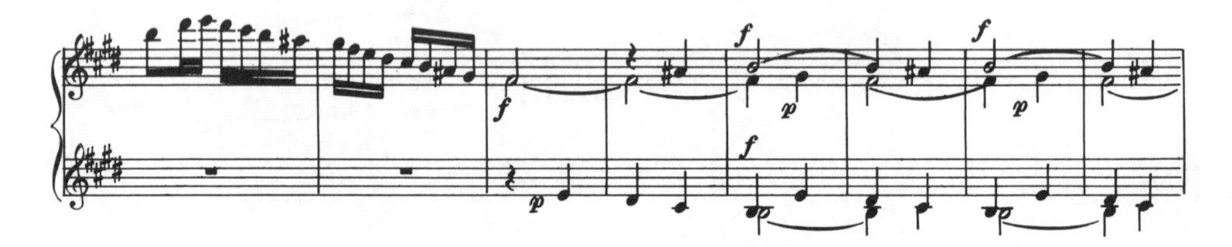

p
f

p
f
f

p

tr

tr
f

Cadenza
tr
adagio

f
f
p
p

Tempo Primo

tr

tr

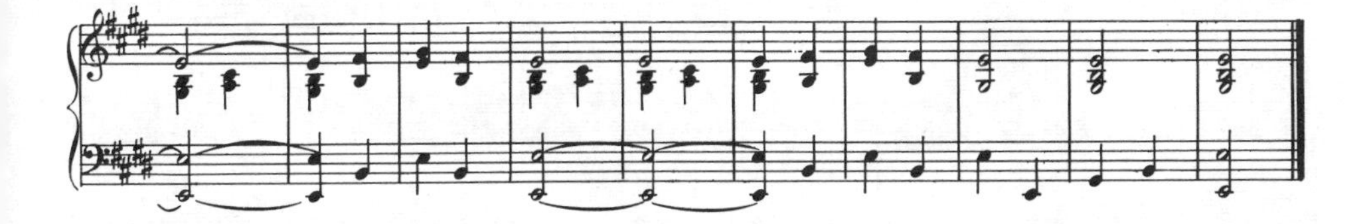

75. SONATA FOR THE PIANO FORTE WITH AN ACCOMPANIMENT FOR A VIOLIN

1797

Carr's Musical Repository
(*Philadelphia*, 1797)

Raynor Taylor
(1747–1825)

tr
mf
f
p
mf
f
mf
p

tr
mf
f
ff
8ths

tr
tr
tr

tr
mf
mf
tr
tr

tr
p
tr
tr
p
tr

f
tr
f

tr
tr
3
3
3
3
p

mf
tr
f
mf
tr
f
mf
tr

Tempo di Menuetto
mf
tr
p
f

76. WHY, HUNTRESS, WHY?

from
The Archers

1796

Musical Journal, Vol. II
Benjamin Carr
(*Philadelphia, 1801*)

Benjamin Carr
(1768–1831)

Ah! think what pangs thy Father still must feel,
What pangs must Arnold know,
When thou'rt expos'd unto the biting steel
Shall rush amid the foe,
Then, Huntress, why wilt thou thy life expose?

William Dunlap
(1796)

77. ALKNOMOOK

The Death Song of the Cherokee Indians
from
Tammany

1794

George Gilfert
(*New York, c. 1800*)

James Hewitt
(1770–1827)

2

Remember the Arrows he shot from his Bow,
Remember your Chiefs by his Hatchet laid low,
Why so slow, do you wait 'till I shrink from the pain,
No, the Son of ALKNOMOOK Will never complain.

3

Remember the wood where in Ambush we lay,
And the Scalps which we bore from your Nation away,
Now the flame rises fast, you Exult in my pain,
But the Son of ALKNOMOOK can never complain.

4

I go to the Land where my Father is gone,
His Ghost shall rejoice in that of his Son;
Death comes like a friend, he relieves me from pain,
And thy Son O! ALKNOMOOK has scorn'd to complain.

Ann Julia Hatton
(1794)

78. FEW ARE THE JOYS

from
Edwin and Angelina

1797

Columbian Melodies
George Willig
(*Philadelphia, 1811*)

Victor Pelissier

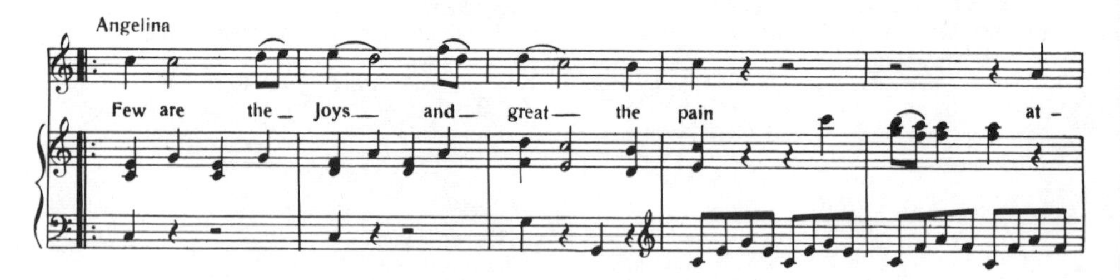

ten - dent on a love sin - cere, I'll try my Free - - dom
to re - gain how - e - 'er the task may prove se -
vere how - e'er the task may
prove se - - vere may prove se - - vere.
p

Yes, hear me Cu - pid
p

I re - solve hence-forth to treat thee

as a foe no more this heart thou

Elihu Hubbard Smith
(1794)

79. SINFONIA

1793

Moller and Capron's
Monthly Numbers
The First Number, 1793

John Christopher Moller
(d. 1803)

Menuetto

Rondo Allegro

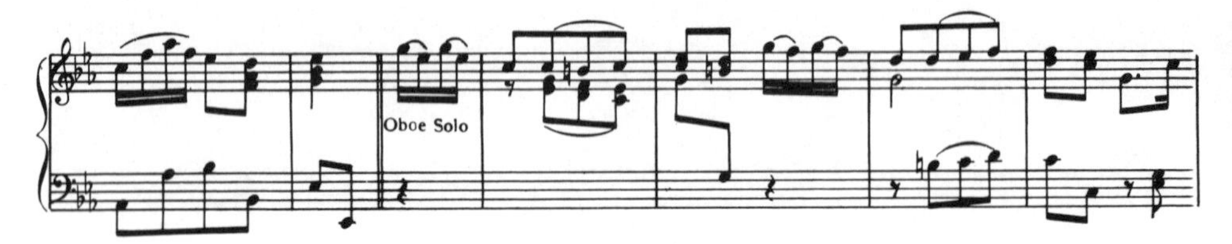

Menuet

80. THE DEATH SONG OF AN INDIAN CHIEF

1791

The Massachusetts Magazine, Vol. II (Boston, March, 1791)

Hans Gram

tenuto
tr
p
f
p
Rear'd — midst the war-em-pur-pled plain, What Il - li - nois sub - mits to pain! How
tenuto
poco f
can the glo-ry - dart - ing fire, The cow- ard chill of death — in - spire, — The

[1] The first two eighth notes are A-flat in the original.

By Philenia, a lady of Boston
[Sarah Wentworth Morton]

80a. THE DEATH SONG OF AN INDIAN CHIEF

1791

Hans Gram
Arranged from the full score

tenuto
plain, What Il - li - nois sub - mits to pain! How
shine, And own their FLAM - ING SOURCE di - vine. Then
fear, Not all your force can start a tear. Think
tenuto
can the glo - ry - dart - - ing fire, The cow - ard chill of
let me hail th' IM - MOR - - TAL FIRE, And in the sa - cred
not with me my tribe de - cays, More glo - rious chiefs the
f
death in - spire, The cow - ard chill of death in -
flames ex - pire; Nor yet those Hu - ron hands re -
hatch - et raise; Not un - re - veng'd their sa - - chem
mf
spire, The cow - ard chill of death in - spire!
strain; This bo - som scorns the throbs of pain.
dies, Not un - at - tend - ed greets the skies.
dim.
p

81. FUNERAL DIRGE ON THE DEATH OF GENERAL WASHINGTON

P. A. van Hagen
(*Boston, 1799*)

1799

Peter A. van Hagen, Sr.
(1750–1803)

Grave

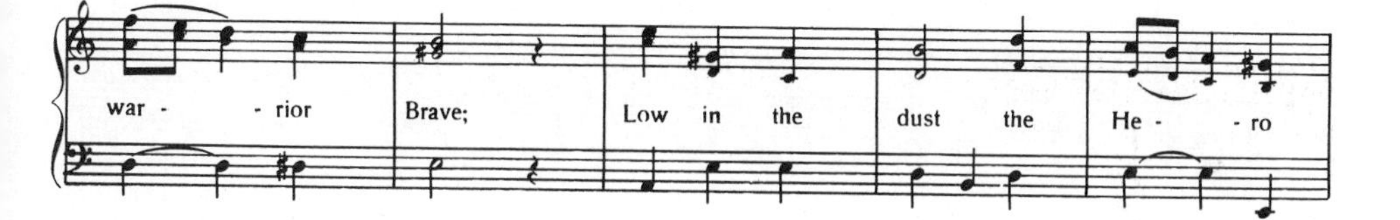

2

By thee inspir'd with warlike art
He urg'd the fight, or bade it cease:
Not less he fill'd the statesman's part:
Our guide in war, our head in Peace.

3

His Country happy, great, and free,
Hail'd him her Father, hope, and pride:
But fix'd, O God, his hope on thee,
He liv'd thy friend, thy servant died.

82. VERSES FOR THE FOURTH OF JULY

Publisher unknown (c. 1803)

George K. Jackson (1745–1822)

When gen-'rous Free-dom leaves her dow-ny

bed, And Proud Be-lo-na droops her Aw-ful

head. Then more than Hap-pi-ness with wide do-

dolce
tr
dolce
main Ex-tends to ev-'ry Maid and Vil-lage

Swain, Ex - tends to ev - 'ry Maid and Vil - lage

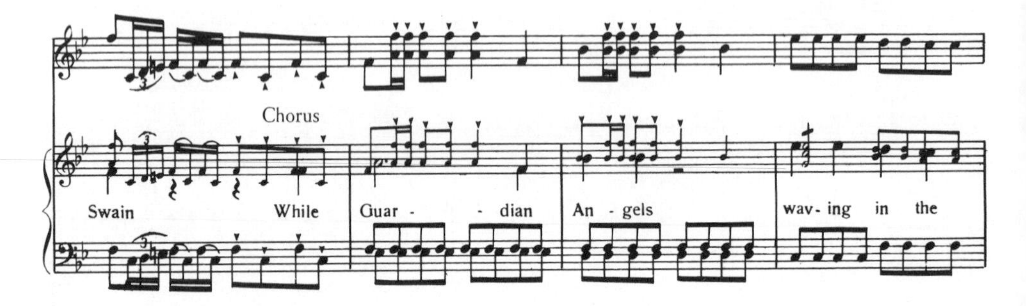
Chorus
Swain While Guar - - dian An - gels wav - ing in the

Air, Fair Free - dom's Ban - ners

high up - lift - ed bear, Fair Free - dom's— Ban - ners high up - lift - - ed

2

The lovely Cherub Contemplation bring,
Let Harmony soft Hymeneals sing
Of gentle Love, and his fantastic toys,
Of Health, Domestic Peace, and all their Joys;
Chorus: While Guardian Angels etc.

3

Their Trumpets, sounding Fame, in Concert hear
Of Washington, Great Washington revere.
Him first, him best, our grateful hours employ
The Great, the Good, and Source of all your Joy.
Chorus: While Guardian Angels etc.

Mrs. George K. Jackson
(c. 1803)

Chapter Six

LOWELL MASON AND HIS CONTEMPORARIES

"The chief value of music . . . in schools or families, will be social and moral."

Lowell Mason

CHURCH and school music and music education were dominated by Lowell Mason (1792–1872) and his contemporaries for at least sixty years of the 19th century. Mason's chief contribution to music in America was the introduction of singing classes in the public schools and the establishment of teacher-training institutes. The singing schools of the early 19th century provided the first teachers and "methods" for this new development. Mason also organized "musical conventions" in various parts of the country and was influential in the establishment of theoretical and practical music in many of the new liberal arts colleges in the Midwest.

These activities required music, and Mason and his co-workers published a large number of collections, which included psalm-tunes, hymns, chants, sentences, motets, and anthems. Tunes from the works of European composers were freely arranged and harmonized by Mason, Hastings, Webb, Bradbury, Woodbury, and others, who also contributed hymns and some anthems of their own. A few tunes by the earlier English composers, such as Tans'ur, Playford, Williams, and the Americans Read, Holden, and others, were retained to satisfy the "old-fashioned" tastes.

It was Mason's desire to bring "music to the masses" and, as he said, to "reform" the church music of the 18th-century singing schools. He did reach the masses through his manifold activities; and the many tunebooks, which always included some of his music and that of his associates, had a wide circulation through the East and Midwest, bringing him both fame and fortune. The psalm-tunes and fuging tunes of his New England predecessors were mostly eliminated in favor of a standard type of "better music" with simple, melodious harmonies which represented "scientific progress."

The hymns of Mason and his contemporaries were probably suited to the needs of their time and represented an improvement over many of the cheap, secular revival songs in current use. However, the sentimental texts and lack of distinction and originality in the music did little to elevate musical taste. Many of their hymns, although appearing less and less frequently in modern hymnals, still have a firm hold on Protestant congregations today.

Typical hymns, included in the *Anthology* in their original version, are Mason's *From Greenland's icy mountains* (*A Missionary Hymn*, No. 83) and *My faith looks up to Thee* (*Olivet*, No. 84), Hastings's *Rock of Ages* (*Toplady*, No. 86), and Bradbury's *Woodworth* (No. 88), best known today with the text "Just as I am, without one plea."

From Greenland's icy mountains was originally composed and published as a solo song and dedicated to Miss Mary W. Howard of Savannah, Georgia. The song was later included in Mason's publications as a three-part, and subsequently as a four-part, hymn.

Mason set a new text to Aaron Williams's tune, *St. Thomas's* (*Anthology*, No. 29), and moved the melody from the tenor to the treble voice (No. 85). He also added a typical "Hallelujah" coda and a figured bass for the organ, an innovation of his that is found for the first time in American tunebooks.

The well-known tune by George Webb is given in its original form as a secular song, *'Tis dawn, the lark is singing* (No. 87). The tune is found in hymnals with the texts, "The morning light is breaking," written in 1832 by Samuel Francis Smith, the author of "My country 'tis of thee," and "Stand up, stand up for Jesus," written by George Duffield in 1858. Webb introduced an unusual and practical way of making a keyboard score for the organist by adding the alto and tenor parts in small notes to the treble and bass parts.

One of the comparatively few collections of secular music of this period was Isaac B. Woodbury's *Song Crown*, a collection of glees, quartets, opera choruses, trios, solos, and miscellaneous pieces. His two glees, *The Farmer's Daughter* (No. 89) and *Stars of the Summer Night* (No. 90), were the outgrowth of his travels with the Bay State Glee Club, which he conducted, and the latter glee is found in many college song books today.

83. FROM GREENLAND'S ICY MOUNTAINS

A Missionary Hymn

1824

Published by G. Willig, Jr.
(*Baltimore, 1824*)

Lowell Mason
(1792–1872)

2

What tho' the spicy breezes blow soft o'er Ceylon's isle;
Tho' ev'ry prospect pleases and only man is vile;
In vain with lavish kindness the gifts of God are strown;
The heathen in his blindness bows down to wood and stone.

3

Shall we, whose souls are lighted by wisdom from on high,
Shall we to men benighted the lamp of life deny?
Salvation! O Salvation! the joyful sound proclaim,
Till earth's remotest nation has learnt Messiah's name.

4

Waft, waft, ye winds, his story, and you, ye waters, roll,
Till like a sea of glory it spreads from pole to pole;
Till o'er our ransom'd nature the Lamb for sinners slain,
Redeemer, King, Creator, returns in bliss to reign.

Bishop Reginald Heber (1819)
(1783–1826)

84. MY FAITH LOOKS UP TO THEE

(Olivet)

1831

Spiritual Songs for Social Worship
Lowell Mason and Thomas Hastings
(Utica, 1831)

Lowell Mason
(1792–1872)

Air
Alto

My faith looks up to thee, Thou Lamb of Cal - va - ry;
Sa - viour di - vine! Now hear me when I pray Take all my
guilt a - way: Oh let me from this day, Be whol - ly thine.

Tenor
Base

Note: The spelling "Base" instead of "Bass" is often found in music of this period.

2

May thy rich grace impart
Strength to my fainting heart,
My zeal inspire;
As thou hast died for me,
Oh may my love to thee,
Pure, warm, and changeless be,
A burning fire.

3

While life's dark maze I tread,
And griefs around me spread,
Be thou my guide;
Bid darkness turn to day,
Wipe sorrow's tears away,
Nor let me ever stray,
From thee aside.

Ray Palmer (1830)
(1808–1887)

85. ST. THOMAS

1841

New Carmina Sacra
Lowell Mason
(*Boston, 1852*)

Aaron Williams
(1731–1776)
Arranged by Lowell Mason
(1792–1872)

Note: The tenors may sing the first three notes of the second phrase in thirds. The pedal point should be played on the organ or a bass instrument. The "Hallelujahs" (added by Lowell Mason) were not only to be used at the close of the hymn, but could be introduced before the first stanza and between the stanzas.

2

His pow'r subdues our sins;
And his forgiving love,
Far as the east is from the west,
Doth all our guilt remove.

4

High as the heav'ns are rais'd
Above the ground we tread,
So far the riches of his grace
Our highest thoughts exceed.

Ps. 103: Isaac Watts (1719)
(1674–1748)

86. ROCK OF AGES

(*Toplady*)

1831

Spiritual Songs for Social Worship
Lowell Mason and Thomas Hastings
(*Utica, 1831*)

Thomas Hastings
(1784–1872)

2

Should my tears for ever flow;
Should my zeal no languor know;
This for sin could not atone:
Thou must save, and thou alone.
In my hand no price I bring;
Simply to thy cross I cling.

3

While I draw this fleeting breath,
When mine eyelids close in death,
When I rise to worlds unknown,
And behold thee on thy throne,
Rock of Ages, cleft for me,
Let me hide myself in thee.

Augustus M. Toplady (1776)
(1740–1778)

87. 'TIS DAWN, THE LARK IS SINGING

1837

The Odeon
George J. Webb
(*Boston, 1837*)

George J. Webb
(1803–1887)

2

The birds, they seem to send,
Their sweetest notes on high,
For benefits that blend
Their being with the sky.
And Oh, may I bestow,
My first, last, thought on heaven;
And may my bosom glow
With thanks each morn and even!

88. WOODWORTH

1849

The Mendelssohn Collection
William Bradbury and Thomas Hastings
(*New York, 1849*)

William B. Bradbury
(1816–1868)

[1] The first note in the alto is B in later editions.

2

Yet not one murmuring wish or thought
Should with our mourning passion blend;
Nor should our bleeding hearts forget
Th'almighty, ever-living Friend.

89. THE FARMER'S DAUGHTER

1856

The Song Crown
Isaac B. Woodbury
(*New York, 1856*)

Isaac B. Woodbury
(1819–1858)

90. STARS OF THE SUMMER NIGHT

1856

The Song Crown
Isaac B. Woodbury
(*New York, 1856*)

Isaac B. Woodbury
(1819–1858)

Henry Wadsworth Longfellow
(1807–1882)

Chapter Seven

SOUTHERN FOLK HYMNS

The watchmen blow the trumpet round,
Come listen to the solemn sound,
And be assured there's danger nigh,
How many are prepared to die?
Your days on earth will soon be o'er,
And time to you return no more;
O think thou hast a soul to save;
What are thy hopes beyond the grave?
"The Watchman's Call" (*Southern Harmony*, 1835)

THE 18TH-CENTURY revival movement in America, which originated among the dissenting groups of various denominations, began its development, especially among the Baptists in Massachusetts, with the "Great Awakening" under Jonathan Edwards and George Whitefield. The psalm-tunes of the early 18th-century Puritans no longer satisfied the revivalists who were "wont to sing with unusual elevation of heart and voice." A number of collections of English vocal music appeared in the second half of the century, and during the last two decades of the century the New England group of composers—Edson, Read, French, and others—wrote many tunes which had the characteristics of folk music.

The true folk hymn is based on a secular folk tune and is sung to a religious text. Only a few of these folk hymns, among them the well-known *Kedron* (No. 95), appeared in Northern collections before the close of the 18th century. Soon, however, tunebooks were published which included many folk hymns and these, as well as the psalm-tunes and fuging tunes of the New England composers, found their way into Southern collections.

The Kentucky Revival of 1800 led to the rapid development of folk hymnody in the South and the publication about 1815 of the first Southern tunebook, *Kentucky Harmony* by Ananias Davisson. This collection was followed by many other tunebooks, among them *The Missouri Harmony* (1820) by Allen D. Carden, *The Southern Harmony* (1835) by William Walker, and *The Sacred Harp* (1844) by B. F. White and E. J. King. These collections went through many editions and the music is still being used in "all-day sings" in rural communities. Irving Lowens [1] has pointed out that John Wyeth's *Repository of Sacred Music, Part Second* (1813) was an important source for the *Kentucky Harmony*. Three of the folk hymns that were originally found in Wyeth's *Repository, Part Second* (*Fairton*, No. 91; *Consolation*, No. 93; and *Primrose*, No. 94) are printed in this chapter of the *Anthology*.

The texts (many by Isaac Watts) of the Southern folk hymns were often adapted to fiddle tunes, ballads, and other secular sources from here and the British Isles. There are also many anonymous tunes and tunes ascribed to men about whom little or nothing is known.[2]

Southern collections of folk hymns are written in "shape-notes," sometimes called "buckwheat" or "patent" notes. The four-shape notation, introduced by William Little and William Smith in *The Easy Instructor* (Philadelphia, 1801), was used in the early tune-books; and later an effort was made to introduce a seven-shape system. The shape-notes are used with a conventional clef and key signature on lines and spaces and can be read as modern notation. The usual time signatures are found and also occasional instances of the use of the inverted C for $\frac{2}{2}$ time. The four shapes for the notes are right triangle (fa), used for the first and fourth degrees of the scale; round (sol), for the second and fifth degrees; square (la), for the third and sixth degrees; and diamond (mi), for the seventh degree.

Printed in score, the music is in three or four parts, with the tune customarily in the tenor. Later collections, notably the Denson Revision of *The Sacred Harp*, often have an alto part that was added to original three-part music. The collections also usually contained "grounds and rudiments of music" borrowed from various sources, including William Tans'ur.

The music was sung without accompaniment, and it was customary for all parts except the bass to be sung by both men and women. In four-part songs this resulted in the upper three parts being doubled at the octave, and, as Billings might have said, a tune so sung (although it has but four parts) is in effect the same as *seven*.

The singers received their tonic pitch from the leader of the group, first singing the song with the syllables represented by the shape-notes, and then with the text. When two notes occurred in one part ("choosing notes"), it was customary to sing both parts, although in some contexts one or the other note might be chosen. The tune in the tenor was often freely ornamented, the singer adding a higher or lower grace note before singing the melody note. Frequent use of slides, scoops, and anticipations is a characteristic performance practice, and only rarely do the ornamentations appear in the printed music.[3] The "coloring" of the intervals by the singers sometimes resulted in the singing of "neutral thirds."

A large majority of the tunes are modal or quasi-modal.[4] The Aeolian (natural minor) is frequently found (*Fairton; Consolation; Kedron* in *Southern Harmony*—No. 95a). *The Converted Thief* (No. 96) is in the Mixolydian mode, and *The Hebrew Children* (No. 97) is in the rarely used Phrygian mode. *Wondrous Love* (No. 101) is usually sung with a lowered sixth which places the tune in the Dorian mode. Melodies in the Ionian (major) mode include *Morality* (No. 92), *Primrose*, *Plenary* (No. 99), and *Gospel Trumpet* (No. 103). *Shouting Song* (No. 102) appears to be in F-sharp minor. The seventh is omitted, however, which leaves the tune with an ambiguous tonality.

Gapped melodies, with one or two scale

[1] Irving Lowens, "John Wyeth's *Repository of Sacred Music, Part Second*," *Journal of the American Musicological Society* V (1952), 114-131.

[2] The books by Dr. George Pullen Jackson should be consulted for a complete history of the Southern folk hymn.

[3] An ornamented version of *Amazing Grace* has been printed in Dr. Jackson's *Spiritual Folk-Songs of Early America* and quoted in *America's Music* by Gilbert Chase (New York, 1955), p. 203.

[4] The reader should remember that it is the tune that is being discussed, not the harmonization.

degrees omitted, are frequently used. The tunes in nine of the thirteen folk hymns printed in the *Anthology* have scale degrees omitted. Pentatonic melodies with the fourth and seventh omitted are found in *The Good Old Way* (No. 98), *Plenary* (No. 99), and *New Britain* (No. 100). The seventh is omitted in *Primrose*, the second in *The Hebrew Children*, the third in *The Converted Thief*, and the sixth in *Gospel Trumpet*.

Dyadic and triadic harmony and second-inversion chords are freely used with open and parallel fifths and octaves (*Fairton*, *Morality*, *Wondrous Love*, *Shouting Song*, and many others). Modulations are extremely rare, and the third is usually omitted in the final cadence, with a preference for the open fifth. The *Gospel Trumpet* exemplifies the rarely used fuging style. Sharp dissonances sometimes result from independent melodic lines as in the music of the earlier New England school of composers.

A number of the folk hymns in the *Anthology* have tunes of special interest. Among these are *Fairton*, with its extraordinary use of open fourths and second-inversion chords, irregular phrase-lengths, and unusually attractive melody; *Primrose*, in which the first, second, and fourth phrases begin with the same notes; *Morality*, which is based on the tune known as *Alknomook* (No. 77); *The Hebrew Children*, which was one of the many tunes taken over by the Negroes that became "spirituals" (No. 97a); the tune of *Kedron* (No. 95), which is found in modern church hymnals; *Plenary*, a setting of *Auld Lang Syne;* and *Wondrous Love*, one of the finest examples of a folk-hymn melody.

The *Shouting Song* and *Good Old Way* are typical examples of revival spirituals with a short, simple tune for the leader followed by a camp-meeting chorus for the entire group. *The Converted Thief* is a religious folk ballad in which the story was originally sung by one voice.

The Southern folk hymn gradually gave way to the commercialized "gospel song" with its sentimental text and stereotyped music with a catchy rhythm. Camp-meeting singing of folk hymns, however, has been preserved in many rural communities in the South, and in recent years there has been a renewed interest in this music as there has been in other indigenous music of America.

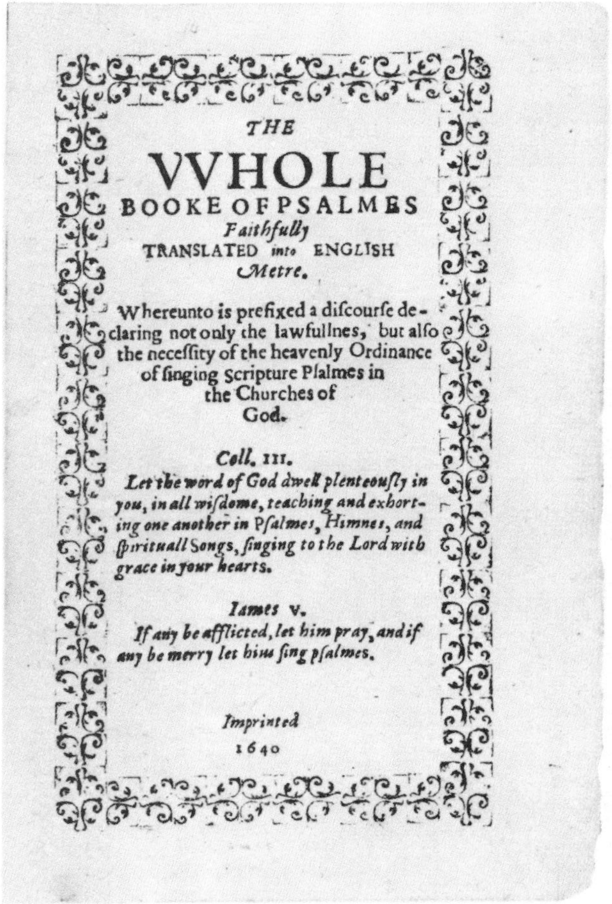

THE

VVHOLE

BOOKE OF PSALMES

Faithfully

TRANSLATED *into* ENGLISH

Metre.

Whereunto is prefixed a discourse declaring not only the lawfullnes, but also the necessity of the heavenly Ordinance of singing Scripture Psalmes in the Churches of God.

Coll. III.

Let the word of God dwell plenteously in you, in all wisdome, teaching and exhorting one another in Psalmes, Himnes, and spirituall Songs, singing to the Lord with grace in your hearts.

Iames V.

If any be afflicted, let him pray, and if any be merry let him sing psalmes.

Imprinted

1640

Title page from the first edition of the *Bay Psalm Book* (Cambridge, 1640).

Psal. 23. *Low Dutch Tune.*

Low Dutch Tune from the *Bay Psalm Book* (Boston, 1698).
See No. 13, p. 34.

266 *The Creede.*

And so he died in the flesh,
But quickned in the spirit:
His body then was buried,
As is our vse and right.
His spirit after this descend
Into the lower parts:
To them that long in darknesse were,
The true light of their hearts.

And in the third day of his death,
He rose to life againe:
To the'nd he might be glorified,
Out of all griefe and paine:
Ascending to the heauens hie,
To sit in glory still.

On Gods right hand his father deere,
According to his will.

Vntill the day of iudgement come,
When he shall come againe:
with Angels, power, yet of that day
We all be vncertaine.
To iudge all people righteously,
Whom he hath dearely bought:
The liuing and the dead also,
Which he hath made of nought.

And in the holy spirit of God,
My faith to satisfie:
The third person in Trinitie

A Prayer to the holy Ghost. CANTVS. Iohn Milton.

Ome holy spirit the God of might, comforter of vs all: Teach vs to know thy word aright, that we doe neuer fall.

Yorke Tune. TENOR, or *Playnsong.*

Ome holy spirit the God of might, comforter of vs all: Teach vs to know thy word aright, that we doe neuer fall.

O holy Ghost visit our coast,
defend vs with thy shield
Against all sinne and wickednesse,
Lord help vs winne the field.

Lord keepe our King and his Counsell,
and giue them will and might
To perseuere in thy Gospell,
Which can put sinne to flight:
O Lord which giuest thy holy word,
send Preachers plenteously:
That in the same we may accord

and therein liue and die.

O holy Spirit direct aright,
the preachers of thy word:
That thou by them must cut downe sinne
as it were with a sword.
Depart not from those pastors pure,
but aide them at all needs:
Which breake to vs the bread of life,
whereon our soules doe feede.

O Blessed Spirit of truth keepe vs

Da pacem. CANTVS. Tho. Rauens. B. of M.

Iue peace in these our dayes O Lord, great dangers are now at hand:

2. *High Dutch Tune.* TENOR, or *Faburden.*

Iue peace in these our dayes O Lord, great dangers are now at hand:

The Creed. 267

Beleeue I stedfastly.
The holy and Catholike Church,
That Gods word doth maintaine:
And holy Scripture doth allow,
Which Satan doth disdaine.

And also I doe trust to haue,
By Iesus Christ his death:
Release and pardon for my sins,
And that onely by faith.
What time all flesh shall rise againe
Before the God of might:
And see him with their bodily eyes
Which now doth giue them light.

And then shall Christ our Sauiour
The Sheepe and Goats diuide:
And giue life euerlastingly
To those whom he hath tride.
Within his realme celestiall,
In glory for to rest:
With all the holy company,
Of Saints and Angels blest.

Which serue the Lord omnipotent
Obediently each houre:
To whom be all dominion,
And prayse for euermore.

A Prayer to the holy Ghost. MEDIVS. Iohn Milton.

Come holy Spirit the God of might comforter of vs all. Teach vs to know thy word aright, that we doe ne- uer fall.

BASSVS.

Ome holy spirit the God of might, comforter of vs all: Teach vs to know thy word aright, that we doe neuer fall.

in peace and vnitie:
Keepe vs from sects and errours all,
and from all Papistry.

Conuert all those that are our foes,
and bring them to thy light:
That they and we may well agree,
and prayse thee day and night.
O Lord increase our faith in vs,
and loue so to abound:
That man and wife be void of strife,
and neighbours about vs round.

In our time giue thy peace (O Lord)
to nations farre and nie:
And teach them all thy holy word,
that we may sing to thee.

All glory to the Trinitie,
that is of mighties most:
The liuing Father and the Sonne,
and eke the holy Ghost.
As it hath beene in all the time,
that hath beene heretofore:
As it is now, and so shall be,
henceforth for euermore.

Da pacem. MEDIVS. Tho. Rauens. B. of M.

Iue peace in these our daies O Lord, great dangers are now at hand:

BASSVS.

Iue peace in these our dayes O Lord, great dangers are now at hand:

S 2

A Prayer to the Holy Ghost (*Yorke Tune*) by John Milton, Sr.
From *The Whole Booke of Psalmes* by Thomas Ravenscroft (London, 1621).
See No. 6, p. 29.

5,

Southwel Tune.

Cantus.

Medius.

Bassus.

Southwel new.

Cantus.

Medius.

Bassus.

B

A page from *The Grounds and Rules of Musick Explained*
by Thomas Walter (Boston, 1721).
See No. 25, p. 52.

10

Cant. 85 Psalm *Tune.*

Med.

Bass.

Cant. 100 Psalm *Tune.*

Med.

Bass.

Cant. 100 Psalm *Tune New*

Med.

Bass.

C 2

A page from *An Introduction to the Singing of Psalm-Tunes*
by John Tufts (Boston, 1721).
See No. 23, p. 50.

GOTT ein Herrscher aller Heyden, der sein Volck bald wird herrlich leiten, und ihr Recht lassen hoch hergehn: wenn ER Zion schön wird schmücken, ihr Heil wird lassen naher rücken, so wird man Freud und Wonne seh

an Seinem Eigenthum, das nun giebt Preiß und Ruhm GOTT dem König, der sie erhöht, ihr Völcker seht! wie GOttes Braut nun einhergeht. 196.

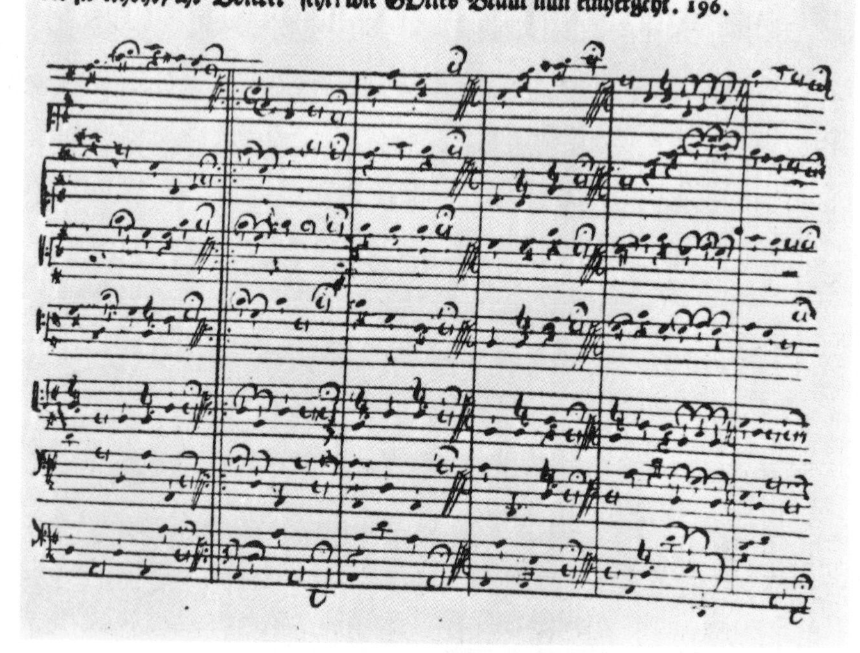

Gott ein Herrscher aller Heyden by Johann Conrad Beissel (Ephrata, 1754).
See No. 31, p. 64.

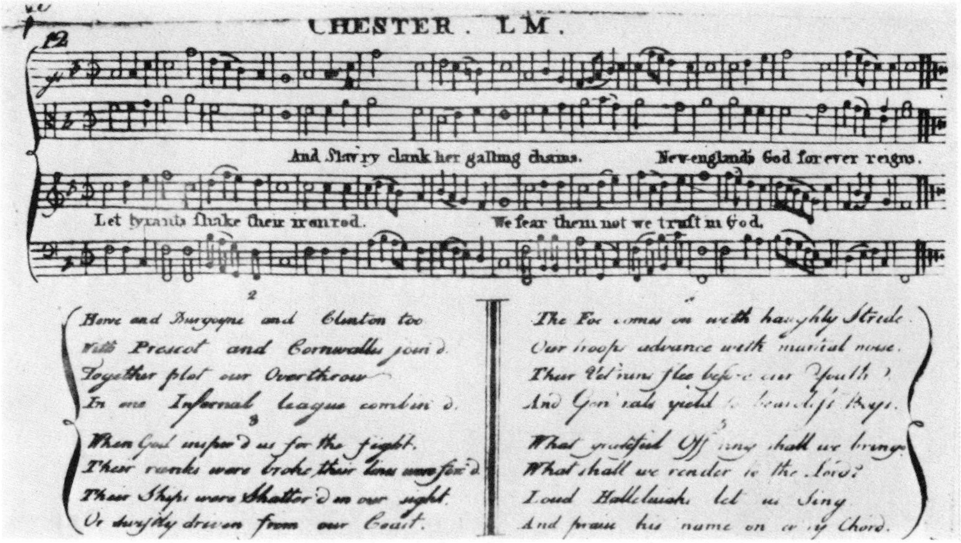

CHESTER. L.M.

And Slav'ry clank her galling chains. New-england's God for ever reigns.

Let tyrants shake their iron rod. We fear them not we trust in God.

2

Howe and Burgoyne and Clinton too
With Prescot and Cornwallis join'd.
Together plot our Overthrow
In one Infernal league combin'd.

3

When God inspir'd us for the fight.
Their ranks were broke their lines were forc'd.
Their Ships were Shatter'd in our sight.
Or swiftly driven from our Coast.

4

The Foe comes on with haughty Stride.
Our troops advance with martial noise.
Their Vet'rans flee before our Youth,
And Gen'rals yield to beardless Boys.

5

What grateful Off'ring shall we bring.
What shall we render to the Lord?
Loud Hallelujahs let us Sing
And praise his name on ev'ry Chord.

Chester by William Billings. From *The Singing Master's Assistant* (Boston, 1778).
See No. 43, p. 112.

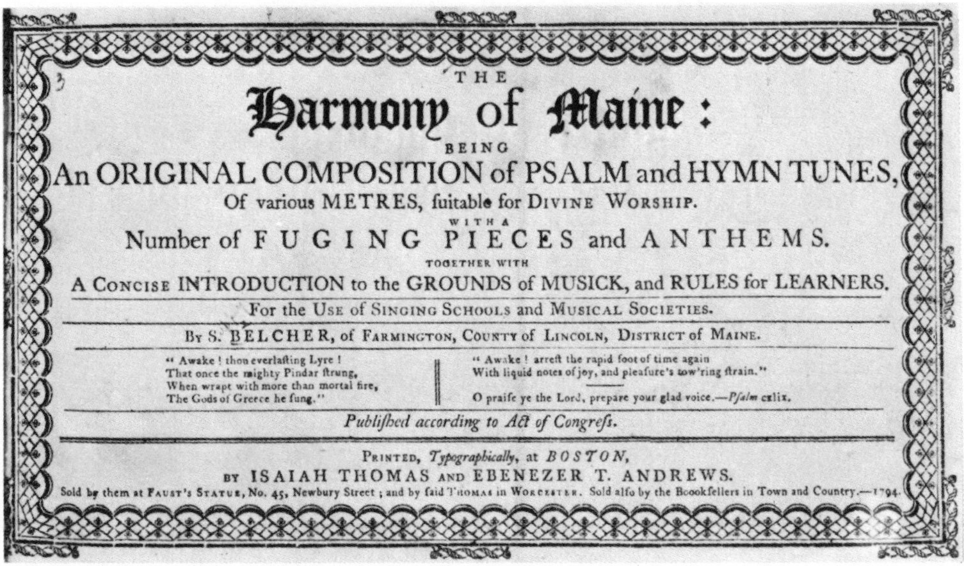

THE

Harmony of Maine:

BEING

An ORIGINAL COMPOSITION of PSALM and HYMN TUNES,

Of various METRES, suitable for DIVINE WORSHIP.

WITH A

Number of FUGING PIECES and ANTHEMS.

TOGETHER WITH

A CONCISE INTRODUCTION to the GROUNDS of MUSICK, and RULES for LEARNERS.

For the USE of SINGING SCHOOLS and MUSICAL SOCIETIES.

BY S. BELCHER, of FARMINGTON, COUNTY of LINCOLN, DISTRICT of MAINE.

"Awake! thou everlasting Lyre!
That once the mighty Pindar strung,
When wrapt with more than mortal fire,
The Gods of Greece he sung."

"Awake! arrest the rapid foot of time again
With liquid notes of joy, and pleasure's tow'ring strain."

O praise ye the Lord, prepare your glad voice.—*Psalm* cxlix.

Published according to Act of Congress.

PRINTED, *Typographically*, at *BOSTON*,
BY ISAIAH THOMAS AND EBENEZER T. ANDREWS.
Sold by them at FAUST'S STATUE, No. 45, Newbury Street; and by said THOMAS in WORCESTER. Sold also by the Booksellers in Town and Country.—1794.

Title page of Supply Belcher's *The Harmony of Maine* (Boston, 1794).
See No. 59, p. 154.

The first page of the Adagio from the original manuscript of the *Sonata in E for the Piano Forte* by Alexander Reinagle.
See No. 74, p. 191.

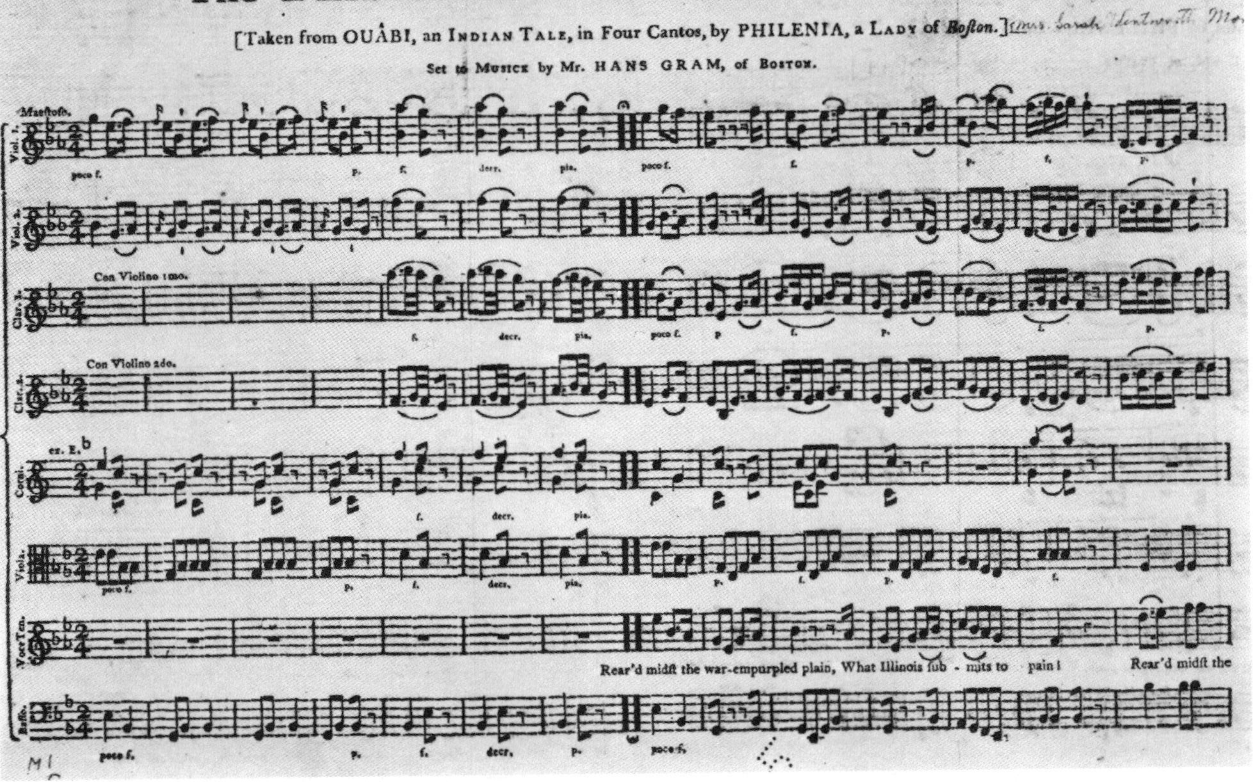

The original score of *The Death Song of an Indian Chief* by Hans Gram.
See No. 80, p. 222.

THE

STAR SPANGLED BANNER

A PARIOTIC SONG.

Baltimore. Printed and Sold at CARRS Music Store 36 Baltimore Street. [1814]

Air, Anacreon in Heaven.

Con Spirito

O! say can you see by the dawn's early light, What so proudly we hail'd at the twilight's last gleaming, Whose broad stripes & bright stars thro' the perilous fight, O'er the ramparts we watch'd, were so gallantly streaming. And the Rockets' red glare, the Bombs bursting in air, Gave proof through the night that our

rf rf

(Adapd. & Arrd. by T.C.)

The original edition of *The Star Spangled Banner*, adapted and

𝄋 2d time Chorus.

Flag was still there, O! say does that star spangled Banner yet wave, O'er the

Land of the free, and the home of the brave.

Sym.

L.H.

(2)

On the shore dimly seen through the mists of the deep,
Where the foe's haughty host in dread silence reposes,
What is that which the breeze, o'er the towering steep,
As it fitfully blows, half conceals, half discloses;
Now it catches the gleam of the morning's first beam,
In full glory reflected new shines in the stream,
'Tis the star spangled banner, O, long may it wave
O'er the land of the free, and the home of the brave.

(3)

And where is that band who so vauntingly swore
That the havoc of war and the battle's confusion,
A home and a country, shall leave us no more,
Their blood has wash'd out their foul footsteps pollution.
No refuge could save the hireling and slave,
From the terror of flight or the gloom of the grave,
And the star spangled banner, in triumph doth wave,
O'er the Land &c.

(4)

O! thus be it ever when freemen shall stand,
Between their lov'd home, and the war's desolation,
Blest with vict'ry and peace, may the Heav'n rescued land,
Praise the Pow'r that hath made and preserv'd us a nation!
Then conquer we must, when our cause it is just,
And this be our motto_"In God is our Trust";
And the star spangled banner, in triumph shall wave,
O'er the Land &c.

For the Flute.

Con Spirito

Song.

(Adapd. & Arrd. by T.C.)

(Pl.2.)

arranged by Thomas Carr (Baltimore, 1814). *See No. 115, p. 291.*

Cover page showing "Mr. T. Rice As the Original Jim Crow" (c. 1832).
See No. 104, p. 262.

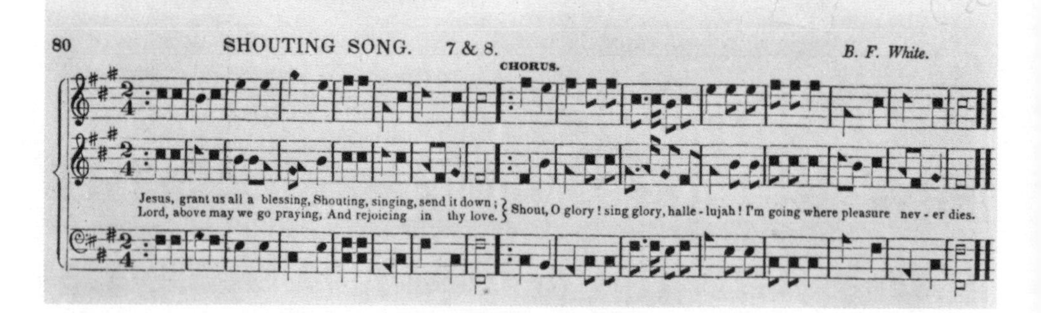

Shouting Song by Benjamin Franklin White.
From *The Sacred Harp* by B. F. White and E. J. King (Philadelphia, 1844).
See No. 102, p. 258.

Cover page of *The Old Arm Chair* by Henry Russell (Boston, 1860).
See No. 123, p. 313.

Cover page of *The Banjo* by Louis Moreau Gottschalk (New York, 1855).
See No. 125, p. 323.

91. FAIRTON

1813

Repository of Sacred Music, Part Second
John Wyeth
(*Harrisburg, Pa., 2nd ed., 1820*)

Elkanah K. Dare
(1782–1826)

[1] This note is F in the original.

2

Give me the presence of thy grace,
  Then my rejoice tongue
Shall speak aloud thy righteousness,
  And make thy praise my song.

4

A soul oppres'd with sin's desert,
  My God will ne'er despise;
A humble groan, a broken heart,
  Is our best sacrifice.

Ps. 51: Isaac Watts (1719)
(1674–1748)

92. MORALITY

1789

The Missouri Harmony
Allen D. Carden
(*Cincinnati, 1820*)

4

For when age steals on me, and youth is no more,
And the moralist time shakes his glass at my door,
What pleasure in beauty or wealth can I find?
My beauty, my wealth, is a sweet peace of mind.

6

And when I the burden of life shall have borne,
And death with his sickle shall cut the ripe corn,
Reascend to my God without murmur or sigh,
I'll bless the kind summons, and lie down and die.

93. CONSOLATION

1813

The Missouri Harmony
Allen D. Carden
(*Cincinnati, 1820*)

Dean?

[1] G in the Bass in the original.
[2] Thus in the original.

2

Night unto night his name repeats,
The day renews the sound,
Wide as the heav'n on which he sits,
To turn the seasons round.

6

Dear God, let all my hours be thine,
Whilst I enjoy the light;
Then shalt my sun in smiles decline,
And bring a pleasant night.

Hymn: Isaac Watts (1707)
(1674–1748)

94. PRIMROSE

Twenty-fourth

1813

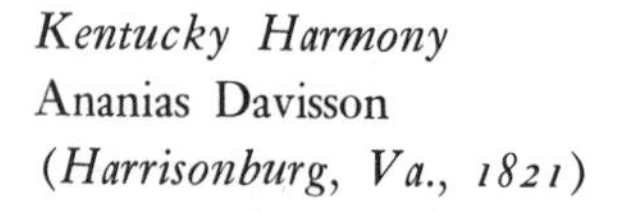

Kentucky Harmony
Ananias Davisson
(*Harrisonburg, Va., 1821*)

[Amzi] Chapin

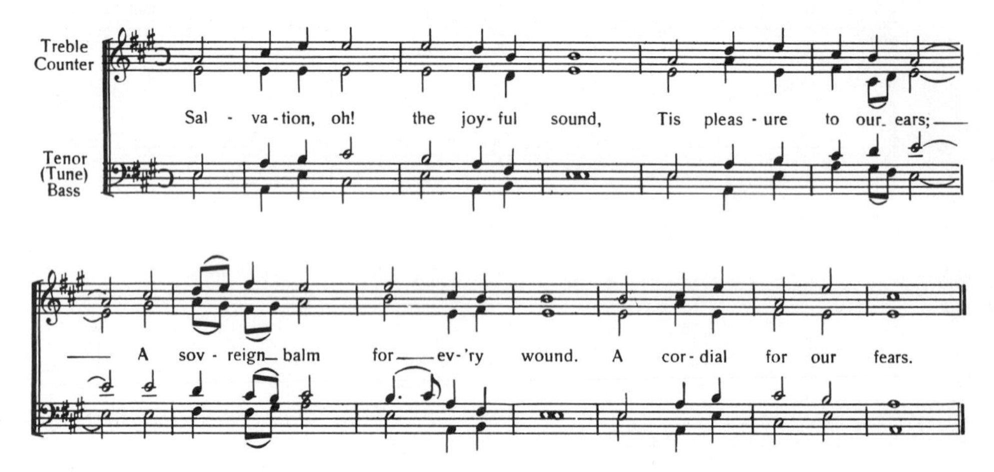

2

Buried in sorrow and in sin
At hell's dark door we lay,
But we arise by grace divine,
To see a heav'nly day.

3

Salvation! let the echo fly
The spacious world around,
While all the armies of the sky
Conspire to raise the sound.

Hymn: Isaac Watts (1707)
(1674–1748)

95. KEDRON

1799

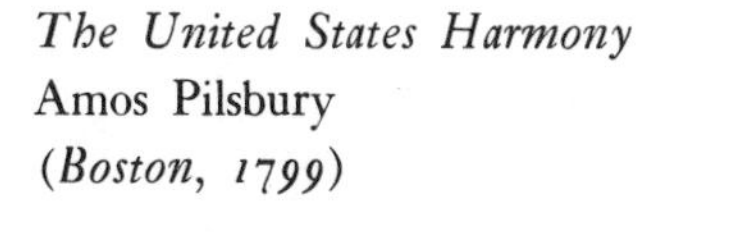
The United States Harmony
Amos Pilsbury
(*Boston, 1799*)

Anonymous

95a. KEDRON

1835

The Southern Harmony
William Walker
(*New Haven, 1835*)

[Elkanah K.] Dare
(1782–1826)

96. THE CONVERTED THIEF

1835

The Southern Harmony
William Walker
(*New Haven, 1835*)

[William] More

2

"Jesus, thou Son and heir of Heav'n!
Thou spotless Lamb of God!
I see thee bathed in sweat and tears,
And welt'ring in thy blood.
Yet quickly from these scenes of woe
In triumph thou shalt rise;
Burst thro' the gloomy shades of death,
And shine above the skies."

3

"Amid the glories of that world,
Dear Saviour, think on me,
And in the victories of thy death,
Let me a sharer be."
His prayer the dying Jesus hears,
And instantly replies,
"Today thy parting soul shall be
With me in Paradise."

Mercer's *Cluster* (c. 1815)

97. THE HEBREW CHILDREN

1841

The Southern Harmony
William Walker
(*Philadelphia, 1847*)

David Walker

97a. NEGRO SPIRITUAL

based on
The Hebrew Children

98. THE GOOD OLD WAY

1835

The Southern Harmony
William Walker
(New Haven, 1835)

William Walker
(1809–1875)

2

Our conflicts here, though great they be,
Shall not prevent our victory,
If we but watch, and strive, and pray,
Like soldiers in the good old way.

Chorus

And I'll sing hallelujah,
And glory be to God on high;
And I'll sing hallelujah,
There's glory beaming from the sky.

3

O good old way, how sweet thou art!
May none of us from thee depart,
But may our actions always say,
We're marching on the good old way.
And I'll sing, etc.

6

Ye valiant souls, for heaven contend;
Remember glory's at the end;
Our God will wipe all tears away,
When we have run the good old way.
And I'll sing, etc.

99. PLENARY

1835

The Southern Harmony
William Walker
(New Haven, 1835)

A. Clark

2
"Princes, this clay must be your bed,
 In spite of all your towers;
The tall, the wise, the reverend head
 Must lie as low as ours"!

3
Great God! is this our certain doom?
 And are we still secure?
Still walking downward to the tomb,
 And yet prepare no more!

4
Grant us the power of quickening grace,
 To fit our souls to fly;
Then, when we drop this dying flesh,
 We'll rise above the sky.

Hymn: Isaac Watts (1707)
(1674–1748)

100. NEW BRITAIN

Amazing Grace

1835

The Southern Harmony
William Walker
(*New Haven, 1835*)

2
'Twas grace that taught my heart to fear,
And grace my fears relieved:
How precious did that grace appear,
The hour I first believed!

3
Thro' many dangers, toils, and snares,
I have already come;
'Tis grace has brought me safe thus far,
And grace will lead me home.

4
The Lord has promised good to me,
His word my hope secures,
He will my shield and portion be,
As long as life endures.

5
Yes, when this flesh and hear shall fail
And mortal life shall cease,
I shall possess, within the veil,
A life of joy and peace.

John Newton (1789)
(1725–1807)

101. WONDROUS LOVE

1835

The Southern Harmony
William Walker
(*New Haven, 1835*)

Christopher

[1] This note is F in the original.
[2] This note is F in the original.

2

When I was sinking down, sinking down, sinking down,
When I was sinking down, sinking down,
When I was sinking down
Beneath God's righteous frown
Christ laid aside His crown for my soul, for my soul,
Christ laid aside His crown for my soul.

4

And when from death I'm free I'll sing on, I'll sing on,
And when from death I'm free I'll sing on,
And when from death I'm free
I'll sing and joyful be,
And thro' eternity I'll sing on, I'll sing on,
And thro' eternity I'll sing on.

102. SHOUTING SONG

1844

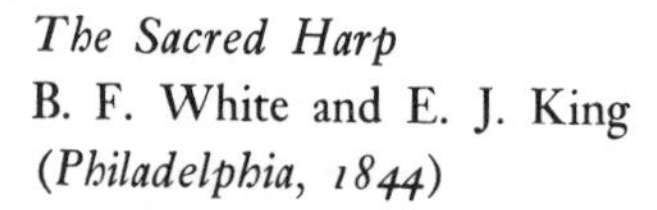
The Sacred Harp
B. F. White and E. J. King
(*Philadelphia, 1844*)

Benjamin Franklin White
(1800–1879)

103. GOSPEL TRUMPET

1844

The Sacred Harp
B. F. White and E. J. King
(*Philadelphia, 1844*)

E. J. King
(c. 1800–c. 1850)

Chapter Eight

MUSIC OF THE MINSTREL SHOWS

De Scriber am pressed wid de vast 'sponsibility ob pesentin' to de whole Popalashun ob dis world de genus ob de colored pofessors ob de' vine art; and did he tink dat de world would be safe widout em, an' dat posterity would not sink down into oblivion, he would most 'spectfully hab declined de honor to be fus' skientific orther ob an Ethiopian Glee Book.

Preface, *The Ethiopian Glee Book* (Boston, 1848)

MINSTREL shows (often called Ethiopian operas) and ballad operas have much in common. Perhaps the most binding feature is their use of borrowed music, which, interspersed as needed, shared the proceedings on the stage with dances, comic repartees, stump speeches, and jokes. The performers with blackened faces, dressed in striped trousers, swallow-tail coats, oversized collars, and wearing white gloves, are often pictured seated in a semicircle singing to the accompaniment of a banjo, violin, tambourine, and bones (castanets). The beginning of the minstrel show can be traced back to about 1820, when white performers impersonated the southern Negro plantation workers and the northern Negroes who tried to imitate the white dandy.

The songs included in the *Anthology* are among the most popular and were performed by such bands as Bryant's Minstrels, Virginia Serenaders, Sable Harmonists, Christy's Minstrels, and Ethiopian Serenaders, to name but a few. Thomas ("Daddy") Rice, A. F. Winnemore, Stephen Foster, and Dan Emmett were fully aware of the publicity and sales opened to their music by the minstrels—the precursors of our contemporary disc-jockeys. Appropriated by these, the songs were catapulted into the realm of immortality. Typical of the minstrel song is the solo-chorus formula with repeated refrains sung in unison or in three or four parts over a simple accompaniment. The song, in a major key, is preceded by an introduction or "vamp" and ends with a "tag," the melody of which may or may not have been drawn from the song.

The "walk-around" was the finale of the minstrel show. The entire troupe assembled on the stage in a semicircle; a few members stepped forward and sang a stanza, during which they were interrupted by "end-men." Then the whole company joined in the final chorus as some danced, some sang, and others clapped or stamped in time with the music. Originally the walk-around was only a dance; later (about 1858) it was danced and sung, and with Bryant's Minstrels it achieved its popularity as the grand finale.

Jim Crow (No. 104), also known as *Jump, Jim Crow,* was perhaps the first black-face song with a dance act to become the mainstay of the minstrel show. Thomas D. Rice wrote the song for his impersonation of a gay, picturesque Negro plantation worker, and it became an overnight sensation.

The tune *Zip Coon* (No. 105), better known as *Turkey in the Straw,* may be of Irish origin, but certainly there is no doubt that in its one hundred and thirty years of existence in the United States it has become a strictly American tune, ideal for square dances. *Zip Coon* represents the other type of Negro impersonation; the character who imitated in his dress and actions the comic white "Broadway swell." "Completely taken in by himself, he talked mainly of his elegant appearance and of his narcotic effect on the ladies."[1]

Stop That Knocking at My Door (No. 106) by A. F. Winnemore is a minstrel song for solo voice, with a few spoken words, a duet, and a chorus. The title page bears the information that the song was "sung and arranged by the Christy Minstrels."

Stephen Foster was only twenty-one when he composed one of his first successes, the "non-sense" song, *Oh! Susanna* (No. 107). It was first performed at Andrew's "Eagle Ice Cream Saloon" in Pittsburgh in 1848, and a year later it was taken over by Christy's Minstrels. The tune became one of the most popular of its day, and it was even carried to California by the forty-niners, who adopted it as their theme song.

Old Folks at Home (No. 108) is without doubt Stephen Foster's most famous song. It first appeared in 1851 as an "Ethiopian Melody as sung by Christy's Minstrels. Written and Composed by E. P. Christy." Not until the song won an incredible popularity both in England and in America did Foster acknowledge himself as the composer. This nostalgic song, written about a plantation on the Suwannee river [2] (Foster spelled it "Swanee"), which he had never seen, offers a sharp contrast to the gay and lively tunes usually associated with the minstrels. It does, however, retain the form of the typical Ethiopian song —namely, three or four stanzas for a solo voice, each followed by a refrain for the chorus.

Dixie's Land (No. 109) was composed by Dan Emmett in 1859 when he was a member of Bryant's Minstrels, and it became a favorite walk-around. The tune achieved such great popularity that it was adopted by the Confederate Army as a battle-song along with *The Bonnie Blue Flag.*

[1] Hans Nathan, *Dan Emmett, and the Rise of Early Negro Minstrelsy* (Norman, Okla., 1962), p. 59.

[2] The Suwannee river rises in Georgia and flows through northern Florida into the Gulf of Mexico.

104. JIM CROW

c. 1832

E. Riley
(*New York, c. 1832*)

Thomas Dartmouth Rice
(1808–1860)

[1] D in the original.
[2] E in the original.
[3] E in the original.

2
I'm a rorer on de fiddle,
 And down in ole Virginny;
Dey say I play de skientific.
 Like massa Pagganninny.

12
O den I go to Washinton,
 Wid bank memorial;
But find dey tork sich nonsense,
 I spen my time wid Sal.

15
I den go to de Presiden,
 He ax me wat I do;
I put de veto on de boot,
 An nullefy de shoe.

17
O den I goes to New York,
 To put dem rite all dare;
But find so many tick heads,
 I gib up in dispair.

19
I take de walk to Niblows,
 Wid Dina by my side;
And dare we see Miss Watson,
 De Paganini bride.

20
She sing so lubly dat my heart,
 Went pit a pat jis so;
I wish she fall in lub wid me,
 I'd let Miss Dina go.

Thomas Dartmouth Rice

105. ZIP COON

1834

G. Willig, Jr. (*Baltimore, 1834*) — Anonymous

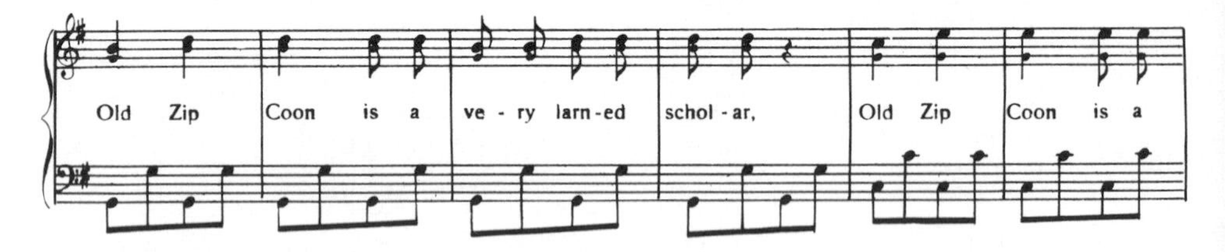

6

Dat tarnal critter Crocket, he never say his
prayers,
He kill all de wild cats de Coons and de Bears,
An den he go to Washington to help to make
de laws,
An dere he find de Congress men sucking of
deir paws.

9

O glory be to Jackson, for he blow up de
Banks,
An glory be to Jackson, for he many funny
pranks,
An glory be to Jackson, for de battle of
Orleans,
For dere he gib de enemy de hot butter beans.

106. STOP THAT KNOCKING AT MY DOOR

1843

George P. Reed
(*Boston, 1843*)

A. F. Winnemore

town, Her eyes so bright dey_ shine at night when de moon am gone_ a
way, She used to call his dark-ey up_ Just a fore de broke of
day: wid a who dar? who dar? who dar? An a who dar a knocking at my
SPOKEN. Why Sam.
door? Am dat you Sam? Am_ dat you Sam? No, you bet-ter stop dat knocking at my
SPOKEN. Aint you gwan to let me in?
By Bass Voice

[1] B in the original.

CHORUS

1.st VOICE
2.nd VOICE
TENOR
BASS
PIANO
Stop that knock-ing, stop that knock-ing, stop that knocking, stop that knocking, Oh! you
Stop that knock-ing, stop that knock-ing, stop that knocking, stop that knocking, Oh! you
Stop that knock-ing, stop that knock-ing, stop that knock-ing, stop that knocking, Oh! you
Stop that knock-ing, stop that knock-ing, stop that knock-ing, stop that knocking, No! I'll
bett - er stop that knock - ing at my door. Stop that
bett - er stop that knock - ing at my door. Stop that
bett - er stop that knock - ing at my door. Stop that
nev - er stop that knock - ing at your door. Let me in. Stop that

knock-ing, stop that knock-ing, stop that knock - ing, stop that knock - ing, Oh! you
knock-ing, stop that knock-ing, stop that knock - ing, stop that knock - ing, Oh! you
knock-ing, stop that knock - ing, stop that knock - ing, stop that knock - ing, Oh! you
knock-ing, stop that knock-ing, stop that knock - ing, stop that knock - ing, No! I'll
bett - er stop that knock-ing at my door.
bett - er stop that knock-ing at my door.
bett - er stop that knock-ing at my door.
nev - er stop that knock- ing at your door.
8va

2

She was the prettiest yaller Gal
That eber I did see,
She never would go walking,
Wid any Colored man but me.
And when I took my Banjo down,
And played three tunes or more,
All at once I heard, three pretty hard raps
Come bang again my door.
Wid who dar? who dar?
Stop that knocking &c.

3

Oh, de first one dat cum in de room
Was a darkey dressed to death,
He looked just like de showman,
What dey used to call Mackbeth.
He said he was a Californi man,
An just arrived on shore,
I ax him whare fore he cum an rap,
So hard against my door.
Wid who dar? who dar?
Stop that knocking &c.

A. F. Winnemore

107. OH! SUSANNA

1848

C. Holt, Jr.
(*New York, 1848*)

Stephen Collins Foster
(1826–1864)

weath - er it was dry, The sun so hot I
frose to death Sus - an - na dont you cry.
Chorus
1st Voice
Oh! Sus an - na Oh! dont you cry for me I've
2nd Voice
Oh! Sus - an - na Oh! dont you cry for me I've
Tenor.
Oh! Sus - an - na Oh! dont you cry for me I've
Bass
Oh! Sus - an - na Oh! dont you cry for me I've
Piano
Forte

2

I jumped aboard de telegrph [*sic*],
And trabbelled down de riber,
De Lectric fluid magnified,
And Killed five Hundred Nigger.
De bull gine buste, de horse run off,
I realy thought I'd die;
I shut my eyes to hold my breath,
Susana [*sic*], dont you cry.
Oh! Susana &c.

3

I had a dream de odder night,
When ebery ting was still;
I thought I saw Susana,
A coming down de hill.
The buckwheat cake war in her mouth,
The tear was in her eye,
Says I, im coming from de South,
Susana, dont you cry.
Oh! Susana &c.

Stephen Collins Foster

108. OLD FOLKS AT HOME

Ethiopian Melody

1851

Firth, Pond & Co.
(*New York, 1851*)

Stephen Collins Foster
(1826–1864)

Sad - - ly I roam, Still long - ing for de old plan - ta - tion,
And for de old folks at home.
Chorus
All de world am sad and drea-ry, Eb - ry where I
roam, Oh! dar - keys how my heart grows wea-ry, Far from de old folks at home.

2

All round de little farm I wandered
  When I was young,
Den many happy days I squandered,
  Many de songs I sung.
When I was playing wid my brudder
  Happy was I,
Oh! take me to my kind old mudder,
  Dere let me live and die.—*Chorus*

3

One little hut among de bushes,
  One dat I love,
Still sadly to my mem'ry rushes,
  No matter where I rove.
When will I see de bees a humming
  All round de comb?
When will I hear de banjo tumming
  Down in my good old home?—*Chorus*

Stephen Collins Foster

109. DIXIE'S LAND

1860

Firth, Pond & Co.
(*New York, 1860*)

Dan. D. Emmett
(1818–1904)
Arranged by
W. L. Hobbs

Land. In— Dix - ie Land—whar— I was born in, Ear - ly on one fros - ty mornin, Look a -
way! Look a - way! Look a - way! Dix - ie Land.
Chorus
Den— I wish I was in Dix - ie, Hoo - ray! Hoo - ray! In— Dix - ie Land, I'll
took my stand, To lib an die in Dix - ie, A - way, A - way, A -

2

Old Missus marry "Will-de-weaber,"
Willium was a gay deceaber;
Look away! &c—
But when he put his arm around'er,
He smilled as fierce as a forty-pound'er.
Look away! &c—
Chorus—Den I wish I was in Dixie, &c—

3

His face was sharp as a butchers cleaber,
But dat did not seem to greab'er;
Look away! &c—
Old Missus acted de foolish part,
And died for a man dat broke her heart.
Look away! &c—
Chorus—Den I wish I was in Dixie, &c—

4

Now here's a health to the next old Missus,
An all de galls dat want to kiss us;
Look away! &c—
But if you want to drive'way sorrow,
Come an hear dis song to-morrow.
Look away! &c—
Chorus—Den I wish I was in Dixie, &c—

5

Dar's buck-wheat cakes an 'Ingen' batter,
Makes you fat or a little fatter;
Look away! &c—
Den hoe it down an scratch your grabble,
To Dixie land I'm bound to trabble.
Look away! &c—
Chorus—Den I wish I was in Dixie, &c—

Daniel Decatur Emmett
(1859)

Chapter Nine

NATIONAL AND PATRIOTIC SONGS

1794-1865

When our land is illumined with liberty's smile,
If a foe from within strikes a blow at her glory,
Down, down with the traitor that dares to defile
The flag of the stars, and the page of her story!
By the millions unchained
Who their birth-right have gained,
We will keep her bright blazon forever unstained;
And the Star-Spangled Banner in triumph shall wave,
While the land of the free is the home of the brave.

Oliver Wendell Holmes, an added stanza to our National Anthem (April 14, 1872)

THE NATIONAL and patriotic songs sung during our wars with England again offer testimony of the indebtedness to the mother country evinced in *Yankee Doodle* and *To Anacreon in Heaven (Star Spangled Banner).* The tune of *God Save the King* was also well known in the Colonies but found its way peacefully into the repertory of national airs with the text *My country, 'tis of thee.* A large number of patriotic songs completely American in spirit, such as *When Johnny comes marching home* and *Marching through Georgia,* emerged during the Civil War.

New Yankee Doodle (No. 110) is possibly the earliest publication in America of the tune with a text. The words of *New Yankee Doodle*, and also *Hail! Columbia* (No. 111), were inspired by the undeclared war with France (1798–1800). First printed in Glasgow in 1782, the tune of *Yankee Doodle* was well known in England long before, and in this country as early as 1767, but was not published here until 1794 when it appeared in Benjamin Carr's *Federal Overture*, a medley of patriotic "airs."

Joseph Hopkinson, son of Francis, wrote the words of *Hail! Columbia* in 1798 at the request of the actor, Gilbert Fox, who wanted them adapted to Philip Phile's *President's March* (1793). The stirring words with the popular tune soon became one of our most famous songs.

Washington's March (No. 112) is the first of many marches to be published in honor of George Washington. The march is known to have been played at a public celebration in Philadelphia in 1794, but it may have been composed and performed before that. The composer is unknown, although the music is sometimes attributed to Francis Hopkinson.

The Anacreontic Song, "To Anacreon in Heav'n" (No. 113), was the constitutional song of the Anacreontic Society of London. The poem, written about 1775 by Ralph Tomlinson, was set to music by a musician whose identity has long been disputed. Addressed to the Grecian poet Anacreon (c. 500 B.C.) and celebrating the delights of Bacchus and Amor, it achieved a popularity so widespread that it reached our shores before the turn of the century. The edition used in the *Anthology* is the first, published in London in 1778 or 1779, and it is included here so that it may be compared with later versions of the tune.

In 1798 Thomas Paine (not related to his namesake, the Anglo-American philosopher and writer) adapted new words to the English drinking song *To Anacreon in Heaven* which he titled *Adams and Liberty* (No. 114), and it was performed in June of the same year at the fourth anniversary of the Massachusetts Charitable Fire Society. The late Richard S. Hill compiled a list of 85 American parodies adapted to *To Anacreon in Heaven* between 1790 and 1818.[1]

The Star Spangled Banner (No. 115) was written by Francis Scott Key on September 14, 1814, immediately following the bombardment of Fort McHenry by the British. It first appeared as a broadside on September 15 bearing the title *Defence of Fort McHenry* and an indication that it was to be sung to the tune *To Anacreon in Heaven.* A short time later the first edition, with both words and music and the title *The Star Spangled Banner*, was printed in Baltimore by [Joseph] Carr. It was, however, not officially declared our national anthem until 1931.

The words to *My country, 'tis of thee* (No. 116) were written in 1831 by the Reverend Samuel Francis Smith of Boston. At the instigation of Lowell Mason, Smith examined many German music books for attractive melodies suitable for children. He selected the melody *Heil dir im Siegerkranz* and wrote his famous poem, naïvely unaware that the tune selected was the British national anthem. The tune, first printed in *Harmonia Anglicana* (London, 1744), has been adopted at one time or another by a number of countries as their official national anthem. Lowell Mason had the song, clad in its new text, performed by children in Park Street Church on July 4, 1831. The singable tune is somewhat in the rhythm and style of a galliard, and it will be noticed that since its first appearance in America in Lyon's *Urania*, the music has undergone slight melodic changes (*Anthology*, No. 40).

The tune of *Glory! Hallelujah!* (No. 117), often attributed to William Steffe, was originally a rousing camp-meeting song with a text beginning, "Say Brothers, will you meet us?" After the raid on Harper's Ferry in 1859, many new texts commemorating the martyr John Brown were set to the tune, and it became the marching song of the Massachusetts volunteers on their way to the battlefields of the South.

Late in 1861 Julia Ward Howe wrote a "new and more dignified text" to the famous tune and submitted it to the editor of the *Atlantic Monthly*, who published it in the February 1862 issue under his own title *The Battle Hymn of the Republic.*

[1] Richard S. Hill, "The Melody of 'The Star Spangled Banner' in the United States before 1820." Offprint from *Essays Honoring Lawrence C. Wroth*, 1951. Washington: The Library of Congress, 1951.

All quiet along the Potomac to-night (No. 118) was composed by John Hill Hewitt in 1861 to a text attributed to Lamar Fontaine of Mississippi. With this song, in which the death of a sentry on duty along the Potomac is romantically and pathetically described, Hewitt achieved a success that placed him in the front rank of ballad composers. Although it was written as a Confederate song, it became popular in the North as well.

Another song of the Civil War, *Tenting on the Old Camp Ground* (No. 119), was composed by a Northerner, Walter Kittredge, soon after he was drafted in 1862. This melancholy song was widely sung by the Hutchinson family, who advertised themselves as the "Tribe of Asa," and it became so popular that it was taken up by the Southern Army as well as the Northern.

When Johnny comes marching home (No. 120), adopted by the North during the Civil War, was composed by the famous bandmaster Patrick Gilmore and published under his pseudonym, Louis Lambert. This enormously popular and vital folksong-like piece is only sixteen measures in length. Its four stanzas are separated by an eight-measure chorus reminiscent of an Irish jig, possibly a part of Gilmore's Irish inheritance.

Marching through Georgia (No. 121) refers to the famous march "from Atlanta to the sea," about 300 miles through Georgia. It was less a campaign than a picnic, for the Union Army encountered no opposition. Henry Clay Work's text is fully descriptive of this memorable event. In ABA form, this jaunty song with its spirited choral refrain is one of the most popular songs to have been inspired by the Civil War.

110. NEW YANKEE DOODLE

1798

James Hewitt
(*New York*, [1798])

Arranged by
J.[ames] Hewitt
(1770–1827)

2

The only way to keep off war,
  And gaard 'gainst persecution,
Is always to be well prepar'd,
  With hearts of resolution.
    Yankee Doodle, let's Unite,
      Yankee Doodle Dandy,
    As patriots, still maintain our right,
      Yankee Doodle Dandy.

3

Great WASHINGTON, who led us on,
  And Liberty effected,
Shall see we'll die or else be free—
  We will not be subjected.
    Yankee Doodle, guard your coast,
      Yankee Doodle Dandy—
    Fear not then or threat or boast,
      Yankee Doodle Dandy.

4

A Band of Brothers let us be,
  While ADAMS guides the nation;
And still our dear bought Freedom guard,
  In ev'ry situation.
    Yankee Doodle, guard your coast,
      Yankee Doodle Dandy—
    Fear not then or threat or boast,
      Yankee Doodle Dandy.

5

May soon the wish'd for hour arrive,
  When PEACE shall rule the nations—
And Commerce, free from fetters prove
  Mankind are all relations.
    Then Yankee Doodle, be divine,
      Yankee Doodle Dandy—
    Beneath the Fig tree and the Vine,
      Sing Yankee Doodle Dandy.

111. THE FAVORITE NEW FEDERAL SONG HAIL! COLUMBIA

1798

Benjamin Carr
(*Philadelphia*, [*1798*])

Philip Phile
(c. 1734–1793)

For the Voice, Piano Forte, Guittar and Clarinett

who fought & bled in
free - doms cause,
and when the storm of
war was gone, en -

joy'd the _ peace your
va - lor won; let
In - de - pen - dence
be _ our _ boast,

ev - er mind - ful
what it cost,
ev - er grate - ful
for _ the _ prize,

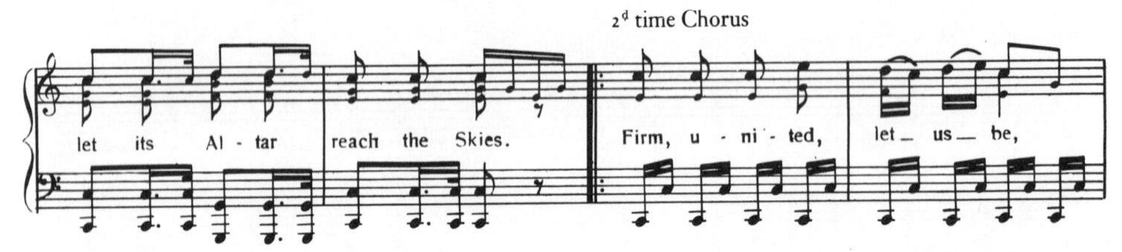
2d time Chorus
let its Al - tar
reach the Skies.
Firm, u - ni - ted,
let _ us _ be,

ral - lying round our
Li - ber - ty,
as a band of _
Bro - thers joind,

2

Immortal Patriots, rise once more!
Defend your rights, defend your shore;
  Let no rude foe with impious hand,
  Let no rude foe with impious hand,
Invade the shrine where sacred lies,
Of toil and blood, the well earn'd prize;
    While offering peace, sincere and just,
    In heav'n we place a manly trust,
    That truth and justice will prevail,
    And every scheme of bondage fail!
      Firm, united. &c.

3

Sound, sound the trump of fame!
Let Washington's great name
  Ring through the world with loud applause!
  Ring through the world with loud applause!
Let every clime to Freedom dear
Listen with a joyful ear;
    With equal skill, with godlike pow'r,
    He governs in the fearful hour
    Of horrid war, or guides with ease
    The happier times of honest peace.
      Firm, united. &c.

4

Behold the Chief who now commands,
Once more to serve his Country, stands
  The rock on which the storm will beat!
  The rock on which the storm will beat!
But arm'd in virtue, firm and true,
His hopes are fix'd on heav'n and you;
    When hope was sinking in dismay,
    When glooms obscur'd Columbia's day,
    His steady mind, from changes free,
    Resolved on Death or Liberty.
      Firm, united. &c.

Joseph Hopkinson
(1798)

112. WASHINGTON'S MARCH

1794/95

G[eorge] Willig's *Musical Magazine* (*Philadelphia, 1794/95*)

[1] The trills (tr) and the sign (∽) may be played [notation] or [notation]
[2] The original has the sign (tr) over the G.

113. THE ANACREONTIC SONG

To Anacreon in Heav'n

1778/79

Longman & Broderip
(*London*, [*1778/79*])

sides, I'll in-struct you like me, to_ in-twine, The Myr-tle of VENUS with BACCHUS'S Vine.
Chorus
And be-sides, I'll in-struct you like me, to en-twine, The
And be-sides, I'll in-struct you like me, to en-twine, The
Myr-tle of VE-NUS with BAC-CHUS-'S Vine."
Myr-tle of VE-NUS with BAC-CHUS-'S Vine."
Ralph Tomlinson
(1778)

114. ADAMS AND LIBERTY

The Boston Patriotic Song

1798

Air: *Anacreon in Heaven*

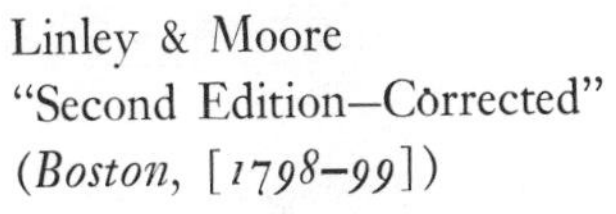

Linley & Moore
"Second Edition–Corrected"
(*Boston*, [*1798–99*])

[1] The first two bass notes are F in the original.

2

In a clime, whose rich vales feed the marts of the world,
Whose shores are unshaken by Europe's commotion,
The Trident of Commerce should never be hurl'd,
To incense the legitimate powers of the ocean.
But should Pirates invade,
Though in thunder array'd,
Let your cannon declare the free charter of TRADE.
For ne'er shall the sons of COLUMBIA be slaves,
While the earth bears a plant, or the sea rolls its waves.

9

Let FAME to the world sound AMERICA's voice;
No intrigue can her sons from their GOVERNMENT sever;
Her Pride is her ADAMS—his LAWS are her CHOICE,
And shall flourish, till LIBERTY slumber forever!
Then unite, heart and hand,
Like Leonidas' band,
And swear to the GOD of the ocean and land,
That ne'er shall the sons of COLUMBIA be slaves,
While the earth bears a plant, or the sea rolls its waves.

Thomas [Robert Treat] Paine
(1798)

115. THE STAR SPANGLED BANNER

A Pa[t]riotic Song

1814

J[oseph] Carr
(*Baltimore, [1814]*)

Air: *Anacreon in Heaven*
Adapted and arranged by
T[homas] C[arr]

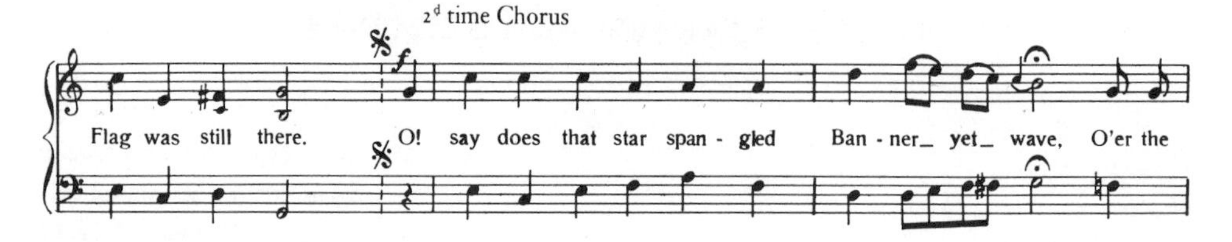

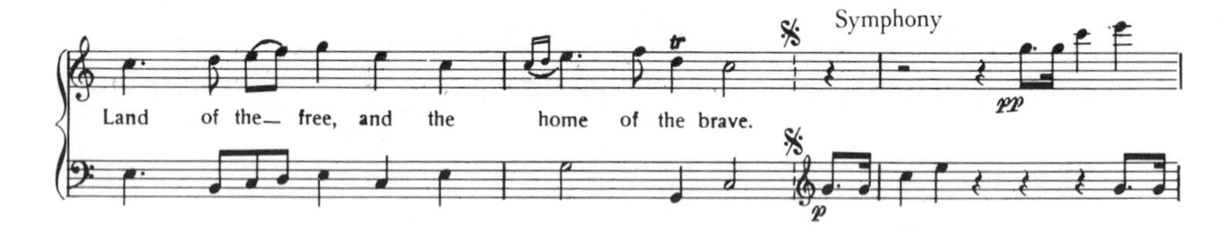

2

On the shore dimly seen through the mists of the deep,
  Where the foe's haughty host in dread silence reposes,
What is that which the breeze, o'er the towering steep,
  As it fitfully blows, half conceals, half discloses;
Now it catches the gleam of the morning's first beam,
In full glory reflected now [1] shines in the stream,
    'Tis the star spangled banner, O! long may it wave
    O'er the Land of the free, and the home of the brave.

3

And where is that band who so vauntingly swore
  That the havoc of war and the battle's confusion,
A home and a country, shall leave us no more,
  Their blood has wash'd out their foul footsteps pollution.
No refuge could save the hireling and slave,
From the terror of flight or the gloom of the grave,
    And the star spangled banner, in triumph doth wave
    O'er the Land of the free, and the home of the brave.

4

O! thus be it ever when free men shall stand,
  Between their lov'd home, and the war's desolation.
Blest with vict'ry and peace, may the Heav'n rescued land,
  Praise the Pow'r that hath made and preserv'd us a nation!
Then conquer we must, when our cause it is just,
And this be our motto—"In God is our Trust";
    And the star spangled banner, in triumph shall wave,
    O'er the Land of the free, and the home of the brave.

[1] The original text reads "new."

Francis Scott Key
(1814)

116. MY COUNTRY! 'TIS OF THEE

1831

C[harles] Bradlee
(*Boston,* [*1831*])

Tune: *God Save the King* (1744)

[1] The original has F-sharp in the middle voice.

2

My native country! thee,
Land of the noble free,
Thy name I love;
I love thy rocks and rills,
Thy woods and templed hills;
My heart with rapture thrills,
Like that above.

3

Let music swell the breeze,
And ring from all the trees
Sweet freedom's song;
Let mortal tongues awake,
Let all that breathe partake,
Let rocks their silence break,
The sound prolong.

4

Our father's God! to thee,
Author of liberty!
To thee we sing;
Long may our land be bright,
With freedom's holy light;
Protect us by thy might,
Great God, our King!

Samuel Francis Smith
(1831)

117. GLORY! HALLELUJAH!

1861

Oliver Ditson & Co.
(*Boston, 1861*)

William Steffe?

Moderato

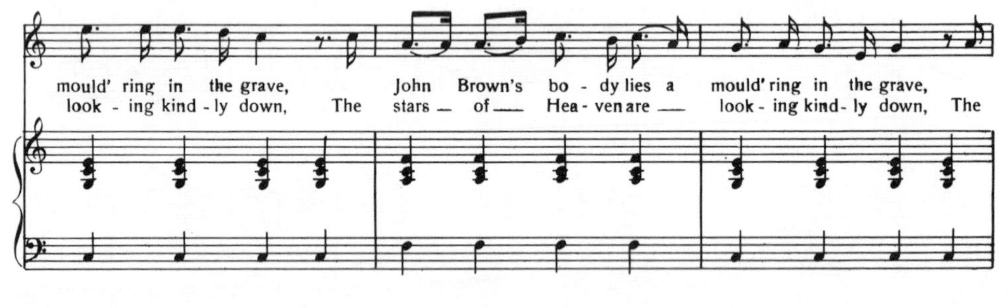

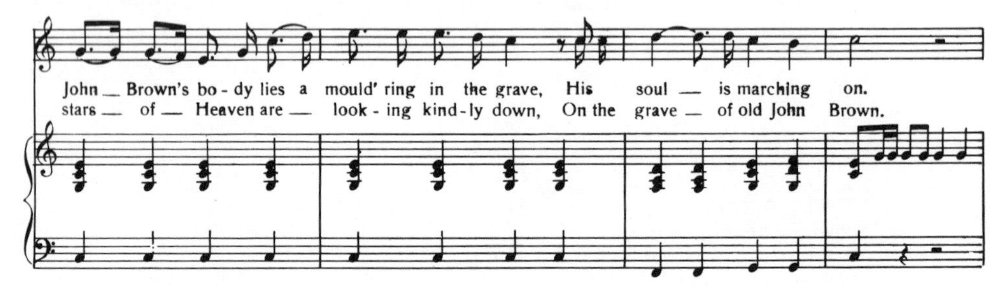

3

He's gone to be a soldier in the army of the
Lord! :||
His soul is marching on.

4

John Brown's knapsack is strapped upon his
back, :||
His soul is marching on.

5

His pet lambs will meet him on the way, :||
And they'll go marching on.

6

They will hang Jeff Davis to a tree, :||
As they march along.

Fort Warren, Boston (1859)

THE BATTLE HYMN OF THE REPUBLIC

1862

Julia Ward Howe
(1819–1910)

1

Mine eyes have seen the glory of the coming of the Lord;
He is trampling out the vintage where the grapes of wrath are stored;
He hath loosed the fateful lightning of His terrible swift sword;
His truth is marching on.

2

I have seen Him in the watch-fires of a hundred circling camps,
They have builded Him an altar in the evening dews and damps;
I can read His righteous sentence by the dim and flaring lamps;
His day is marching on.

3

I have read a fiery gospel writ in burnished rows of steel;
"As ye deal with my contemners, so with you my grace shall deal:"
Let the Hero, born of woman crush the serpent with his heel,
Since God is marching on.

4

He has sounded forth the trumpet that shall never call retreat;
He is sifting out the hearts of men before His judgment seat;
Oh, be swift, my soul, to answer Him! be jubilant my feet!
Our God is marching on.

5

In the beauty of the lilies Christ was born across the sea,
With a glory in his bosom that transfigures you and me;
As he died to make men holy, let us die to make men free,
While God is marching on.

Julia Ward Howe
(1862)

118. ALL QUIET ALONG THE POTOMAC TO-NIGHT

Julian A. Selby
(*Columbia*, S.C. [*c. 1864*])

John Hill Hewitt
(1801–1890)

2

"All quiet along the Potomac to-night,"
Where the soldiers lie peacefully dreaming,
And their tents in the rays of the clear autumn moon,
And the light of the camp fires are gleaming.
A tremulous sigh, as the gentle night wind
Thro' the forest leaves slowly is creeping,
While the stars up above, with their glittering eyes,
Keep guard o'er the army while sleeping.

3

There's only the sound of the lone sentry's tread,
As he tramps from the rock to the fountain,
And thinks of the two on the low trundle bed,
Far away in the cot on the mountain.
His musket falls slack—his face, dark and grim,
Grows gentle with memories tender,
As he mutters a prayer for the children asleep,
And their mother—"may Heaven defend her."

4

Then drawing his sleeve roughly over his eyes,
He dashes off the tears that are welling;
And gathers his gun close up to his breast,
As if to keep down the heart's swelling.
He passes the fountain, the blasted pine tree,
And his footstep is lagging and weary:
Yet onward he goes, thro' the broad belt of light,
Towards the shades of the forest so dreary.

5

Hark! was it the night wind that rustles the leaves?
Was it the moonlight so wondrously flashing?
It looked like a rifle! "Ha! Mary, good-bye!"
And his life-blood is ebbing and [s]plashing.
"All quiet along the Potomac to-night,"
No sound save the rush of the river;
While soft falls the dew on the face of the dead,
"The Picket's" off duty forever.

E. B. [Ethel Lynn Beers]
(1861)

119. TENTING ON THE OLD CAMP GROUND

1864

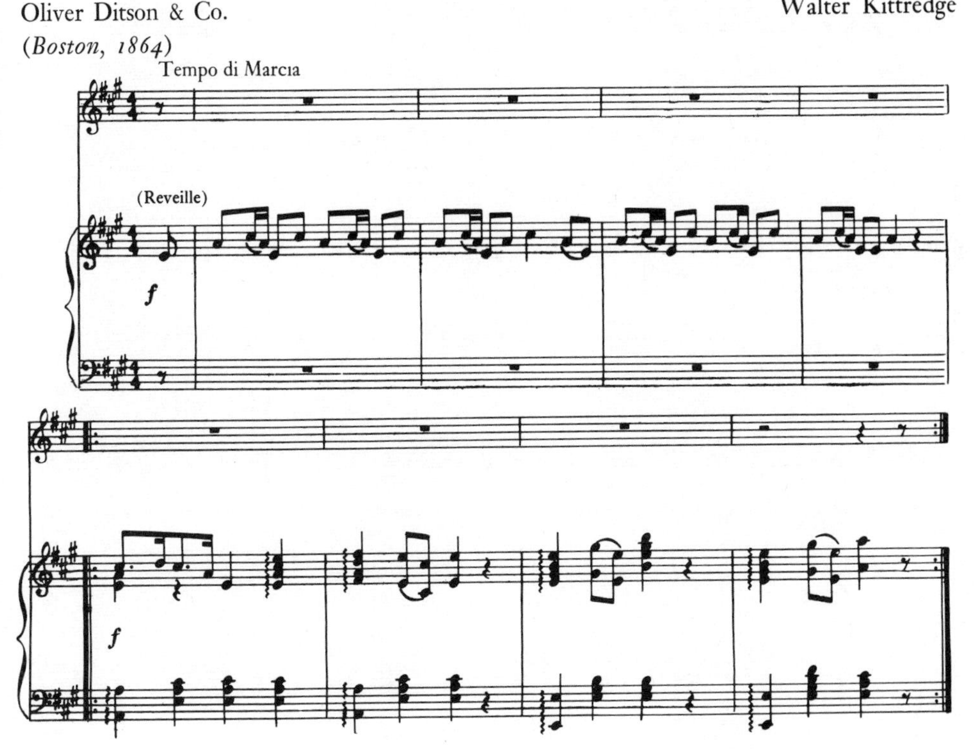

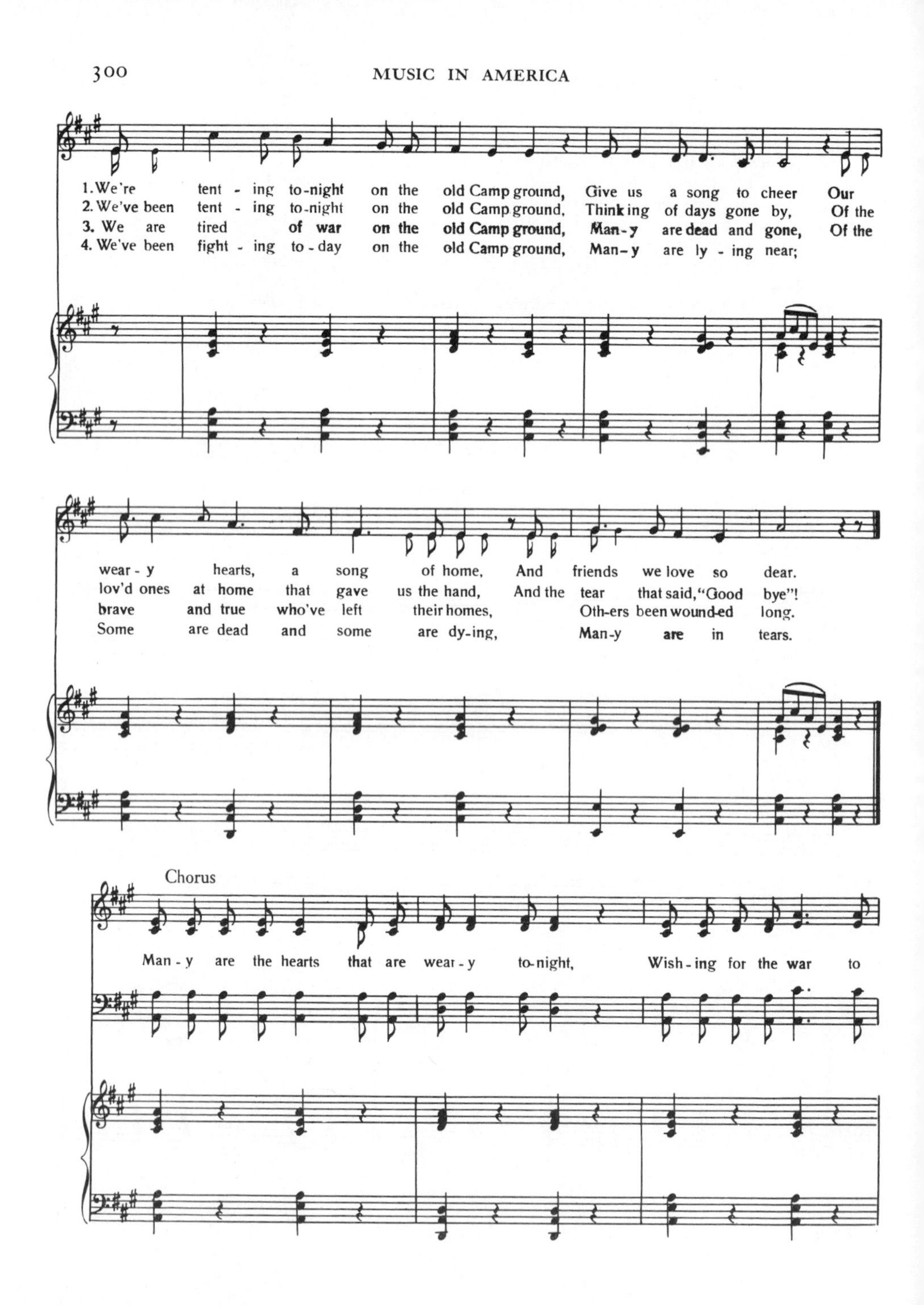
1. We're tent - ing to-night on the old Camp ground, Give us a song to cheer Our weary hearts, a song of home, And friends we love so dear.
2. We've been tent - ing to-night on the old Camp ground, Thinking of days gone by, Of the lov'd ones at home that gave us the hand, And the tear that said, "Good bye"!
3. We are tired of war on the old Camp ground, Man-y are dead and gone, Of the brave and true who've left their homes, Oth-ers been wound-ed long.
4. We've been fight - ing to - day on the old Camp ground, Man - y are ly - ing near; Some are dead and some are dy-ing, Man-y are in tears.
Chorus
Man - y are the hearts that are wear - y to-night, Wish - ing for the war to

Walter Kittredge
(1862)

120. WHEN JOHNNY COMES MARCHING HOME

1863

Henry Tolman & Co.
(*Boston, 1863*)

Louis Lambert
(Patrick S. Gilmore)
(1829–1892)

Louis Lambert (Patrick S. Gilmore)

121. MARCHING THROUGH GEORGIA

1865

Root & Cady
(*Chicago, 1865*)

Henry Clay Work
(1832–1884)

Introduction

start the world a - long
com - mis - sa - ry found!
had not seen for years;
'twas a hand - some boast,
hun - dred to the main;
Sing it as we used to sing it,
How the sweet po - ta - toes e - ven
Hard - ly could they be re - strained from
Had they not for - got, a - las! to
Trea - son fled be - fore us, for re -
fif - ty thou - sand strong,
start - ed from the ground,
break - ing forth in cheers,
reck - on with the host,
sis - tance was in vain,
While we were march - ing through Geor - gia.
Chorus
Air.
"Hur - rah! Hur - rah! we bring the Ju - bi - lee! Hur - rah! Hur - rah! the
Alto.
ff
Tenor.
"Hur - rah! Hur - rah! we bring the Ju - bi - lee! Hur - rah! Hur - rah! the
Base.
ff

Henry Clay Work
(1864)

Chapter Ten

ROMANTIC BALLADS AND NATIONALIST COMPOSERS

1821-1857

"I was dreadfully sorry to hear of poor Gottschalk's death. He had a golden touch, and equal to any in the world, I think. But what a romantic way to die!—to fall senseless at his instrument, while he was playing "La Morte." It was very strange. If anything more is in the papers about him you must send it to me, for the infatuation that I and 99,999 other American girls once felt for him, still lingers in my breast."

From the diary of Amy Fay, *Music Study in Germany* (Chicago, 1881).

THE 19TH CENTURY found musicians in the United States actively engaged in various kinds of music-making for large and receptive audiences. Lowell Mason dominated church music, and the English ballad singer Henry Russell, and the American, Septimus Winner, were unbelievably popular. The exotic Louis Moreau Gottschalk, an exponent of the Creole songs of Louisiana and the salon music of Paris, was causing young ladies to swoon with his romantic pianism, and William Mason was introducing sound principles of piano technique, and composing and playing music of popular appeal. Avowed champions of American music arose, among them the Bohemian composer Anton Philip Heinrich and the

American-born William Henry Fry and George F. Bristow.

America could now boast of such organizations as the Handel and Haydn Society of Boston, founded in 1815, the Philharmonic Society of Boston, 1810, the Musical Fund Society of Philadelphia, 1820, and the Philharmonic Society of New York, 1842. The ambitious character of the Handel and Haydn Society is indicated by the fact that in 1823 it commissioned an oratorio from Beethoven, a work that unfortunately failed to materialize. New York City presented operas only two years after they were first performed in Italy and France. Famous European concert artists began to appear in 1848 (some of whom included California on their itinerary), demonstrated their dazzling techniques, and returned to Europe rich. Touring European orchestras presented a repertory of serious and light music, Classic and contemporary, played with impeccable precision and discipline. At the conclusion of their tours, many a group disbanded, its personnel for the greater part remaining in this country, and each member contributing enormously to the musical progress of his community.

One of our most famous songs, *Home! Sweet Home!* (No. 122), was composed by an Englishman, Henry R. Bishop. The words were written by an itinerant American actor, John Howard Payne, during his residence in London. On a commission by the manager of Covent Garden Theatre, Bishop adapted a French play into an opera, *Clari, or, The Maid of Milan*, and it was produced on May 8, 1823, and published in New York in the same year. Although the opera has long since fallen into obscurity, the air *Home! Sweet Home!* has achieved immortality. The melody is presented several times during the opera; it is heard in the overture, it is sung by Clari in the first act, in the third act by the peasants, and lastly by the chorus backstage. The title page of Bishop's score tells us that *Home! Sweet Home!* was "composed and partly founded on a Sicilian Air," and that "the air is from Bishop's collection of *Melodies of various Nations*."

The Old Arm Chair (No. 123), by the Englishman Henry Russell, who came to America in 1833, is typical of the sentimental ballad genre and is one of the earliest examples of a "mother song." Poignant words, a sentimental melody, an overly well-done performance, was Russell's technique to draw torrential applause from his receptive audience. The popularity of the sentimental ballad was enormous, and there were few melodeons and pianos that did not have copies on the music rack. Not everyone, however, was captivated by these drippingly sentimental songs, and Russell and other ballad writers had their critics.

Septimus Winner, a native-born American, credited the tune of his song *Listen to the Mocking Bird* (No. 124) to a colored boy, Richard Milburn, whom he heard whistling it. The song, with its mournful text and cheerful tune, was published under Winner's pen name of Alice Hawthorne and described as "a sentimental Ethiopian ballad." It became popular with both minstrel and ballad singers, and its refrain made it a favorite song for whistlers.

Louis Moreau Gottschalk was America's first internationally known musician and the first American composer to recognize the value of the native music in the United States. When Chopin heard Gottschalk play in Paris in 1845 he predicted that the young boy would become the "king of pianists." This prediction was soon to become a reality, and in Europe, the United States, the Caribbean Islands, and South America Gottschalk met with astounding success as a virtuoso, composer, and matinee idol.

In his compositions Gottschalk used the Creole songs (*Bamboula*) of his native New Orleans, Spanish folk melodies (*Minuit à Seville*), Latin American songs and rhythms (*Souvenir de Porto Rico*), American national airs (*L'Union*), and folk themes (*The Banjo*). Compositions like *The Last Hope* and *The Dying Poet* represent Gottschalk at his worst and were written, as he said, "to please others, even if not myself."

The Banjo (No. 125) was published in 1855,

two years after Gottschalk's return to America from Europe. The introduction and coda bear a strong resemblance to the pentatonic melodies of the Negro Spiritual *Roll, Jordan, Roll* and Stephen Foster's *Camptown Races* (1850); the remainder of *The Banjo* is original. The realistic strumming of the banjo, motoric drive, ostinato figures, and melodic coloration of this brilliant concert piece are skillfully joined to achieve a highly unified and exciting composition.

William Mason's piano pieces were designed for the public taste of his time, in spite of his high ideals as a musician. The Chopinesque *Lullaby*, Opus 10 (No. 126), with its ostinato left-hand figure, is typical of the works that achieved popularity. It is as a piano pedagogue, however, that William Mason will be remembered.

Yankeedoodle [*sic*] is the coda of an extended composition called *The Hickory, or Last Ideas in America* by that eccentric Bohemian champion of American music, Anton Philip Heinrich. The piece (No. 127) is a paraphrase on the famous *Yankee Doodle* tune, which Heinrich first presents in a minor key. However, he fluctuates rapidly from minor to major throughout, introducing some arresting modulations on the 16th-note ostinato beginning in measure 40. Heinrich's penchant for detailed dynamic markings knew no bounds, for almost every note and phrase is minutely explained or modified through the conventional markings.

The libretto used by William Henry Fry for his opera *Leonora* was prepared by his brother, Joseph, who drew his material from Bulwer-Lytton's novel *The Lady of Lyons* (1838). According to the composer, certain changes were made in the scenes and characters for musical reasons. These modifications include the omission of some characters, the increased prominence given to others, and a change of place and time in order to achieve a more romantic setting. The first performance of *Leonora* took place on June 4, 1845, in Philadelphia. The locale of the opera is Spain in 1530. Revengeful Montalvo, a wealthy nobleman spurned by Leonora, persuades Giulio, a poor but handsome peasant, to masquerade as a wealthy prince and to court Leonora. The enterprise leads to marriage. Later, the remorseful Giulio confesses his part in the plot, returns his bride to her father, Valdor, and sails for South America to seek his fortune. Three years elapse and Leonora, believing Giulio will never return, accepts Montalvo's marriage proposal, providing that he save her father from imminent bankruptcy. As the marriage banns are announced, Giulio arrives with the wealth and honors of a successful adventurer. Learning that Leonora still loves him, he makes his presence known and declares himself able to redeem his wife and to save her father from his creditors. The wicked Montalvo sings *My triumph's nigh* (No. 128) as his marriage to Leonora is announced, and the aria, *Every doubt and danger over* (No. 129), sung by Leonora, brings the opera to a joyous conclusion.

Rip Van Winkle is the first opera composed by an American to be based on a libretto of American lore. The librettist, T. W. Wainwright, retained the original plot of Washington Irving's legend of Rip Van Winkle, but in the 1882 edition of the vocal score, J. W. Shannon is credited with having "reconstructed" the libretto. Bristow's opera had its successful première at Niblo's Theatre in New York on September 27, 1855, and ran for four weeks. In spite of its American origin and subject, the music is stylistically Italianate, with an "easy flow of melody, free from effort and spontaneous." The critic in the *Musical World* also wrote that "in none of the arias [or choruses] do we meet with large conception or rich development of ideas; none of them is shaped after a large pattern." The aria, *Alas! they know me not* (No. 130), in ternary form, is sung by Rip in the last act upon his belated return to the village. The opera concludes with an aria, *List! the merry bells are ringing* (No. 131), sung by Alice, followed by a chorus in which the three principals join.

122. HOME! SWEET HOME!

Aria from
Clari, or, The Maid of Milan

1823

George Bacon
(*Philadelphia, 1823*)

Henry R. Bishop
(1786–1855)

hal - low us there, Which seek through the world, is ne'er met with else -

espress.
where! Home! Home! sweet, sweet, Home! There's
pp

Largo
tr
Tempo I.
no place like Home! There's no place like Home!
pp
colla voce
ff

più animato
An Ex - ile from Home, Splen-dour daz - zles in
ff
p

John Howard Payne

123. THE OLD ARM CHAIR

1840

George P. Reed
(Boston, 23rd ed., 1860)

Henry Russell
(1812–1900)

dew'd — it with tears, and em - balm'd — it with sighs; 'Tis bound — by a thou - sand
bands — to my heart, Not a tie will break, not a link will start. Would ye
learn the spell, a moth-er sat there, And a sa - cred — thing is that
Old Arm — Chair.

I sat and watch'd her man - y a day, When her eyes grew dim, and her
locks — were — grey, And I al - most worshipp'd her when she — smil'd And
turn'd from her bi - ble to bless her child. Years — roll'd on but the
last one sped, My i - dol was shatter'd my — earth star fled: I

learnt how much the heart can _ bear, When I saw her _ die in that
f
p

Old Arm _ Chair.
mf
p

'Tis past! 'tis past! but I gaze on it now With quiv-er - ing breath, and

throb - ing _ brow, 'Twas there she nurs'd me, 'twas there she _ died; And

Eliza Cook
(1818–1889)

124. LISTEN TO THE MOCKING BIRD

1855

Winner & Schuster
(*Philadelphia, 1855*)

Alice Hawthorne
(Septimus Winner)
(1827–1902)

dream - ing now of — Hal-ly, — For the thought of her is one that nev-er dies: She's
well I yet re - mem-ber, — When we ga-ther'd in the cot-ton side by side: 'Twas
sleep - ing in the — val-ley, — the — val-ley, — the — val-ley; — She's
in the mild Sep - tem-ber, — Sep - tem-ber, — Sep - tem-ber, — 'Twas
sleep - ing in the — val-ley. — And the mock-ing bird is sing-ing where she lies —
in the mild Sep - tem-ber. — And the mock-ing bird was sing-ing far and wide. —
CHORUS
SOLO
Lis-ten to the mock - ing bird, Lis - ten to the mock-ing bird. The
PIANO

mock - ing bird still sing - ing o'er her grave; Lis-ten to the mock-ing bird, Lis-ten to the

mock - ing bird, Still sing - ing where the weep - ing will - ows wave.

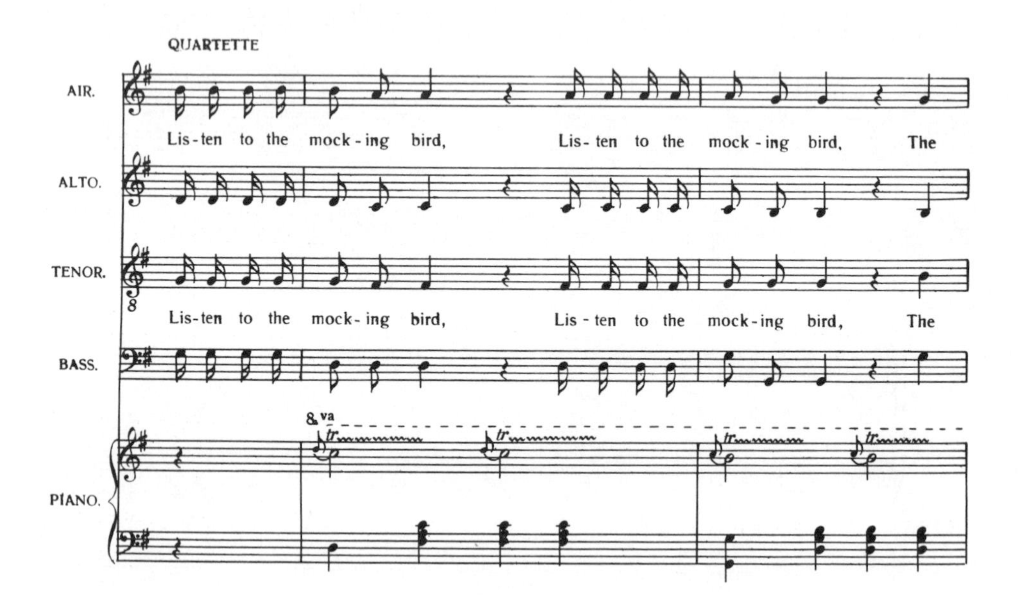
QUARTETTE
AIR.
Lis-ten to the mock - ing bird, Lis- ten to the mock - ing bird, The
ALTO.
TENOR.
Lis-ten to the mock- ing bird, Lis - ten to the mock-ing bird, The
BASS.
PIANO.
8va
tr

mock-ing bird still sing-ing o'er her grave: Lis-ten to the mock-ing bird, Lis-ten to the
mock-ing bird still sing-ing o'er her grave; Lis-ten to the mock-ing bird, Lis-ten to the
8.va
tr
mock - ing bird, Still sing - ing where the weep-ing will - ows wave.
mock - ing bird, Still sing - ing where the weep-ing will - ows wave.
8.va
tr

3

When the charms of spring awaken,
And the mocking bird is singing on the bough,
I feel like one forsaken,
Since my Hally is no longer with me now.

Septimus Winner

125. THE BANJO

Grotesque Fantasie

1855

Wm. Hall & Son
(*New York, 1855*)

Louis Moreau Gottschalk
(1829–1869)

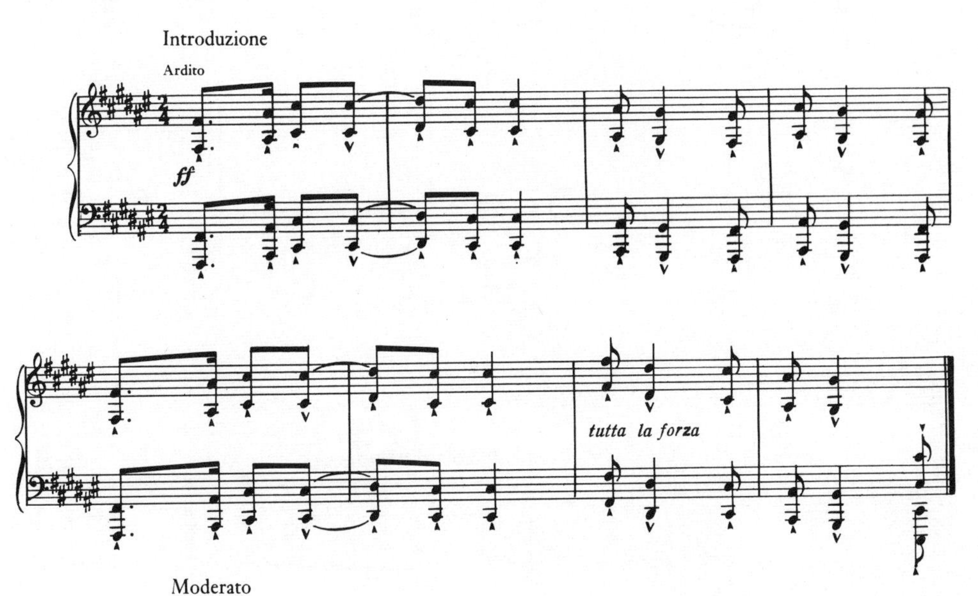

pp

pp

6
6

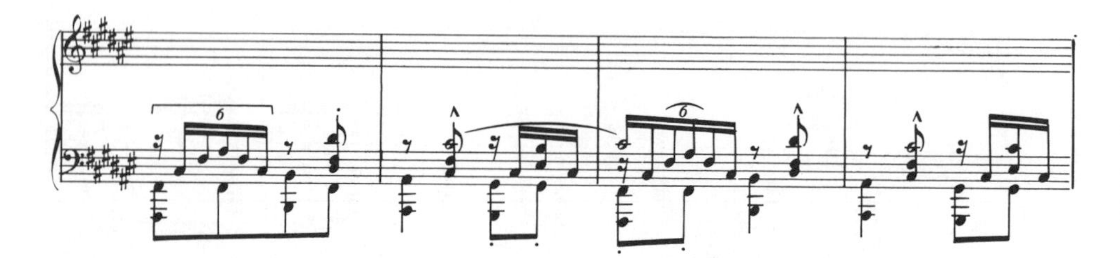
6
6

cresc.

f
pp

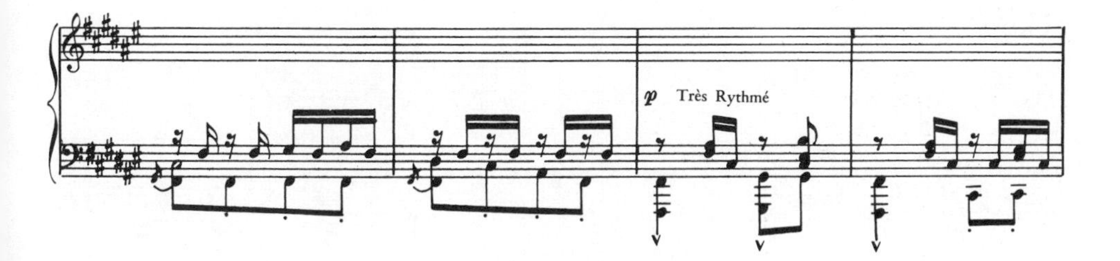
p Très Rythmé

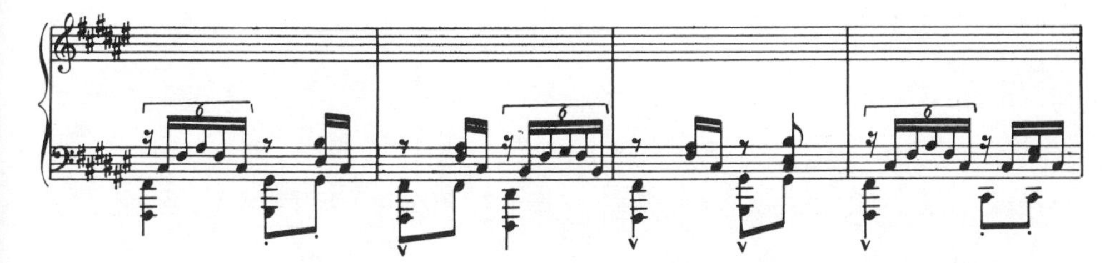

ben misurato
f brillante

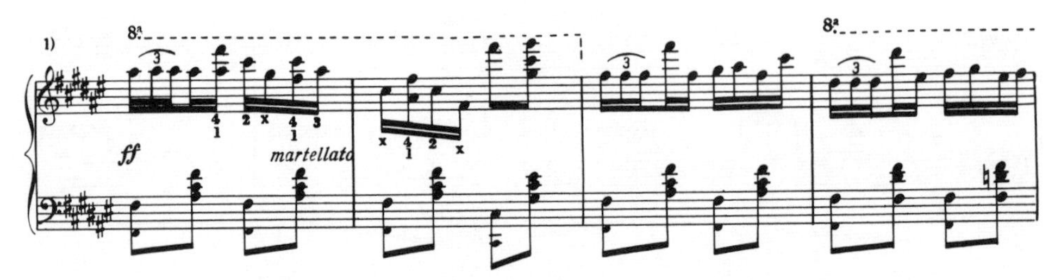

[1] The *facilité* (ossia) of 27 measures is omitted here. The cross indicates the thumb, and the other fingers are numbered from 1 to 4.

strepitoso
cresc.
martellato tutta la forza
fff
fff
ff
p subito

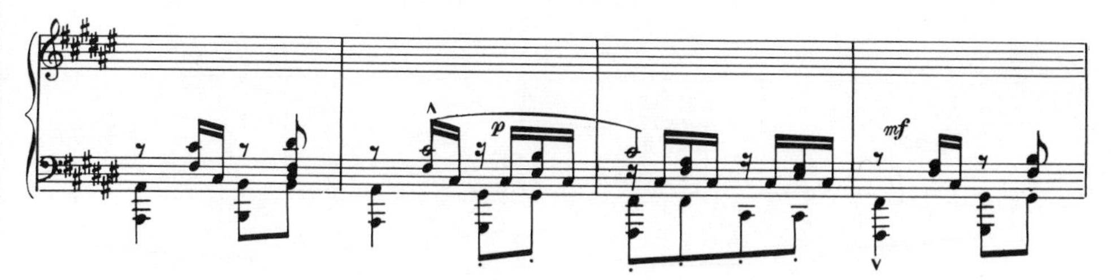
p
mf

p

6

6
rfz

rfz
pp

martellato
6

6

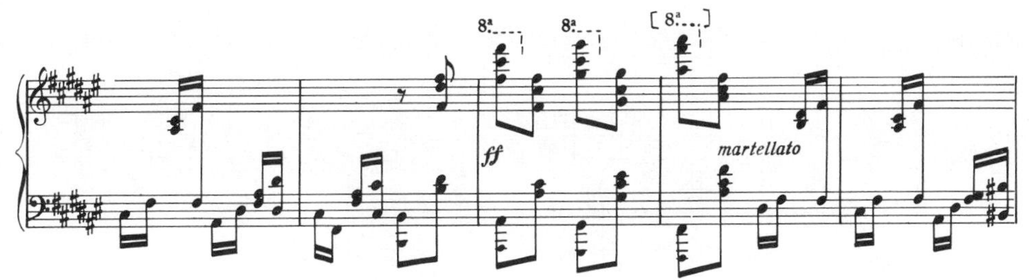

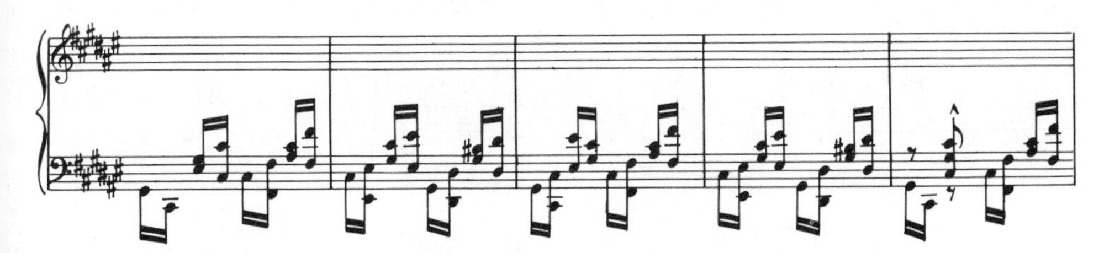

[2] The *facilité* (ossia) of 27 measures is omitted here.

ben misurato

cresc.
strepitoso
martellato
tutta la forza
fff
fff
ff
p subito

p

dim.

pp
pp
cres

cen
do
ben misurato e tranquillo

p
dim.

animato
un poco più f
ben misurato
martellato

un poco più f

più presto
sempre più presto

Prestissimo
ff
cresc.

Velocissimo
tutta la forza

fff

Prestissimo
ben martellato

8a
ffff

126. LULLABY

1857

Oliver Ditson & Co.
(*Boston, 1857*)

William Mason
(1829–1908)

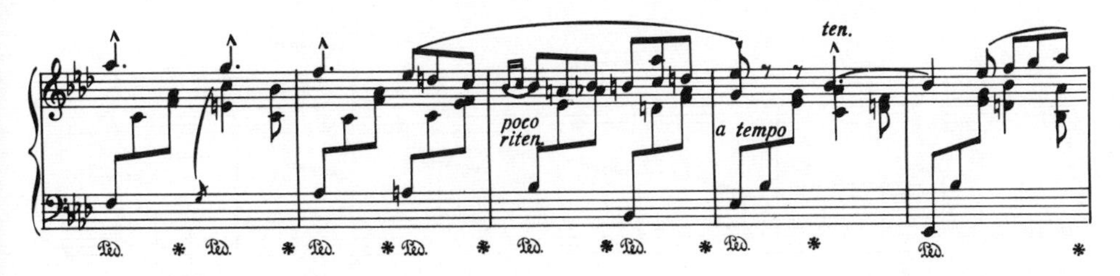
ten.
poco
riten.
a tempo

cresc.

poco riten. e dim.
pp a tempo

poco cresc.
poco cresc.

ten.
sfz
ten.

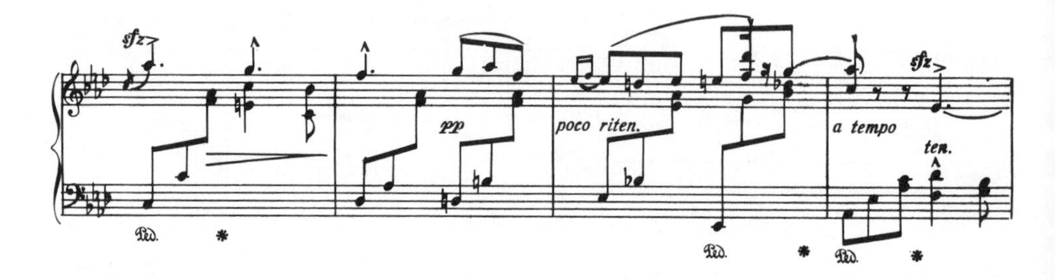
sfz
pp
poco riten.
a tempo
sfz
ten.

sfz
ten.

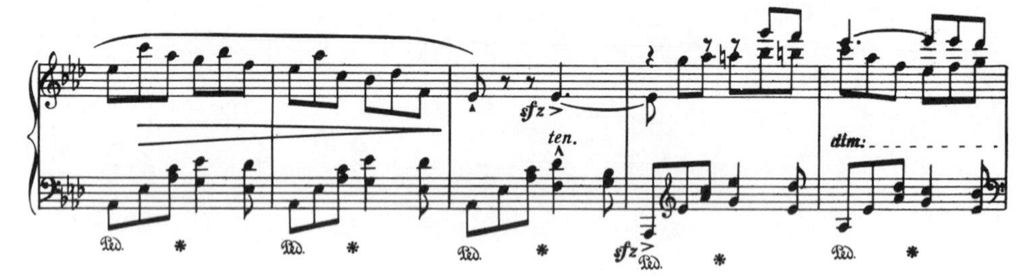
sfz
ten.
sfz
dim.

sfz
ten.
pp
sfz
poco a poco
ritenuto

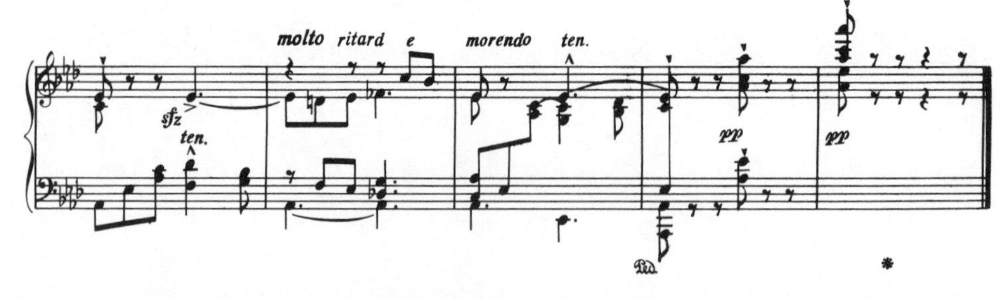
molto ritard e morendo ten.
sfz
ten.
pp
pp

127. YANKEEDOODLE

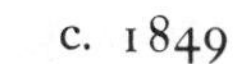
c. 1849

Presentazioni Musicali
Published by the Author
(*New York, 1853*)

Anthony Philip Heinrich
(1781-1861)

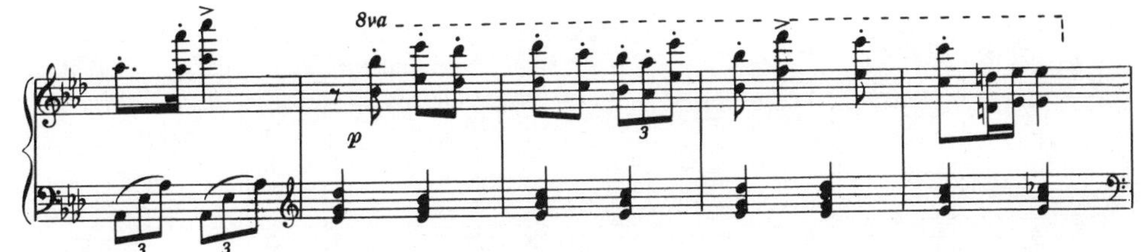

8va
a tempo
mf
3
3
p
3
3

loco
mf
3
p

8va
mf

f stringendo

8va
loco
ff

f
mf

tr
tr

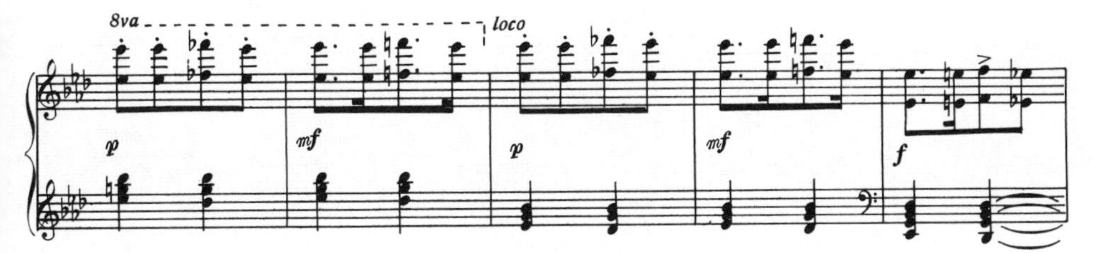
8va
loco
p
mf
p
mf
f

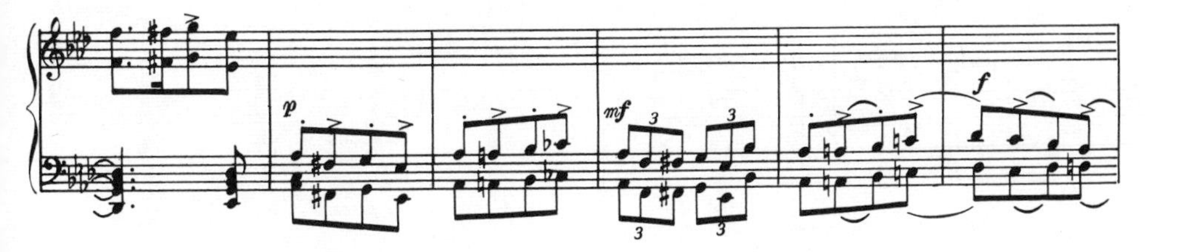
p
mf
f

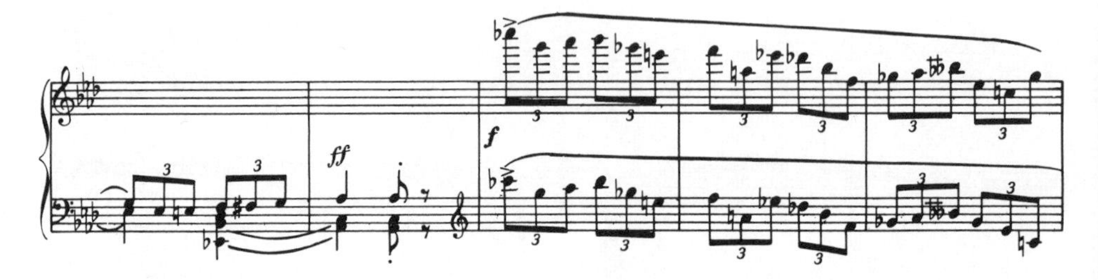
ff
f

mf
p
mf

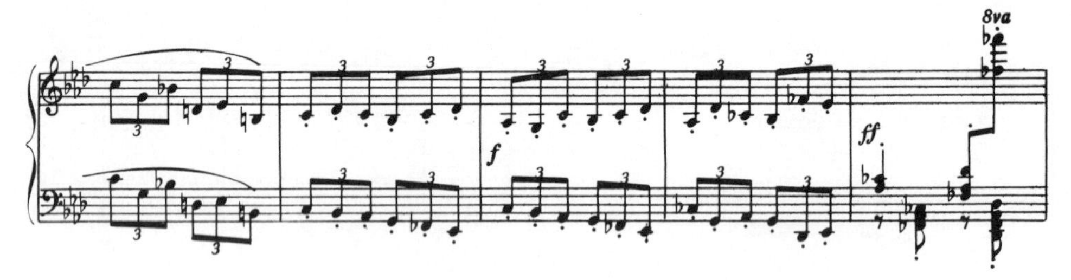
8va
f
ff

Adagio
Metronome ♪ = 50
2
p legato

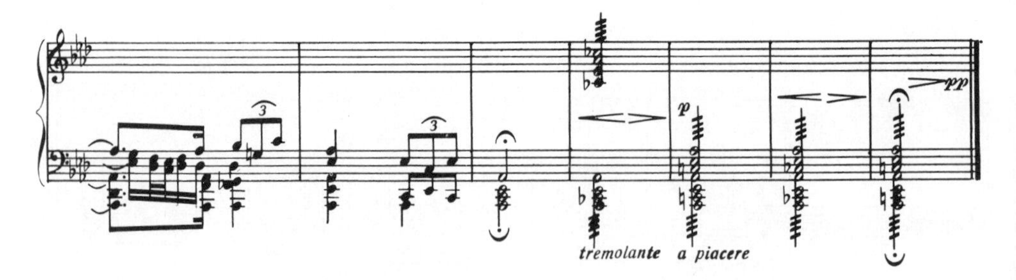
p
pp
tremolante a piacere

128. MY TRIUMPH'S NIGH

Aria from
Leonora

1845

E. Ferret & Co. (Vocal Score)
(*New York, 1846*)

William Henry Fry
(1813–1864)

con ferocia
con fremito
ff
ni - ted To one whom soon she must ab - hor;
f
fp
fp
fp
My pride was stung, my pas- sion slight - ed,
p
voce soffocata
Too deep a wrong to be for - giv - en:
Agitato
Now like my hope shall thine be

blighted, Im - pe - rious, wretch - ed Le - o - nore! Now like my
hope shall thine be blight — ed, Im - pe - rious, wretched Le - o -
- nore! Ah Le - o -
- nore, Im - pe - rious, wretched, wretch - ed Le - o - nore!
f
p
ff

Joseph R. Fry

129. EVERY DOUBT AND DANGER OVER

Aria from
Leonora

1845

F. Ferret & Co. (Vocal Score)
(New York, 1846)

William Henry Fry
(1813–1864)

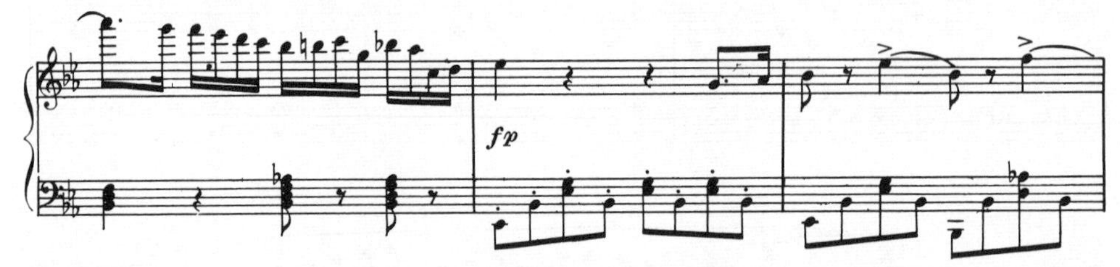

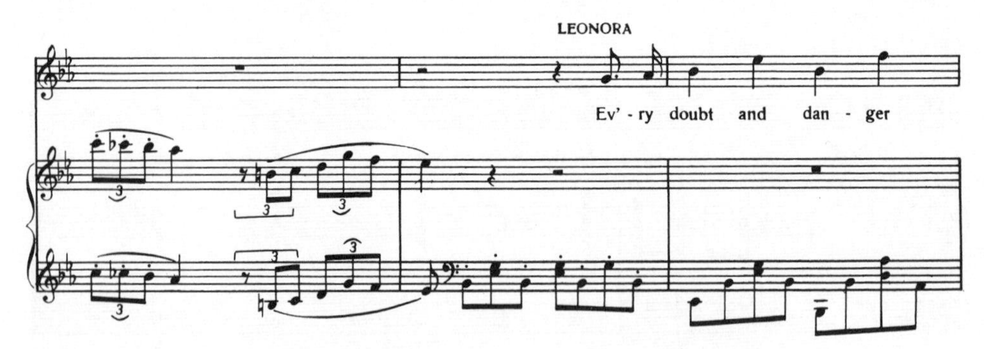

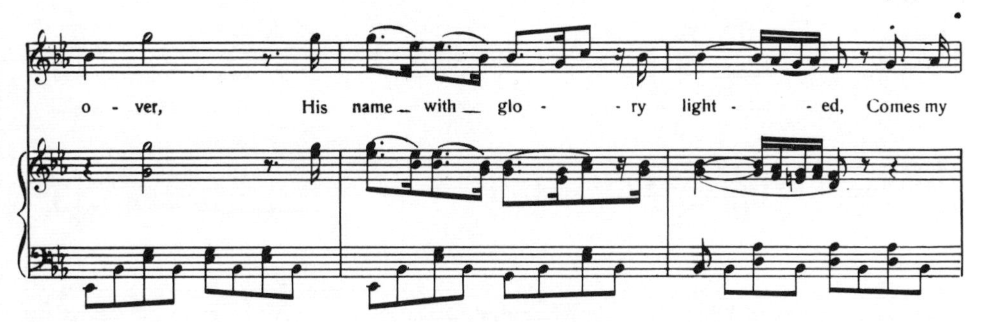
o - ver, His name with glo - - ry light - - ed, Comes my

he - ro and my lov - er To my con - stant arms a -

gain! Years of an - guish are all re - qui - - ted In this

mo - ment of ex - ta - tic joy! For by hal - lowed bond u -

[1] This ornament is written in 16th notes in the original.

Joseph R. Fry

130. ALAS! THEY KNOW ME NOT

Aria from
Rip Van Winkle

1855

G. Schirmer (Vocal Score)
(*New York, 1882*)

George Frederick Bristow
(1825–1898)

in the sphere of ma-ny a mile, Full ev-'ry one I know, Not
Clar Oboe
p

con passione
f
one, not one of these give me a
cresc.
f
dim.
Tutti

poco animato e agitato
smile, Strange fears up-on me grow, Strange
Oboe Fag.

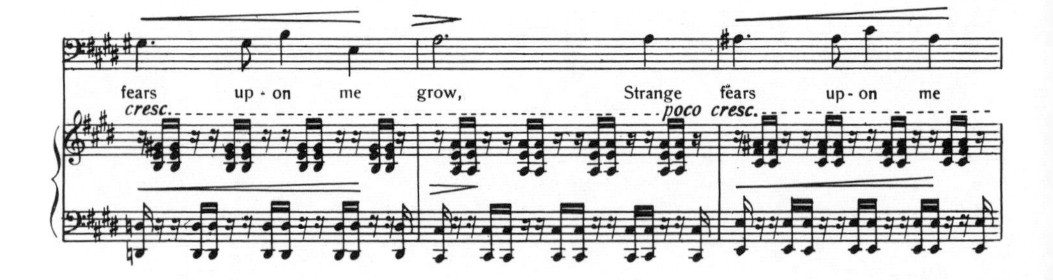
fears up-on me grow, Strange fears up-on me
cresc.
poco cresc.

grow, Strange fears, strange fears up on — me grow, up -
cresc.
f
ff
rit.
tempo
dim.
Tutti
dim.

p
- on me grow.
A -
mf
Corno
Clar.
pp

con espress.
- las! a - las they know me not, Stran - gers are they are they — to me, — Am I my -
pp

con anima
self or am I not, — What can the mat-ter, What can the mat - ter be? — Am I my -

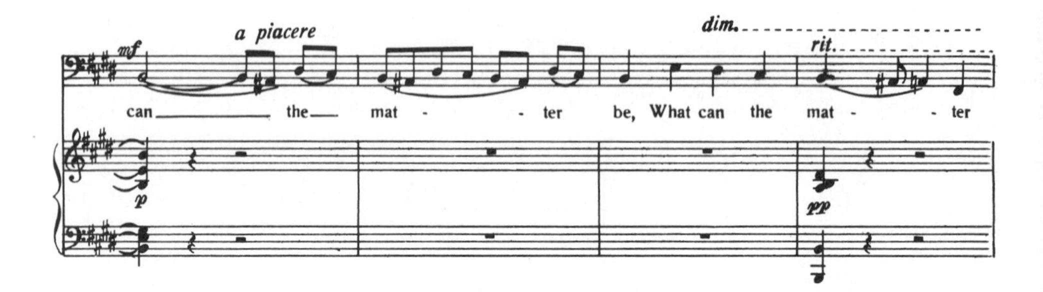

T. W. Wainwright

131. LIST! THE MERRY BELLS

Aria and Chorus from
Rip Van Winkle

1855

G. Schirmer (Vocal Score)
(*New York, 1882*)

George Frederick Bristow
(1825–1898)

round.
Gay hearts to the bri - dal
bring - ing, Birds on eve - ry tree are sing - ing, Birds on eve - ry tree are
cresc.
sing - ing, Glad-ness smiles on all a - round, on all a -

round. All our griefs and woes are end - ing, Peace and hope with joy are

blend - ing, Smiles and bless - ings us at - tend - ing, Love's hap - py heav - en
cresc.
ff
now is found, now is found, is
Più mosso
ALICE
Soprani
found. Now Love's hap - py heav'n is found. Now Love's hap - py heav'n is
Alti
EDWARD
Tenori
Now Love's hap - py heav'n is found, Now Love's hap - py heav'n is
Now Love's hap - py heav'n is found. Now Love's hap - py heav'n is
RIP.
Bassi
Now Love's hap - py heav'n is found, Now Love's hap - py heav'n is
Più mosso
ff

T. W. Wainwright

Biographical Notes

John ANTES (b. Frederick, Penn., 1740; d. Bristol, England, 1811) was a Moravian minister, watchmaker, violinmaker, composer, and inventor. In 1752 he was a student in a boys' school in Bethlehem. In 1764 he was called to Herrnhut, Saxony, the international center of the Moravians. He was ordained a Moravian minister in 1769 and spent the years 1770–1781 in Cairo as the first American missionary in Egypt. He returned to Heernhut again and then about 1783 went to Fulneck, England, where he remained for 25 years, moving to Bristol in 1808. Antes is known to have written at least 25 sacred, concerted vocal compositions, thirteen chorales, and three trios for two violins and cello.

Supply BELCHER (b. Stoughton, Mass., 1751; d. Farmington, Maine, 1836), a distinguished man of his time, was a Justice of the Peace, member of the state legislature, school teacher, choir leader, violinist, and composer. He was called by his contemporaries "The Handel of Maine." He fought in the early days of the Revolution, and in 1788 acquired a tavern that became a meeting place for local singers. He attended Billings's singing classes in Stoughton and was strongly influenced by Billings's music. In 1785 Belcher moved to Maine, and in 1794 he published *The Harmony of Maine*. This is his only known publication, and it is devoted entirely to his own compositions.

Daniel BELKNAP (b. Framingham, Mass., 1771; d. Pawtucket, R.I., 1815) began his career as a farmer and mechanic and had little opportunity for instruction in music. He developed his natural voice, however, and soon was teaching singing and the rudiments of music in and near his native town. He published three collections (1797, 1800, 1806), often using his own texts, and a number of his tunes were published by other composer-compilers.

William BILLINGS (b. Boston, 1746; d. there, 1800) was apprenticed to a tanner and, in spite of his love for music, he continued to practice that trade. Ugly in appearance and physically deformed, he was a self-taught, original, and enthusiastic musician, and succeeded in exerting a strong influence on the musical life of New England and beyond. He organized and conducted singing schools and composed and published six collections of music which contained over 250 psalm-tunes and about 50 anthems, almost all sacred music. His popularity, however, did not last; he died in poverty and was buried in an unmarked grave on Boston Common.

Henry Rowley BISHOP (b. London, 1786; d. there, 1855) was a famous opera conductor and composer. He was a professor of music at the Universities of Edinburgh and Oxford and was knighted by Queen Victoria in 1842. Bishop composed about 130 operas (mostly in ballad style), farces, ballets, and various adaptations.

Louis BOURGEOIS (b. Paris, c. 1510; d. there, c. 1561) was a follower of Calvin and lived with him at Geneva from 1545 to 1557, when he returned to Paris. He composed or adapted most of the melodies for Marot's and Bèze's French versifications of the psalms.

William Batchelder BRADBURY (b. York, Maine, 1816; d. Montclair, N.J., 1868) received his first musical instruction from Sumner Hill in Boston. He later became associated with Lowell Mason and George J. Webb of the Boston Academy of Music and after a few years went to Machias, Maine, where he taught singing. He went to New York as an organist and choirmaster, and in 1847 to Leipzig, where he studied for two years with Moscheles and others. In 1854 he joined his brother in the manufacture and selling of pianos. Bradbury edited more than fifty collections of music between 1841 and 1867, and it has been estimated that over 2,000,000 copies of these books were sold.

George Frederick BRISTOW (b. Brooklyn, N.Y., 1825; d. New York, 1898) became a *cause célèbre* when he resigned his position as violinist with the New York Philharmonic Society orchestra in protest over the failure of that Society to perform works by American composers. He was re-engaged a short time later, and in 1856 the Society performed his Second Symphony, in D minor. During the next eighteen years his Third and Fourth Symphonies were programmed. While he was a member of the Philharmonic Society, he conducted the Harmonic Society, and this choral group performed one of his two oratorios, *Praise to God*, among other American works. Bristow also composed two operas, *Rip Van Winkle* and the unfinished *Columbus*, two cantatas, six symphonies, two overtures, two string quartets, anthems, songs, and pieces for organ, piano, and violin.

Benjamin CARR (b. London, 1768; d. Philadelphia, 1831) was the son of Joseph Carr and the brother of Thomas. The three Carrs became successful music publishers and dealers in Philadelphia, where they established a "Musical Repository" in 1793, Baltimore, and New York. Benjamin Carr was editor of the *Musical Journal*, which published his song, *Why, Huntress, why?*, and *The Gentleman's Amusement*, which published *The President's March*, later used for *Hail! Columbia*. He was also active as a composer, singer, organist, and pianist. Carr was associated with Raynor Taylor in the founding of the Musical Fund Society in Philadelphia in 1820, and he was one of the most influential of the European musicians who came to the United States after the Revolution.

A[mzi] CHAPIN may have been an early 19th-century singing master who traveled through Pennsylvania, Virginia, and Kentucky and died in Ohio. His music is found in Wyeth's *Repository, Part Second* and many Southern tunebooks.

William CROFT (b. Warwickshire, England, 1678; d. Bath, 1727) was a chorister in the Chapel Royal and became organist in 1707. He succeeded his master, John Blow, as organist at Westminster Abbey in 1708. Croft was also organist at St. Anne's, Soho, from 1700 to 1712. He composed songs, instrumental music, odes, and music for the services of the church.

Elkanah Kelsay DARE (1782–1826), a Methodist minister and a musician, served for a time as dean of boys at Wilmington College, Delaware.

Eliakim DOOLITTLE (b. Connecticut, 1772; d. Argyle, N.Y., 1850) was active as a composer and singing teacher. His elder brother, Amos, also a musician, was a business partner of Daniel Read.

Jacob ECKHARD (b. Eschwege, Germany, 1757; d. Charleston, S.C., 1833), a church organist and composer, came to America in 1776 and after the Revolution settled in Richmond, where he taught music and was organist at St. John's Episcopal Church. In 1786 he became organist and choir director of the German Lutheran Church in Charleston, and in 1809 he assumed similar duties at St. Michael's Episcopal Church. Here he compiled a manuscript tunebook for the use of the choir and in 1816 the *Choral Book* was published. This collection contained 110 psalm-tunes and hymns, principally from English and German sources. A few American tunes, among them Lewis Edson's popular *Lenox*, were included.

Lewis EDSON, Sr. (b. Bridgewater, Mass., 1748; d. near Woodstock, N.Y., 1820) was a blacksmith by trade, but early in life became an amateur musician. He first taught singing school and by 1780 had won considerable fame in Massachusetts, New York, and Connecticut as a singer. He was highly regarded by his contemporaries, although he compiled no tunebooks and composed comparatively little music. He did, however, write three of the most popular fuging tunes of his time. These were included in almost all later collections, and one of them, *Lenox*, may be found in modern hymnals. Edson's son, Lewis, Jr. (1771–1845), was a school teacher and singing master and published a collection called the *Social Harmonist* (New York, 1800).

Daniel Decatur EMMETT (b. Mt. Vernon, Ohio, 1815; d. there, 1904) was perhaps the most famous of the black-face performers. His entire life was spent in travel, first with a circus troupe at the age of eighteen and subsequently as a minstrel with several minstrel groups. In 1858 he led his own Emmett's Minstrels in a short-lived tour, but it was not until his association with Bryant's Minstrels in the same year that he began the composition of his famous minstrel songs and "walk-arounds."

Josiah FLAGG (b. Woburn, Mass., 1738; d. 1794) was a teacher, director of a military band, compiler-publisher of two collections, and an impresario. He organized concerts of "vocal and instrumental musick" and as early as 1771 performed music of Bach and Handel. His *Collection of the Best Psalm Tunes* (1764) included two anthems. In 1766 Flagg published a second collection, entitled *A Collection of All Tans'ur's and a number of other Anthems* . . . , which included upwards of twenty anthems, the first extensive collection of anthems published in America.

Stephen Collins FOSTER (b. Lawrenceville, near Pittsburgh, Penn., 1826; d. New York, 1864) showed an interest in music early in life but had little, if any, formal instruction. His first composition, *The Tioga Waltz*, was written at the age of fourteen while he was in school at Athens near Towanda. His first published song was composed when he was sixteen, and his interest in Negro melodies and black-face songs led to the composition in 1845 of the first of a large number of "Ethiopian" or minstrel songs. Foster lived with his parents in Allegheny from 1841 to 1846 and then moved to Cincinnati as a bookkeeper for his brother. He returned to Allegheny in 1848 and married Jane McDowell in 1850. In 1860 he went to New York with his wife and daughter and feverishly tried to make a living by selling his songs. Foster's limited education, inability to hold a position, and lack of business acumen, however, kept him in a perpetual state of debt. He finally became an alcoholic and died destitute in Bellevue Hospital. During his short lifetime of 38 years, Foster composed 188 songs (many to his own texts), twelve instrumental compositions, and a number of arrangements.

Jacob FRENCH (b. Stoughton, Mass., 1754; d. Northampton, Mass., 1817) was a singing master and an able and sensitive composer. He compiled three tunebooks (1789, 1793, 1802), but his own compositions were not often included in collections compiled by others.

William Henry FRY (b. Philadelphia, 1813, d. Santa Cruz, West Indies, 1864) was a composer, journalist, and champion of American music and opera in English. He went to Europe about 1845 as foreign editor of the New York *Tribune* and met several European composers, among them Berlioz. He returned to America in 1852 as music editor of the *Tribune*, which afforded him the opportunity to attack the indifference of artists and audiences to their own native composers. Fry's compositions include four symphonies—*Santa Claus*, *The Breaking Heart*, *Childe Harold*, and *A Day in the Country* (all performed by the eccentric Frenchman, Louis Antoine Jullien)—two operas, cantatas, and songs.

Patrick Sarsfield GILMORE (Louis Lambert) (b. Dublin, Ireland, 1829; d. St. Louis, Mo., 1892) came to the United States via Canada and became a bandmaster with the Union Army. He organized "Gilmore's Band" in 1859 and became famous for his mammoth "Peace Jubilees" requiring thousands of musicians. The "Worlds Peace Jubilee" held in Boston in 1882 required an orchestra of 2000 and a chorus of 20,000! His compositions include military music, songs, and arrangements for band.

Louis Moreau GOTTSCHALK (b. New Orleans, 1829; d. Tijuca, near Rio de Janeiro, 1869) was the son of an aristocratic Creole mother and an affluent English father. His parents recognized his extraordinary musical talent and he was sent to Paris to study in 1842. At the age of sixteen he was presented in a private concert in Salle Pleyel and in 1847 he made his professional début in Sedan, France, and in 1849 in Paris. Returning to the United States early in 1853, he gave his first New York recital at Niblo's Saloon and began a tour of the United States, invariably arousing his audiences, especially the ladies, to a high pitch of enthusiasm.

Gottschalk made a short Cuban tour in 1854, and from 1857 to 1862 he resided in Cuba, composing, wandering throughout the Caribbean islands giving concerts, and "enjoying the good life." On his return to the United States in 1862, he made his second début at Niblo's Garden and embarked on an even more hectic concert life than before.

From 1865 until his death, Gottschalk lived in South America, settling finally in Rio de Janeiro. Although stricken with yellow fever, he continued to give concerts and directed a gala festival concert on November 24, 1869, in which 650 musicians participated. He was invited to play during a concert by the Philharmonic Society the following day, and while playing his *Morte* he was taken ill and was unable to complete the composition. He died on December 18 and his body was interred in Rio de Janeiro. A year later his remains were returned to the United States and buried in Green-Wood Cemetery, Brooklyn.

Gottschalk's works (over 150) include pieces for piano, two operas, two symphonies, various works for orchestra, and a few songs.

Hans GRAM (b. Denmark, dates unknown) was educated in Stockholm and about 1789 settled in Boston, where he became organist of the Brattle Street Church. He collaborated with Oliver Holden and Samuel Holyoke in the publication of *The Massachusetts Compiler* (1795), a progressive and comprehensive work on psalmody which included a musical dictionary. Gram also composed a number of anthems and some songs that appeared in *The Massachusetts Magazine*.

Alice HAWTHORNE. See Septimus Winner.

Peter Albrecht van (von) HAGEN, Sr. (b. 1750, Holland; d. Boston, 1803), music teacher, organist, violinist, and composer, lived in Charleston, S.C., from 1774 to 1789. He then moved to New York with his musical family, which included his equally famous son, Peter Albrecht, Jr. (1781–1837). In 1796 he went to Boston, where he conducted the Haymarket Theatre Orchestra, became organist at the Stone Chapel (1800), taught music, and established a music shop and publishing house. His compositions include a number of patriotic songs and pieces and music for the theater.

Thomas HASTINGS (b. Washington, Conn., 1784; d. New York, 1872) was a self-taught composer of hymn-tunes and a compiler of successful tunebooks. His first collection appeared in 1816, and during the course of the years he brought out 50 volumes of music, some in collaboration with others. He is said to have composed some 1000 hymn-tunes and 600 hymn texts. Hastings was editor of the *Western Recorder* of Utica from 1823 to 1832. He then settled in New York, where he became associated with Lowell Mason and in 1836 founded the *Musical Magazine*. His *Dissertation on Musical Taste* appeared in 1822 and *The History of Forty Choirs* in 1854. In 1858 he received from the University of the City of New York one of the first honorary Doctor of Music degrees to be awarded in America.

Anton (Anthony) Philip HEINRICH (b. Schönbüchel, Bohemia, 1781; d. New York, 1861) arrived in the United States about 1818; his continuous search for employment and recognition for his compositions took him to Philadelphia, Boston, Pittsburgh, Lexington (Kentucky), London, and New York. He found inspiration for his grandiose compositions in the Indians and in the history and natural beauty of his adopted country. In the Preface to his *Dawning of Music in Kentucky, or the Pleasures of Harmony in the Solitudes of Nature* he states that "no one would ever be more proud than himself, to be called an *American Musician*." After his many travels, Heinrich finally settled in New York and devoted himself to composing his American music and promoting his efforts by taking an active part in the musical life of the city. He composed an enormous number of orchestral compositions, cantatas, and songs, most of them with fanciful titles that were sometimes foreign or a mixture of languages. Heinrich met with many disappointments and some successes, but his lack of talent and training was all too apparent. He will be remembered, however, as one of the first to promote American nationalism.

James HEWITT (b. Dartmoor, England, 1770; d. Boston, 1827) left for the New World in 1792. A fine musician, he became a dominant personality in New York, where in addition to his activities as an organist, violinist, conductor, and composer, he operated a Musical Repository which he purchased from Benjamin Carr. In 1812 Hewitt moved to Boston, where he became associated with the Federal Street Theater, was organist of Trinity Church, and continued his other musical activities both in New York and Boston. Hewitt's compositions include sentimental ballads and other songs, keyboard pieces, among them *The Battle of Trenton*, and various orchestral works and theater music.

John Hill HEWITT (b. New York, 1801; d. Baltimore, 1890) was the eldest son of James Hewitt. Active as a theatrical manager, composer, and journalist, he achieved a modicum of fame when he bested Edgar Allen Poe in a literary contest with his poem *The Song of the Wind*. His compositions include about 300 songs, an oratorio, four cantatas, and four operas.

Oliver HOLDEN (b. Shirley, Mass., 1765; d. Charlestown, 1844) was a carpenter and Justice of the Peace in Charlestown. From about 1792 he began to teach music and operate a music store. He later became a preacher in the Puritan Church, and was elected to the Massachusetts House of Representatives. Many of his hymn-tunes were published in the *Union Harmony* (1793), and he contributed to some nine other collections between 1792 and 1807.

Samuel HOLYOKE (b. Boxford, Mass., 1762; d. Concord, N.H., 1820) was one of the few New England composers to whom music was more than an avocation. He graduated from Harvard in 1789 and after 1800 lived in Salem, teaching, conducting, and promoting concerts there and in other New England towns. Holyoke taught music at Phillips Andover Academy (1809–1810) and was active as a composer-compiler of tunebooks. His instruction book, *The Instrumental Assistant* (Exeter, New Hampshire, Vol. I, 1800; Vol. II, 1807), was one of the first to contain detailed instructions on the art of playing the violin, German flute, clarinet, hautboy, and bass-viol.

Francis HOPKINSON (b. Philadelphia, 1737; d. there, 1791), a member of a prominent Philadelphia family, graduated from the College of Philadelphia (now University of Pennsylvania). He was a poet, satirist, inventor, painter, and one of the signers of the Declaration of Independence. He was appointed Judge of the Admiralty, and found time to receive musical instruction from James Bremner, to compose, and to perform at the harpsichord. His compositions include a number of songs, a few odes, and two of the earliest anthems by an American composer. He brought out a *Collection of Psalm Tunes* in 1763, and in 1767 he adapted psalms from the "New Version of Tate and Brady for the use of the Reformed Protestant Church in New York."

Jeremiah INGALLS (b. Andover, Mass., 1764; d. Hancock, Vt., 1828) was a tavern-keeper, farmer, cooper, singing-school teacher, composer, compiler, and choirmaster. He moved to Vermont in 1800, living successively in Newbury, Rochester, and Hancock. His compositions, some of them folk hymns, are found in his only collection, *The Christian Harmony* (Exeter, 1805), and other tunebooks, particularly in the South.

George K. JACKSON (b. Oxford, England, 1745; d. Boston, 1822) was awarded a Doctor of Music degree from Saint Andrews College in 1791 and left England for Virginia in 1796. He was in New York in 1804 as organist of St. George's Chapel, and in 1812 he settled in Boston and became the organist of the newly organized Handel and Haydn Choral Society. A prolific writer, he published hymn books, a treatise on music theory, and numerous compositions.

Stephen JENKS (b. New Canaan, Conn., 1772; d. Thompson, Ohio, 1856), composer and compiler of hymn-tunes, confined his activity principally to the state of Connecticut, although many of his tunes were well known in New England and the South. He compiled at least five tunebooks between 1800 and 1824.

Simeon JOCELIN (JOCELYN) (b. Branford, Conn., 1746; d. New Haven, 1823). Little is known about the life of this composer, but he compiled three collections (one with Amos Doolittle) between 1780 and 1793.

Jacob KIMBALL (b. Topsfield, Mass., 1761; d. there, 1826) graduated in law from Harvard in 1780 and was admitted to the bar in Stratford, N.H., but abandoned the profession for music. He studied with Hans Gram, organized singing classes, and taught in many New England towns. Kimball left two collections, *The Rural Harmony* (Boston, 1793), which contained over 70 of his tunes, and *The Essex Harmony* (Exeter, N.H., 1800).

E. J. KING (c. 1800–c. 1850) was associated with B. F. White in the publication of *The Sacred Harp* (Philadelphia, 1844).

Walter KITTREDGE (dates unknown) was called to the Northern Army in 1862, but rejected because of rheumatic fever. He is known today for his song *Tenting on the Old Camp Ground*, which met with great popular success.

Louis LAMBERT. See Patrick S. Gilmore

Andrew LAW (b. Milford, Conn., 1748; d. Cheshire, Conn., 1821) was educated at Rhode Island College (Brown University), where he received a master's degree. He became an ordained minister in 1787, but his interest in music led him to the profession of singing master, compiler, and composer. He invented a new system of notation (1802) which employed four (later seven) shape notes without the use of a staff and adopted—for the first time in American tunebooks—the idea of setting the melody in the treble instead of the tenor. Between 1767 and 1812 Law compiled a considerable number of tunebooks which went into several editions. His popular *Art of Singing* (1794) included in its three parts the *Musical Primer*, *Christian Harmony*, and *Musical Magazine*.

James LYON (b. Newark, N.J., 1735; d. Machias, Maine, 1794) was a student at New Jersey College

(Nassau Hall) which moved to Princeton in 1756 and became known as Princeton University. He graduated in 1759 with a B.A. degree and in 1762, while living in Philadelphia, he received his M.A. degree. He was ordained a Presbyterian minister in 1764 and was sent to Nova Scotia and in 1771 to Machias, Maine, where he remained until his death. His first composition was an ode, which was performed in 1759 at the time of his graduation from Princeton. In 1761 an anthem of his and an ode by Francis Hopkinson were performed at a commencement program given by the College of Pennsylvania in Philadelphia. Ten of Lyon's compositions have been preserved, six of them in *Urania* (Philadelphia, 1761)—his only collection.

Lowell MASON (b. Medfield, Mass., 1792; d. Orange, N.J., 1872) was largely a self-taught musician, although he received some instruction from Oliver Shaw and others. In 1812 he moved to Savannah, Georgia, where he worked in a bank and was organist and choirmaster at the First Presbyterian Church. While there he studied harmony and composition and compiled his first collection, published in Boston in 1822. In 1827 Mason moved to Boston, where he was elected president of the Handel and Haydn Society and became organist of Lyman Beecher's Church. He established the Boston Academy of Music in 1832 and in 1838 succeeded in introducing music in the public schools. His teachers' institutes, normal institutes, and musical conventions spread his work throughout the country. Mason made two trips to Europe; in 1837 to study the Pestalozzian system of teaching and from 1851 to 1853 to lecture. He received an honorary Doctor of Music degree from New York University in 1855, the second to be awarded in this country. Mason composed a large number of hymns and published about eighteen collections of sacred music, some in collaboration with his colleagues, which brought him enormous profits. He also compiled fifteen books for children and a number of collections of secular part-songs and glees.

William MASON (b. Boston, 1829; d. New York, 1908) was the youngest son of Lowell Mason. After piano instruction with Henry Schmidt in Boston, Mason went to Europe in 1849. He studied in Leipzig with Moscheles, Hauptmann, and Richter; in Prague with Dreyschock and with Liszt in Weimar. Mason played a number of recitals in Europe—not always with unqualified success—before returning to New York in 1854. He took up the career of a piano virtuoso, but disliked the taste of a public that demanded such improvisations as the playing of *Old Hundredth* and *Yankee Doodle* at the same time. With Theodore Thomas he founded in 1855 the "Soirées of Chamber-music" for the performance of Classical music, a series that continued until 1868. He devoted himself more and more to teaching and composing and achieved an enviable reputation as a piano pedagogue. In addition to his well-known textbooks on piano playing, including the important *Touch and Technic* (1891), Mason composed about 40 piano pieces and a *Serenata* for cello and piano.

David Moritz MICHAEL (b. Kienhausen [Erfurt], Germany, 1751; d. Neuwied, Germany, 1827) arrived in America in 1795. He became a dominant figure in Moravian music, first in Nazareth and then in Bethlehem. He was much interested in contemporary European music and gave the first American performance of Haydn's *The Creation* at Bethlehem in 1811. Michael composed anthems, songs, and sixteen pieces for wind instruments.

John MILTON, Sr. (b. near Oxford c. 1563; d. London, 1647), father of the poet, was a chorister at Christ Church, Oxford (c. 1573–77), and in 1585 went to London, where he was admitted to the Scriveners' Company. His compositions include a madrigal, anthems, motets, three psalm-settings in Ravenscroft's Psalter, and two *Fantazias* for viols.

John Christopher MOLLER (probably born in Germany; d. New York, 1803) arrived in New York from London in 1790 and made his first appearance as a harpsichordist. Shortly thereafter he was appointed organist at Zion Church in Philadelphia and took an active part in the City Concerts. Besides his activities as a keyboard performer, composer, and teacher, he founded with Capron the first publishing firm in Philadelphia which he also used as a music school. He was in New York in 1796; there he succeeded Hewitt as manager of the New York City Concerts with the van Hagens. Moller published a considerable number of compositions including string quartets, keyboard sonatas, and instruction books.

Justin MORGAN (b. West Springfield, Mass., 1747; d. Randolph, Vt., 1798) is perhaps better known as a horse breeder than as a hymn-tune writer. He did not publish any collections, and his many tunes are found in the compilations of others.

Victor PELISSIER (dates unknown), a horn virtuoso and composer, was a post-Revolutionary emigrant from France. He first worked in Philadelphia and in 1793 he went to New York, where he was principal horn-player and composer and arranger for the Old American Company. He wrote a number of ballad operas and incidental music for plays and pantomimes.

Johann Friedrich (John Frederik) PETER (b. Heerendijk, Holland, 1746, of German parents; d. Bethlehem, 1813) came to Pennsylvania in 1770, served in various capacities in Nazareth, Bethlehem, and Lititz, and became director of the Collegium Musicum in Salem, N.C., where he lived from 1780 to 1790. He spent a few years in Graceham, Maryland, and Hope, New Jersey, after which he returned to Bethlehem. Peter composed some 116 anthems and six string quintets and copied and performed a considerable amount of music by Stamitz, C. P. E. Bach, and others.

Philip PHILE (b. c. 1734; d. Philadelphia, 1793) was a German violinist and teacher who came to Philadelphia early in the 1780s. He served in the Pennsylvania regiment during the Revolutionary War and participated in musical affairs as a violinist and conductor in New York and Philadelphia.

Daniel READ (b. Reheboth, Mass., 1757; d. New Haven, Conn., 1836) spent the greater part of his life in New Haven as a comb-maker, owner of a general store, and singing master. He was one of the most capable composers of the late 18th century, and his tunebooks were widely known. Read's two principal collections were *The American Singing Book* (New Haven, 1785 to 1796) with its *Supplement* (1787) and *The Columbian Harmonist* (New Haven, 1793 to 1810).

Alexander REINAGLE (b. Portsmouth, England, 1756; d. Baltimore, 1809) was born of Austrian parents. He was a pupil of Raynor Taylor in London and counted among his close friends C. P. E. Bach, whose musical style he greatly admired. Coming to America in 1786, he settled in Philadelphia and established himself as a pianist, composer, conductor, theatrical manager, and teacher. He was one of the founders and musical director for fifteen years of a company organized for the production of ballad operas. Reinagle wrote instrumental works for keyboard, strings, pantomimes, and stage plays, and a collection of songs.

Thomas Dartmouth ("Daddy") RICE (b. New York, 1808; d. there, 1860), singer and comedian, popularized black-face characterizations with his routine, which he called "Jump Jim Crow."

Henry RUSSELL (b. Sheerness, England, 1812; d. London, 1900) was an organist, singer, and composer of sentimental ballads. He spent some time in Italy and Paris, where he met many of the famous musicians of the time. He came to America in 1833 and was organist of the First Presbyterian Church in Rochester, N.Y., until 1841, when he returned to England. During this time he composed hundreds of ballads and traveled extensively throughout the United States, singing his songs to his own accompaniments and meeting with extraordinary success.

William SELBY (b. England, 1738; d. Boston, 1798) was an organist, harpsichordist, composer, teacher, and concert manager. He came to Boston about 1771 and, except for a short time in Newport, R.I., remained there the rest of his life. Shortly after his arrival he was appointed organist at King's Chapel, and during the Revolution he made his living as a liquor dealer and grocer. After the war he resumed his career and played an important part in the rapid development of music in Boston. Selby's compositions include songs, anthems, and instrumental pieces.

Oliver SHAW (b. Middleboro, Mass., 1779; d. Providence, R.I., 1848) was for a time a dealer in pianofortes, music, and fish, advertising the piscatorial product in his *Melodia Sacra* (Providence, 1819) as "one Barrel extra No. 1 Mackeral." A good part of his musical education was received from Gottlieb Graupner, who arrived in Boston in 1796. In 1807 he settled in Providence as a singing teacher and organist of the First Congregational Church. Deprived of his sight at twenty-one, he nevertheless acquired an enviable reputation as a composer and teacher, numbering among his many pupils Lowell Mason. Shaw composed mostly sacred music—hymns, psalm-tunes, songs—and compiled three collections of sacred music. His secular compositions include instrumental ensembles published in *For the Gentlemen* (Dedham, 1807) and a few songs.

William STEFFE (dates unknown) of Charleston, S. C., was a composer of popular Sunday School songs. The tune of the famous *Battle Hymn of the Republic* is attributed to him.

Timothy SWAN (b. Worcester, Mass., 1758; d. Northfield, Mass., 1842) was a carpenter and virtually a self-taught composer. His musical education consisted of a few weeks in a singing school, and while serving in the Continental Army he learned to play the fife. In 1773 he was living in Suffield, Conn., and in 1807 he moved to Northfield, Mass. Between 1785 and 1803 Swan compiled two and possibly three collections, which included a number of his own hymn-tunes and a few secular songs.

William TANS'UR (Tanzer) (b. Dunchurch, Warwickshire, 1706; d. St. Neot's, Huntingdonshire, 1783) was a bookbinder, theoretician, teacher of psalmody, and a composer-compiler of psalm-tunes and anthems. His publications were numerous and went into many editions.

Raynor TAYLOR (b. England, 1747; d. Philadelphia, 1825) was trained as a chorister of the King's Royal Chapel and in 1765 became organist of a church in Chelmsford. In the same year he was appointed music director of Sadler's Wells Theatre in London. He came to the United States in 1792 and was well-equipped to serve in the roles of conductor, impresario, organist, singer, and composer. He first lived in Baltimore, then Annapolis, and from 1793 in Philadelphia, where he played a dual role as organist of St. Peter's Church and impresario-entertainer of comic skits known as "Olios." His works are mostly secular and include a ballad opera, cantatas, songs, and instrumental pieces.

William TUCKEY (b. Somersetshire, England, 1708; d. Philadelphia, 1781) played an important part in the musical life of New York from his arrival there in 1753. He organized the choir at Trinity Church, taught music, and was active as a concert artist. In 1770 he presented the Overture and sixteen numbers from Handel's *Messiah* for the first time in America. Tuckey's compositions, widely known in his lifetime, include anthems, odes, and psalm-tunes. He published none of his own music, however, but his works are found in the compilations of others.

John TUFTS (b. Medford, Mass., 1689; d. Amesbury, Mass., 1750) graduated from Harvard College in 1708. He was a Congregational minister in Newbury, Mass., from 1714 until his retirement in 1738 to Amesbury, where he became a shopkeeper. He was a pioneer in music instruction and tunebooks.

William WALKER (b. Cross Keys, S.C., 1809; d. Spartansburg, S.C., 1875) was born of humble parents and received very little education. His ambition to "perfect the vocal modes of praise" resulted in the compilation of *The Southern Harmony* (1835). This enormously popular collection contained 209 tunes, of which Walker claimed the authorship of 25. Later editions included fifteen more of his folk hymns.

Thomas WALTER (b. Roxbury, Mass., 1696; d. there, 1725) received his M.A. degree from Harvard College in 1713, and in 1718 he became an ordained minister. Like Tufts, he recognized the need for music instruction books, and in 1721, just four years before his death at the age of twenty-nine, he published his *Grounds and Rules of Musick Explained.*

George James WEBB (b. near Salisbury, England, 1803; d. Orange, N.J., 1887) studied piano, violin, and organ in his youth and in 1830 came to Boston. He was appointed organist of the Old South Church and helped Lowell Mason organize the Boston Academy of Music. He became famous as a choral and orchestral conductor and in 1840 was made president of the Handel and Haydn Society. In 1870 he followed Mason to New York, where he taught voice and conducted normal courses for teachers. Webb's compositions include sacred songs, glees, cantatas, and hymn-tunes. He compiled a number of collections of church music, some with Mason, and edited two periodicals, *The Musical Library* (1835–1836) and *The Musical Cabinet* (1837–1840).

Benjamin Franklin WHITE (b. Spartansburg, S.C., 1800; d. Atlanta, Ga., 1879) was a newspaper editor and a self-taught musician. He became a singing teacher, composer, arranger, and published *The Sacred Harp* (1844) with E. J. King.

Aaron WILLIAMS (b. London, 1731; d. there, 1776) was a music teacher, engraver, publisher, and a clerk at the Scottish Church in London Wall. He composed anthems and hymn-tunes and published four collections between 1763 and 1780 for use in Nonconformist churches.

Septimus WINNER (Alice Hawthorne) (b. Philadelphia, 1827; d. there, 1902) began to earn his living as a music teacher, giving lessons in violin, banjo, guitar, and other instruments. In 1847 he opened a publishing house and music store in Philadelphia. He is said to have composed over 200 volumes of music, including instruction books for 23 different instruments, arrangements for violin and pianoforte, and over 100 songs. His most famous song, *Listen to the Mocking Bird*, sold over 20 million copies in 50 years.

Abraham WOOD (b. Northboro, Mass., 1752; d. there, 1804) was a fuller, or dresser of cloth, a singer, and a self-taught composer. During the Revolutionary War he served as a drummer. He published his *Divine Songs* in 1789, and was co-author of the *Columbian Harmony* (1793) with Joseph Stone. Twenty-six of his tunes appeared in the latter collection and a number were published in other tunebooks.

Isaac Baker WOODBURY (b. Beverley, Mass., 1819; d. Columbia, S.C., 1858) was originally apprenticed to a blacksmith. He early became interested in music, however, and in 1838 went to Europe, where he studied in Paris and London. After a year he returned to America and settled in Boston as a music teacher and traveled with the Bay State Glee Club. He became known as a conductor in Vermont and later went to New York as a choirmaster at the Rutgers Street Church and became editor of *The Musical Review.* Woodbury wrote hymn-tunes, sacred and secular songs, and glees. He published a number of tunebooks that were extremely popular and a *Self-instructor in Musical Composition and Thorough-Bass.*

Henry Clay WORK (b. Middletown, Conn., 1832; d. Hartford, 1884) was a printer, an abolitionist, and a temperance advocate, but is remembered today as a self-taught composer of popular songs. Work is best known for his Civil War songs, but he was also a successful composer of minstrel and temperance songs.

General Index

Classified Index

S-Soprano; A-Alto; T-Tenor; B-Bass

I. VOCAL (unaccompanied)

SOLO OR UNISON

TWO VOICES (SB)

TWO VOICES (SB) WITH CHORUS (STB)

THREE VOICES (STB)

FOUR VOICES (SATB)

Index of First Lines

Introductory Readings on Language

Introductory Readings on Language

WALLACE L. ANDERSON
NORMAN C. STAGEBERG
State College of Iowa

New York
HOLT, RINEHART AND WINSTON, INC.

Library of Congress Catalog Card Number: 62-9502
20409–0112

Printed in the United States of America

TO THE INSTRUCTOR

This book is designed primarily as a text for freshman English, though it should also prove useful in the increasing number of undergraduate English courses devoted to the study of language. It has three major purposes:

1. To present basic information about language as a subject interesting and important in its own right. The intent is to make the students aware of the nature of language and some of its multifarious aspects.
2. To arouse the students' intellectual curiosity about language to the point where they want to know more about it.
3. To influence the students' own use of language and to enable them to cope more successfully with the welter of words, both spoken and written, that surrounds us all.

It is our conviction that the major concern of freshman English should be language. Most freshman English courses are planned to help students to write with clarity, if not with grace, and to read with understanding and discrimination. Usually, composition is taught in conjunction with a book of readings containing examples of good writing in a variety of styles and on a variety of topics. This variety of topics can prove troublesome. Oftentimes discussion tends to center in the content of the essays, so that the instructor finds himself of necessity taking on the role of sociologist, historian, scientist, and philosopher. The topics dealt with are important ones, to be sure, but they are probably better treated elsewhere by specialists in those fields. To the extent that this shift in roles occurs, the course becomes blurred; it loses its focus. Moreover, it inhibits the instructor's dealing with one of the subjects in which he is at home, namely, language. And this is one thing students need to know more about.

College freshman are, for the most part, linguistically unsophisticated. Their attitudes toward language are often naïve; indeed, they have many misconceptions about language—misconceptions which they share with the general populace. One function of the English instructor is to rid college students of these misconceptions, to replace false beliefs with a more enlightened view of language in general, and of their own language in particular. For many college students, the freshman course is the sole course in English that they will take. Freshman English is the only place where these students will have the opportunity to gain real insight into the workings of language. They should not come to us naïve and leave older but still naïve in a matter of such vital import. Hence this book of readings on language.

We realize that other kinds of content may be justifiably defended in a freshman English course, but we also believe that the rationale offered here has a cogency that cannot be lightly dismissed.

These essays constitute an introductory course in language. Although they deal with various linguistic topics, they are not a course in linguistics. They are intended to be complementary to a composition text or handbook; hence matters of rhetoric and mechanics have for the most part been excluded. The readings have been selected on the basis of three criteria: (1) that they be soundly informative, (2) that they be in line with current linguistic thought, and (3) that they be within the intellectual reach of the average freshman. We have been particularly mindful that these readings are for beginning college students. The topics chosen are basic to an understanding of the nature of language; yet they do not presuppose previous technical knowledge. In the main the selections themselves are nontechnical. The single exception is Charlton Laird's essay on the classification of English vowels and consonants; here of necessity phonetic terminology and symbols are used. (This essay should precede the others in the section.) The few technical terms that do occur are clearly defined in the text or in footnotes of definition and illustration which we have provided.

In addition to the explanatory footnotes, we have included three kinds of editorial assistance: headnotes, suggested assignments, and lists of further readings. These are an integral part of the book. The headnotes prepare the students for the reading to follow by providing background material and by raising questions. Their purpose is to arouse interest, to stimulate thought, and to direct attention to the particular issues involved. The "assignments" are in a sense extensions of the readings themselves. Their purpose is to make the readings more meaningful by giving the students an opportunity to come to grips with specific issues by means of a variety of oral and written assignments. Many of the assignments are adaptable to either discussion or written work. The readings are included as a source of information for research papers; they may also serve to open more doors for those students desirous of gaining further insight into the nature of language.

The arrangement of topics is one that makes sense to us. However, it is not inflexible. The most appropriate order will depend, as it should, on the ingenuity of the instructor and his view of the course.

W. L. A.
N. C. S.

Cedar Falls, Iowa
March, 1962

TO THE STUDENT

To use language is the mark of a man; to understand language, in the deepest sense, is the mark of an educated man. From about the age of six, you have been using language with really a high degree of efficiency. And so have 300 million other speakers of English. But your understanding of your native tongue is probably fragmentary and riddled with misconceptions. In the course of twelve years of schooling, if you are like many college freshmen, you have gathered into your intellectual granary sundry notions about language, varying in worth from known truths to halftruths down to palpable nontruths. An illustration will make this clear. With which of the following propositions would you agree?

1. When writing, one finds his thoughts and then puts them into words.
2. The languages of primitive peoples are simpler than those of more advanced nations.
3. An excellent way to find the correct pronunciation of a word is to look it up in the dictionary.
4. If you pronounce *pursuing* to rime with *ruin*, you are dropping the *g*.
5. The word *humor* should be pronounced with an *h* because it is spelled with an *h*.
6. Since the real meaning of *awful* is "full of awe," this word should not be used as a general term of condemnation.
7. Many words have a specific and universal connotation.
8. In the question "Who is it for?" one should say *whom* because it is the object of the preposition *for*.

If you agree with any of these, you are in error, for each states or implies a concept that is to some degree untrue. These errors, however, are no cause for alarm, since each of us entertains misconceptions in areas of knowledge with which he is unfamiliar. But the situation is one that demands correction because, as you go through college, you will gain much of your education through the medium of language. You will listen to classroom lectures where you will have to catch and interpret words on the fly. You will have heavy reading assignments where you will have to read closely, wtih sharp attention to nuances of meaning and validity of reasoning. You will have compositions to write where you must use language with scrupulous precision. You will have to do serious thinking, which can be done only through language. All of these activities you should be able to perform more capably when you understand the language matters presented in this book—such matters, for example, as the symbolic nature of language, the basis of good usage, the uses of metaphor, the ever-present hazards of ambiguity, the pitfalls of analogy, the uniqueness of meanings, and the fallacies of causal reasoning.

Language study, in addition to being a practical pursuit, is also a cultural subject. It is a social science, concerned with an aspect of man's behavior that sets him apart from the lower animals—his use of an intricate system of speech sounds to communicate with his peers and his use of written symbols to transmit the accumulated knowledge of the race to his descendants. You will get an inkling of the scientific side of language study when you read the selections on linguistic geography, usage, and structural grammar. You will discover fragments of history embedded in words when you dig into etymology. You will touch upon philosophy when you inquire into the symbolic nature of words. And if you were to venture into the higher reaches of descriptive linguistics, you would become involved with mathematics.

Of the whole fascinating drama of language behavior, you will receive a series of quick, revealing glances as scholars draw the curtain aside on various scenes. And you will emerge, it is hoped, with a deepened comprehension of the foundation stone of man's humanity—language.

TABLE OF CONTENTS

6 Usage

7 Linguistic Geography

8 Structural Grammar

9 Clear Thinking

Introductory Readings on Language

1. The Nature of Language

LANGUAGE DEFINED

Edward Sapir

Language is so much a part of us that we tend to regard it as both natural and simple. Moreover, because education in our culture is carried on primarily by means of books, many of us think of language primarily in its written form—black marks imprinted on paper, or wiggly lines made with pen or pencil. But in many parts of the world it is impossible for people to communicate in that way. They have no written language; they communicate solely by means of the spoken word—sound waves in the air. Are we to conclude, then, that writing is not language? Or are there two kinds of language? What is the relationship between speech and writing? And how, in either case, does communication take place? How do these sound waves or wiggly lines mean anything? These are some of the basic questions that Edward Sapir deals with. One of the pioneers of modern linguistic science, Sapir was an authority on American-Indian languages; he was also one of the first to study the relationships between linguistics and anthropology.

SPEECH IS so familiar a feature of daily life that we rarely pause to define it. It seems as natural to man as walking, and only less so than breathing. Yet it needs but a moment's reflection to convince us that this naturalness of speech is but an illusory feeling. The process of acquiring speech is, in sober fact, an utterly different sort of thing from the process of learning to walk. In the case of the latter function, culture, in other words, the traditional body of social usage, is not seriously brought into play. The child is individually equipped, by the complex set of factors that we term biological heredity, to make all the needed muscular and nervous adjustments that result in walking. Indeed, the very conformation of these muscles and of the appropriate parts of the nervous system may be said to be primarily adapted to the movements made in walking and in similar activities. In a very real sense the normal human being is predestined to walk, not because his elders will assist him to learn the art, but because his organism is prepared from birth, or even from the moment of conception, to take on all those expenditures of nervous energy and all those muscular adaptations that result in walking. To put it concisely, walking is an inherent, biological function of man.

Not so language. It is of course true that in a certain sense the individual is predestined to talk, but that is due entirely to the circumstance that he is born not merely in nature, but in the lap of a society that is certain, reasonably certain, to lead him to its traditions. Eliminate society and there is every reason to believe that he will learn to walk, if, indeed, he survives at all. But it is just as certain that he will never learn to talk, that is, to communicate ideas according to the traditional system of a particular society. Or, again, remove the new-born individual from the social environment into which he has come and transplant him to an utterly alien one. He will develop the art of walking in his new environment very much as he would have developed it in the old. But his speech will be completely at variance with the speech of his native environment. Walking, then, is a general human activity that varies only within circumscribed limits as we pass from individual to individual. Its variability is involuntary and purposeless. Speech is a human activity that varies without assignable limit as we pass from social group to social group, because it is a purely historical heritage of the group, the product of long-continued social usage. It varies as all creative effort varies—not as consciously, perhaps, but none the less as truly as do the religions, the beliefs, the customs, and the arts of different peoples. Walking is an organic, an instinctive, function (not, of course, itself an instinct); speech is a non-instinctive, acquired, "cultural" function.

There is one fact that has frequently tended to prevent the recognition of language as a merely conventional system of sound symbols, that has seduced the popular mind into attributing to it an instinctive basis that it does not really possess. This is the well-known observation that under the stress of emotion, say of a sudden twinge of pain or of unbridled joy, we do involuntarily give utterance to sounds that the hearer interprets as indicative of the emotion itself. But there is all the difference in the world between such involuntary expression of feeling and the normal type of communication of ideas that is speech. The former kind of utterance is indeed instinctive, but it is non-symbolic; in other words, the sound of pain or the sound of joy does not, as such, indicate the emotion, it does not stand aloof, as it were, and announce that such and such an emotion is being felt. What it does is to serve as a more or less automatic overflow of the emotional energy; in a sense, it is part and parcel of the emotion itself. Moreover, such instinctive cries hardly constitute communication in any strict sense. They are not addressed to any one, they are merely overheard, if heard at all, as the bark of a dog, the sound of approaching footsteps, or the rustling of the wind is heard. If they convey certain ideas to the hearer, it is only in the very general sense in which any and every sound or even any phenomenon in our environment may be said to convey an idea to the perceiving mind. If the involuntary cry of pain which is conventionally represented by "Oh!" be looked upon as a true speech symbol equivalent to some such idea as "I am in great pain," it is just as allowable to interpret the appearance of clouds as an equivalent symbol that carries the definite message "It is likely to rain." A definition of language, however, that is so extended as to cover every type of inference becomes utterly meaningless.

The mistake must not be made of identifying our conventional interjections (our "oh!" and "ah!" and "sh!") with the instinctive cries themselves. These interjections are merely conventional fixations of the natural sounds. They therefore differ widely in various languages in accordance with the specific phonetic genius of each of these. As such they may be considered an integral portion of speech, in the properly cultural sense of the term, being no more identical with the instinctive cries themselves than such words as "cuckoo" and "killdeer" are identical with the cries of the birds they denote or than Rossini's treatment of a storm in the overture to "William Tell" is in fact a storm. In other words, the interjections and sound-imitative words of normal speech are related to their natural prototypes as is art, a purely social or cultural thing, to nature. It may be objected that, though the interjections differ somewhat as we pass from language to language, they do nevertheless offer striking family resemblances and may therefore be looked upon as having grown up out of a common instinctive base. But their case is nowise different from that, say, of the varying national modes of pictorial representation. A Japanese picture of a hill both differs from and resembles a typical modern European painting of the same kind of hill. Both are suggested by and both "imitate" the same natural feature. Neither the one nor the other is the same thing as, or, in any intelligible sense, a direct outgrowth of, this natural feature. The two modes of representation are not identical because they proceed from differing historical traditions, are executed with differing pictorial techniques. The interjections of Japanese and English are, just so, suggested by a common natural prototype, the instinctive cries, and are thus unavoidably suggestive of each other. They differ, now greatly, now but little, because they are builded out of historically diverse materials or techniques, the respective linguistic traditions, phonetic systems, speech habits of the two peoples. Yet the instinctive cries as such are practically identical for all humanity, just as the human skeleton or nervous system is to all intents and purposes a "fixed," that is, an only slightly and "accidentally" variable, feature of man's organism.

Interjections are among the least important of speech elements. Their discussion is valuable mainly because it can be shown that even they, avowedly the nearest of all language sounds to instinctive utterance, are only superficially of an instinctive nature. Were it therefore possible to demonstrate that the whole of language is traceable, in its ultimate historical and psychological foundations, to the interjections, it would still not follow that language is an instinctive activity. But, as a matter of fact, all attempts so to explain the origin of speech have been fruitless. There is no tangible evidence, historical or otherwise, tending to show that the mass of speech elements and speech processes has evolved out of the interjections. These are a very small and functionally insignificant proportion of the vocabulary of language; at no time and in no linguistic province that we have record of do we see a noticeable tendency towards their elaboration into the primary warp and woof of language. They are never more, at best, than a decorative edging to the ample, complex fabric.

What applies to the interjections applies with even greater force to the sound-imitative words. Such words as "whippoorwill," "to mew," "to caw" are in no sense natural sounds that man has instinctively or automatically reproduced. They are just as truly creations of the human mind, flights of the human fancy, as anything else in language. They do not directly grow out of nature, they are suggested by it and play with it. Hence the onomatopoetic theory of the origin of speech, the theory that would explain all speech as a gradual evolution from sounds of an imitative character, really brings us no nearer to the instinctive level than is language as we know it to-day. As to the theory itself, it is scarcely more credible than its interjectional counterpart. It is true that a number of words which we do not now feel to have a sound-imitative value can be shown to have once had a phonetic form that strongly suggests their origin as imitations of natural sounds. Such is the English word "to laugh." For all that, it is quite impossible to show, nor does it seem intrinsically reasonable to suppose, that more than a negligible proportion of the elements of speech or anything at all of its formal apparatus is derivable from an onomatopoetic source. However much we may be disposed on general principles to assign a fundamental importance in the languages of primitive peoples to the imitation of natural sounds, the actual fact of the matter is that these languages show no particular preference for imitative words. Among the most primitive peoples of aboriginal America, the Athabaskan tribes of the Mackenzie River speak languages in which such words seem to be nearly or entirely absent, while they are used freely enough in languages as sophisticated as English and German. Such an instance shows how little the essential nature of speech is concerned with the mere imitation of things.

The way is now cleared for a serviceable definition of language. Language is a purely human and non-instinctive method of communicating ideas, emotions, and desires by means of a system of voluntarily produced symbols. These symbols are, in the first instance, auditory and they are produced by the so-called "organs of speech." There is no discernible instinctive basis in human speech as such, however much instinctive expressions and the natural environment may serve as a stimulus for the development of certain elements of speech, however much instinctive tendencies, motor and other, may give a predetermined range or mold to linguistic expression. Such human or animal communication, if "communication" it may be called, as is brought about by involuntary, instinctive cries is not, in our sense, language at all.

I have just referred to the "organs of speech," and it would seem at first blush that this is tantamount to an admission that speech itself is an instinctive, biologically predetermined activity. We must not be misled by the mere term. There are, properly speaking, no organs of speech; there are only organs that are incidentally useful in the production of speech sounds.[1] The lungs, the larynx, the palate, the nose, the tongue, the teeth, and the lips, are all so utilized, but they are no more to be thought of as primary organs of speech than are the fingers to be considered as essentially organs of piano-playing or the knees as organs of prayer. Speech is not a simple activity that is carried on by one or more organs biologically adapted to the purpose. It is an extremely complex and ever-shifting network of adjustments—in the brain, in the nervous system, and in the articulating and auditory organs—tending towards the desired end of communication. The lungs developed, roughly speaking, in connection with the necessary biological function known as breathing; the nose, as an organ of smell; the teeth, as organs useful in breaking up food before it was ready for digestion. If, then, these and other organs are being constantly utilized in speech, it is only because any organ, once existent and in so far as it is subject to voluntary control, can be utilized by man for secondary purposes. Physiologically, speech is an overlaid function, or, to be more precise, a group of overlaid functions. It gets what service it can out of organs and functions, nervous and muscular, that have come into being and are maintained for very different ends than its own.

It is true that physiological psychologists speak of the localization of speech in the brain. This can only mean that the sounds of speech are localized in the auditory tract of the brain, or in some circumscribed portion of it, precisely as other classes of sounds are localized; and that the motor processes involved in speech (such as the movements of the glottal cords in the larynx, the movements of the tongue required to pronounce the vowels, lip movements required

[1] For a diagram of the speech organs, and a further discussion of the production of speech sounds, see pp. 224-237. [eds.]

to articulate certain consonants, and numerous others) are localized in the motor tract precisely as are all other impulses to special motor activities. In the same way control is lodged in the visual tract of the brain over all those processes of visual recognition involved in reading. Naturally the particular points or clusters of points of localization in the several tracts that refer to any element of language are connected in the brain by paths of association, so that the outward, or psycho-physical, aspect of language, is of a vast network of associated localizations in the brain and lower nervous tracts, the auditory localizations being without doubt the most fundamental of all for speech. However, a speech-sound localized in the brain, even when associated with the particular movements of the "speech organs" that are required to produce it, is very far from being an element of language. It must be further associated with some element or group of elements of experience, say a visual image or a class of visual images or a feeling of relation, before it has even rudimentary linguistic significance. This "element" of experience is the content or "meaning" of the linguistic unit; the associated auditory, motor, and other cerebral processes that lie immediately back of the act of speaking and the act of hearing speech are merely a complicated symbol of or signal for these "meanings." . . . We see therefore at once that language as such is not and cannot be definitely localized, for it consists of a peculiar symbolic relation—physiologically an arbitrary one—between all possible elements of consciousness on the one hand and certain selected elements localized in the auditory, motor, and other cerebral and nervous tracts on the other. If language can be said to be definitely "localized" in the brain, it is only in that general and rather useless sense in which all aspects of consciousness, all human interest and activity, may be said to be "in the brain." Hence, we have no recourse but to accept language as a fully formed functional system within man's psychic or "spiritual" constitution. We cannot define it as an entity in psycho-physical terms alone, however much the psycho-physical basis is essential to its functioning in the individual.

From the physiologist's or psychologist's point of view we may seem to be making an unwarrantable abstraction in desiring to handle the subject of speech without constant and explicit reference to that basis. However, such an abstraction is justifiable. We can profitably discuss the intention, the form, and the history of speech, precisely as we discuss the nature of any other phase of human culture—say art or religion—as an institutional or cultural entity, leaving the organic and psychological mechanisms back of it as something to be taken for granted. . . .

I have already pointed out that the essence of language consists in the assigning of conventional, voluntarily articulated, sounds, or of their equivalents, to the diverse elements of experience. The word "house" is not a linguistic fact if by it is meant merely the acoustic effect produced on the ear by its constituent consonants and vowels, pronounced in a certain order; nor the motor processes and tactile feelings which make up the articulation of the word; nor the visual perception on the part of the hearer of this articulation; nor the visual perception of the word "house" on the written or printed page; nor the motor processes and tactile feelings which enter into the writing of the word; nor the memory of any or all of these experiences. It is only when these, and possibly still other, associated experiences are automatically associated with the image of a house that they begin to take on the nature of a symbol, a word, an element of language. But the mere fact of such an association is not enough. One might have heard a particular word spoken in an individual house under such impressive circumstances that neither the word nor the image of the house ever recur in consciousness without the other becoming present at the same time. This type of association does not constitute speech. The association must be a purely symbolic one; in other words, the word must denote, tag off, the image, must have no other significance than to serve as a counter to refer to it whenever it is necessary or convenient to do so. Such an association, voluntary and, in a sense, arbitrary as it is, demands a considerable exercise of self-conscious attention. At least to begin with, for habit soon makes the association nearly as automatic as any and more rapid than most.

But we have traveled a little too fast. Were the symbol "house"—whether an auditory, motor, or visual experience or image—attached but to the single image of a particular house once seen, it might perhaps, by an indulgent criticism, be termed an element of speech, yet it is obvious at the outset that speech so constituted would have little or no value for purposes of communication. The world of our experiences must be enormously simplified and generalized before it is possible to make a symbolic inventory of all our experiences of things and relations; and this inventory is imperative before we can convey ideas. The elements of language, the symbols that ticket off experience, must therefore be associated with whole groups, delimited classes, of experience rather than with the single experiences themselves. Only so is communication possible, for the single experience lodges in an individual consciousness and is, strictly speaking, incommunicable. To be communicated it needs to be referred to a class which is tacitly accepted by the community as an identity. Thus, the single impression which I have had of a particular house must be identified with all my other impressions of it. Further, my generalized memory or my "notion" of this house must be merged with the notions that all other individuals who have seen the house have formed of it. The particular experience that we started with has now been widened so as to embrace all possible impressions or images that sentient beings have formed or may form of the house in question.[2] This first simplification of experience is at the bottom of a large number of elements of speech, the so-called proper nouns or names of single individuals or objects. It is, essentially, the type of simplification which underlies, or forms the crude subject of, history and art. But we cannot be content with this measure of reduction of the infinity of experience. We must cut to the bone of things, we must more or less arbitrarily throw whole masses of experience together as similar enough to warrant their being looked upon—mistakenly, but conveniently—as identical. This house and that house and thousands of other phenomena of like character are thought of as having enough in common, in spite of great and obvious differences of detail, to be classed under the same heading. In other words, the speech element "house" is the symbol, first and foremost, not of a single perception, nor even of the notion of a particular object, but of a "concept," in other words, of a convenient capsule of thought that embraces thousands of distinct experiences and that is ready to take in thousands more. If the single significant elements of speech are the symbols of concepts, the actual flow of speech may be interpreted as a record of the setting of these concepts into mutual relations. . . .

Language is primarily an auditory system of symbols. In so far as it is articulated it is also a motor system, but the motor aspect of speech is clearly secondary to the auditory. In normal individuals the impulse to speech first takes effect in the sphere of auditory

[2] Sapir is here discussing the processes of abstraction and clarification. For a more complete discussion of this topic, see pp. 179-188. [eds.]

imagery and is then transmitted to the motor nerves that control the organs of speech. The motor processes and the accompanying motor feelings are not, however, the end, the final resting point. They are merely a means and a control leading to auditory perception in both speaker and hearer. Communication, which is the very object of speech, is successfully effected only when the hearer's auditory perceptions are translated into the appropriate and intended flow of imagery or thought or both combined. Hence the cycle of speech, in so far as we may look upon it as a purely external instrument, begins and ends in the realm of sounds. The concordance between the initial auditory imagery and the final auditory perceptions is the social seal or warrant of the successful issue of the process. As we have already seen, the typical course of this process may undergo endless modifications or transfers into equivalent systems without thereby losing its essential formal characteristics.

The most important of these modifications is the abbreviation of the speech process involved in thinking. This has doubtless many forms, according to the structural or functional peculiarities of the individual mind. The least modified form is that known as "talking to one's self" or "thinking aloud." Here the speaker and the hearer are identified in a single person, who may be said to communicate with himself. More significant is the still further abbreviated form in which the sounds of speech are not articulated at all. To this belong all the varieties of silent speech and of normal thinking. The auditory centers alone may be excited; or the impulse to linguistic expression may be communicated as well to the motor nerves that communicate with the organs of speech but be inhibited either in the muscles of these organs or at some point in the motor nerves themselves; or, possibly, the auditory centers may be only slightly, if at all, affected, the speech process manifesting itself directly in the motor sphere. There must be still other types of abbreviation. How common is the excitation of the motor nerves in silent speech, in which no audible or visible articulations result, is shown by the frequent experience of fatigue in the speech organs, particularly in the larynx, after unusually stimulating reading or intensive thinking.

All the modifications so far considered are directly patterned on the typical process of normal speech. Of very great interest and importance is the possibility of transferring the whole system of speech symbolism into other terms than those that are involved in the typical process. This process, as we have seen, is a matter of sounds and of movements intended to produce these sounds. The sense of vision is not brought into play. But let us suppose that one not only hears the articulated sounds but sees the articulations themselves as they are being executed by the speaker. Clearly, if one can only gain a sufficiently high degree of adroitness in perceiving these movements of the speech organs, the way is opened for a new type of speech symbolism—that in which the sound is replaced by the visual image of the articulations that correspond to the sound. This sort of system has no great value for most of us because we are already possessed of the auditory-motor system of which it is at best but an imperfect translation, not all the articulations being visible to the eye. However, it is well known what excellent use deaf-mutes can make of "reading from the lips" as a subsidiary method of apprehending speech. The most important of all visual speech symbolisms is, of course, that of the written or printed word, to which, on the motor side, corresponds the system of delicately adjusted movements which result in the writing or typewriting or other graphic method of recording speech. The significant feature for our recognition in these new types of symbolism, apart from the fact that they are no longer a by-product of normal speech itself, is that each element (letter or written word) in the system corresponds to a specific element (sound or sound-group or spoken word) in the primary system. Written language is thus a point-to-point equivalence, to borrow a mathematical phrase, to its spoken counterpart. The written forms are secondary symbols of the spoken ones—symbols of symbols—yet so close is the correspondence that they may, not only in theory but in the actual practice of certain eye-readers and, possibly, in certain types of thinking, be entirely substituted for the spoken ones. Yet the auditory-motor associations are probably always latent at the least, that is, they are unconsciously brought into play. Even those who read and think without the slightest use of sound imagery are, at last analysis, dependent on it. They are merely handling the circulating medium, the money, of visual symbols as a convenient substitute for the economic goods and services of the fundamental auditory symbols.

The possibilities of linguistic transfer are practically unlimited. A familiar example is the Morse telegraph code, in which the letters of written speech are represented by a conventionally fixed sequence of longer or shorter ticks. Here the transfer takes place from the written word rather than directly from the sounds of spoken speech. The letter of the telegraph code is thus a symbol of a symbol of a symbol. It does not, of course, in the least follow that the skilled operator, in order to arrive at an understanding of a telegraphic message, needs to transpose the individual sequence of ticks into a visual image of the word before he experiences its normal auditory image. The precise method of reading off speech from the telegraphic communication undoubtedly varies widely with the individual. It is even conceivable, if not exactly likely, that certain operators may have learned to think directly, so far as the purely conscious part of the process of thought is concerned, in terms of the tick-auditory symbolism or, if they happen to have a strong natural bent toward motor symbolism, in terms of the correlated tactile-motor symbolism developed in the sending of telegraphic messages.

Still another interesting group of transfers are the different gesture languages, developed for the use of deaf-mutes, of Trappist monks vowed to perpetual silence, or of communicating parties that are within seeing distance of each other but are out of earshot. Some of these systems are one-to-one equivalences of the normal system of speech; others, like military gesture-symbolism or the gesture language of the Plains Indians of North America (understood by tribes of mutually unintelligible forms of speech) are imperfect transfers, limiting themselves to the rendering of such grosser speech elements as are an imperative minimum under difficult circumstances. In these latter systems, as in such still more imperfect symbolisms as those used at sea or in the woods, it may be contended that language no longer properly plays a part but that the ideas are directly conveyed by an utterly unrelated symbolic process or by a quasi-instinctive imitativeness. Such an interpretation would be erroneous. The intelligibility of these vaguer symbolisms can hardly be due to anything but their automatic and silent translation into the terms of a fuller flow of speech.

We shall no doubt conclude that all voluntary communication of ideas, aside from normal speech, is either a transfer, direct or indirect, from the typical symbolism of language as spoken and heard or, at the least, involves the intermediary of truly linguistic symbolism. This is a fact of the highest importance. Auditory imagery and the correlated motor imagery leading to articulation are, by whatever devious ways we follow the process, the historic fountain-head of all speech and of all thinking. One other point is of still greater importance. The ease with which speech symbolism can be transferred from one sense to another, from technique to technique, itself indicates that the mere sounds of speech are not the essential fact of language, which lies rather in the classification, in the formal patterning, and in the relating of concepts. Once more, language, as a structure, is on its inner face the mold of thought. . . .

There is no more striking general fact about language than its universality. One may argue as to whether a particular tribe engages in activities that are worthy of the name of religion or of art, but we know of no people that is not possessed of a fully developed language. The lowliest South African Bushman speaks in the forms of a rich symbolic system that is in essence perfectly comparable to the speech of the cultivated Frenchman. It goes without saying that the more abstract concepts are not nearly so plentifully represented in the language of the savage, nor is there the rich terminology and the finer definition of nuances that reflect the higher culture. Yet the sort of linguistic development that parallels the historic growth of culture and which, in its later stages, we associate with literature is, at best, but a superficial thing. The fundamental groundwork of language—the development of a clear-cut phonetic system, the specific association of speech elements with concepts, and the delicate provision for the formal expression of all manner of relations—all this meets us rigidly perfected and systematized in every language known to us. Many primitive languages have a formal richness, a latent luxuriance of expression, that eclipses anything known to the languages of modern civilization. Even in the mere matter of the inventory of speech the layman must be prepared for strange surprises. Popular statements as to the extreme poverty of expression to which primitive languages are doomed are simply myths. Scarcely less impressive than the universality of speech is its almost incredible diversity. Those of us that have studied French or German, or, better yet, Latin or Greek, know in what varied forms a thought may run. The formal divergences between the English plan and the Latin plan, however, are comparatively slight in the perspective of what we know of more exotic linguistic patterns. The universality and the diversity of speech lead to a significant inference. We are forced to believe that language is an immensely ancient heritage of the human race, whether or not all forms of speech are the historical outgrowth of a single pristine form. It is doubtful if any other cultural asset of man, be it the art of drilling for fire or of chipping stone, may lay claim to a greater age. I am inclined to believe that it antedated even the lowliest developments of material culture, that these developments, in fact, were not strictly possible until language, the tool of significant expression, had itself taken shape.

SUGGESTED ASSIGNMENTS

1. Montaigne, a famous sixteenth-century French writer, learned to speak Latin before his native tongue. "I was above six years of age," he wrote, "before I understood either French or Perigordin, any more than Arabic." Yet he was born of French parents, brought up in France, and lived in a house with many servants, one of whom was German by birth. What circumstances must have been present to account for the writer's learning to speak Latin first? For the facts of the case, read Montaigne's essay "Of the Education of Children."
2. Human beings are not the only creatures that communicate with each other. Some animals have elaborate signalling systems. Bees, for example, have a systematic dance routine to indicate the source of food; jackdaws have a group of calls that apparently are meaningful. Look up one of the following references and make a report to the class: On bees, see Karl von Frisch, *Bees, Their Vision, Chemical Senses, and Language*; on jackdaws, see Konrad Lorenz, *King Solomon's Ring.* Both of these studies are summarized and discussed in Roger Brown's *Words and Things*, Chapter 5.
3. Commenting on the interjectional and onomatopoetic elements in language, Sapir remarked that "all attempts so to explain the origin of speech have been fruitless." Although evidence about the origin of speech will always remain theoretical and inconclusive, nonetheless the various theories are of interest because they reveal something of the complexity of the problem and because they show us some of the approaches linguists have taken in their attempts to solve the problem. See, for example, Otto Jespersen, *Language, Its Nature, Development, and Origin*, Chapter 21; Edgar H. Sturtevant, *Linguistic Science*, Chapter 5; and Roger Brown, *Words and Things*, pp. 131-136.
4. At first glance the following statement will not make much sense to you:

The reason is that you do not know what the symbols represent. Once you know the code, however, you can easily decipher the message. Use the following code to discover it:

A D G
B E H
C F I

J M P
K N Q
L O R

S
T U
V

W
X Y
Z

How many steps is the coded statement removed from the speech act itself?

5. Study these three definitions of language:
   a. Language is the expression of thought by means of speech sounds.
   b. Language is the instrument for the expression and communication of human thought.
   c. Language is nothing but a set of human habits, the purpose of which is to give expression to thoughts and feelings, and especially to impart them to others.

   Choose one and write a theme explaining its deficiencies.
6. Write a single-paragraph definition of *pond*, *gymnasium*, or *cottage*. In class the paragraphs will be compared in an effort to discover which characteristics the group attributes to this class of objects, and which characteristics are merely personal.
7. Write a theme telling which language skills, both general and specific, you think will be most valuable to you in your college work. At the end of the first semester, if you re-read this theme, you may be surprised at how you misjudged your needs.

SIGNS AND SYMBOLS

Stephen Ullmann

Language binds us together as men; yet, paradoxically, it also divides us. The French speak French, Germans speak German, Italians speak Italian, and the Swiss speak—French, German, Italian, or Rhaeto-Romance. Nor is there any necessary correlation between nationality and language or between race and language. Yet in order to communicate with each other, members of the same speech community must use the same symbols. We say bread, *the French* pain, *the Germans* Brot, *and the Italians* pane *to refer to the same thing. In each language the symbols are different, but they are equally effective because the symbolic process is the same regardless of the language. Clearly, in order to understand the nature of language, we must know what a symbol is and how it operates. Stephen Ullman's essay, "Signs and Symbols," will serve as an introduction to this topic. Ullman is Professor of Romance Philology at the University of Leeds.*

THE MECHANISM of language can best be seen at work in a simple speech-situation. Suppose for instance that a child notices an apple and feels an urge to pick it and eat it. To satisfy this desire, the child can do one of two things. If the apple is easily accessible and there are no other obstacles, he can go and get it without any outside help. If he cannot reach it, or if special permission is required, then the collaboration of some second person will have to be enlisted. The child will then articulate a series of sounds arranged into a certain pattern of rhythm and intonation, and forming an utterance such as: "Could you please get me that apple?" The vibrations of air started by the speaker will reach the ear of the hearer who, when the message has been understood, will react. In the simplest case, this reaction will take the form of some practical step, such as the picking of the apple as requested. There may also be more complicated patterns of further linguistic exchanges, with some practical result, positive or negative, at the end.

This situation has been analysed by the late Professor Leonard Bloomfield in "behaviourist" terms, *i.e.* as a chain of stimuli and responses. When the child can pick the apple by himself, there is a simple chain. The sight of the apple acts as an external stimulus and elicits an immediate and practical reaction. When co-operation is required, the external stimulus (S) sets off a linguistic reaction (r): the speaker produces a series of articulate sounds. The sound-waves reach the hearer and act on him as a linguistic stimulus (s). This in its turn gives rise to a practical, external reaction (R) on the hearer's part. Thus: S———r . . . s———R. Between the original stimulus and the final response, a linguistic exchange, an act of speech and interpretation has been fitted in, and as a result, the practical step will be taken by someone other than the recipient of the initial stimulus. In other words, a *division of labour* will have been ensured.

On closer inspection, our simple speech-situation will yield further information concerning the linguistic exchange. It shows, for instance, that three factors are involved in any utterance: the speaker, the hearer, and the message. For the speaker, the act of speech is an expression, a means of conveying his thoughts, feelings, or desires. For the hearer, it is a stimulus to take some action or to adopt some kind of attitude. From the point of view of the message itself, it is an act of communication. To use a terse formula advanced by the Austrian psychologist K. Bühler, the act of speech is a *symptom* of the speaker's state of mind, a *symbol* of the message conveyed, and a *signal* to the hearer.

The basic functions of human speech clearly emerge from this analysis. As there are three terms and three aspects, the functions also are three in number: expressive, communicative, and effective, according to whether it is viewed from the angle of the speaker, the message, or the hearer.

One crucial point, however, remains unexplained in our speech-situation. Why and how did the string of sounds "Could you please get me that apple?" induce the hearer to pick the fruit? To narrow down the problem to its central point, why and how does the string of sounds "apple" denote that particular object and no other, or for that matter any object at all? Clearly there is no natural link between form and meaning in this case. Not only does one fail to see what that link could be, but if a hidden connection did exist, then one would be at a loss to explain the diversity of names for the same object in different languages: *apple*, *pomme* in French, *manzana* in Spanish, *mar* in Rumanian, *alma* in Hungarian, etc. How did it happen that the word *apple* has, in the minds of all English speakers, become closely associated with that fruit, that it has established itself as its symbol?

To answer this question it will be necessary to consider signs and symbols on a more general plane, since it is common knowledge that there are many non-linguistic signs and symbols, and that the words of human speech merely take their place in the wider framework of symbolic processes.

If I see heavy clouds in the sky, I interpret this as a *sign* of impending rain. If a dog wants to go out of the room, he signifies his desire by scratching at the door. In the former case, a natural phenomenon has been analysed as an indication of some other phenomenon; in the latter, a sign has been deliberately produced for the benefit of some recipient or recipients. More important, however, is the process of interpretation itself. The famous experiments carried out by the Russian physiologist Pavlov have thrown fresh light on this process. On repeated occasions, Pavlov blew a whistle at a certain pitch when giving food to his dog. Thus, an associative link was established between the sight of the food, its smell, its taste, and the sound regularly accompanying its consumption. All these sense-impressions formed part of one common and recurring experience. Having established this context of sensations, Pavlov one day blew the whistle without producing the food, and found that the dog showed every sign of expectancy, including salivation, which the presence of food would normally evoke. What had happened was that part of an experience had been detached from the rest and, standing by itself, this isolated part was sufficient to call up the remainder of the context. To bring out the most salient feature of signs, Dr. Richards has coined the expressive if somewhat ponderous phrase: "delegated efficacy." An element in a complex experience is singled out to act for the whole, "by proxy", so to speak. We shall then define a sign as *some part of an experience, which is capable of calling up the remainder of that experience.*

A great many signs are used by men in their intercourse with each other. It is convenient to mark off these signs from the rest and to label them *symbols.* Symbols will be defined, for the purposes of our enquiry, as "*those signs which men use to communicate one with another*" (Ogden-Richards). Such symbols can be classified from various viewpoints. They may appeal to different *senses;* sound and sight are of course the most privileged, as their organs are most highly developed, but other sense-impressions may also be brought into play, such as touch in the braille alphabet. There may even arise combinations of diverse sensations, as in an operatic performance where musical effects are accompanied and enhanced by visual devices. From a different point of view, symbols are found to be either *natural* or *conventional.* Natural symbols have some kind of intrinsic link with the thing symbolised. Thus, some gestures are descriptive of the states of mind they reflect. Pictorial or sculptural representations of, say, the goddess of Justice are allegorical, *i.e.*, based on some internal analogy. Again, the cross is a natural symbol of Christendom, not—or at least not primarily—because of any allegorical implications, but through its historical associations, because of the significance of the crucifixion of Christ. On the other hand, the spoken and the written word, the siren as a time-signal or as an air raid warning, the use of black as a sign of mourning, the shaking of the head as a sign of negation, are purely conventional devices; they become unintelligible outside the community where they are established. In China, white and not black is the colour of mourning, and in Turkey, the shaking of the head signifies assent. Finally, some symbols are *isolated,* whereas others form complex and intricate *systems* such as road signals, naval signals, codes, the deaf-and-dumb alphabet, language, and writing. In recent years, the American philosopher Charles Morris and others have begun to explore the possibility of a comprehensive *theory of signs,* which would examine, classify and correlate all symbolic processes, including human language which is their supreme and most elaborate example.

SUGGESTED ASSIGNMENTS

1. Ullmann divides symbols into two classes, natural or conventional. The letters of our alphabet are conventional symbols, but we use a great many other conventional but nonalphabetic symbols to communicate with each other as well. Our response to these symbols is so automatic that we rarely think about them. Indeed, we hardly seem to notice them, yet they are constantly functioning, and they play an important part in our lives. No matter where we are, whether in college, at home, or on the highway, on a bus or train or plane, even asleep in bed, we are surrounded by symbols of one kind or another. Shopkeepers frequently identify the nature of their wares or services by symbolic means, e.g., a boot in front of a shoe store, a watch in front of a jeweler's. Look about you in the course of a day and make a list of nonalphabetic symbols that you notice. Classify them as natural or conventional, and visual or auditory. For those that you list as natural symbols, describe the intrinsic link between the symbol and what it stands for.
2. In the list you made for Assignment 1, you may have included the familiar red and white striped barbershop pole. Did you classify it as a conventional symbol? Today most people would. Years ago, however, it was regarded as a natural symbol. To find out why, look up the story of its origin.
3. Gestures, either as accompaniment to speech or alone, are a part of our system of communication. We tend to think of gestures as natural movements that are universally understandable, regardless of the language that people happen to use. Some of them may be, e.g., grimaces of pain and smiles of joy. But some of them are quite clearly just as conventional as language, and vary with different groups of people. In the United States, for example, the "wolf" whistle is commonly understood as a signal that a pretty girl is passing by; in Portugal a man might pinch his ear to indicate the same thing. In our society what do the following gestures mean (there may be more than one meaning, depending on the context): a handshake, a shrug of the shoulders, a shake of the fist, thumbing the nose, thumbs down (note that we even use this as a verbal expression), scratching the head, pursing the lips, tapping a foot? What others can you think of?
4. As an interesting experiment, observe the behavior of a person making a phone call. Be sure you cannot overhear the conversation. Jot down all the gestures you notice—bodily movements as well as facial

expressions. To what extent could you make a fairly accurate statement about the conversation? (It would be wise *not* to compare notes afterwards with the speaker.) If the telephone assignment is not feasible, watch a program on TV with the volume turned off and do the same thing.

5. Playing charades is fun. It is also an example of nonverbal communication in which the mimer uses symbols that have to be interpreted by the audience. Either alone or with some of your classmates, choose a song title and present it as a charade. Ask the first person who interprets it correctly to explain how he knew the answer, that is, to analyze the specific symbolic devices used.
6. A recent term in our language is *status symbol,* a symbol used to convey prestige upon the possessor, e.g., an imported sports car, a Greek-letter fraternity pin, or membership in an exclusive club. Write a theme on one of the following topics:

   a. The Use and Abuse of Status Symbols
   b. Status Symbols—a Symbol of Inferiority
   c. Unusual Status Symbols I Have Observed
   d. The Ladder of Status Symbols

LANGUAGE, LOGIC, AND GRAMMAR

L. M. Myers

Language, we have seen, is a system of conventionalized symbols by which we communicate with each other. One would think that, since we use the same symbols, we would always understand one another. Yet we do not always say what we mean, nor do we always understand what other people mean. If we do not know the meaning of a particular word, we are told, we can always consult

From *American English, a Twentieth-Century Grammar* by L. M. Myers. Reprinted by permission of the author, copyright 1952. Published by Prentice-Hall, Inc.

the dictionary. But what do we find in the dictionary? Other words! In one sense these other words are the meaning of the first word. But aren't we only saying that both mean the same thing? What is this other meaning? Is meaning only verbal? This whole question of the meaning of meaning is of fundamental importance in the study of language. In the following essay, L. M. Myers, Professor of English at Arizona State University, identifies three kinds of meaning.

A LANGUAGE may be defined roughly as consisting of a set of words and some habitual ways of putting them together. Dictionaries deal primarily with the individual words; grammars with characteristic forms and with ways of arranging words in coherent communications. There is inevitably some overlapping between the two.

WORD-FORM AND WORD-ORDER

In some languages the connections between words are shown largely by changes in form. Thus in Latin, "Marcus vidit Quintum" and "Marcum vidit Quintus" mean quite different things, although the same three words are used in the same order. The first means that Marcus saw Quintus; the second, that Quintus saw Marcus. The endings in *-us* and *-um* show which is the subject and which is the object of the action, regardless of the order.

In some other languages, like Chinese, words never change their form. The meaning of a group of words therefore depends on the choice of words and the order in which they are arranged.

Originally, English was very much like Latin in this respect. Most words were *inflected;* that is, they had a number of forms that showed variations in their basic meanings, and indicated their relations to each other. Now most of these inflections have been lost, and the structure of the language has become more like that of Chinese. Even the endings that remain have lost most of their power to show distinctions. Look at the following sentences:

He and I saw it yesterday.
Him and me seen it yesterday.

There are good reasons . . . for avoiding the second. But we understand it as readily as the first, and take it to mean the same thing. Our usual way of showing differences in meaning is by varying the *order* of words, as in the following sentences.

John hit Tom.
Tom hit John.

On the other hand, there are times when changes in the forms of words make a considerable difference in the meaning:

The man helps the boys.
The men helped the boy.

A study of English grammar therefore involves both the forms and the order of words.

THE PROBLEM OF MEANING

If we want to keep our feet on the ground while we are making such a study, we had better begin by trying to understand something about how words come to "mean" anything at all. If we simply take it for granted that they do and go on from there, we will never have any real understanding of the language, no matter how many grammatical rules we memorize.

Let us suppose that on an uninhabited island a freak rock-formation has resulted in the white streaks on a cliff forming the letters P A I N. This would mean absolutely nothing to the animals, the trees, or the rocks themselves. It would still mean nothing if an illiterate savage landed on the island and looked at it. But if an American landed, the letters would look to him like a familiar word, and would call up reactions connected with earlier acquaintance with that word. For the first time the letters would suggest a meaning—"pain." This meaning would occur in the man's mind. The cliffs and the letters would be no more intelligent than before.

If a Frenchman landed on the island and noticed the same letters, an entirely different meaning would be suggested, since it happens that in French the letters P A I N also form a word—but the word means "bread," and not an uncomfortable sensation.

Most of us probably have a feeling that the letters must somehow mean something all by themselves, even if there is nobody there to appreciate them; but it is hard to see how they could mean two such different things as "pain" and "bread." If we think the matter over, we are forced to agree that meaning is the product of human nervous systems, and does not reside in the letters on the cliff.

The next question that comes up is, would the letters on the cliff have a meaning of their own if they had been deliberately written to form a word? Suppose the American had written down the sentence, "I have a *pain* in my back," and had then torn up the paper so that one piece contained just the word "pain." If the Frenchman happened to pick that piece up, it would suggest to him the idea "bread." Would the word "really" mean what the American intended to convey, or what it happened to suggest to the Frenchman?

THREE KINDS OF MEANING

We could argue this point forever without getting anywhere, for the fact is that we use the words *mean* and *meaning* in a number of different ways; and if we don't keep at least three of these carefully separated in our minds, we can become badly confused.

Meaning (1) What the speaker intends to indicate.
Meaning (2) What is suggested to a particular listener.
Meaning (3) A more or less general habit of using a given word to indicate a given thing.

A good many writers on the language neglect the first two of these and treat the third far too rigidly, as if the connection between the word and the thing were absolute, instead of a never-quite-uniform habit. You have probably heard such statements as: "*Buffalo* does not mean the American bison, but an entirely different animal"; or: "*Penny* really means an English coin—the American coin is a *cent*."

This is putting the cart before the horse. We can discover meaning (3)—often referred to as the "real" meaning—only by observing the occurrences of meanings (1) and (2). To deny that these meanings are real is as unreasonable as it would be to deny the reality of a family of two or eleven on the grounds that the "average" family consists of five. It is quite true that the English used the word *penny* for one kind of a coin before we used it for another. But it is equally true that the newer meaning is very common in America; and it is *not* true (in spite of what some dictionaries say) that this meaning is merely "colloquial." Even our most formal writers might say, "He had a dime, two nickels, and three *pennies*," though they probably express the total by saying "twenty-three *cents*."

Of course we could not communicate at all without some sort of agreement that certain words are to be used to stand for certain things. Therefore meaning (3)—"a more or less general habit of using a given word to indicate a given thing"—is also perfectly legitimate. But we should not pretend that this more or less general habit is absolutely uniform, or that any number of books or teachers can ever make it so.

We can only guess how the habit started, and a number of very different guesses have been made. A linguist can trace the connection between English *father* and Latin *pater*, or between English *fish* and Latin *piscis;* but he cannot give a satisfactory reason why one of these pairs of words should be applied to male parents and the other to animals that live in the water. They would work exactly as well if their meanings were reversed. This last point is important. The "agreement" to use certain words for certain things is basically arbitrary. It is also, in the main, informal, habitual, and unenforceable.

WHY COMMUNICATION IS NEVER PERFECT

We cannot understand each other unless we approximate the habits of those with whom we communicate; but we can only approximate. Until we find two people with identical physical equipment, nervous systems, and backgrounds of past experience, we cannot expect to find even two people who use a language in exactly the same way. Schools and other forces tend to keep our language habits somewhat similar, but perfect uniformity is not even theoretically possible. This is true of both individual words and of ways of putting them together. Moreover, it is true of the ways we react to language as well as of the ways we express it.

Let us look at a single short sentence:

John hurt Mary.

Most of us would say offhand that we understand this perfectly. Yet it conveys, by itself, very little definite information, as we can see by trying to answer the following questions: Are John and

Mary people, pigs, or one of each? Are they real or imaginary? Was the hurting mental, physical, or what?

Suppose that as I wrote the sentence I was thinking of one pig biting another; that Jim Smith, as he reads it, gets the impression of one child scratching and kicking another; and that Sally Jones builds up the picture of a love affair marked by deep spiritual suffering. Each of these "meanings" is perfectly legitimate; but unless we can somehow get closer together, our communication will not be very successful. From the *words themselves* we get only the following information:

(1) *John* is presumably male and animate, and there is some probability that he is human. He may be either real or imaginary.

(2) *Mary* is presumably female. Her other possibilities are parallel to John's.

(3) *Hurt* indicates some sort of action with an unpleasant effect that has already occurred.

(4) The position of the words indicates that the direction of the action was from John to Mary.

Thus each word, by itself, *limits the possibilities* a good deal; and the relative position of the words limits them still further. The question is, can we limit them enough to communicate our ideas accurately and effectively?

We can make some progress in this direction by using additional words. Suppose I expand the sentence to read: "My little black pig, John, hurt my little white pig, Mary, by biting her in the left ear." This answers two of the questions listed above—John and Mary are pigs rather than people, and the hurting was physical. The reader may even accept the fact that the pigs are real rather than imaginary, although this cannot be proved by words alone. But other questions remain— how big is *little*, how much it hurt, and so forth. No matter how many words we use, or how carefully we arrange them, we can never directly transfer an idea from one mind to another. We can only hope to stimulate in the second mind an idea *similar* to that in the first. The words pass through our minds. The pigs, we hope, stay in their pens. And the exact nature of the connection between the words, the minds, and the pigs is not the easiest thing in the world to explain. At the very least we have to consider:

(1) The relation between the words and the minds of the people who use them.

(2) The relations between the words and the things and activities they stand for.

(3) The relations of the words to each other.[1] . . .

WORDS AND THE HUMAN NERVOUS SYSTEM

The human brain operates something like an electronic computing machine. It contains millions of short nerve-lengths comparable to wires, and millions of nerve-connections comparable to switches. The workings of this complex system are not fully understood, but we do know that electrical impulses pass through it at a very regular speed of about four hundred feet per second. It is the passage of these impulses that constitutes our thinking.

Even the simplest thought requires the passage of a current over a complicated circuit containing innumerable switches. When an impulse starts, it might follow any one of an enormous number of routes, depending on how the switches click. But once a route has been selected, there is some tendency for the switches to set, so that a second impulse starting from the same point as the first can more easily duplicate the route than pick out a new one of its own. It is by this setting of the switches that memory and habits develop. It may take a number of repetitions to have a significant effect.

A switch may be set so firmly that a possible connection is blocked out temporarily, or even permanently. For instance, most of us have had the experience of doing a complicated problem of arithmetic, in the midst of which we have made a very obvious mistake, such as multiplying two by two and getting two as the result. We have then checked it over several times without finding the error—two times two still seems to give us two. One of our switches has temporarily been jammed in the wrong position. Fortunately, not every passage of a nerve impulse jams a switch; it merely makes it easier for it to turn one way than another.

There are always a number of impulses passing through different circuits, and these affect each other. The way we think at a given time is therefore determined largely by our previous experiences—not only the things we have encountered, but the particular paths

[1] Myers' discussion of this topic is not included here, since it is dealt with in the section on structural grammar. [eds.]

that our nerve impulses have followed as a result of encountering them. No two of us started out with exactly the same wiring system, and the original differences have been increased by later activity.

The explanation just given is greatly oversimplified, but perhaps it will help us to understand something about the way we use words. Early in life we learn to associate words with people, things, events, and relations. Words as such are not permanently stored in the brain like cards in a filing cabinet. When a man hears or sees a word he receives an impulse which must pass along some circuit, determined by his previous experience with both words and things. When he hears it again, the new impulse tends to follow approximately the same circuit, unless some intervening experience modifies it. On the other hand, when some other stimulus sends an impulse along part of the same circuit, he "remembers" the word. Meanwhile it, as a word, has completely disappeared from his mind. But the affect it has had on his nervous system, by operating some of the switches, persists. Consequently, if he has associated the word with a given situation, the recurrence of some aspect of that situation, either in physical fact or in mental review, is likely to reactivate the circuit, and he is again conscious of the word.

For instance, I look into a pen and see one animal bite another, and hear the second one squeal. I would not say anything, even to myself, unless I was to some extent interested in the activity. But if I was interested enough to notice it, part of the reaction of noticing would probably be the passing of words through my mind. The particular words that passed would be determined by my previous experiences. If I had seen similar animals before, I might say "One pig bit the other," or "One pig hurt the other," depending on whether I was more impressed by the action or its effect. If they were my own animals I would probably think of them as individuals rather than simply as pigs, and might therefore say, "John hurt Mary."

Simple as this sentence is, I could not possibly have said it without having had a number of past experiences—enough to guess at the probable effect of John's teeth on Mary's ear and nervous system, and the significance of her squeal. Not being, myself, a small female pig, I must base my guess on a whole chain of assumptions; but I can be reasonably confident of its accuracy.

Certain events in the outside world have made impressions on my nervous system. I have associated words with these *impressions*, and not directly with the events themselves. If I attempt to communicate by the use of words, I must try to arouse *similar impressions in the nervous system* of the man I am talking to. Similar, not identical. His own past experiences, which cannot possibly be exactly the same as mine, are bound to affect his reactions. Even if he realizes that I am talking about my two pigs, his internal response may be quite surprising. I am expecting him to feel something like "Isn't that too bad?" but his actual sentiments may be "So what?" or even "Three cheers for John!"

We may be tempted to say: "Oh, he understands, all right. He just reacts differently." But what we call his understanding is merely a part of his total reaction, and cannot be separated, except verbally, from the rest of it. If you don't believe this, try telling a mother some time: "Oh, your boy is all right; he just broke a leg and a couple of ribs." The only thing she will understand from the word *just* is that you are an inhuman brute. As for the rest of the sentence, you have sent out a message saying "The damage to your son is temporary, so there is nothing to worry about." She has received one saying: "My darling is suffering, and there is no justice, and how do I know that one of his ribs hasn't punctured a lung?" And if you try to tell her that that is not a reasonable interpretation of your words, she will simply say (if she is still bothering to speak to you), "You have never been a mother." Her past experiences and her set of values are different from yours, especially where her son is concerned. Even if you had been more tactful in your report, your words could not possibly "mean" to her what they "mean" to you.

WORDS AND THINGS

The second relation—between words and the things they stand for—also needs some attention. We have already seen that the connection between a word and a thing is neither necessary nor direct. It is also important to realize that it is never quite the same twice, because the thing itself is always changing. If you buy a quart of milk, drink half of it, leave the rest in a warm kitchen for a couple of days, and then drink *that*, are you drinking the *same* milk?

The question cannot be answered intelligently without realizing that two quite different ideas are indicated by the word *same*. In the sense of continuity, it *is* the same milk you left there. In the sense of identity of structure, it is *not*. Important changes have taken place, and your tongue recognizes the effect of some of these changes at the first sip. Moreover, these changes have been taking place every instant that the milk has been there, and other changes have been taking place in the bottle. Such changes are not always perceptible, and we can often afford to disregard them, but they are inevitably taking place *all the time;* and the fact that we don't notice them does not prevent them from being real. It does no good to say that for "all practical purposes" a thing remains the same, unless we are quite sure that we can predict in advance what "all practical purposes" will be. If the bottle crystallizes and breaks at a tiny jar, or the milk picks up and multiplies germs that kill us, we cannot dispose of the unfortunate results by insisting that the "same" things were perfectly all right a while ago.

To go one step further into the matter, we may bring up the question of whether anything is the same, even at a given instant, to two different observers. Again the answer seems to be no. Since our senses, nervous systems, and backgrounds of past experience vary, no two people can get identical impressions of the "same" thing. The actual thing (unless it is something like a bullet or an axe) does not get into our heads. What does get in—what we are conscious of and what we talk about—is merely the impression made on our nervous system. Therefore when two people look at a Pekingese dog, and she says, "Oh, the cute little darling!" while he says "What a disgusting little slug," they are not applying different words to the *same* thing. Each of them is describing, not the physical dog, but the impression created in his own mind by a combination of his present sense-perceptions and his past experiences. Even if they agree verbally that it is a Pekingese, the meeting of their minds is not complete; because the word Pekingese still "means" something different to each of them.

It follows that "using the same words for the same things" is not even theoretically possible, because there simply aren't any "same things." The best we can hope for is a reasonable approximation. Our remote ancestors, when they developed the language, did not know this. A few of them had imaginative glimpses of the truth, but on the whole they believed very firmly that many things were identical, permanent, and alike to all observers; and the structure of the language, like the structure of their physical theories, reflected this belief. Until the development of modern physics and neurology there was no definite proof that they were wrong.

A good many men, for a good many centuries, have been trying to devise and encourage the use of a language suitable for perfect communication—a language in which every word has a fixed meaning, which any properly trained person can recognize; and in which the arrangement of words is completely systematic and "logical."[2] We can now see that such a language would be possible only if words operated in a vacuum, or at least in a perfectly uniform medium, of which each human skull somehow contained a part. We must therefore lower our sights.

Of course an approximate agreement as to the significance of words and word-arrangements is possible, or we could not communicate at all; and among people of similar backgrounds and training, communication over a limited range of subjects may reach a high degree of reliability. Dictionaries and grammars, if they are well made and sensibly used, may increase the uniformity of our language habits and thus improve the quality of our communication. But they may do us more harm than good if we let them blind us to the fact that language is not, and never can be, an independent, objective structure governed by its own laws. At its theoretical best, language can only stimulate similar (never identical) reactions in necessarily different nervous systems. Aside from its effect on these nervous systems, it has no importance at all.

The man who goes through life complaining that his friends (*a*) don't say what they mean, and (*b*) don't understand him when he speaks plain English, deserves pity rather than blame. He suffers from a delusion that makes it hard for him to look through the words and find out what the man behind them means; and equally hard for him to select and arrange his own words with some attention to the response that they probably will arouse, rather than the one they "should" arouse. If his delusion makes him haughty and ill-tempered, it is probably because of continual frustration rather than natural viciousness.

[2] A large number of artificial languages for international use have been invented, fifty-three between 1880 and 1907. Volapük and Esperanto are the two most notable. Recently the International Auxiliary Association of New York proposed a new one, Interlingua, made up of components common to the languages most widely used today. [eds.]

SUGGESTED ASSIGNMENTS

1. According to Myers, the same word means different things to different people, depending on their experience. To a metallurgist, *gold* means a heavy, yellowish, metallic chemical element (Au), with a high degree of ductility and malleability, and an atomic weight of 197.2. What differences in meaning would you assume the term *gold* to have for a jeweler, a guard at Fort Knox, the Secretary of the U.S. Treasury, a woman who has just received some in the form of a wedding ring, a worker in a gold mine, and an Eskimo untouched by civilization?
2. $E=mc^2$ was rather meaningless to most people until a few years ago. What does it mean to an atomic physicist? To you? To a Bantu warrior? To a victim of Hiroshima? To what do you attribute these differences in meaning?
3. Both *dog* and *cur* refer to the same quadruped known to zoologists as *Canis familiaris*. Do they mean the same thing? If not, explain the difference. Similarly, explain the differences between the words in each of the following pairs: *horse, nag; stingy, thrifty; cocky, confident.*
4. Compare the different meanings of the word *dog* in each of the following contexts:

   a. A dog is man's best friend.
   b. He leads a dog's life.
   c. You are a dirty dog!
   d. He is always putting on the dog.
   e. Let sleeping dogs lie.

5. Construct five sentences in which you use the same word in five different contexts.
6. Write a brief theme in which you describe a personal experience of a misunderstanding caused by the speaker and the listener understanding a word in different senses.
7. A Greek philosopher once said, "You cannot walk through the same river twice." Write a theme interpreting this saying in relation to words.

THE USES OF LANGUAGE

Irving M. Copi

Language is often referred to as a tool. The implication is that, like a hammer, drill, or saw, it can be used to perform certain jobs. Most tools, however, have a single function; each job requires a special tool. We use a hammer to drive nails, a drill to bore holes, and a saw to cut wood. If language is a tool, it is the most remarkable invention we have; it will beat any combination knife, can opener, screwdriver, bottlecap remover, or other gadget on the market. What jobs does language perform? To reply "speech and writing" misses the point; it merely says that language has two ways of doing its various jobs. To reply "poetry and prose" comes closer, but it is still an oversimplification. If we classify all that is not poetry as prose, does that mean that the language of prose has a single function? Think of the language of science, newspaper reporting, advertising, political oratory, the language of the church—prayers and the litany. Depending on the job at hand, we use language differently, and we respond differently to the various uses of language. What these uses are and how they differ one from another are discussed by Irving M. Copi in his essay. Copi, a logician, is Professor of Philosophy at the University of Michigan.

I. THREE BASIC FUNCTIONS OF LANGUAGE

LANGUAGE IS so subtle and complicated an instrument that the multiplicity of its uses is often lost sight of. Here, as in many other situations, there is danger in our tendency to oversimplify things.

A not uncommon complaint of those who take too narrow a view of the legitimate uses of language concerns the way in which words are "wasted" at social functions. "So much talk, and so little said!" sums up this kind of criticism. And more than one person has been heard to remark, "So and so asked me how I felt. What a hypocrite! He doesn't care in the least how I feel!" Such remarks reveal a failure to understand the complex purposes for which language is used. It is shown also in the deplorable conduct of the bore, who, when asked how he feels, actually proceeds to tell about the state of his health—usually at great length and in much detail. But people do not usually talk at parties to instruct each other. And ordinarily the question "How are you?" is a friendly greeting, not a request for a medical report.

One very important use of language is to communicate information. Ordinarily this is accomplished by formulating and affirming (or denying) propositions. Language used to affirm or deny propositions, or to present arguments, is said to be serving the *informative function.* In this context we use the word "information" to include misinformation: false as well as true propositions, incorrect as well as correct arguments. Informative discourse is used to *describe* the world, and to reason about it. Whether the alleged facts that are being described are important or unimportant, general or particular, does not matter; in any case the language used to describe or report them is being used informatively.

We may distinguish two basic uses or functions of language in addition to the informative, and refer to them as the *expressive* and the *directive.* Just as science provides us with the clearest examples of informative discourse, so poetry furnishes us the best examples of language serving an *expressive* function. The following lines of Burns:

> O my Luve's like a red, red rose
> That's newly sprung in June:
> O my Luve's like the melodie
> That's sweetly play'd in tune!

are definitely not intended to inform us of any facts or theories concerning the world. The poet's purpose is to communicate not knowledge but feelings and attitudes. The passage was not written to report any information but to *express* certain emotions that the poet felt very keenly and to evoke feelings of a similar kind in the reader. Language serves the *expressive* function whenever it is used to vent or communicate feelings or emotions.

Not all expressive language is poetry, however. We express sorrow by saying "That's too bad," or "Oh my," and enthusiasm by shouting "Wow!" or "Oh boy!" The lover expresses his delicate passion by murmuring "Darling!" or "Oh baby!" The poet expresses his complex and concentrated emotions in a sonnet or some other verse form. A worshipper may express his feeling of wonder and awe at the vastness and mystery of the universe by reciting the Lord's Prayer or the twenty-third Psalm of David. All these are uses of language not to communicate information but to express emotions, feelings, or attitudes. Expressive discourse *as expressive* is neither true nor false. For a person to apply only the criteria of truth or falsehood, correctness or incorrectness, to expressive discourse like a poem is to miss its point and to lose much of its value. The student whose enjoyment of Keats' sonnet *On first looking into Chapman's Homer* is marred by his historical knowledge that Balboa rather than Cortez discovered the Pacific Ocean is a "poor reader" of poetry. The purpose of the poem is not to teach history, but something else entirely. This is not to say that poetry can have no literal significance. Some poems *do* have an informative content which may be an important ingredient in their total effect. Some poetry may well be "criticism of life," in the words of a great poet. But such poems are more than merely expressive, as we are using the term here. Such poetry may be said to have a "mixed usage," or to serve a multiple function. This notion will be explained further in the following section.

Expression may be analyzed into two components. When a man curses to himself when he is alone, or a poet writes poems which he shows to no one, or a man prays in solitude, his language functions to express or evince his own attitude but does not serve to evoke a similar attitude in anyone else. On the other hand, when an orator seeks to inspire his audience—not to action, but to share enthusiasm; when a lover courts his beloved in poetic language; when the crowd cheers its athletic team; the language used not only evinces the attitudes of the speakers but also is intended to evoke the same attitudes in the hearers. Expressive discourse, then, is used either to *evince* the speaker's feelings or to *evoke* certain feelings on the part of the auditor. Of course it may do both.

Language serves the *directive* function when it is used for the purpose of causing (or preventing) overt action. The clearest examples of directive discourse are commands and requests. When a mother tells her little boy to wash his hands before supper, she does not intend to communicate any information to him or to evince or evoke any particular emotion. Her language is intended to get results, to cause action of the indicated kind. When the same mother asks the grocer to deliver certain goods to her house, she is again using language directively, to motivate or effect *action.* To ask a question is ordinarily to request an answer, and is also to be classified as directive discourse. The difference between a command and a request is a rather subtle one, for almost any command can be translated into a request by adding the word "please," or by suitable changes in tone of voice or in facial expression.

In its nakedly imperative form, directive discourse is neither true nor false. A command such as "Close the window" cannot be either true or false in any literal sense. Whether the command is obeyed or disobeyed does not affect or determine its truth-value, for it has none. We may disagree about whether a command has been obeyed or not; we may disagree about whether a command should be obeyed or not; but we never disagree about whether a command is true or false, for it cannot be either. However, the reasonableness or propriety, the unreasonableness or impropriety of commands are properties somewhat analogous to the truth or falsehood of informative discourse. And questions of the propriety of given commands can be raised and resolved in ways that are strictly within the scope of logic.

II. DISCOURSE SERVING MULTIPLE FUNCTIONS

In the preceding section the examples presented were chemically pure specimens, so to speak, of the three basic kinds of communication. The threefold division proposed is illuminating and valuable, but it cannot be applied mechanically, because almost any ordinary communication will probably exemplify, to a greater or less extent, all three uses of language. Thus a poem, which is primarily expressive discourse, may have a moral and be in effect a command to the reader (or hearer) to lead a certain kind of life, and may also convey a certain amount of information. On the other hand, although a sermon is predominantly directive, seeking to cause certain appropriate action by members of the congregation (whether to abandon their evil ways, or to contribute money to the church, or what not), it may evince and evoke sentiments, thus serving the expressive function, and may also include some information, communicating some factual material. And a scientific treatise, essentially informative, may evince something of the writer's own enthusiasm, thus serving an expressive function, and may also, at least implicitly, serve some directive function or other, perhaps bidding the reader to verify independently the author's conclusion. Most ordinary uses of language are mixed.

It is not always the result of any confusion on the part of the speaker when his language serves mixed or multiple functions. It is rather the case that *effective* communication demands certain combinations of function. Few of us stand to each other in the relation of parent to child or employer to employee. And outside the context of such formal relationships as these, one cannot simply issue an order with any expectation of having it obeyed. Consequently a certain indirection must be employed: a bald command would arouse antagonism or resentment and be self-defeating. One cannot cause action by merely voicing an imperative; it is necessary to use a more subtle method of stimulating the desired action.

Action may be said to have very complex causes. Motivation is more properly to be discussed by a psychologist than a logician, but it is common knowledge that actions are usually caused by both desires and beliefs. A man who *desires* to eat food will not touch what is on his plate unless he *believes* it to be food; and even though he *believes* it to be food he will not touch it unless he *desires* to eat. This fact is relevant to our present discussion because desires are a special type of what we have been calling "attitudes."

Consequently actions may be caused by evoking appropriate attitudes *and* communicating relevant information. Assuming your listeners to be benevolent, you may cause them to contribute to a given charity by informing them of its effectiveness in accomplishing benevolent results. In such a case your use of language is ultimately directive, since its purpose is to cause action. But a naked command would be far less effective in this situation than the informative discourse used. Suppose, on the other hand, that your listeners are already persuaded that the charity in question does accomplish benevolent results. Here again you cannot simply command with any great hope of being obeyed, but you may succeed in causing them to act in the desired fashion by somehow arousing a sufficiently benevolent feeling or emotion in them. The discourse you use to realize your end is expressive discourse; you must make a "moving appeal." Thus your language will have a mixed use, functioning both expressively and directively. Or finally, let us suppose that you are seeking a donation from people who have *neither* a benevolent attitude *nor* a belief that the charity serves a benevolent purpose. Here you must use *both* informative and expressive language. In such a case the language used serves all three functions, being directive, informative, and expressive all at once, not accidentally as a mere mixture that just happens to occur, but essentially, as necessary to successful communication.

Some writers on language have suggested that discourse serves more than these three distinct functions. It is possible, however, to understand any other function as a mixture or combination of two or possibly all three of the basic uses that have been distinguished here. The most important of these others has frequently been called the "ceremonial" use of language. Included within this category are many different kinds of phrases, ranging from relatively trivial words of greeting to the more portentous discourse of the marriage ceremony, phrasings of state documents, and the verbal rituals performed on holy days in houses of worship. But these can all be regarded as mixtures of expressive and directive discourse, rather than some altogether different and unique kind. For example, the usual ceremonial greetings and chit-chat at social gatherings serve the purpose of evincing and evoking goodwill and sociability. Perhaps for some speakers they are intended also to serve the directive purpose of causing their hearers to act in certain definite ways, to patronize the speaker's business, to offer him employment, or to invite him to dinner. At the other extreme, the impressive language of the marriage ceremony is intended to emphasize the solemnity of the occasion (its expressive function), and also to cause the bride and groom to perform in their new roles with heightened appreciation of the seriousness of the marriage contract (its directive function).

SUGGESTED ASSIGNMENTS

1. Classify the following selections in terms of function, i.e., informative, expressive, directive. Substantiate your judgments. Remember that language may serve multiple functions.

a. In the beginning God created the heaven and the earth.
And the earth was without form, and void; and darkness was upon the face of the deep. And the Spirit of God moved upon the face of the waters.
And God said, Let there be light: and there was light.
And God saw the light, that it was good: and God divided the light from the darkness.
And God called the light Day, and the darkness he called Night. And the evening and the morning were the first day.
And God said, Let there be a firmament in the midst of the waters, and let it divide the waters from the waters.

(Genesis 1:1-6)

b. Save me, O God; for the waters are come in unto my soul.
I sink in deep mire, where there is no standing: I am come into deep waters, where the floods overflow me.
I am weary of my crying: my throat is dried: mine eyes fail while I wait for my God.
They that hate me without a cause are more than the hairs of mine head: they that would destroy me, being mine enemies wrongfully, are mighty: then I restored that which I took not away.

(Psalm 69:1-4)

c. A Birthday

My heart is like a singing bird
Whose nest is in a watered shoot:
My heart is like an apple-tree
Whose boughs are bent with thickset fruit;
My heart is like a rainbow shell
That paddles in a halcyon sea;
My heart is gladder than all these
Because my love is come to me.

Raise me a dais of silk and down;
Hang it with vair and purple dyes;
Carve it in doves and pomegranates,
And peacocks with a hundred eyes;
Work it in gold and silver grapes,
In leaves and silver fleurs-de-lys;
Because the birthday of my life
Is come, my love is come to me.

(Christina Rossetti)

d. Sea King Sailing Surf Board. Wonderful for summer sailing—you don't have to be an expert. Easy to handle aluminum boom. Non-sinkable balsa wood flotation. Special non-skid deck for safety; removable centerboard, kick-up rudder for shallow water. 14-ft. Fiberglass covered hull. With

3-ft. beam. Maximum 10 in. deep 14-ft. gunwale length; transom 18 in. wide by 4 in. deep.

(A mail-order catalog)

e. Every Price Cut $1. Famous Pinehurst at Low Prices. It's like walking on air. Heel-to-toe foam rubber shock absorbing cushion for greater foot ease. Fashioned of extra fine leathers. Finest Goodyear welt construction. Supertex lining resists athlete's foot. $11.99.

(A mail-order catalog)

f. I dug my cellar in the side of a hill sloping to the south, where a woodchuck had formerly dug his burrow, down through sumach and blackberry roots, and the lowest stain of vegetation, six feet square by seven deep, to a fine sand where potatoes would not freeze in any winter. The sides were left shelving, and not stoned; but the sun having never shone on them, the sand still keeps its place. It was but two hours' work. I took particular pleasure in this breaking of ground, for in almost all latitudes men dig into the earth for an equable temperature. Under the most splendid house in the city is still to be found the cellar where they store their roots as of old, and long after the superstructure has disappeared posterity remark its dent in the earth. The house is still but a sort of porch at the entrance of a burrow.

(Thoreau's *Walden*)

g. None of them knew the color of the sky. Their eyes glanced level, and were fastened upon the waves that swept toward them. These waves were of the hue of slate, save for the tops, which were of foaming white, and all of the men knew the colors of the sea. The horizon narrowed and widened, and dipped and rose, and at all times its edge was jagged with waves that seemed thrust up in points like rocks. Many a man ought to have a bath-tub larger than the boat which here rode upon the sea. These waves were most wrongfully and barbarously abrupt and tall, and each froth-top was a problem in small-boat navigation.

(Stephen Crane's "The Open Boat")

h. These are the times that try men's souls. The summer soldier and the sunshine patriot will, in this crisis, shrink from the service of their country; but he that stands it *now*, deserves the love and thanks of man and woman. Tyranny, like hell, is not easily conquered; yet we have this consolation with us, that the harder the conflict, the more glorious the triumph. What we obtain too cheap, we esteem too lightly; it is dearness only that gives every thing its value. Heaven knows how to put a proper price upon its goods; and it would be strange indeed if so celestial an article as FREEDOM should not be highly rated.

(Thomas Paine's "The Crisis")

2. Choose two of the above passages which differ in function and write a paper explaining in some detail exactly how they differ.
3. Assume that you are the representative of a business firm that has sent

you to investigate Community X as a possibility for future expansion of the business—a branch office, a new factory, or something of the sort. Write a theme in the form of a report to the company, making either a positive or negative recommendation. Your intent is to be informative. As a contrastive exercise, assume that you are the Secretary of the Chamber of Commerce of Community X. Write a theme in the form of a letter to the same company. Your purpose is to induce the company to establish its business in Community X. Make an analysis of how the two themes differ in their use of language.

4. Assume that you are Chairman of the Board of Student Governors at your college. You are disturbed at the apathy of some student organizations for failing to send representatives to the monthly meeting of the Board. Write a letter, directive in intent, to the presidents of the sluggard organizations, announcing the next meeting. You want their representatives to attend the meeting. Keep in mind as you write that you want to gain their support, not to lose it completely.

THE GIFT OF TONGUES

Clyde Kluckhohn

It is often assumed that what can be expressed in one language can be expressed in another; all one has to do is to substitute the words of one language for equivalents in the other. The matter is not so simple. What if there are no equivalents? Cultures differ not only in dress and behavior, in political, economic, and social institutions, but also in language, which is a form of social behavior. Each language is a product of a particular culture, and it reflects the culture of the people and their view of the world. This Weltanschauung *is built into the very structure of a language. Whether language determines the way a person thinks is a moot question, but it is believed*

With permission of the publishers from *Mirror for Man* by Clyde Kluckhohn. Copyright, 1949, by the McGraw-Hill Book Co., Inc.

by many that it does affect his perception of the world about him. It is not, as Harry Hoijer has pointed out, "that linguistic patterns limit sensory patterns but that they direct perception and thinking into certain habitual channels." The fascinating topic of the relationship between language and culture is discussed by the late Clyde Kluckhohn, eminent Professor of Anthropology at Harvard.

Our misapprehension of the nature of language has occasioned a greater waste of time, and effort, and genius, than all the other mistakes and delusions with which humanity has been afflicted. It has retarded immeasurably our physical knowledge of every kind, and vitiated what it could not retard.

—A. B. Johnson,
Treatise on Language[1]

IT'S A PITY that so few of us have lived down our childhood struggles with grammar. We have been made to suffer so much from memorizing rules by rote and from approaching language in a mechanical, unimaginative way that we tend to think of grammar as the most inhuman of studies. Probably Americans, who dramatize themselves and their independence, have a kind of unconscious resentment against all patterns that are so set as to constitute a gratuitous insult to the principle of free will. For whatever reasons, Americans have been characteristically inept at foreign languages. Like the British, we have expected everybody else to learn English.

Yet nothing is more human than the speech of an individual or of a folk. Human speech, unlike the cry of an animal, does not occur as a mere element in a larger response. Only the human animal can communicate abstract ideas and converse about conditions that are contrary to fact. Indeed the purely conventional element in speech is so large that language can be regarded as pure culture. A Burmese weaver, moved to Mexico, would know at once what a fellow craftsman in Mexico was doing, but would not understand one word of the Nahuatl tongue. No clues are so helpful as those of language in pointing to ultimate, unconscious psychological attitudes. More-

[1] Alexander Bryan Johnson, *A Treatise on Language*, edited by David Rynin, The University of California Press, 1947.

over, much of the friction between groups and between nations arises because in both the literal and the slangy senses they don't speak the same language.

We live in an environment which is largely verbal in the sense that we spend the most of our waking hours uttering words or responding actively or passively to the words of others. We talk to ourselves. We talk to our families and friends—partly to communicate to them and to persuade them, partly just to express ourselves. We read newspapers, magazines, books, and other written matter. We listen to the radio, to sermons, lectures, and movies. As Edward Sapir says:

> Language completely interpenetrates direct experience. For most persons every experience, real or potential, is saturated with verbalism. This perhaps explains why so many nature lovers do not feel that they are truly in touch with nature until they have mastered the names of a great many flowers and trees, as though the primary world of reality were a verbal one, and as though one could not get close to nature unless one first mastered the terminology that somehow magically expresses it. It is this constant interplay between language and experience which removes language from the cold status of such purely and simply symbolic systems as mathematical symbolism or flag signalling.[2]

The dictionaries still say that "language is a device for communicating ideas." The semanticists and the anthropologists agree that this is a tiny, specialized function of speech. Mainly, language is an instrument for action. The meaning of a word or phrase is not its dictionary equivalent but the difference its utterance brings about in a situation. We use words to comfort and cajole ourselves in fantasy and daydream, to let off steam, to goad ourselves into one type of activity and to deny ourselves another. We use words to promote our own purposes in dealing with others. We build up verbal pictures of ourselves and our motives. We coax, wheedle, protest, invite, and threaten. Even the most intellectual of intellectuals employs only a minute fraction of his total utterance in symbolizing and communicating ideas that are divorced from emotion and action. The primary social value of speech lies in getting individuals to work more effectively together and in easing social

[2] From "Language," by Edward Sapir, *Encyclopedia of the Social Sciences*, Vol. ix. Copyright 1933 by The Macmillan Company and used with their permission.

tensions. Very often what is said matters much less than that something is said.

To the manipulation of this verbal environment, the anthropological linguist has made some immediately practical contributions. Forced by the absence of written materials and by other circumstances attendant upon work with primitives, he has become an expert on "the direct method." He knows how to learn a language by using it. Though sensitive to the broader implications of the subtler, rarer forms of a language, he is skilled in the socially practical. He knows how to dodge the subjunctive when the immediate objective is to get a conversation going. The training of the conventional teacher of languages tempts him to his besetting sin of preoccupation with the niceties. He loves complicated rules and even more the exceptions to those rules. This is one of the principal reasons that after eight years of instruction in French an American can read a French novel with pleasure but is terrified to ask street directions in Paris. The anthropologist can't look up the rules in the book. He is hardened to making small and large mistakes. His tradition is to break through, to concentrate on the essential, to get on with the talk at all costs.

Since many odd languages were of military significance during World War II, the anthropological linguist had a chance to introduce his method of working directly with the native informant. He prepared educational materials that highlighted anthropological short cuts in learning how to speak languages. The results have influenced the traditional methods of language instruction in the United States. The anthropological linguist has also worked out ways of teaching adults who have no written language and ways of teaching illiterates to write and read their own tongue.

Because anthropological linguists have usually been trained as ethnologists and have often done general field work, they have tended less than other students of language to isolate speech from the total life of the people. To the anthropologist, language is just one kind of cultural behavior with many interesting connections to other aspects of action and thought. Analysis of a vocabulary shows the principal emphases of a culture and reflects culture history. In Arabic, for example, there are more than six thousand different words for camel, its parts, and equipment. The crudity and the special local words of the vocabulary of Spanish-speaking villages in New Mexico reflect the long isolation of these groups from the main stream of Latin culture. The particular archaisms used show that the break with the main continuity of the Spanish language occurred during the eighteenth century. The fact that the Boorabbee Indians of Panama use words like *gadsoot* (gadzooks), *forsoo'* (forsooth), *chee-ah* (cheer), and *mai-api* (mayhap) suggests a possible connection with Elizabethan buccaneers.

A great deal is now known about the history of languages, especially those languages that have been the great carriers of culture: Greek, Latin, Sanskrit, Arabic, Chinese, and English. Certain regularities have been discovered. In contrast to the general course of cultural evolution, languages move from the complex to the simple. Chinese and English have today lost almost all inflections. The uniformities of phonetic change are most encouraging to those who believe that there is a discoverable order in human events. As Bloomfield has said:

> These correspondences are a matter of historical detail, but their significance was overwhelming, since they showed that human action, in the mass, is not altogether haphazard, but may proceed with regularity even in so unimportant a matter as the manner of pronouncing the individual sounds within the flow of speech.[3]

The phonetic side of language beautifully illustrates both the selective nature of culture and the omnipresence of patterning. The sound of the p in pin is uttered with a slight puff of breath that is lacking when we sound the p in spin. Yet the speakers of English have entered into an unconscious agreement to treat them as the same signals, though they are not acoustically identical. It is like the motorist trained to stop at a light that is any shade of red. If I am investigating an unknown language and discover two sounds that are somewhat similar to those represented by English "b" and "d" but differ in being softly whispered, I can immediately predict that sounds in the new language of "g" type will conform to the same pattern.

Language is as consistently nonrational as any aspect of culture. We cling stubbornly to functionless capital letters. One may also instance our absurd English spelling. "Ghiti" ought to spell fish—gh as in laugh, ti as in ambition. In hiccough, gh has a p sound. "Ghoughteighteau" could be read as potato—figure it out yourself.

[3] Leonard Bloomfield, *Language*, Holt, Rinehart and Winston, Inc., 1933.

We say "five houses" when "five house" would be simpler and convey the meaning equally well.

Small pecularities of linguistic usage are very revealing. It is no accident that French Catholics address the deity with the familiar form of the personal pronoun (*tu*) and Protestants with the formal (*vous*). In all sectors of French society save the old aristocracy spouses use *tu* to each other. But in the *Faubourg St. Germain* the duke calls his duchess *vous*—it being well understood between them that he reserves *tu* for his mistress.

A whole monograph could well be written on differences in the social structure of European nations as exposed by linguistic habits relating to the second personal pronoun. In France one comes to *tutoyer* few people after adolesence. This familiarity is restricted to immediate relatives and to a few intimate friends of childhood. In the German-speaking world, however, a student who did not soon come to use the familiar *Du* with those whom he saw frequently would be regarded as stuffy. In the army of imperial Austria all officers in the same regiment called each other *Du* regardless of rank. Failure to use the familiar form was equivalent to a challenge to the duel. In Austria and in other European countries the initiation of the familiar usage between adults is formalized in a ceremony. There is an embrace and a drink from each other's glasses. In Spain and Italy the introduction of the *tu* relationship in later life is considerably easier than in France but less frequent than in southern Germany and Austria. In Italy there is the further complication of a special form of respectful address (*Lei*). Choice of *Lei* or the more common formal pronoun became a political issue. The Fascist Party forbade the use of *Lei*. In Sweden also, passions have been aroused over the pronoun *ni* which is used toward those of lower social status—and, in accord with the familiar principle of inverted snobbery,[4] toward royal personages. Clubs were formed to abolish this word. Individuals wore buttons saying, "I don't use *ni* and I hope you don't either." Persons were brought into court for using *ni* toward people who considered themselves the equals or superiors of those who derogated them by using *ni* in address. "You are *ni* to me; I am not *ni* to you."

[4] Another illustration of the "principle of inverted snobbery": In an American college that is small or struggling for prestige, faculty members who are members of Phi Beta Kappa would as soon appear on the campus without their pants as without their keys. In old, well-established universities, ΦBK keys are worn only by a few older professors.

These are also instances of the intensely emotional symbolism of language. During the course of the development of nationalism and the romantic movement, every tongue was seized upon as the tangible manifestation of each culture's uniqueness. In the earlier part of the nineteenth century Magyar nobles spoke Latin in the Hungarian Parliament because they could not speak Magyar and would not speak German. Magyar, Irish, Lithuanian, and other tongues have been revived within the last hundred years from the category of practically dead languages. This tendency is about as old as written history. In the Bible we learn that the Gileadites slew everyone at the passages of Jordan who said *sibboleth* instead of *shibboleth*.

Groups within a culture emphasize their unity by a special language. Criminals have their own argot. So, indeed, do all the professions. One school in England (Winchester) has a language, compounded of medieval Latin and the accretions of the slang of many generations, that is utterly unintelligible to the uninitiated. "The linguistic community" is no meaningless phrase. The use of speech forms in common implies other things in common. The hunting or "county" set in England affects the dropping of final g's as a badge of their being set apart. Understatement is the mark of unshakable psychological security. If a member of the English upper classes is a member of the Davis Cup team he says "Yes, I play a little tennis." Individuals of many countries pronounce words in certain ways in order to associate themselves with particular social classes. The extent to which an elderly or middle-aged Englishman is still identifiable as Harrow or Rugby—and not as a Yorkshireman nor even as an Oxonian nor as an army man—proves the identification of distinctive language with social status. You can pretty well place an Englishman by his tie and his accent. Idiomatic turns of speech identify to society at large the special positions and roles of its various members. Cliques and classes unconsciously use this device to prevent absorption into the larger group. "He talks like one of us" is a declaration of acceptance. Euphemisms, special terms of endearment, and slang are class labels.

The essential aroma of each culture or subculture may be caught as a fragrance of language. In the Berlin of 1930, when one met an acquaintance on the street one bowed and stiffly said, "Good day." In Vienna one called out, "I have the honor," to a superior; "May God greet thee (you)," to an intimate; or "Your servant," to a fellow student or fellow aristocrat. That *gewisse Liebenswürdigkeit* (a certain graciousness) which was the hallmark of Viennese culture came out most clearly and immediately in certain phrases that were not unknown in northern and Protestant Germany but were much less frequent in the stuff of daily conversation: "Live well," "the lady mother," "I kiss the hand, noble lady," and many others. In Austria when the delivery boy brought the groceries to the kitchen he said, "May God greet thee," if the maid received them; "Kiss the hand, noble lady," if the mistress were there.

Although one could press this point of view too far, there is *something* significant in the lists of words from each European language that have become widely current in other languages. From English: gentleman, fair play, week end, sport. From French: *liaison, maitresse, cuisine.* From Italian: *diva, bravo, bel canto.* From German: *Weltschmerz, Sehnsucht, Weltanschauung, Gemutlichkeit.* In *Englishmen, Frenchmen, and Spaniards,* de Madariaga has suggested that the words, fair play, *le droit,* and *el honor* are the keys to the respective cultures. Here is a sample of his discussion of English:

> There is deep satisfaction in the thought that English—the language of the man of action—is a monosyllabic language. For the man of action, as we know, lives in the present, and the present is an instant with room for no more than one syllable. Words of more than one syllable are sometimes called in English "dictionary" words, *i.e.*, words for the intellectual, for the bookworm, for the crank, almost for the un-English. They are marvellous, those English monosyllables, particularly, of course, those which represent acts. Their fidelity to the act which they represent is so perfect that one is tempted to think English words are the right and proper names which those acts are meant to have, and all other words but pitiable failures. How could one improve on splash, smash, ooze, shriek, slush, glide, speak, coo? Who could find anything better than hum or buzz or howl or whir? Who could think of anything more sloppy than slop? Is not the word sweet a kiss in itself and what could suggest a more peremptory obstacle than stop?[5]

Certainly the recurrent turns of phrase, the bromides, of each culture and of different time periods in the same culture are illuminating. They embody in capsule form the central strains and stresses of the society, major cultural interests, the characteristic

[5] S. de Madariaga, *Englishmen, Frenchmen, and Spaniards,* Oxford University Press, 1929.

definitions of the situation, the prime motivations. You can't swear effectively in British to an American audience and vice versa. The Navaho greeting is "All is well"; the Japanese, "There is respectful earliness"; the American, "How do you do?" "How are you getting on?" Each epoch has its stock phrases. As Carl Becker has written:

> If we would discover the little backstairs door that for any age serves as the secret entranceway to knowledge, we will do well to look for certain unobtrusive words with uncertain meanings that are permitted to slip off the tongue or pen without fear and without research; words which, having from constant repetition lost their metaphorical significance, are unconsciously mistaken for objective realities. . . . In each age these magic words have their entrances and their exits.[6]

In a way there is nothing very new about semantics. The Roman grammarian, Varro, pointed out in a learned treatise that he had discovered 228 distinct meanings for the word "good." His basic point was the same as Aldous Huxley's: "There ought to be some way of dry-cleaning and disinfecting words. Love, purity, goodness, spirit—a pile of dirty linen waiting for the laundress." We are always bringing together by words things that are different and separating verbally things that are, in fact, the same. A Christian Scientist refused to take vitamin tablets on the ground that they were "medicine"; he willingly accepted them when it was explained that they were "food." An insurance company discovered that behavior toward "gasoline drums" was ordinarily circumspect, that toward "empty gasoline drums" habitually careless. Actually, the "empty" drums are the more dangerous because they contain explosive vapor.

The semantic problem is almost insoluble because, as John Locke said, "So difficult is it to show the various meaning and imperfections of words when we have nothing else but words to do it by." This is one of the reasons that a cross-cultural approach is imperative. Anyone who has struggled with translation is made to realize that there is more to a language than its dictionary. The Italian proverb "*traduttore, tradittore*" (the translator is a betrayer) is all too correct. I asked a Japanese with a fair knowledge of English to translate back from the Japanese that phrase in the new Japanese constitution that represents our "life, liberty, and the pursuit of

[6] Carl Becker, *Heavenly City of the Eighteenth Century Philosophers*, Yale University Press, 1935.

happiness." He rendered, "license to commit lustful pleasure." English to Russian and Russian back to English transmuted a cablegram "Genevieve suspended for prank" into "Genevieve hanged for juvenile delinquency."

These are obvious crudities. But look at translations into half-a-dozen languages of the same passage in the Old Testament. The sheer difference in length will show that translation is not just a matter of finding a word in the second language that exactly matches a word in the original. Renderings of poetry are especially misleading. The best metrical translation of Homer is probably the fragment done by Hawtrey. The final two lines of the famous "Helen on the wall" passage of the third book in the *Iliad* goes as follows:

> So said she; but they long since in earth's soft arms were reposing
> There in their own dear land, their fatherland, Lacedaemon.

Hawtrey has caught the musical effect of Greek hexameter about as well as it is possible to do in English. But the Greek says literally, "but them, on the other hand, the life-giving earth held fast." The original is realistic—Helen's brothers were dead and that was that. The English is sentimental.

Once in Paris I saw a play called "The Weak Sex." I found it charmingly risqué. A year later in Vienna I took a girl to see a German translation of the same play. Though she was no prude, I was embarrassed because the play was vulgar if not obscene in German.

I think I got my first genuine insight into the nature of language when my tutor at Oxford asked me to translate into Greek a few pages from an eighteenth-century British rhetorician which contained the following phrase, "she heaped the utmost virulence of her invective upon him." I struggled with this and finally committed the unforgivable sin of looking up each word in an English-Greek dictionary. My tutor glanced at the resultant monstrosity and looked up at me with mingled disgust, pity, and amazement. "My dear boy," he said, "don't you know that the only possible way you can render that is *deinos aedeitai*, she blamed very strongly?"

Really, there are three kinds of translation. There is the literal or word-for-word variety which is always distorted except perhaps between languages that are very similar in structure and vocabulary. Second, there is the official type where certain conventions as to idiomatic equivalents are respected. The third, or psychological type of translation, where the words produce approximately the same effects in the speakers of the second language as they did in those of the original, is next to impossible. At best, the rendering must be extremely free, with elaborate circumlocutions and explanations. I once heard Einstein make a slip of the tongue that stated the deeper truth. He said, "I shall speak in English this evening, but if I get excited during the discussion I shall break into German and Professor Lindeman will traduce me."

If words referred only to things, translation would be relatively simple. But they refer also to relations between things and the subjective as well as the objective aspects of these relationships. In different tongues relationships are variously conceived. The Balinese word *tis* means not to be cold when it is cold. The Balinese word *paling* designates the state of a trance or drunkenness or a condition of not knowing where you are, what day it is, where the center of the island is, the caste of the person to whom you are talking. The subjective aspects arise from the fact that we use words not only to express things and relationships but to express ourselves; words refer not only to events but to the attitudes of the speakers toward those events.

The words prostitute and whore have exactly the same denotation. The connotation, however, is very different. And a word's connotation is at least as important as the denotation in rousing feeling and producing action. Examine carefully the richest field of modern verbal magic—advertisements.

The same words often don't mean the same thing to different generations within the same culture. Margaret Mead writes:

Take the word *job*. To the parents a job was something you got when you finished school—the next step, a little grim, a little exciting, the end of carefree school days. A job was something you were going to get, bound to get, something that waited for you at the end of school, just as certainly as autumn follows summer. But job—to those born in 1914, 1915? Something that you might never get, something to be longed for and prayed for, to starve for and steal for, almost—a job. There weren't any. When these two generations talk together and the word *job* is used, how will they understand each other? Suppose the issue is the draft—"A shame a fellow has to give up his job." To the elders this is arrant unpatriotic selfishness. To the young it is obvious sense. They find it strange that older people can see the sacrifice involved when married men with children must leave their families to go away in the defense service. Yet these same people don't see that any one should mind leaving a job. "Don't they know what a *job* means now, in the thinking of those born in 1915, 1916, 1917? Don't they know that just as among the ancients one was not a man until one had begotten a male child, so today one can't think of one's self as a full human being, without a job? We didn't say a guy wouldn't go because he had a job. We just said it was tough on him. We weren't saying anything they wouldn't say themselves about a man with kids. But gee–how they blew up!"[7]

The British and the Americans are still under the delusion that they speak the same language. With some qualifications this is true as far as denotations are concerned, though there are concepts like "sissy" in American for which there are no precise English equivalents. Connotations, however, are often importantly different, and this makes for the more misunderstanding because both languages are still called "English" (treating alike by words things that are different). An excellent illustration is again supplied by Margaret Mead:

. . . in Britain, the word "compromise" is a good word, and one may speak approvingly of any arrangement which has been a compromise, including, very often, one in which the other side has gained more than fifty per cent of the points at issue. On the other hand, in the United States, the minority position is still the position from which everyone speaks: the President *versus* Congress, Congress *versus* the President, the State government *versus* the metropolis and the metropolis *versus* the State government. This is congruent with the American doctrine of checks and balances, but it does not permit the word "compromise" to gain the same ethical halo which it has in Britain. Where, in Britain, to compromise means to work out a good solution, in America it usually means to work out a bad one, a solution in which all the points of importance (to both sides) are lost. Thus, in negotiations between the United States and Britain, all of which had, in the nature of the case, to be compromises, as two sovereignties were involved, the British could always speak approvingly and proudly of the result, while the Americans had to emphasize their losses.[8]

The words, then, that pass so readily from mouth to mouth are not entirely trustworthy substitutes for the facts of the physical world. The smooth-worn standard coins are slippery steppingstones

[7] Margaret Mead, "When Were You Born," *Child Study*, Spring, 1941.
[8] *Ibid.*

from mind to mind. Nor is thinking simply a matter of choosing words to express thoughts. The selected words always mirror social situation as well as objective fact. Two men go into a bar in New York and are overcharged for bad liquor: "This is a gyp joint." The same thing happens in Paris: "The French are a bunch of chiselers."

Perhaps the most important contribution of anthropological linguistics has come from the difficulties the anthropologist goes through in trying to express the meanings contained in speech structures completely foreign to the pattern of all European tongues. This study and this experience has forced upon the anthropologist a rather startling discovery which is fraught with meaning for a world where peoples speaking many different idioms are trying to communicate without distortion. Every language is something more than a vehicle for exchanging ideas and information—more even than a tool for self-expression and for letting off emotional steam or for getting other people to do what we want.

Every language is also a special way of looking at the world and interpreting experience. Concealed in the structure of each different language are a whole set of unconscious assumptions about the world and life in it. The anthropological linguist has come to realize that the general ideas one has about what happens in the world outside oneself are not altogether "given" by external events. Rather, up to a point, one sees and hears what the grammatical system of one's language has made one sensitive to, has trained one to look for in experience. This bias is the more insidious because everyone is so unconscious of his native language as a system. To one brought up to speak a certain language it is part of the very nature of things, remaining always in the class of background phenomena. It is as natural that experience should be organized and interpreted in these language-defined classes as it is that the seasons change. In fact the naïve view is that anyone who thinks in any other way is unnatural or stupid, or even vicious—and most certainly illogical.

In point of fact, traditional or Aristotelian logic has been mainly the analysis of consistencies in the structures of languages like Greek and Latin. The subject-predicate form of speech has implied a changeless world of fixed relations between "substances" and their "qualities." This view, as Korzybski[9] has insisted, is quite inadequate

[9] Alfred Korzybski, foremost proponent of General Semantics, wrote *Science and Sanity: An Introduction to Non-Aristotelian Systems and General Semantics,* a difficult but significant book on language and human behavior. [eds.]

to modern physical knowledge which shows that the properties of an atom alter from instant to instant in accord with the shifting relationships of its component elements. The little word "is" has brought us much confusion because sometimes it signifies that the subject exists, sometimes that it is a member of a designated class, sometimes that subject and predicate are identical. Aristotelian logic teaches us that something is or isn't. Such a statement is often false to reality, for both-and is more often true than either-or. "Evil" ranges all the way from black through an infinite number of shades of gray. Actual experience does not present clear-cut entities like "good" and "bad," "mind" and "body"; the sharp split remains verbal. Modern physics has shown that even in the inanimate world there are many questions that cannot be answered by an unrestricted "yes" or an unqualified "no."

From the anthropological point of view there are as many different worlds upon the earth as there are languages. Each language is an instrument which guides people in observing, in reacting, in expressing themselves in a special way. The pie of experience can be sliced in many different ways, and language is the principal directive force in the background. You can't say in Chinese, "answer me yes or no," for there aren't words for yes and no. Chinese gives priority to "how?" and nonexclusive categories; European languages to "what?" and exclusive categories. In English we have both real plurals and imaginary plurals, "ten men" and "ten days"; in Hopi plurals and cardinal numbers may be used only for things that can be seen together as an objective group. The fundamental categories of the French verb are before and after (tense) and potentiality vs. actuality (mood); the fundamental categories of one American Indian language (Wintu) are subjectivity vs. objectivity, knowledge vs. belief, freedom vs. actual necessity.

In the Haida language of British Columbia there are more than twenty verbal prefixes that indicate whether an action was performed by carrying, shooting, hammering, pushing, pulling, floating, stamping, picking, chopping, or the like. Some languages have different verbs, adjectives, and pronouns for animate and inanimate things. In Melanesia there are as many as four variant forms for each possessive pronoun. One may be used for the speaker's body and mind, another for illegitimate relatives and his loincloth, a third his

---

Korzybski's views have been popularized by S. I. Hayakawa, Stuart Chase, and others. [eds.]

possessions and gifts. The underlying conceptual images of each language tend to constitute a coherent though unconscious philosophy.

Where in English one word, "rough," may equally well be used to describe a road, a rock, or the business surface of a file, the Navaho language finds a need for three different words which may not be used interchangeably. While the general tendency is for Navaho to make finer and more concrete distinctions, this is not inevitably the case. The same stem is used for rip, light beam, and echo, ideas which seem diverse to speakers of European languages. One word is used to designate a medicine bundle with all its contents, the skin quiver in which the contents are wrapped, the contents as a whole, and some of the distinct items. Sometimes the point is not that the images of Navahos are less fluid and more delimited but rather just that the external world is dissected along different lines. For example, the same Navaho word is used to describe both a pimply face and a nodule-covered rock. In English a complexion might be termed "rough" or "coarse," but a rock would never, except facetiously, be described as pimply. Navaho differentiates two types of rough rock: the kind which is rough in the manner in which a file is rough and the kind which is nodule-encrusted. In these cases the differences between the Navaho and the English ways of seeing the world cannot be disposed of merely by saying that the Navaho language is more precise. The variations rest in the features which the two languages see as essential. Cases can indeed be given where the Navaho is notably less precise. Navaho gets along with a single word for flint, metal, knife, and certain other objects of metal. This, to be sure, is due to the historical accident that, after European contact, metal in general and knives in particular took the place of flint.

Navahos are perfectly satisfied with what seem to Europeans rather imprecise discriminations in the realm of time sequences. On the other hand, they are the fussiest people in the world about always making explicit in the forms of the language many distinctions which English makes only occasionally and vaguely. In English one says, "I eat," meaning, "I eat something." The Navaho point of view is different. If the object thought of is actually indefinite, then "something" must be tacked on to the verb.

The nature of their language forces the Navaho to notice and report many other distinctions in physical events which the nature of the English language allows speakers to neglect in most cases, even though their senses are just as capable as those of the Navaho to register the smaller details of what goes on in the external world. For example, suppose a Navaho range rider and a white supervisor see that a wire fence needs repair. The supervisor will probably write in his notebook, "Fence at such and such a place must be fixed." If the Navaho reports the break, he must choose between forms that indicate whether the damage was caused by some person or by a nonhuman agency, whether the fence was of one or several strands of wire.

In general, the difference between Navaho thought and English thought—both as manifested in the language and as forced by the very nature of the linguistic forms into such patterns—is that Navaho thought is ordinarily much more specific. The ideas expressed by the English verb "to go" provide a nice example. When a Navaho says that he went somewhere he never fails to specify whether it was afoot, astride, by wagon, auto, train, airplane, or boat. If it be a boat, it must be specified whether the boat floats off with the current, is propelled by the speaker, or is made to move by an indefinite or unstated agency. The speed of a horse (walk, trot, gallop, run) is expressed by the verb form chosen. He differentiates between starting to go, going along, arriving at, returning from a point. It is not, of course, that these distinctions *cannot* be made in English, but that they *are not* made consistently. They seem of importance to English speakers only under special circumstances.

A cross-cultural view of the category of time is highly instructive. Beginners in the study of classical Greek are often troubled by the fact that the word *opiso* sometimes means "behind," sometimes "in the future." Speakers of English find this baffling because they are accustomed to think of themselves as moving through time. The Greeks, however, conceived of themselves as stationary, of time as coming up behind them, overtaking them, and then, still moving on, becoming the "past" that lay before their eyes.

Present European languages emphasize time distinctions. The tense systems are usually thought of as the most basic of verbal inflections. However, this was not always so. Streitberg says that in primitive Indo-European a special indicator for the present was usually lacking. In many languages, certainly, time distinctions are only irregularly present or are of distinctly secondary importance. In Hopi the first question answered by the verb form is that of the type of information conveyed by the assertion. Is a situation reported as actuality, as anticipated, or as a general truth? In the anticipatory form there is no necessary distinction between past, present, and future. The English translation must choose from context between "was about to run," "is about to run," and "will run." The Wintu language of California carries this stress upon implications of validity much farther. The sentence "Harry is chopping wood" must be translated in five different ways, depending upon whether the speaker knows this by hearsay, by direct observation, or by inference of three degrees of plausibility.

In no language are the whole of a sense experience and all possible interpretations of it expressed. What people think and feel and how they report what they think and feel are determined, to be sure, by their personal history, and by what actually happens in the outside world. But they are also determined by a factor which is often overlooked; namely, the pattern of linguistic habits which people acquire as members of a particular society. It makes a difference whether or not a language is rich in metaphors and conventional imagery.

Our imaginations are restricted in some directions, free in others. The linguistic particularization of detail along one line will mean the neglect of other aspects of the situation. Our thoughts are directed in one way if we speak a language where all objects are classified according to sex, in another if the classification is by social position or the form of the object. Grammars are devices for expressing relations. It makes a difference what is treated as object, as attribute, as state, as act. In Hopi, ideas referring to the seasons are not grouped with what we call nouns but rather with what we call adverbs. Because of our grammar it is easy to personify summer, to think of it as a thing or a state.

Even as between closely related tongues, the conceptual picture may be different. Let us take one final example from Margaret Mead:

> Americans tend to arrange objects on a single scale of value, from best to worst, biggest to smallest, cheapest to most expensive, etc., and are able to express a preference among very complex objects on such a single scale. The question, "What is your favorite color?" so intelligible to an American, is meaningless in Britain, and such a question is countered by: "Favorite color for what? A flower? A necktie?" Each object is thought of as having a most complex set of qualities, and color is merely

a quality of an object, not something from a color chart on which one can make a choice which is transferable to a large number of different sorts of objects. The American reduction of complexities to single scales is entirely comprehensible in terms of the great diversity of value systems which different immigrant groups brought to the American scene. Some common denominator among the incommensurables was very much needed, and over-simplification was almost inevitable. But, as a result, Americans think in terms of qualities which have uni-dimensional scales, while the British, when they think of a complex object or event, even if they reduce it to parts, think of each part as retaining all of the complexities of the whole. Americans subdivide the scale; the British subdivide the object.[10]

Language and its changes cannot be understood unless linguistic behavior is related to other behavioral facts. Conversely, one can gain many subtle insights into those national habits and thought ways of which one is ordinarily unconscious by looking closely at special idioms and turns of speech in one's own and other languages. What a Russian says to an American doesn't really get across just from shuffling words—much is twisted or blunted or lost unless the American knows something about Russia and Russian life, a good deal more than the sheer linguistic skill needed for a formally correct translation. The American must indeed have gained some entrance to that foreign world of values and significances which are pointed up by the emphases of the Russian vocabulary, crystalized in the forms of Russian grammar, implicit in the little distinctions of meaning in the Russian language.

Any language is more than an instrument for conveying ideas, more even than an instrument for working upon the feelings of others and for self-expression. Every language is also a means of categorizing experience. The events of the "real" world are never felt or reported as a machine would do it. There is a selection process and an interpretation in the very act of response. Some features of the external situation are highlighted; others are ignored or not fully discriminated.

Every people has its own characteristic classes in which individuals pigeonhole their experiences. These classes are established primarily

[10] Margaret Mead, "The Application of Anthropological Techniques to Cross-National Communication," *Transactions of the New York Academy of Sciences*, February, 1947.

by the language through the types of objects, processes, or qualities which receive special emphasis in the vocabulary and equally, though more subtly, through the types of differentiation or activity which are distinguished in grammatical forms. The language says, as it were, "notice this," "always consider this separate from that," "such and such things belong together." Since persons are trained from infancy to respond in these ways, they take such discriminations for granted as part of the inescapable stuff of life. When we see two peoples with different social traditions respond in different ways to what appear to the outsider to be identical stimulus situations, we realize that experience is much less an objective absolute than we thought. Every language has an effect upon what the people who use it see, what they feel, how they think, what they can talk about.

"Common sense" holds that different languages are parallel methods for expressing the same "thoughts." "Common sense," however, itself implies talking so as to be readily understood by one's fellows—in the same culture. Anglo-American "common sense" is actually very sophisticated, deriving from Aristotle and the speculations of scholastic and modern philosophers. The fact that all sorts of basic philosophic questions are begged in the most cavalier fashion is obscured by the conspiracy of silent acceptance which always attends the system of conventional understandings that we call culture.

The lack of true equivalences between any two languages is merely the outward expression of inward differences between two peoples in premises, in basic categories, in the training of fundamental sensitivities, and in general view of the world. The way the Russians put their thoughts together shows the impress of linguistic habits, of characteristic ways of organizing experience, for

> Human beings do not live in the objective world alone, nor alone in the world of social activity as ordinarily understood, but are very much at the mercy of the particular language which has become the medium of expression for their society. It is quite an illusion to imagine that one adjusts to reality essentially without the use of language and that language is merely an incidental means of solving specific problems of communication or reflection. The fact of the matter is that the 'real world' is to a large extent unconsciously built up on the language habits of the group. . . . We see and hear and otherwise experience very

largely as we do because the language habits of our community predispose certain choices of interpretation.[11]

—Edward Sapir

A language is, in a sense, a philosophy.

SUGGESTED ASSIGNMENTS

1. Kluckhohn informs us that different languages divide the perceptual world in different ways. The way "you," the person spoken to, is handled is a convenient example. In English we have one word *you* which serves as singular and plural and as subject and object. But in some other languages, e.g., French, Italian, Spanish, Dutch, German, Russian, there are three, four and more forms to express "you," and these forms can express subtle shades of meaning and attitude. If you are acquainted with such a language, write a comparative description of the use of "you" in that language and in English. Include in your paper an evaluation of the two systems.
2. English once had four forms for "you" where we now have only one word in ordinary English. Look this matter up in *The Development of Modern English* by Stuart Robertson and Frederic Cassidy, pp. 125-126. Then find examples of all four forms in the King James version of the *Bible*. Write a short theme in which you explain and illustrate the Elizabethan uses of "you." If you wish to go a little further with this subject, turn to *A Shakespearean Grammar* by E. A. Abbott, p. 153 ff., to discover some of the shades of meaning expressed by these pronouns. For an extended paper using a primary source, you might read a play by Shakespeare, say *Romeo* and *Juliet*, and discuss Shakespeare's use and confusion of the pronouns, correlating the choice of *thou-thee* and *ye-you* with the attitudes of the characters.
3. Under what circumstances are *thou* and *thee* still used in present-day English?
4. How do you account for the development of such forms as "you-all" and "yous"?
5. In English we have the forms *whither*, *where*, and *whence* to express the meanings "to where," "where," and "from where," but only *where* is in common use. In some languages, notably German, separate words are regularly used for these meanings. Can you think of cases in which English is less precise for having abandoned *whither* and *whence?* What would you say about the parallel cases of *hither*, *here*, *hence* and *thither*, *there*, *thence?*

[11] Edward Sapir, "Language," *Encyclopedia of the Social Sciences*, vol. ix, The Macmillan Company, 1933.

6. Languages divide the world of family relatives in various ways. For example, French has separate masculine and feminine words, *le cousin* and *la cousine*, for our single *cousin;* and for our *uncle* Latin has two separate words, *avunculus* for a mother's brother and *patruus* for a father's brother. Do you think we are handicapped in expression by not having the distinctions of French and Latin?
7. When white light is passed through a prism or other diffracting medium it produces a spectrum, a series of colors shading from red to violet. Undoubtedly all people of normal vision are able to perceive variations of color produced in this way, but they do not necessarily make their divisions at the same places in the scale. In English the color names most frequently used are *red*, *orange*, *yellow*, *green*, *blue*, *purple*, *pink*, and *brown*. Look up the following references and write a short paper on how colors are categorized in other languages: Harry Hoijer, "The Relation of Language to Culture," in *Anthropology Today*, edited by A. L. Kroeber, pp. 558-559; Willis D. Wallis, *An Introduction to Anthropology*, pp. 420-421; and Lucien Lévy-Bruhl, *How Natives Think*, p. 171.
8. The vocabulary of a language is an index of items culturally important to the people speaking that language. Snow and ice play an important part in the lives of the Eskimos and the Lapps; consequently there are many specific words for snow and ice in various forms in the languages of these people. The Eskimos have separate words for snow on the ground, falling snow, drifting snow, melting snow, and so on. Lévy-Bruhl reports that the Lapps have 20 words for ice, 11 for cold, 41 for snow, and 26 verbs to express freezing and thawing. To most of us snow, no matter what its condition, is *snow*. We have at least one group, however, to whom snow is important enough to warrant specialized terminology. Interview a skier, or consult a book on skiing, and make a list of words referring to different snow conditions.

FURTHER READINGS

1. Abbott, E. A. *A Shakespearean Grammar*. London: Macmillan and Co., 1878.
2. Bloomfield, Leonard. *Language*. New York: Holt, Rinehart and Winston, Inc., 1933. On meaning, see Chapters 2 and 9.
3. Brown, Roger. *Words and Things*. New York: The Free Press of Glencoe, Inc., 1958. On the origin of speech, see pp. 131-136; on animal "languages," pp. 155-172; on the *Weltanschauung* theory, pp. 229-263.
4. Carroll, John B. *The Study of Language*. Cambridge: Harvard Uni-

versity Press, 1953. For a definition of language and a discussion of the work of linguistic scientists, see pp. 7-15; on the *Weltanschauung* theory, see pp. 43-48.

5. Gleason, H. A., Jr. *An Introduction to Descriptive Linguistics.* New York: Holt, Rinehart and Winston, Inc., 1955. On language, see Chapter 1.
6. Gode, Alexander, and Hugh E. Blair. *Interlingua: A Grammar of the International Language.* New York: Storm Publishers, 1951.
7. Guérard, Albert Léon. *A Short History of the International Language Movement.* New York: Liveright Publishing Corporation, 1922.
8. Hayakawa, S. I. *Language in Thought and Action.* New York: Harcourt, Brace & World, Inc., 1949. On the uses of language, see Chapters 5-7.
9. Hoijer, Harry. "The Relation of Language to Culture," in *Anthropology Today*, edited by A. L. Kroeber. Chicago: University of Chicago Press, 1953.
10. Jespersen, Otto. *Language, Its Nature, Development and Origin.* New York: The Macmillan Company, 1922. On the origin of speech, see Chapter 21.
11. Lee, Irving J. *Language Habits in Human Affairs.* New York: Harper & Brothers, 1941. On meaning, see pp. 29-51.
12. Lévy-Bruhl, Lucien. *How Natives Think.* New York: Alfred A. Knopf, Inc., 1925.
13. Lorenz, Konrad. *King Solomon's Ring.* New York: Thomas Y. Crowell Company, 1952.
14. Robertson, Stuart, and Frederic G. Cassidy. *The Development of Modern English*, 2d ed. Englewood Cliffs, New Jersey: Prentice-Hall, Inc., 1954.
15. Sturtevant, Edgar H. *Linguistic Science.* New Haven: Yale University Press, 1947. On the origin of speech, see Chapter 5.
16. Von Frisch, Karl. *Bees, Their Vision, Chemical Senses, and Language.* Ithaca, New York: Cornell University Press, 1950.
17. Wallis, Willis D. *An Introduction to Anthropology.* New York: Harper & Brothers, 1926.
18. Whatmough, Joshua. *Language, A Modern Synthesis.* New York: St. Martin's Press, Inc., 1956. On the uses of language, see Chapter 6.

2. Words: Forms and Meanings

WORD-MAKING IN ENGLISH

Henry Bradley

As language continues to grow, its word stock is constantly changing. While some words sink into disuse and disappear, others are being added to meet new needs. Your grandfather, for instance, could have driven a run-about *or* touring-car, *whereas now, two generations later, you are likely to be behind the wheel of a* hardtop *or a* station wagon. *The additions to our word stock are of two kinds. One consists of borrowings from other languages. In English this borrowing has gone on without stop ever since our language first appeared in England 1,500 years ago. It is illustrated in the selection by Thomas Pyles on page 93. The second kind of addition consists of new words formed from existing materials. That is to say, words and word-parts are re-formed into new combinations, and sometimes entirely new words are created from the repertory of English speech sounds. It is this second group that Mr. Bradley discusses here as he describes the three major processes by which new words come into being. Henry Bradley was one of the distinguished editors of that monumental lexicon, the* Oxford English Dictionary.

The English language has augmented its resources not only by the adoption of words from other tongues, but also by the making of new words. There are three possible ways in which a new word can

From *The Making of English* by Henry Bradley. Reprinted by permission of Macmillan and Company Ltd., and St. Martin's Press, Inc., copyright 1904.

be made: (1) by *Composition*, which means the joining together of two existing words to form a compound; (2) by *Derivation*, which means the making of a new word out of an old one, usually by the addition of some prefix or suffix which is not itself a word, but is significant in combination; and (3) by *Root-creation*, which is the invention of an entirely new word, usually either imitative of some inarticulate noise, or suggested by some instinctive feeling of expressiveness.

1. COMPOSITION.

A compound word is a word formed by joining two or more words to express a meaning that could be rendered by a phrase of which the simple words form part. Some languages have no compound words at all; and those which have them do not all form them after the same manner. The principles of English word-compounding are, to a great extent, inherited from the primitive Indo-Germanic language. In those kinds of compounds that most frequently occur, the last element expresses a general meaning, which the prefixed element renders less general. Thus an *apple-tree* is a tree, but only a particular kind of tree. In the original Indo-Germanic language the prefixed element in a compound of this sort was not, properly speaking, a *word*, but a word-stem: that is to say, a word deprived of those grammatical characters—case, number, gender, mood, tense, person, etc., which it would possess if it occurred separately in a sentence.[1] It has still this character, so far as meaning is concerned, in those English compounds that are formed on the inherited pattern. Thus *apple-* in *apple-tree* is neither singular nor plural, neither nominative, accusative, nor genitive. Hence the phrase for which such a compound is the condensed expression admits of great variety of form; the former of the two words may occur in it in any case or in either number; and the meaning of the compound varies accordingly. A *tree-frog* is a frog that lives in trees; a *tree-fern* is a fern that is a tree; a *tree-fruit* is the fruit produced by a tree. As a general rule, our knowledge of the things denoted by the simple words guides us at

[1] This comes out clearly in such a language as Greek, which has preserved the primitive Indo-Germanic system of inflexions. Thus *oikodespotēs* is Greek for 'master of a house'; but while *despotēs* 'master,' is a real word, *oiko-*, 'house,' is only a stem. To make it into a word, capable of being used in a sentence, we must add the endings that mark case and number, as in *oikos*, nom. sing., *oikon*, acc. sing., *oikou*, gen. sing., *oikoi*, nom. pl., *oikous*, acc. plural.

once to a correct understanding of the meaning of the compound. This, however, is not always the case. A *house-boat* might very well mean a sort of boat usually kept in a boat-house, or a boat that belongs to a house, or that supplies the needs of houses. It is only custom that has decided that the compound word shall mean a boat that serves as a house. The general meaning of this class of compounds might be expressed by saying that the noun which is formed of the two nouns A and B means "a B which has some sort of relation to an A or to A's in general."

The compounds formed by prefixing one noun to another, however, constitute only one out of the many classes of compounds which exist in English. There are compounds of adjective and noun, as *blackbird*, *hotbed;* of adverb and noun, as *downfall;* of noun and adjective, as *grass-green*, *purse-proud*, *penny-wise;* of adjective or adverb and adjective, as *dark-blue*, *ever-young;* and of noun or adjective and verb, as *wiredraw*, *whitewash;* and the very many compounds of adverb and verb, such as *overcome*, *inlay*, *outlive*, *upturn*. In all these cases the literal meaning of the compound is that of the last element, only limited or specialised. . . . From the fifteenth century onwards many compound nouns and adjectives have been formed in imitation of French, in which the first element is a verb-stem (in the original examples it was the imperative of a verb) and the second element is a noun denoting the object of the action, as in *breakfast*, *breakneck*, *kill-joy*, *makeshift*, *save-all*, *scapegrace*, *scarecrow*, *spendthrift*, *tosspot*, *turnkey*. We have also many nouns and adjectives compounded with a verb-stem and an adverb, as *break-up*, *come-down*, *knock-out*, *run-away*.

. . . As any page of an "Anglo-Saxon" dictionary will show, compound words were abundant in Old English; and in every succeeding age of the language a multitude of new compounds have come into existence. And yet, if we take a page of modern German and place beside it a good translation into English, we shall not fail to perceive that the compound words are very much more numerous in the German original than in the English rendering. Another noteworthy fact is that a great number of compounds, once generally used, are now obsolete, although the simple words composing them are still universally familiar. It may be worth while to inquire why this has happened.

Although word-composition, in those languages which freely admit it, is one of the readiest means of supplying the need for new words, compounds are often somewhat awkward in actual use. A compound word is a description, often an imperfect description; and when an object of perception or thought is familiar to us, we desire that its name shall suggest the thing to our minds directly, and not through the intervention of irrelevant ideas. Accordingly, a compound word for a simple notion gives a certain sense of inconvenience, unless we are able to forget its literal meaning. It is true that we frequently succeed in doing this: we use multitudes of compound words without mentally analysing them at all. In such cases the compound often undergoes processes of phonetic change which a distinct consciousness of its etymological meaning would not have allowed to take place. Thus the Old English *gōdspel,* literally "good tidings" (which early became *gŏdspel,* through misreading the first element as "God" instead of "good"), is now *gospel;* the late Old English *hūsbonda,* a compound of *hūs* house and *bonda* dweller, cultivator, is now not *housebond* but *husband;* the poetical designation *day's eye* is now *daisy,* a word which we never think of as containing two elements; *holy day* has become *holiday; Christ's mass* is now *Christmas,* with an altered pronunciation which quite disguises the first word. This process is especially observable in place-names, where, even more than in ordinary compound words, the original descriptive meaning is a palpable irrelevance. Very few names of English places are now intelligible to persons unlearned in etymology, even when the separate words of which they are composed are still familiar in everyday speech. The Old English *stān* survives as "stone," and *tūn* as "town"; but the place-name *Stāntūn* is now not "Stonetown" but "Stanton." *Pedridan-tūn,* the "town" or farm enclosure on the river Pedride, is now Petherton, though the name of the river has come to be pronounced "Parret."

A consideration of these and similar examples will show that compound words have often the disadvantage that their etymological meaning has to be forgotten before they can become quite satisfactory instruments of expression. It would appear that the English are, from whatever cause, more conscious of this inconvenience than are the speakers of some other languages. At any rate, although many new compounds have been formed in every period of the language, a large proportion of them have been short-lived or of very limited currency: the general tendency has been to replace them by other words. In the Middle English period this tendency was fostered by the circumstance that the two fashionable languages, French and

Latin, make very little use of composition; and the common practice of adopting words from these languages made it easy to find substitutes for the native compounds. The Old English names for arts and sciences—such as *læcecrǣft* (leechcraft) for medicine, *scopcræft* for poetry, *tungolcræft* for astronomy, *rīmcrǣft* for arithmetic—disappeared early from the language, their places being taken by words adopted through French from Latin, or through French and Latin from Greek. The fourteenth century monk who wrote *ayenbite (of inwyt)* for "remorse (of conscience)" did not succeed in inducing any other writer to use his new word: the Latin-French synonym was felt to be better for its purpose. Even now, a well-established compound is often partly superseded by a simple word or a derivative: for example, we use the word *steamer* more frequently than *steamboat* or *steamship.*

The habit of freely adopting foreign words, which has been produced by the conditions under which the English language has been developed, has had the good effect of relieving us from the necessity of having recourse to composition in cases where a compound, as such, is less suitable for our purpose than a simple word. But, on the other hand, our language has lost something of its capacity for forming compounds even where they would be useful. When Carlyle, imitating the German *Schadenfreude,* speaks of "a mischief-joy, which is often a justice-joy," we somehow feel that these formations are alien to the genius of the language, though if it were not for this the words would have been welcome additions to our vocabulary. It would seem un-English to say that a person was *rank-proud,* though the apparently analogous *purse-proud* has long been a recognised word; and *country-love* or *virtue-love* for "love of country," "love of virtue," would be equally inadmissible. And yet not only does modern English possess an enormous number of compounds, but new ones are continually introduced; and, what is still more remarkable, many of these additions to our language, when we first hear them, do not seem in the slightest degree novel. Probably nobody has ever used or ever will use the word *purple-eared;* but if the meaning ever needs to be expressed no one will say that the word is not English. It is not easy to say definitely what kinds of compounds are rejected by the instinct of the language and what kinds are freely admitted. In general, the new compounds that find ready acceptance are those which belong to some particular type or pattern which is exemplified in a large number of common words. One such type is that of the so-called "parasynthetic" formation, like *blue-eyed*, *long-haired*, *swallow-tailed*. English idiom leaves us almost as free to invent new compounds of the type of *blue-eyed* as to invent new phrases of the type of *with blue eyes*. When one or both the elements happen to be very commonly used in combinations of this kind, the compound adjective, whether we have met with it before or not, is quite as natural a mode of expression as the equivalent phrase. . . .

There are several other types of composition which are so familiar to us from the multitude of existing specimens that we can employ them almost without restriction to form new words. For instance, we seldom hesitate to make, whenever we feel the need of it, a new compound on the pattern of *coach-house*, *hair-brush*, *water-jug*, where the first element indicates the particular use to which the object designated is adapted. It may be remarked that the composition of long polysyllables is generally avoided as ungraceful: and, further, that most of the words derived from French and Latin appear somewhat unfrequently in compounds, probably because in the periods when word-composition was most frequent they were still felt to be more or less exotic.

With reference to the formation of compound verbs, modern English is somewhat peculiar in its usages. Perhaps the reader may be familiar with the practice of modern German in dealing with what are called separable prefixes. In the German dictionaries we find a verb *aufgeben*, compounded of the adverb *auf* "up" and the verb *geben* "to give." In the infinitive this is written as one word, the adverbial part coming first. So it is, under certain conditions, in the indicative and subjunctive; but "I give it up" is ordinarily rendered in German by *ich gebe es auf*, where the two elements are treated as separate words, the adverb coming last, with the object-pronoun between it and the verb. Now combinations of this sort may, from one point of view, be regarded as phrases rather than as compounds; the adverb and the verb are really separate words. The idiom of the language requires that under some conditions the adverb shall precede the verb and that under other conditions it shall follow it; and in the former case custom has ordered that the two words shall be written as one. In Old English the position of the adverb was similarly variable (though the rules for its position were not so strict as in German); but in modern English prose we must always put the adverb last. In poetry, indeed, there are exceptions. Browning writes:

> "Then a beam of fun *outbroke*
> On the bearded mouth that spoke."

But *outbroke* is merely poetical: in plain prose we must say "broke out." We can, if we please, call *give up, break out, set up, put through,* and such like, "compound verbs"; and in a certain sense the appellation is quite justifiable. If we adopt this nomenclature the number of compound verbs in English is beyond all calculation, and in fact we are continually inventing new ones. In its power of expressing fine distinctions of meaning by this method English vies with Greek and German, and has a great advantage over the Romanic languages, which have hardly any compound verbs at all.

But alongside these "virtual compounds," English has a considerable number of verbs formed with prefixed adverbs, such as *overtake, upset, understand.* In most cases their meaning is not obvious from their composition, and it is usually quite different from that of the combination of the verb with the following adverb. "To overtake a person" does not mean the same as "to take a person over"; "to upset a thing" happens to have a meaning quite opposite to that of "to set a thing up." Compounds of this class originated in an older stage of the language; the principle of composition which they represent has almost died out, so that as a rule we cannot form any new words on the same pattern. We can, it is true, with some degree of freedom, prefix *over,* and *under,* with the sense "too much," "too little," to verbs; but in general the modern feeling of the language resists the introduction of compounds of this kind, and very few of them have come in since the sixteenth century.

It is equally foreign to the spirit of the modern language to add to the number of those compound nouns or adjectives which are formed by prefixing an adverb to a verb-stem, a verbal noun, or a participle, such as *outbreak, outfit, income, downfall, downsitting, uprising, onlooker, outfit, forthcoming, downtrodden.* The method of formation of these words is a relic of the time when in a verbal phrase the adverb could precede the verb—when, for instance, it was as natural to say "to out break" as "to break out"; but new compounds of the kind could be easily formed down to the seventeenth century. They are fairly abundant, and admirably expressive; but we have almost[2] en-

[2] A word of this formation which has recently gained some currency in journalistic use is *upkeep,* meaning "(cost of) keeping-up." It appears to have been imported from the Scottish dialect, in which this mode of composition has been more generally used than in standard English. From the same source we have obtained *outcome* (brought into literary English by Carlyle) and *uptake.*

tirely ceased to form new words on the same pattern. Although we perhaps more frequently say "to fit up" than "to fit out," it would seem very eccentric to speak of an *upfit*, or an *upfitter;* and we should not think of using *downbroken* as a parallel to *downtrodden.* Cyclists talk of "lighting-up time," not of "uplighting time," which would be quite un-idiomatic. Indeed many such compounds that were once current are now gone out of general use. The translators of our Bible could write "My downsitting and mine uprising"; but in natural modern English the equivalent expression would be "my sitting down and my rising up." Not long ago a very able foreign scholar, writing a grammatical treatise in English, puzzled his readers by using the word *down-toners* as a name for the class of adverbs which (like *rather, somewhat)* "tone down" the force of the words to which they are prefixed. No doubt, if the phrase "to tone down" had existed in the sixteenth century, a writer of that period could have spoken of a "down-toner" without any risk of not being understood. But in this respect the language has undergone a change, which may be a change for the worse, but which it would be vain to try to resist.

The composition of an agent-noun with a *following* adverb, which was foreign to English in its earliest stages, has been fairly common from the fourteenth century onwards. Chaucer has "*holdere up* of Troye"; Lydgate speaks of Nimrod as "*fynder up* of false religions"; Shakespeare has "the *finder-out* of this secret"; the Bible of 1611 has "a *setter-forth* of strange gods"; later examples of this mode of formation are *cutter-out, hanger-on, filler-in, fitter-up.* . . .

2. DERIVATION.

Old English was considerably less rich than modern English in methods of making new words by derivation. It is true that a large portion of the Old English vocabulary consists of words derived from other words that existed in the language. But very many of these derivatives had been already formed before the English came over from the continent, and the processes by which they were made had become obsolete before the date of the earliest Old English literature. Perhaps this statement may need a little illustration to make it clear to readers unacquainted with philology. Everybody can see that the word *laughter* is derived from the verb *laugh;* and yet we should never think of forming a new substantive by the same process from any other verb. One of Mr. F. R. Stockton's personages, indeed, speaks of a dog "bursting into *barkter*," but nobody would seriously propose to coin a new word of this kind. The ending *-ter* is no longer "a living suffix," and, in fact, it had ceased to be such before Old English existed as a separate language. Many other suffixes which appear in Old English derivatives were, in like manner, never used in the formation of new words.

There is in English a large class of derivative verbs which, if there were no other evidence but that afforded by Old English itself, we should have to regard as formed from other Old English words, either nouns, adjectives, or verbs, by altering their vowel. Thus we find a noun *talu*, tale (in both senses, "number" and "story") and a verb *tellan*, to tell (again in both senses, "to count" and "to narrate"); a noun *salu*, sale, and a verb *sellan*, to sell. *Tȳnan*, to enclose, is derived from *tūn*, enclosure; *blēdan*, to bleed, from *blōd*, blood; *blǣcan*, to bleach, from *blāc*, white or pale; *fiellan*, to fell, cause to fall, from *feallan*, to fall. A comparison of these words with their equivalents in the other Germanic languages teaches us that the true account of their origin is as follows: By the addition of a suffix *-jo* (pronounced *yo*) to the stem of the substantive adjective or verb, a new verb-stem was formed, to which the endings of mood, tense, and person were appended. The earlier forms of the verbs above mentioned were *taljan, saljan, tūnjan, blōdjan, blaikjan, falljan.* In prehistoric Old English the *j* in this position always produced an alteration in the vowel of the preceding syllable (unless that vowel was *i*), and caused the preceding consonant to be lengthened or doubled if the vowel before it was short. Hence *taljan* became first *telljan* and then *tellan*, *blōdjan* became *blēdan;* and so with the rest. But all this had already taken place before Old English became a written language; and when it had taken place there was an end to the possibility of forming any new "verbs of making or causing" by the process which had previously been so easy. All the verbs apparently formed by vowel change that existed in Old English were inherited from prehistoric times. Perhaps we might have expected that new derivatives would have been formed by vowel-change, in imitation of those which already existed (for instance, a verb *gēdan*, to make good, might have been formed from *gōd*, imitating the relation between *cōl* cool and *cēlan* to cool); but, so far as we know, nothing of the sort ever happened. The Old English language, at the earliest period at which it is known to us, had already lost one of the most useful of the means for word-making which it originally possessed.

Almost all those modes of derivation which were actually current in Old English have continued in constant use down to the present time. Only a few of the most important of them need be mentioned here. In Old English, a verb could be formed from a noun by attaching the conjugational endings to the stem of the noun: thus, from *wilcuma*, a welcome guest, was formed the verb *wilcumian* to welcome (*ic wilcumige* I welcome, *ic wilcumode* I welcomed). In later English, through the dropping away of final syllables, the infinitive, the imperative, and the plural and the first person singular of the present indicative of the derived verb have the same form as the primary noun, so that what takes place seems to be not the making of a new word but the using of a noun as a verb. Hence the operation has become, in modern English, so easy that we perform it almost unconsciously. In colloquial language, we can make new verbs with extraordinary freedom, not only from nouns, but even from phrases. "He *my-dear-fellow*-ed me all the day," for instance, is quite permissible conversational English. Conversely, in modern English, we have an almost unlimited number of nouns which are merely verbs used substantively to denote an act. We can speak of "a wash," "a shave," "a think," "a tumble down," "a dig in the ribs." Occasionally it happens that a noun in this way gives rise to a verb, which in its turn gives rise to another noun, all three words being exactly alike in sound and spelling. Thus, in the following examples: (1) "The *smoke* of a pipe," (2) "To *smoke* a pipe," (3) "To have a *smoke*," the noun of (1) is not, strictly speaking, the same word as the noun of (3). . . .

The following words of modern origin may serve to illustrate the freedom with which we can still form new derivatives by means of suffixes inherited from Old English: clever*ness*, clever*ly*, gentleman*ly*, rogu*ish*, think*er*, nois*y*, horseman*ship*. The English reader will be able at once to recollect many other words formed with each of these suffixes, and will perceive also that he might, without seeming at all eccentric in so doing, venture to use any one of them to form quite new words. Similarly, we can prefix the Old English negative particle *un-* to almost any descriptive adjective. There is another prefix *un-* (of different origin) which we can prefix quite freely to verbs to express a reversal of the action, as in *unfasten*, *uncover;* and the list of verbs formed with *be-* (like *befog*, *bemuddle*) is almost interminable.

There are one or two Old English suffixes for which the later language has discovered new uses. The ending *-isc* (now *-ish*) was in

Old English chiefly used to form adjectives from names of places or peoples, as in *Englisc* English, *Lundenisc* Londonish. It was also appended in a few instances to common nouns to form adjectives of quality, as in *folcisc* popular (from *folc*, "folk," people), *cildisc* childish. The suffix *-ish* is still a living formative in both these uses. But about 1400 it began to be attached to names of colour, to form adjectives denoting a colour approaching that expressed by the simple word, as in *bluish*, *blackish*. On the analogy of the adjectives thus formed it afterwards became common to add *-ish* to any sort of descriptive adjective, in order to express a slight degree of the quality which they indicate. It was thenceforth possible, instead of saying "somewhat good" or "somewhat bad," to express the idea by the single word *goodish* or *baddish*. To the characteristic English love of brevity this innovation was welcome; and in modern English we can append the suffix to any adjective denoting a quality that admits of degrees.

The ending *-ly*, representing the Old English *-līce*, forming adverbs of manner from adjectives, became in Middle English much more common, because the final *-e*, which in Old English was the ordinary adverbial suffix, ceased to be pronounced, so that the adjective and its related adverb became identical in form.[3] Early in the sixteenth century, the need was felt for adverbs to indicate position in a numbered series; that is to say, for single words with such meanings as "in the first, second, or third place." The need was supplied by the addition of the adverbial ending *-ly* to the ordinal numeral, as in *firstly*, *secondly*, *thirdly*, *fourthly*, which were unknown to the older language.

Since the close of the Old English period, the vocabulary of our language has been enriched by a multitude of new derivatives formed with the prefixes and suffixes that already existed in Old English; and there can be no doubt that the formation of new words by this

[3] For example, in Old English the adjective form was *hlūd* and the adverb *hlūde*, pronounced with two syllables. When the adverbial ending *-e* was no longer sounded in Middle English, the two forms became indistinguishable. But the other Middle English adverbial form in *-ly*, like *sweetly*, could be used to distinguish the adverb from the adjective *sweet*.

Another adverb of manner has been recently revived, that using the suffix *-wise* in expressions like *student-wise*. The Old English *wīse* meant manner. Later it was combined with nouns in the sense of "in the manner of," as in "Let us try once more to argue Cardinalwise," i.e., in the manner of a Cardinal. For further details consult the *Oxford English Dictionary*. [eds.]

means will continue in the future. But the native machinery of derivation, though very little of it has become obsolete, has not been found sufficient for the necessities of the language, and has been largely supplemented by additions obtained from other languages. The adoption of foreign formative machinery has been rendered possible by the fact that many Latin and French primitive words have been taken into the English language along with their derivatives, formed with French or Latin suffixes. When such pairs of words as *derive* and *derivation*, *esteem* and *estimation*, *laud* and *laudation*, *condemn* and *condemnation*, had found their way into the English vocabulary, it was natural that the suffix *-ation* should be recognised by English speakers as an allowable means of making "nouns of action" out of verbs. This particular suffix supplied a real want, because the only native means of forming nouns of action was the suffix *-ing*, which was not quite definite enough in meaning. It is true that this foreign suffix has not been very extensively attached to native words; as a rule, it has been felt to be more in accordance with fitness to adopt French or Latin nouns of action ready made. Still, such words as *botheration*, *starvation*, *fairation*, *flirtation*, *backwardation*, show that *-ation* has to some extent been regarded as an English formative. Another foreign suffix, *-ative*, though very common in words of Latin derivation, has been appended to a native verb only in one instance, viz. *talkative*. Such formations as *unwalkative* have been employed jocularly, but have never taken root in the language.

In some instances the attempt to naturalise a foreign suffix has failed because there was no real need to be supplied. Wycliff's *everlastingtee* (suggested by *eternitee* from *eterne*) did not find acceptance; the suffix *-tee* (now *-ty*) is confined to words either taken from French or Latin, or at least formed from French or Latin words. The native *-ness* answered all purposes, and the introduction of a foreign synonym was not required.

It was otherwise with many other French suffixes, such as *-age*, *-al* (as used in *withdrawal*, *upheaval*, *betrothal*), *-ment*, *-able*, which had nothing corresponding to them in English, and which have been used to form great numbers of words that the language could badly afford to do without. The endings *-ise*, *-ist*, *-ism*, *-ite*, originally Greek, have been very extensively used in the formation of English derivatives.

Old English, in comparison with most other Indo-Germanic languages, was remarkably poor in diminutive endings, and those which did exist were sparingly used. One of them was *-incel*, as in *tūnincel* a little "town" or homestead; but this did not survive into Middle English. The ending *-ling* can hardly be said to have had a diminutive force in Old English, but it was frequently so used in Old Norse, as in *gǣslingr*, which was adopted into English as *gosling* (dialectally *gesling*). The Norse suffix has in modern English become quite common as a means of forming diminutive nouns. We have *kingling, princeling, squireling*, and many similar words. In the fourteenth century the Dutch or Flemish diminutive ending *-kin* (identical with the German *-chen*) came into English use, chiefly from nicknames like *Willekin*, little William, *Jankin*, little John. The fashion of forming such nicknames from Christian names became exceedingly popular, and has left abundant traces in modern surnames like Jenkins, Atkins, Dawkins, Wilkins. In imitation of these proper names, the suffix was afterwards attached to ordinary substantives, and in modern English we can, at least in jocular speech, add *-kin* to almost any noun to form a diminutive. Even more common than *-kin*, and more dignified in use, is *-let*, which we have adopted from French, and have appended to many native words, as in *cloudlet, streamlet, brooklet, leaflet, ringlet, booklet.*

There are two or three foreign prefixes that have been so completely taken into English that we use them almost or quite as freely as we do those of native origin. The most useful of these is the Latin *re-*, again. No dictionary will ever contain all the words formed with this prefix that have been used by English writers; the compounds of *re-* with verbs and nouns of action are as innumerable as those of *un-* with adjectives. In Middle English *again-* was often used as a prefix, but the words so formed have become obsolete: the English love of brevity has caused the native prefix to be supplanted by the foreigner. The Latin and French *dis-* comes next in frequency of use. Although Lydgate, writing about 1430, uses the word *distrust*, it was not until a hundred years later that it became a common practice to attach this prefix to native words. In 1659 a grammarian writes that *dis-* like *un-* and *re-*, "may be prefixed at pleasure." Perhaps this statement was even at that time somewhat exaggerated, and it would certainly be far from correct now. Of the multitude of words beginning with this prefix coined in the sixteenth and seventeenth centuries the greater part are obsolete (though many are still current, amongst them being such familiar words as *dislike*, *distaste*, *dispraise*), and since 1700 very few new ones have come into use. The prefix, however, is still felt to be quite English: no one would find any difficulty in understanding such a word as *dislove*, though it has perhaps never been used for centuries. Writers of the nineteenth century have used the verbs *disgod*, *dishero*, and the nouns *dishealth*, *discharity;* but formations of this kind have now an appearance of being affected. The French *en-* or *em-* has been used to form several English derivatives, as *endear*, *embody*, *embog*, *enliven*, *ensnare*, *entangle.* In recent times the Greek *anti-*, against, has become thoroughly naturalised. Words like *anti-slavery*, *anti-vaccinator*, *anti-income-tax*, *anti-corn-law*, *anti-radical*, are intelligible to every one, and their number is constantly increasing. Perhaps these formations should be placed rather under the head of combination than under that of derivation, though as the preposition *anti* has no separate existence in English this is a debatable question. There are other foreign elements which have in the same manner come into use as prefixes in the formation of English words, such as the Latin *pro* in *pro-Russian*, *pro-Boer; post* in *post-Norman*, *post-date; ante* in *antedate*, *anteroom* (imitating *ante-chamber*, which is French); *præ* in *pre-Roman*, *pre-Conquest; co-* in *co-mate; sub* in *sub-let; ex* in *ex-king; inter* in *interlock*, *interleave; non* in *non-conductor*, *nonconformist*, *non-existence*, *non-natural.*

From these examples, to which many more might be added, it will be seen that the English language has not only very greatly enriched its vocabulary by direct borrowing from other tongues, but has also largely availed itself of foreign aid to increase its power of forming new words. There is very little in the borrowed machinery of suffixes and prefixes that can fairly be called superfluous. Almost without exception, it has been adopted, not out of foolish affectation, but because it supplied the means of expressing necessary meanings with a degree either of precision or of brevity to which the native resources of the language were inadequate.

According to the definition which we gave of Derivation, "the making of a new word out of an old one," it includes two processes which have not hitherto been mentioned, but which have had a considerable share in the formation of the English vocabulary. These are *Back-formation* and *Shortening*.

BACK-FORMATION

There are many words in English which have a fallacious appearance of containing some well-known derivative suffix. It has not unfrequently happened that a word of this kind has been popularly supposed to imply the existence of a primary word from which it has been derived in the usual way. The result of this supposition is the unconscious creation of a new word, which is made out of the old one by depriving it of what is thought to be its suffix, or sometimes by the substitution of a different suffix. According to some eminent scholars, the verb *to beg* has been in this way formed from *beggar*, which is thought to be adopted from the old French *begar*, a member of the religious order called Beghards, who supported themselves, like the friars, by begging. This etymology is disputed; but there are many other instances of the process which are not open to question. The noun *butcher* is really from the French *boucher*, and the ending is not etymologically identical with the common English suffix of agent-nouns;[4] but in many dialects people have come to use the verb *to butch*, and to speak of "the butching business." Other dialectal back-formations are *buttle*, to pour out liquor, from *butler*, and *cuttle*, to make knives, from *cutler*. The noun *pedlar* is older than the verb *to peddle* or the adjective *peddling*, and *broker* than the verb *to broke* (now obsolete) and the verbal noun *broking*. *Grovelling* was originally an adverb, meaning "face downwards"; it was formed out of the old phrase *on grufe* (which had the same meaning) by adding the suffix *-ling*, which occurs in many other adverbs, now mostly obsolete, such as *backling*, backwards, *headling*, head-first. But *grovelling* was misunderstood as a present participle, and the verb *grovel* was formed from it. Similarly the verbs *sidle* and *darkle* have been formed out of the old adverbs *sideling* and *darkling*. Probably the modern verb *nestle* is not, as is commonly said, the same as the Old English *nestlian* to build a nest, but has been evolved from *nestling*, an inhabitant of a nest, used adjectively as in "nestling brood." Many of the words that have been formed by this process are so happily expressive that the misunderstanding that has given rise to them must be accounted a fortunate accident. . . .

An excellent illustration of the working of this process is seen in the origin of the verb *edit*. The Latin *ēditor*, literally "one who gives

[4] The English agent-noun suffix is *-er*, as in *writer*, *singer*. It indicates one who performs the action named by the stem of the word. [eds.]

out," from the verb *ēdere* to give out, was after the invention of printing often employed in a special sense as denoting the person who "gives to the world" a book or other literary work of which he is not the author. In this sense it has passed into English and other modern languages. But under modern conditions there are two different classes of persons concerned in the production of a book, to either of whom the word might be applied in its literal meaning with equal propriety. The "giver-out" of a book—for instance, of a classical text which has never before been printed—may mean what we now call the "publisher," the man who bears the expense of printing it and makes the arrangements for its circulation among the public, or it may mean the scholar who puts the text into order for publication and provides it with such illustrative matter as it is deemed to require. In early times these two functions were often united in the same person, but they are now ordinarily divided. Now while in French *éditeur* ("editor") has come to mean "publisher," in English it has become restricted to the other of its possible applications. When we use it we no longer think of its literal sense: the prominent function of an "editor" is not that of issuing a literary work to the public, but that of bringing it into the form in which it is to appear. Although *editor* is not a word of English formation, it has an ending which coincides in form with that of English agent-nouns, so that it has naturally suggested the coinage of a verb "to edit," meaning "to prepare for publication as an editor does," *i.e.*, to put into such a form as is thought suitable for the public to read. . . .

Shortening

The substitution, in hurried, careless, jocular or vulgar speech, of a part of a word for the whole, is common in most languages, and is especially congenial to the English fondness for brevity of utterance. It does not, by itself, constitute a mode of word-formation: the vulgar *taters* and *bacca*, for *potatoes* and *tobacco*, cannot be called new words, any more than any other mispronunciations can be so called. But when, as very often happens, the original word and its shortened form come both to be generally used by the same speakers with different meanings, or even only with a difference in the implied tone of feeling, a real addition has been made to the vocabulary of the language, and the lexicographer is bound to recognise the shortened form as a distinct word. Shortening, in such cases, is in the strictest sense a kind of derivation; and it is a process which has contributed not a little to increase the English store of words.

Even when the abbreviated form expresses precisely the same meaning as the original form, the two must often be reckoned as separate words, because the longer form is reserved for more dignified or more serious use. *Omnibus* and *bus* are synonymous in the sense that they denote the same objects; but they are not absolute synonyms, because the one is more familiar in tone than the other; the two are used on different occasions. The same thing may be said of *photograph* and *photo*, or *bicycle* and *bike*, though here the abbreviated forms are not universally accepted by educated people as legitimate. Sometimes what was at first only a jocular abbreviation has ousted the longer form from general use, as in the case of *wig* for *periwig*, which was originally an altered pronunciation of *peruke*.

But very frequently a word which has been formed by shortening undergoes a sense-development of its own, in which the original word does not share. Even if anybody is pedantic enough to deny that *bus* is a distinct word from *omnibus*, he cannot refuse to admit that *cab* is a real word, though it was originally a shortened pronunciation of *cabriolet*. A cab and a cabriolet are not the same kind of vehicle at all. So, too, *Miss*, the title given to an unmarried woman, and *Mrs.* (pronounced *Missis*) are now quite different in meaning from each other, and from *mistress*, from which both are derived by shortening. There was a time when *gent* was used by educated people as a familiar abbreviation for *gentleman*, without any depreciatory implication. But in this use it was gradually discarded from the speech of the upper classes, and came to be a contemptuous designation for the vulgar pretenders to gentility in whose vocabulary it still survived. . . .

Some words that originated as playful abbreviations of other words are now used without any consciousness of their origin. *Extra*, in such phases as "an extra allowance," is not the Latin word, but an abbreviation of *extraordinary*. An *extra*, meaning an edition of a newspaper out of the usual course, was at one time called "an *extraordinary*.". . . And only students of etymology know that *chap* is a shortening of *chapman*, properly meaning "trader."

In the Middle English and early Modern English periods it was very common, in the hurry of pronunciation, to drop an initial vowel which immediately preceded the stressed syllable of a word. In this way many words beginning with a vowel came to have an alternative form from which the first syllable was omitted; and almost in every case in which both forms have survived a difference of meaning has been developed. *Assize* and *size* are so different in sense that no one could think of them as the same word, and yet the one is only a shortened pronunciation of the other. The standard magnitude of an article of commerce was settled by an "assize" or sitting of some constituted authority. Hence the standard or authorised magnitude of anything was called its *assize* or *size*, and afterwards the latter form came to mean magnitude in general. *Tend*, as in the phrase "to tend the sick," was originally the same word as *attend*; but the two verbs are no longer synonymous. *Alone*, which stands for an earlier *all one*, was in the Elizabethan period shortened into *lone* when used as an adjective. The Middle English phrase *on live*, equivalent to "in life," was commonly pronounced *alive*, and this, by shortening, afterwards yielded the adjective *live*. *Mend* was originally the same word as *amend*. The shorter form, as usual, serves for the trivial occasions of ordinary life, while the longer form is of more dignified application. We speak of *mending* a stocking, but of *amending* an Act of Parliament. Sometimes other prefixes than those consisting only of a vowel were dropped in the same way. The verb to *vie* is shortened from *envie*—not the same word as the modern *envy*, but adopted from the French *envier*, which comes from the Latin *invitare* to challenge; so that *vie* and *invite* are in ultimate etymology the same. *Fence* is *defence* without its prefix; and *fend*, from which *fender* is derived, is short for *defend*. Several words that originally began with *dis-* or *des-* now begin with *s*. *Stain* is a shorter form of *distain*, which is the Old French *desteindre*, to take out the dye of anything, from the prefix *des-*, *dis-*, and *teindre* to dye. *Despite*, from the Old French *despit*, the Latin *despectus*, a looking down, despising, has become *spite*. No word now sounds more thoroughly English than *sport*, which has, indeed, been adopted from English into foreign languages; yet it is a shortening of *disport*, which is a word of French origin. To "disport oneself" is, literally interpreted, "to carry oneself in a different direction" from that of one's ordinary business; and hence *disport* and *sport* came to mean amusement or pastime.

Besides the new words that owe their origin to shortening in pronunciation, there are others which have arisen out of abbreviations used in writing. Sometimes the mere initials of a phrase come to be treated as a word, the written letters being represented in pronunciations by their names. Thus we speak of "a question of £ s. d. (*el ess dee*)"; or, again, of "an M.P. (*em pee*)," or "a D. C. L. (*dee cee el*)," meaning a person who is entitled to write those initials after his name. Sometimes, again, a word or phrase as abbreviated in writing happens to yield a pronounceable sequence of letters, and takes its place in the language as a word.[5] This occurs most frequently with Latin phrases. Many of the shortened forms are vulgar[6] or jocular, as *infra dig*, *incog*, *nem. con.*, "the *pros and cons*." But *per cent*, *cent per cent*, from the Latin (*centum*) *per centum*, are part of the ordinary English vocabulary. The most curious instance of the formation of a word by this process is *culprit*. Its origin is to be found in the strange corrupt Norman French once used in our courts of justice. When a prisoner had pleaded "not guilty," the reply made on behalf of the Crown was "culpable; prest." This meant "(he is) guilty, (and we are) ready (to prove it)." In the reports of criminal cases the phrase was commonly abbreviated *cul. prest*, and afterwards corruptly *cul. prit*. Then in some way, not very clearly understood, it seems to have come about that the clerks of the Crown, modelling their procedure on the pattern set in the written reports, fell into the practice of using the syllables *cul prit* as an oral formula; and as this formula was followed by the question, "How will you be tried?" addressed to the prisoner, it was popularly apprehended to mean "guilty man." The custom survived in the courts down to the eighteenth century; but when *culprit* became a current word with a new sense, it was probably felt that there was an injustice in addressing a prisoner by a term which presumed his guilt, and the use of the formula was discontinued.

3. ROOT-CREATION.

Perhaps few, even among professed students of language, are aware how large a portion of the English vocabulary has, in the ordinary sense of the word, no etymology at all. We do not mean merely that there are many words the origin of which is and will always remain unknown because of the imperfection of our means of discovery. This is no doubt quite true. But there are also many words which were neither inherited from Old English, nor adopted from

[5] Such a word is now called an acronym. Examples: AWOL, NATO, RADAR. Many acronyms appeared during and after World War II. [eds.]

[6] By *vulgar* Bradley does not mean "indecent." He is using the word in the linguists' sense of "belonging to the common people." [eds.]

any foreign language, nor formed out of any older English or foreign words by any process of composition or derivation. It is to instances of this kind that the name of "root-creation" may be fitly applied.

One of the principal forms of root-creation is that which is known by the name of Onomatopoeia. The word is Greek, and literally means "name-making." It was used by the Greeks to express the fact (common in their own as in other languages) that a noise, or the object producing it, sometimes *makes its own name:* that is to say, is denoted by a word formed in imitation of the sound.

The number of "echoic" words (as they have been called by Dr. Murray) which have arisen in Middle and Modern English is very considerable. We may mention as examples *bang*, *boo*, *boom*, *cackle*, *cheep*, *fizz*, *gibber*, *giggle*, *hiss*, *hum*, *mumble*, *pop*, *quack*, *rumble*, *simmer*, *sizzle*, *titter*, *twitter*, *whirr*, *whiz*, *whip-poor-will*, and the reduplicated words *bow-wow*, *ding-dong*, *flip-flop*, *hee-haw*, *ping-pong*, *pom-pom*, *rub-a-dub*, *tick-tack*.

It is possible that some of the words in the first part of this list may go back to Old English; words of this kind are much more common in speech than in literature, and we are certainly far from knowing the whole of the Old English vocabulary. However, even if they are much older than they can be proved to be, there is no doubt that they are imitative in origin.

The imitation of inarticulate by articulate sounds can never be accurate. Perhaps one or two birds *do* really "make their names"; though even in the case of the cuckoo it is not quite certain that we actually hear the two consonants. But the cries of birds and animals, produced by organs having more or less similarity to our own, may be regarded as in some measure articulate. In general the rendering of noises into the sounds of human speech involves some play of fancy, like that which is exercised when we see faces in the fire, or landscapes in the clouds. The resemblance which an imitative word is felt to bear to the inarticulate noise which it names consists not so much in similarity of impression on the ear as in similarity of mental suggestion. For instance, it is not at all literally true that a gun, or a heavy body impinging on a door, says "*bang*." But the sequence of three sounds of which the word consists is of such a nature that it can easily be uttered with force, so as to suggest the startling effect of a sudden violent noise, while the final consonant admits of being prolonged to express the notion of a continued resonance. In this instance and in many others, the so-called "imitative" word represents an inarticulate noise not so much by way of an echo as *symbolically*. That is to say, the elements composing the sound of the word combine to produce a mental effect which we recognise as analogous to that produced by the noise.

In much the same way, the sound of a word may suggest "symbolically" a particular kind of movement or a particular shape of an object. We often feel that a word has a peculiar natural fitness for expressing its meaning, though it is not always possible to tell why we have this feeling, and the reasons, when we can trace them, are different in different cases. Sometimes the notion of natural fitness is an illusion, due to the fact that the word obscurely reminds us of the sound of several other words which happen to have meanings somewhat similar to that which it expresses. But quite often the sound of a word has a real intrinsic significance. For instance, a word with long vowels, which we naturally utter slowly, suggests the idea of slow movement.[7] A repetition of the same consonant suggests a repetition of movement, slow if the vowels be long, and rapid if the vowels be short.[8] The vowels that are produced by the passage of the breath through a narrow opening, such as *ee* or *ĭ*, are suited to convey the notion of something slender or slight, while a full vowel such as *oo* suggests a massive object.[9] A syllable ending in a stopped consonant, especially an unvoiced one like *p*, *t*, *k*, preceded by a short vowel, affords a natural expression for the idea of some quick and abrupt action.[10] Sequences of consonants which are harsh to the ear, or involve difficult muscular effort in utterance, are felt to be appropriate in words descriptive of harsh or violent movement.[11] It would be possible to say a great deal more about the inherent symbolism of sounds; but it is not necessary here to pursue the subject in further detail. The point that needs to be remarked is that this phonetic symbolism (which probably had a large share in the primary origin of human language) has led to a very large amount of root-creation in Middle and Modern English. It is worthy of note that many of the words that have in this way been invented as instinctive descriptions of action or form occur in groups of two or three, in which the consonants are alike, while the vowel is varied to express differences of

[7] E.g., water *seeps*. [eds.]
[8] E.g., *cock-a-doodle-doo, titter*. [eds.]
[9] E.g., for smallness: *little, slim, bit, teeny, wee*. [eds.]
[10] E.g., *clap, flap, pat, crack, strike, knock, flick*. [eds.]
[11] E.g., "When Ajax strives some rock's vast weight to throw." Pope [eds.]

mental effect. Thus we have *bleb*, *blob*, *blub-cheeked*, all denoting something inflated. The initial *bl* was perhaps suggested by the verb *blow;* the pronunciation of the syllables involves an inflation of the cheeks which is symbolical of the notion common to the three words, and the different degrees of fulness in the vowels are obviously significant of differences of size in the object denoted. Other instances in which the notion expressed by the consonantal skeleton is modified by difference in the vowel are *jiggle*, *joggle; flip*, *flap*, *flop; chip*, *chap*, *chop; fimble*, *famble*, *fumble; flash*, *flush*.

Among the many words that owe their origin to a sense of the intrinsic expressiveness of particular combinations of sounds are *bob*, *brob*, *bunch*, *dab*, *dodder*, *fiddle-faddle*, *fidge*, *fidget*, *flabbergast*, *fudge*, *hug*, *hugger-mugger*, *hump*, *jog*, *see-saw*, *squander*, *squelch*, *throb*, *thump*, *thwack*, *twiddle*, *wobble*. Some of these, it is true, may in a certain sense be said to have an etymology; but their actual meaning is not due to the word, native or foreign, that may have suggested their formation in the first instance, but to the impression which is made by their mere sound.

Many excellent examples of intentional root-creation may be found among the invented words (not intended to be permanent additions to the language) in Lewis Carroll's *Alice in Wonderland*, *Through the Looking-Glass*, and *The Hunting of the Snark*. These clever coinages derive their effect partly from their suggestion of obscure reminiscences of existing words, and partly from real phonetic expressiveness. Two of them, *galumphing* and the verb *to chortle*,[12] have come into pretty general use, and have found their way into our dictionaries.

SUGGESTED ASSIGNMENTS

1. One important kind of compound word is exemplified by *bláckbird*. The first part is given the stronger stress, and this part modifies the second part. This type of compound is sometimes printed as two words, e.g., *hót dog*, but it is nevertheless considered a single compound word if it meets the two qualifications mentioned. Thus both *sídewalk* and *drúg store* are compounds. Some compounds like these have a counterpart in a two-word combination of modifier plus noun. In these the stronger stress is on the second part, as in *black bírd*

[12] *Chortle* is composed of *chuckle* telescoped with *snort*. Such words are called blends. Examples: *telecast* (televised broadcast), *motel* (motor hotel). [eds.]

(any bird that is black in color) and *hot dóg* (a dog that is hot). The left-hand list below is composed of compounds and the right-hand list of their two-word counterparts. Explain the difference in meaning.

bláckberry	black bérry
Whíte House	white hóuse
géntleman	gentle mán
gáme fish	game físh
blúe book	blue boók
hígh chair	high cháir
súrplus store	surplus stóre
dáncing girl	dancing gírl
móving van	moving ván

2. In the light of the exercise above, explain the ambiguity in these sentences:
   a. The lawyer lost a brief case.
   b. I am an outdoor lover.
   c. Our school has two French teachers.
   d. The firemen burst into the smoking room.
   e. In the old creek bed he found a mammoth tooth.
3. Several uses of the suffix *-ish* are mentioned by Professor Bradley. In addition, it is used today to form pejoratives, that is, words with a derogatory meaning. For example, *womanish* is uncomplimentary while *womanly* is complimentary. You might say, "Now don't be teacherish," or "Now don't be baby brotherish," even though no one had ever before used these terms, and they would be accepted and understood. Write ten sentences in which you use the *-ish* suffix to make pejoratives.
4. Look up the following words in the *New English Dictionary* or the *Oxford English Dictionary* to find out their first recorded use: *typewrite, typewriter; donate, donation; subedit, subeditor; burgle, burglar.* Which of them seem to be back-formations?
5. What do you think is the source of the following back-formations: *to advance register, to henpeck, to laze, to bootleg, to coronate, to orate, to reminisce?*
6. What full words do these shortened forms represent: *lab, exam, co-ed, prom, deb, varsity, bus, cab, still, flu, taxi, gin?*
7. Shortened forms like those above are often called clipped words or clippings. What clippings are a part of your everyday campus jargon?
8. What do these acronyms mean: WAC, SHAPE, ALCOA? What others do you know?
9. The language of the military services is filled with acronyms. Inter-

view a veteran of World War II or of the Korean War and get a list of acronyms that he used in the service.

10. What onomatopoetic words do you find in these quotations?
    a. And the silken, sad, uncertain rustling of each purple curtain. (Poe)
    b. And murmuring of innumerable bees. (Tennyson)
    c. I hear lake water lapping with low sounds by the shore. (Yeats)
    d. And the plashing of waterdrops
    In the marble fountain. (Amy Lowell)
    e. With lisp of leaves and ripple of rain. (Swinburne)
11. Are any of these words not onomatopoetic: *thunder, tinkle, clink, boom, bubble, tick, whisper, wheeze, chug, coo, pop?*
12. Write a short paragraph describing something that is heard, using onomatopoeia to make vivid your description. You might use such topics as a train departing from a station, fast-running water in a stream, bird sounds in a wood, a child playing with metal toys, or starting a car engine on a cold winter morning.
13. What words were used to form the following blends: *brunch, smog, splatter, escalator, blurt, electrocute?*

ANALOGICAL CHANGE

Eugene Nida

New word forms in language are created by a simple but important linguistic process called analogy or analogical change. You will understand analogy when you know why a child says goed *for* went *or* deers *for* deer, *or why you sometimes make a slip of the tongue with a form like* teached. *You will hear examples of analogy nearly every day if you listen attentively to the language around you. Eugene Nida explains this process by means of a dialogue between a professor and four students. Dr. Nida—a specialist in New Testament Greek and in Mexican-*

From *Linguistic Interludes* by Eugene Nida, published by the Summer Institute of Linguistics, Glendale, California. Reprinted by permission of the author,

Indian and African languages—is the author of two valuable books on linguistics: A Synopsis of English Syntax *and* Morphology: A Descriptive Analysis of Words.

Ann Ferrell: What do you mean by analogies and analogical changes?

Dr. Thompson: Your question is a good one. But let us turn to mathematics for a moment. It will be easier for us to understand. Note the following proportion:

$$2 : 4 = 3 : 6 = 4 : x$$

You do not have to hesitate a moment before answering that x equals 8. The relationships between 2 and 4 and between 3 and 6 establish a pattern, so that x is equal to 8. In mathematics this is an analogical proportion. We have similar situations in languages.

Ann Ferrell: I only wish that languages were as simple.

Dr. Thompson: In some ways they are. A linguistic analogy is only the statement of a proportion or pattern in language. Let us suppose that one has heard the word *radio* for the first time and has never heard the plural of this word. He probably will not hesitate long in forming a plural for the word, for he has a pattern or proportion to guide him. For example,

banjo : banjos = billow : billows = radio : x

With practically no hesitation the speaker will say *radios.*

Bill Downing: But why specifically wouldn't he relate this word to a pattern with *-en,* as in *oxen?*

Dr. Thompson: In the first place, the *-en* occurs regularly with only one word, namely, *oxen.* It constitutes a very limited pattern, even when one includes the words *children* and *brethren.* But there is another feature. The speaker has no doubt had occasion before to note that if he formed a new word on the *s* plural pattern, his choice was correct. He has discovered then that the *s* plural pattern is the productive pattern and that the *-en* pattern is fixed and limited.

Richard North: Then, if one makes up a word such as *educationalize,* does he do so simply by following analogies?

Dr. Thompson: Right. I do not know if I have ever before heard the word *educationalize,* but it makes some "sense," because it is built up on the analogy of other words. There is a pattern and a very extensive one which permits the addition of *-al* to almost any noun ending in *-ion.* In turn, the pattern, or analogical proportion, is very extensive for adding the "factitive" suffix *-ize* to any adjective ending in this suffix *-al.*[1]

Bill Downing: Then the person who wishes to translate from one language into another, especially if he has to construct new words in the language into which he is translating, must by all means know the patterns of formation.

Dr. Thompson: That is absolutely imperative, but few translators are fully aware of the importance of it.

Jack Sheridan: You mentioned, Dr. Thompson, that analogy affects all parts of a language. How does this involve the syntax?

Dr. Thompson: Every language is filled with such examples. One, however, which becomes involved in so much discussion is the matter of *like* employed as a conjunction.

Ann Ferrell: Dr. Zilch is especially opposed to such "corruption," as he calls it.

Dr. Thompson: Instead of corruption it is purely a matter of the pattern and the pressure of the pattern toward conformity. We have a word *than* which introduces a clause or a phrase. *Like* is employed generally in phrases and is analogically extended to introduce clauses. This conforms the function of *than* and *like.*

I work more than John : I work more than John works =
I work more like John: I work more like John works.

The fact that the word *more* is employed somewhat differently on the two sides of the equation does not alter the value of this analogical pattern. . . .

Bill Downing: Why is it that a language does not reach the static point where no further analogic change will take place?

Dr. Thompson: For one thing, phonetic change takes place continually. This means that items which would otherwise be in analogical conformity are thrown out of line. Moreover, languages cannot live to themselves; they borrow from other languages or dialects, and this necessitates the assimilation and adaptation of material. Furthermore, analogy must have free operation. If it were not for analogy in languages, there would be no such thing as speech; no one would be able to say anything which he had not heard before. Complex communications are only possible because languages are systems of patterns into which we can fit various lexical items in different arrangements from those we have heard before. The only

[1] Here the factitive suffix *-ize* has the meaning of make. Examples of this pattern are *legalize, rationalize, civilize.* [eds.]

way to prevent change is to stop life. Analogical change ceases only in a "dead" language.

Richard North: I remember that in the King James Version of the Bible *cow* is employed for singular and *kine* for plural. Does the fact that we no longer use *kine* for the plural of *cow* indicate the working of analogy?

Dr. Thompson: It does. An analogical pattern for *cow* : *cows* may have existed in *sow* : *sows*. Moreover, the *s* type of plural was at the time of this change growing in popularity. The *s* plural had become the productive pattern. We are not leveling plural formations now, except perhaps in a class of words such as *rooves* [ˈruwvz] versus *roofs* [ˈrufs] and *laths* [ˈlæðz], versus *laths* [ˈlæθs]. The operation of analogical leveling or pressure toward conformity will occur in one area of the language for a time and then in another.

Bill Downing: Can we tell in advance which part of the language is going to be subject to such leveling influence of analogical change?

Dr. Thompson: We cannot know. We only know that analogy operates in those parts of the language which are out of equilibrium with the general structure as a whole. At present in English considerable leveling appears to be operating in the matter of the so-called perfect participles. Note the fluctuation in the word *proved* versus *proven*. In a high percentage of words in English the form of the perfect participle and the past tense are identical.[2] This situation constitutes a pattern for leveling. At present many speakers employ *proven* in adjectival usage and *proved* in the verb phrase, as in *the proven fact* and *I have proved it*. Compare this with *a shaven face* and *I have shaved*.

Ann Ferrell: Why is it, if analogy attacks the parts of the language that are out of line, that it does not level such items as the irregular parts of the verb *to be?* It would seem that *am*, *are*, *is*, *was*, *were*, and *be* would be good objects for this analogical change.

Dr. Thompson: Your reaction is a good one, but it so happens that the more frequently employed words of a language resist analogical leveling the most. In many languages one finds that irregular forms appear chiefly among the commonest words and phrases of the language. The reason for this is not difficult to find. Let us presume that one has heard both *proved* and *proven*, but he has

[2] E.g., *moved, have moved; loved, have loved; seemed, have seemed; made, have made.* [eds.]

not heard them sufficiently often and in enough contexts so as to be sure precisely which one is to be used in a particular situation. He is more likely to choose the form *proved,* which fits the predominant pattern of formation. If the hearer reacts to the situation at all, his reaction will probably be more or less the same as the speaker's, for these forms *proven* and *proved* are probably not too common in his speech and hence the analogical pattern of conformity of past tense and "perfect passive participle" forms has more opportunity to operate. The speaker is easily understood and meets with no derision as to his choice of forms. Each time he uses *proved* in place of *proven* he meets with a similar experience, so continues to use the form representing the more common pattern. But if on the other hand the speaker should say *I is trying,* having chosen a less frequently employed form, but one which he may have heard from some speakers of sub-standard English, he may be somewhat misunderstood, and certainly he will not make the most favorable impression upon a speaker of standard English. The forms of the verb *to be* are too common to be objects of doubt. One who says *I is trying* may suffer derision or loss of prestige by such an expression. In many circumstances of life it is important that a speaker make a favorable impression upon those who speak standard English, for these standard-English speakers are those who more or less carry on the affairs of the English-speaking world. They are the ones of social and economic prestige and power. Hence conformity to such a standard will add to the prestige of the speaker and at the same time be a means of obtaining social and economic advantages.

Bill Downing: Does analogy account for the development of some new morphological element, such as *-ly,* which I understand came from *like?*

Dr. Thompson: You are right. The *-like* in such compounds as *man-like* and *woman-like* was changed phonetically to the present *-ly,* and it has become a productive affix which we may add to many nouns to form adjectives and to many adjectives to form adverbs.

Richard North: But if the *-like* in *man-like* changed to *-ly,* how is it that we still have the compound *man-like?* It doesn't seem to make sense to say that something changes, when it remains the same.

Dr. Thompson: The fact that we have *man-like* along with *manly* indicates that a new compound has been formed with the constituents *man* and *like.* The phonemic modification of elements of a compound and then the re-formation of a compound like the first is not uncommon. The compound [ˈhu·s-wi·f] "house-wife" has become modern *hussy*. However, another compound with the same constituents has been made so that we have both *house-wife* and *hussy*

Ann Ferrell: I should imagine that people might get their analogies twisted at times, even as they do in popular etymologies.

Dr. Thompson: That is so, if you mean that the analogical formations are contrary to the historical pattern of derivation.

Jack Sheridan: You couldn't expect the common run of people to know the history of the language. Even the so-called scholars are caught making mistakes in etymology.

Dr. Thompson: We cannot expect people to follow historical principles, but we can expect them to follow analogical principles, and they do. People are always re-making a language to fit the patterns which they imagine should exist. As an example of this, one may cite the English forms *cherry* and *cherries*. These forms come from Old French *cherise*, borrowed as Middle English *cheris*. But this *s* ending evidently seemed to be a plural, for the speakers formed a new singular on the analogy of the *s* plural type, so that we have now *cherry* singular and *cherries* plural. This is called a back-formation. Note a similar situation in the verb *burgle* derived from the noun *burglar*.

Bill Downing: But do the speakers of a language actually reason out these types of analogies, or is it all quite accidental?

Dr. Thompson: We must never suppose that people apply any strict logistic methodology to their linguistic decisions. Most analogical formations are made quite unconsciously. People "slip" into a pattern without realizing just why they have said what they have. For a moment a speaker may have forgotten which form he has heard in a particular construction. But in normal speech one does not hesitate long, and so a form is produced which is in keeping with what seems to fit the general pattern. Perhaps a speaker wishes to use a past tense form of *dive*. He may have the impression that the vowel changes somewhat, but he doesn't remember exactly what form it is. He shifts then to the regular pattern and says *dived*.[3] Using this form he will probably meet with an understanding response and little if any unfavorable reaction from the hearers.

[3] The speaker might be moved to say *dove* by analogy with the pattern *ride, rode; drive, drove; write, wrote;* etc. [eds.]

Jack Sheridan: But what is the relationship between analogy and fluctuations? Let us say that the speaker has heard both forms *dove* and *dived.* What is the factor which would induce him to say *dived* rather than *dove?*

Dr. Thompson: It is convenient to recognize as analogical formation the first occurrence of such an analogical form. From then on, if one has heard both forms, the choice of one or the other is a matter of fluctuation between forms.

Bill Downing: But doesn't analogy play an important role in the fluctuation of forms and the ultimate discarding of one or the other?

Dr. Thompson: It does. If the speaker has heard both *dove* and *dived,* he is very likely to choose *dived* because of the predominance of the regular pattern. In the fluctuation between forms we have to recognize the pressure of the pattern which influences the choice in accordance with the analogical conformity.

SUGGESTED ASSIGNMENTS

1. The better desk dictionaries of the 1950's indicate that after *babysitter* had entered English, the back-formation *babysit* followed. To form the past tense, which analogical pattern would you expect users of English to follow–*pit, pitted* or *sit, sat?* Why?
2. The word *spatial* is sometimes misspelled *spacial.* What analogy might account for this misspelling?
3. If you wished to use the past tense of *ding,* a verb employed by Robert Burns, what two forms would first come to your mind? What is the analogical basis of each one?
4. What analogical patterns might bring about the use of the following nonstandard forms: *knowed* for *knew; brang* for *brought; hisn* for *his?*
5. Collect any unusual word-forms or slips of the tongue that you notice in speech. Some of these probably have their source in analogy. Write a paragraph that will account for the forms that you consider analogical.
6. In the second-year English class of a Dutch high school, the students were heard to use the forms *oneth, twoth,* and *threeth* instead of *first, second,* and *third.* What was the source of these forms?

EARLY AMERICAN SPEECH: ADOPTIONS FROM FOREIGN TONGUES

Thomas Pyles

The English language is one of the great word-borrowers in history. About one-half of our word stock has been borrowed into English from Latin and its Romance descendants, and in the Renaissance alone words were adopted into English from more than fifty languages. This process did not stop when the English language was brought to our shores, and in the selection below Thomas Pyles describes how our early settlers took over the words they needed from the tongues with which they came in contact. Mr. Pyles is Professor of English at the University of Florida and has contributed numerous articles to learned journals.

BEFORE THERE WAS any permanent settlement of English-speaking folk in this land, a number of Indian words had made their way into the language of England by way of Spanish or Portuguese—words from Nahuatl, the tongue of the Aztecs, who were the most highly advanced of the Indians that the Spanish found in Mexico, as well as from various Indian dialects spoken in Central and South America and the West Indies. Some of these words came in time to be current in all the languages of Europe.

The English language in those exuberant days of Elizabeth, of Raleigh, Drake, Hawkins, Bacon, Marlowe, Jonson, and Shakespeare, had been particularly receptive to augmentations of its already rich word stock from foreign sources—the so-called "inkhorn" terms from the classical languages, along with words from French, Spanish, Italian, and Portuguese. Words from the New World must have had all the charm of lush exoticisms in a period when the language was being enriched from so many nearby Continental sources, though they seem for the most part commonplace enough today—words like *potato*, *tomato*, *chocolate*, *cocoa*, *canoe*, *cannibal*, *barbecue*, *maize*, and *savannah*, which must have been known to the first Englishmen to come to these shores with any intention of staying. One of them, *maize*, was by a strange perversity of linguistic fate to be replaced by *corn* in the English of America. The British use *corn* in the sense "wheat," while retaining the older meaning of "grain," as in the "Corn Laws." Another of them, *cannibal*, a modification of *Caribal* "Caribbean native," was used in slightly different form by Shakespeare in his play about the "vexed Bermoothes," for *Caliban*, if not simply a metathesized[1] form of *can(n)ibal*, is a variant of *Cariban*, itself a variant of *Caribal*. *Barbecue*, while appearing first in British English, is nevertheless much more familiar in America, and its use to designate an outdoor social or political meeting at which animals are roasted whole is exclusively American. But these words, while native to the New World, must be distinguished from those which entered the language of Englishmen who chose or were forced to transplant themselves permanently in this strange and savage land.

The colonizers of this country were confronted with a land whose topography, meteorological phenomena, trees, plants, birds, and animals were frequently quite different from what they had known in England. Inasmuch as an understanding of the principles of semantics is not congenital, people generally are wont to ask when they see some new object, "What is it?" and expect in answer to be told its name, supposing then that they have learned something really significant about it. This procedure, or something very similar to it, must have been gone through a great many times in the early days of the colonization of America when Indians were friendly enough to be asked and bright enough to divine what was being asked of them. Sometimes, too, these first white Americans made up their own names for what they saw, if there was no one to tell them the "true" names or if the "true" names were too difficult for them to pronounce. . . . They frequently combined or modified English words, as in *bullfrog* and *jimson weed* (originally *Jamestown weed*); sometimes they made use of sound alone, as in *bobolink*.

The situation with regard to the American Indian languages, with

[1] Metathesis is a transposition of sounds (or letters), as in *aksed* for *asked*. [eds.]

many tribes speaking apparently unrelated languages which are in turn subdivided into dialects, is extremely complex. Fortunately it need not concern us here, for to American English only one stock, the Algonquian, is important. This huge group of tribes, comprising among others the Arapaho, Blackfoot, Cheyenne, Cree, Delaware, Fox, Micmac, Ojibwa (Chippewa), and Penobscot, formerly occupied a larger area than any other North American Indian stock. It was they whom the first English settlers in Virginia and Massachusetts came in contact with.

As early as 1608 Captain John Smith in his *True Relation of . . . Virginia Since the First Planting of That Collony* recorded *raccoon*, though he did not spell it that way. He wrote it in various ways—for instance, *raugroughcun* and later, in his *General Historie of Virginia, New-England and the Summer Isles* of 1624, *rarowcun*—in his effort to reduce to symbols, which were, incidentally, ill-adapted to that purpose, what he heard or thought he heard from the Indians. It is highly unlikely, as a matter of fact, that a single English word of Indian origin would be immediately intelligible to an Indian today, for words have been clipped, like *squash* (the vegetable), which was originally *askutasquash*, folk-etymologized[2] like *whiskey-John* "blue jay" from *wisketjan*, or in one way or another made to conform to English speechways.

Early Indian loan words naming creatures neglected by Adam are *opossum*, *moose*, *skunk*, *menhaden*, *terrapin*, *woodchuck*, and *caribou*. *Opossum* usually occurs in speech and often in writing in an aphetic form as *possum*, as does *raccoon* as *coon*. *Woodchuck* is a folk-etymologizing of Cree or Ojibwa *otchek* or *odjik*. Noah Webster was quite proud, by the way, of deriving *woodchuck* from an Avestan word meaning "pig" and made frequent reference to this acute etymological discovery in lectures and prefaces. *Caribou*, as the spelling of its final syllable indicates, comes to us by way of Canadian French; an Englishman would have been more likely to write *cariboo*. These words, all of Algonquian origin, designate creatures indigenous to North America. Ojibwa *chipmunk* would seem to belong to this group, though it was first recorded considerably later, in Cooper's *Deerslayer* (1841); it was certainly in use much earlier.

[2] Folk etymology is a change in the form of a word that is new or strange to a speaker to make it conform to a familiar word. For example, *Welsh rabbit* (melted cheese over toast), was a humorous expression like *Cape Cod turkey* for codfish or *prairie oysters* for eggs. Because it seemed a strange word for its referent, the more reasonable *Welsh rarebit* was substituted. [eds.]

A good many native plants, vegetables, trees and shrubs bear names of Indian origin: *hickory*, *pecan*, *poke(weed)*, *chinquapin*, *squash*, *persimmon*, and *catalpa*, all but one of which are Algonquian. That one, *catalpa*, is of Muskhogean origin. A good many Southern place names are of this linguistic stock, which includes Creek, Chickasaw, and Choctaw, but *catalpa* (with its variant *catawba*) and the topographical *bayou* (from Choctaw *bayuk* "stream," coming to us by way of Louisiana French) are the only widely known words other than place names taken from the languages of these Indians, who formerly occupied an area of our country including most of Georgia, Alabama, and Mississippi and parts of Tennessee, Kentucky, Louisiana, and Florida.

Other early borrowings from the Indians include words denoting foods, customs, relationships, or artifacts peculiar to the Indians at the time of borrowing: *hominy*, *succotash*, *johnnycake*, *pone*, *pemmican*, *moccasin*, *tomahawk*, *totem*, *wigwam*, *toboggan*, *powwow*, *mackinaw*, *caucus* (perhaps), *wampum*, *sachem*, *papoose*, and *squaw*. *Toboggan* and *mackinaw* are first recorded later than the others in this group, though their earliest use in English certainly goes back considerably beyond their first recording. Both entered English by way of Canadian French; the latter word has a half-French spelling, *Mackinac*, when used as a name for the strait, the island, and the town in Michigan. The first element of *johnnycake* is probably from *jonakin* or *jonikin*, apparently of Indian origin and meaning a thin griddle cake made of corn meal. *Johnnycake* was folk-etymologized to *journey cake*, which Noah Webster thought the original form; he assumed that it meant cake to eat when one went on a journey. It has also been suggested that the word is a corruption of *Shawnee cake*, a kind of cake supposed to have been eaten by the Shawnee Indians—an explanation which Mr. Mencken in *The American Language, Supplement One* (New York, 1945) considers "much more plausible" than any other. *Jonikin* (usually spelled *johnnikin*) is still used for a corn griddle cake in the eastern part of the Carolinas and on the Eastern Shore of Maryland. . . .

All the other words in this last group save *johnnycake* have made the Atlantic crossing, and most of them are now about as familiar to the English as they are to us. In fact, all of them except *mackinaw* are listed in Wyld's *Universal Dictionary;* only *succotash* and *johnnycake* are labeled "U.S.A." The usual British pronunciation of *wigwam* rimes with *big dam*, a pronunciation never heard in this country. *Pemmican*, the Indian name for dried meat pounded into paste, mixed with fat and dried fruits, and then compressed into cakes, has even acquired the figurative meaning in British English of "condensed statement." On the continent of Europe also, most of these words are quite well known as a result of literary transmission, for generations of European children have thrilled to the novels of James Fenimore Cooper, as well as of his European imitators.

Tammany as a political designation is a well-known Americanism of Indian origin. Tammany was a Delaware chief who flourished in the latter part of the seventeenth century and who was jocularly canonized as an American saint in 1771. His name was later used to designate a political club which ultimately grew into the present powerful Democratic organization in New York City. References to *Tammany* as the name of the club, which was founded in 1789, occur from 1790 onwards. The organization uses *the Wigwam* as a designation for Tammany Hall, *sachem* for a high official of the society, and *brave* (not of Indian origin, but long used to mean an Indian warrior) for a rank-and-file member.

A good many other words of Indian origin are included in the *Dictionary of American English*, but most of them are not in wide current use: *tuckahoe* "edible part of a fungus found on roots of trees," which is also used to designate a poor white in Virginia and West Virginia, *carcajou* "wolverine," *manito* or *manitou* "a god," *quahog* or *quahaug* "hard clam," *sagamore* "chief," *samp* "corn porridge," *tamarack* "the American larch," *mugwump* "great man," and others considerably less familiar. *Mugwump*, though known much earlier, came into real prominence in the presidential campaign of 1884, when it was applied to those independent Republicans who, affecting an attitude of superiority, refused to support James G. Blaine as their party nominee. Nowadays the word is chiefly notable for the oft-recorded definition by a Congressional wag (would there were more of his kidney!) to the effect that a mugwump was one who always had his *mug* on one side of the fence and his *wump* on the other.

Some early Americanisms were translations or supposed translations of Indian words or phrases, for example, *paleface* (first used by James Fenimore Cooper), *war paint*, *warpath*, *firewater*, *pipe of peace*, *medicine man*, *Great Spirit*, *big chief*, *to scalp*, and *to bury the hatchet*. Frequently *Indian* was used in conjunction with another word, as in *Indian meal*, *Indian file*, *Indian summer*, and *Indian gift*, originally a gift for which one expected something of more value in return, but later a gift which the giver took back. *Indian giver* is first recorded, as far as we know, in Bartlett's *Glossary* of 1848, with the notation that "this term is applied by children to a child who, after having given away a thing, wishes it back again," though *Indian gift* occurs much earlier. The *Dictionary of American English* lists almost a hundred such combinations, though not all are early, for instance, *honest Injun*, which is not recorded until 1875. . . .

Before passing on to other non-English influences it is interesting to note that British English borrowed *Mohawk*, which it usually spelled *mohock*, early in the eighteenth century to designate, according to the *Oxford English Dictionary*, "one of a class of aristocratic ruffians who infested the streets of London at night," but the term has only a historical interest today. It has never had any currency in American English save among professors of eighteenth-century English literature. The *Apache* of *Apache dance*, a rowdy, sexy dance performed by a pair of dancers attired as a Parisian gangster and his "moll," did not come to us directly from the well-known American aborigines of that name. It came instead by way of French, which in the early nineteenth century borrowed the name of the Indian tribe, Gallicized its pronunciation, and used it to designate a Parisian street bully.

It is perhaps not surprising, considering the ultimate reduction of the American Indians to the status of a conquered people, that the Indian element in American English is no larger than it is. As a matter of fact, if we leave out of consideration place names, of which there are an overwhelming number—more than half of our states bear Indian names, and a large portion of our rivers, lakes, mountains, towns, and cities as well—the Indian influence on our vocabulary must be characterized as slight.

The Indian languages were not, however, the only non-European influence upon the English of America in colonial days. More than a year before the Pilgrims landed on Plymouth Rock in search of religious freedom, a group of people were against their will brought here from the west coast of Africa—principally from Senegal, Gambia, Sierra Leone, Liberia, the Gold Coast, Togo, Dahomey, Nigeria, and Angola—and forthwith sold into slavery. The traffic in Negro slaves continued until shortly before the Civil War, though slackening somewhat after 1808, when the Slave Trade Act went into effect. A great majority of these Negroes were brought direct from Africa;

some, however, had previously lived in the British West Indies, where they had picked up a bare working knowledge of English.

Most of the descendants of these transplanted Africans living in the South now speak conventional American English. Because of lack of social contacts with whites and lack of schooling, relics of older standard speech may occasionally be heard from them, such as the pronunciation *deef* for *deaf* and *obleege* for *oblige*. When a colored charwoman with some embarrassment informed me that her small daughter had suffered an injury in her *grine*, she was not using an un-English, "darky" pronunciation, but merely saying *groin* in a manner which went out of fashion in more sophisticated usage years ago. There is, of course, no connection whatever between race and the ability to articulate given speech sounds, though it is popularly believed that the Southern Negro speaks as he does because of a peculiar conformation of speech organs, aided and abetted by indolence and stupidity. I was once gravely informed by a professor of government that the Negro does not have an *r* sound (my informant was of course referring only to *r* before a consonant sound and in final position) because the "letter *r*" did not exist in African languages—not one of which he had any acquaintance with, incidentally. When I presumed to disagree with his explanation, a corollary of which was that the speech of white Southerners was *r*-less because of the linguistic influence of Negro "mammies," and to point out that an Ohio-bred Negro has no difficulty whatsoever pronouncing *r* in all positions, he was grievously offended with me. The fact is that uneducated Negroes in the South by and large differ little in their speech from the uneducated whites. As for the presence of archaisms, they may also be heard from whites who have lived for a long time in cultural isolation, for instance, the Southern mountain folk.

There are, however, communities of Negro Americans engaged largely in the cultivation of rice, cotton, and indigo along the coastal region of South Carolina and Georgia, both on the Sea Islands and on the mainland, who have lived in cultural and geographical isolation for many generations. Most of them have had little contact with whites; some, indeed, have seldom seen white people. These Negroes, numbering about a quarter of a million, speak a type of English which has been so heavily influenced by the African languages native to their remote ancestors that it is not readily intelligible to people, white or colored, from other parts of the country. Their language, Gullah or Geechee, retains a good many African characteristics in its system of sounds, its syntax, its morphology, its vocabulary, its methods of forming words, and, most striking of all to one hearing it for the first time, its intonation. The word *Gullah* is probably either from *Gola*, the name of a Liberian tribe and its language, or from *Angola*. *Geechee*, also used in the upcountry of South Carolina as a derisive nickname for a low-country white, particularly one living in the Charleston area, is probably derived from the name of another Liberian tribe and language.

It was very unlikely that Africans from the same tribe or language area would find themselves thrown together on a single plantation in sufficient numbers to enable them to maintain their native languages. The chances were all that they would be considerably dispersed upon their arrival at the various southern ports. Consequently, it became necessary for them to learn English as well as they could. It is not likely that anyone helped them to do so, unless there were prototypes of Mrs. Stowe's Little Eva gliding or floating about the plantations (for Little Eva seldom merely walked) in the seventeenth and eighteenth centuries. The only English many of them ever heard from native speakers was that of the illiterate or semiliterate white indentured servants with whom they worked in the fields or who were set over them as overseers. It was for them not simply a matter of translating word for word their native idioms into English. This cannot be done successfully even with related languages, where it may result in something intelligible if un-English, like *the bread is all*, a Pennsylvania Germanism (though heard in other parts of the country) from German *das Brot ist alles*. It was for these Negroes a matter of acquiring a quite different linguistic psychology, a new attitude towards the phenomena of life as expressed by language. It is not surprising that their accomplishment fell considerably short of perfect. Their English was a sort of jargon or pidgin, which passed into use by their descendants as a native language. This type of so-called creolized language has been preserved largely in the speech of the Gullahs, Negroes who "stayed put" in a region in which they have always been far more numerous than whites and in which they have developed the only distinctive Negro speech in this country.

The principal importance of Gullah, aside from its intrinsic interest as a remarkable linguistic development, is that recent studies of it have been the means of identifying beyond doubt the African source of a number of words in Southern American English, a few of which have passed into other types of American English and one of which, *banjo,* if it is indeed of African origin, is part of the English language wherever it is spoken. Until Lorenzo Dow Turner began his investigations about twenty years ago, Gullah was traditionally regarded as "a quaint linguistic mongrel," to quote from one serious commentator; it was thought to be characterized by "intellectual indolence," "slovenly and careless," a debased form of the "peasant English" of poor whites, a sort of baby talk. One writer even went so far as to attribute its phonological characteristics to the "clumsy tongues," "flat noses," and "thick lips" of the Negroes who speak it.

Professor Turner's studies of Gullah, culminating in his *Africanisms in the Gullah Dialect* (Chicago, 1949), identify thousands of words in Gullah which have or may have African sources. Unlike earlier commentators, who assumed that many words which seemed strange to them were either nonsense words or mispronunciations of English words, Turner, himself of African descent, took the trouble to acquire a good working knowledge of West African languages. His studies and conclusions have made short shrift of some of the theories of previous writers, who assumed, for instance, that a Gullah word for "tooth" which sounded to them something like *bong* was merely a childish, clumsy-tongued, flat-nosed, thick-lipped mispronunciation of English *bone*, and that the Gullah word *det* or the expression *det rain* "a long, hard rain" was really *death rain*, which involved the further assumption that to the Gullahs a long, hard rain is an omen of death to come—as it were, folklore made to order. The fact that in the Wolof language, spoken in Senegal and Gambia, the word for "tooth" is very like *bong* (it is impossible to indicate the exact pronunciation of the un-English final sound of this word, a palatal nasal, without using phonetic symbols) and that in the same language the word for "long, hard rain" is *det* ought to dispose of the "baby talk" explanation for good and all—though of course it will not, for most people prefer "quaint" explanations of linguistic phenomena to the true ones.

From many Gullah informants, some of them bearing names which are a delight to contemplate—among them Saki Sweetwine, Prince Smith, Samuel Polite, Sanko Singleton, Balaam Walker, Scotia Washington, Shad Hall, and Paris Capers—Dr. Turner collected more than five thousand African words in the Gullah region. About four-fifths of these are now used only as personal names, but most of the remainder are everyday words in the speech of the Gullahs. Some of these words, doubtless the common possession of Negroes in all the slaveholding states, passed into the vocabulary of whites at what must have been a very early date.

How did words from the language of humble slaves get into the speech of their white masters? M. M. Mathews, who devotes the final chapter of his *Some Sources of Southernisms* (University, Ala., 1948) to Africanisms in the word stock of Southern American English, speculates with some reason that such words were transmitted by white children, who would not have resisted the influences of what their elders considered an inferior culture. Dr. Mathews cites his aged aunt's aversion to the "Negro word" *cooter* "turtle" and her regret that her brother, Mathew's father, had sullied the "purity" of his speech by ever using the word.

Actually, the African contribution is rather meager. The remarkable thing is, considering the social and economic relationship of black to white, that there should have been any contribution. Many a white Southerner has imbedded in his vocabulary words whose African origin he probably never suspects. *Banjo* and *cooter* have already been cited. The first word has usually been considered as originating in a Negro mispronunciation of *bandore*, an English word of Spanish transmission denoting a musical instrument whose similarity to the banjo consisted mainly in the fact that it had strings to be plucked. According to Turner, the most probable source is Kimbundu, a language spoken in Angola, in which the word *mbanza* refers to an instrument very similar to the banjo. *Cooter* is very likely from *kuta*, a word appearing in two French West African languages, Bambara and Malinke, in which it has the same meaning as in the language of the Gullahs and in the English of many white Southerners.

Goober "peanut" is a modification of Kimbundu *nguba*, with similar forms occurring in Imbundu (also spoken in Angola) and Kongo (Belgian Congo and Angola). *Pinder*, with the same meaning, is from Kongo *mpinda*. Both these words are freely used on a colloquial level in the South; the first has probably gained a limited national currency.

A number of gustatory and culinary terms of African origin testify to the skill of Negro cooks. Many of these, however, are local terms, like *cush* "corn meal stuffing" and *cala* "sweetened rice"—the latter term confined to the New Orleans area. *Gumbo* is confined to no locality or region, nor is *yam*, which is found also in British English and which is of Portuguese transmission; in Scotland it is used for the common white potato. If the word *yam* was brought to these shores by our early settlers, as it may have been, it is of course not to be regarded as belonging with the group of words under discussion; but there is no reason to insist that, because it occurs also in British English, we could not have got it independently. The same people from whom the Portuguese got the word were right here, and the word might well have entered the American vocabulary, as Dr. Mathews points out, from the language of the slaves. At the least, its use in American English would have been reinforced by their use of it. The word survives as an Africanism in the Gullah dialect (in the form *yambi*) to mean a red sweet potato, which is its usual meaning in Southern American English.

Buckra "white man" is also of African origin, appearing as *mbakara* in Efik and Ibibio, spoken in Southern Nigeria. Loss of the initial nasal sound in the word probably occurred in Negro speech before the word was transmitted to whites and is due to the influence of English on the speech of the Negroes. Simplification of the initial consonant combinations *mb-*, *mp-*, *nd-*, *nt-*, and *ng-*, which do not occur in this position in English, is frequent in the Gullah pronunciation of African words.

The great blue heron is frequently called *poor Joe* (or *po' Joe*) in those regions of the South in which the bird is found. There can be no doubt that this is the same word as Vai (Liberia and Sierra Leone) *pojo* "heron." It is likely that *chigger* and its variant *jigger*—the dictionaries give a spelling *chigoe* which suggests a pronunciation seldom if ever heard—are of African transmission as far as their use in American English is concerned, and perhaps of African origin as well. At any rate, *jiga* "flea" is found in a number of African languages spoken in Senegal, Gambia, Togo, Dahomey, and Northern and Southern Nigeria. The word got into British English probably by way of the British West Indies and has been thought to be of Carib origin. It is likely, however, that its use in American English is due independently to Negro transmission, regardless of its ultimate origin.

Pickaninny, which is probably used nowadays by whites more frequently than by Negroes, is of African transmission, but its source is Portuguese *pequenino* "very little." It is not impossible that the last part of the Portuguese word may have been identified by the Negroes with the Mende (Sierra Leone) word *nini* "female breast," *pequenino* being folk-etymologized into *pickaninny* after these Negroes acquired their English. The word is not exclusively American (the same is true of *buckra*, *jigger*, and others), though it is probably more commonly used here than elsewhere. It is, nevertheless, recorded in British English almost a century and a half earlier than in American English.

Hoodoo and its New Orleans variant *voodoo* are Africanisms. Both forms are in use by the Gullahs. They have, however, become somewhat differentiated in meaning, the latter usually referring to the cult which flourished in the West Indies and was later introduced into this country. *Hoodoo* is applied to a person or object that is thought to bring bad luck, *to hoodoo* consequently meaning "to bring bad luck to someone." Voodoo worship was introduced into Louisiana very early by slaves from the French colonies of Martinique, Guadeloupe, and Santo Domingo, where the cult—probably of African origin, as its name would indicate—raged furiously. It would seem to have grown rather slowly at first, but was a source of worry among the whites by 1782, when the Spanish governor of Louisiana prohibited further importation of Negroes from Martinique because slaves from there were thought to be "too much given to voudouism and make the lives of the citizens unsafe." Later, and partly for the same reason, a similar prohibition was extended to Negroes from Santo Domingo. After the American occupation, however, there were no such restrictions, and with the sudden influx of Negroes into Louisiana by way of New Orleans between 1806 and 1810, voodoo began to exert a strong influence upon the Louisiana Negroes. For a long time thereafter—until well after the Civil War, in fact—voodoo "queens" and "doctors" were persons of tremendous power and prestige among the Negroes, and even to some extent among the lower-class whites.

The most famous of the queens, who were the priestesses of the cult and much more influential than the doctors who shared with them their powers of sorcery, was the remarkable Marie Laveau, a free mulatto of striking beauty in her younger years, who was by profession a hairdresser and by avocation a procuresss for white gentlemen. For more than forty years absolute ruler of the cult, she has remained a legend to this day. The visitor to New Orleans, if he is lucky, may still hear old Oscar "Papa" Celestin, a Robert Frost in ebony, sing *Marie Laveau*, an original composition which recounts some of the miracles performed by this celebrated "cunjer-lady."

Transmission into general use of African *zombi*, a word intimately associated with voodooism, is probably rather recent, though it must have been known to whites in certain areas of the South at an early date. Its present familiarity may well be credited to the cycle of "horror" films some years ago. The word originally designated the snake god which was the object of adoration in the voodoo cult. It later came to mean a supernatural force thought to restore corpses to life, and ultimately a corpse brought to life by means of this force. Recently it has been used, with an obvious appropriateness, to designate a mixed drink of (usually) rum and brandy.

Juke, which has come into general use among whites comparatively recently, mainly in the compounds *juke box* and *juke joint*, has been a part of the vocabulary of the Gullahs for a long time in the sense "disorderly," particularly in the combination *juke house*. Turner shows that the word is of African origin. In standard colloquial use its meaning has been considerably toned down, as has been that of *jazz*, which, though of unknown origin, is said to have been long used by Negroes, particularly in the New Orleans region. *Jazz* is very likely of African origin, though no African etymon has been found. These two words are included here because they have probably appeared in the English or creolized English speech of Negroes since pre-Revolutionary days, even though they may have been late in reaching the standard language. Their very nature would of course sufficiently explain the fact that they were not earlier transmitted to whites. *Jazz* as a verb is, as a matter of fact, sometimes used by whites, though only on a rather low social level, in the sexual sense which it seems originally to have had among the Negroes.

It would be pleasant to be able to record that Professor Turner's researches in Gullah have cleared up the origin of *to tote*, long an etymological puzzle, but there are circumstances in respect to it which indicate that final judgment had better be reserved. It is true that no satisfactory English etymon has been found. *Tote* is one of that sizable number of words of which the dictionaries can say only "orig. uncert.," "unknown origin," or something to that effect. Professor Turner found possible African sources in Kongo and Kikongo *tota* "to pick up," with related words in other West African languages mean "to carry." The fact that *tote* is used in Gullah does not rule out the possibility of an unknown English source, for very many English words are used by the Gullahs. It is likely, however, that if the word is not of African origin, its use has been reinforced, at least in the South and particularly among the Gullahs, by the African words. Though it is usually thought of as a Southernism, *tote* was first recorded in New England in the seventeenth century; it has also been found in upstate New York, northern Michigan, and northern Minnesota, occurring alone and in the combinations *tote road*, *tote wagon*, *tote team*, and *tote sled*. The fact that the word crops up in parts of the country where Negro influence is highly unlikely suggests that there may after all be an English source for the word which has been lost to us. If so, the fact that words of similar sound and meaning occur in West African languages would have to be due to sheer coincidence, like the similarity in American Indian *Potomac* and Greek *potamos* "river."

Contacts with other colonizing peoples have also contributed to the American vocabulary. Relations between the English and the New Amsterdam Dutch were, it is true, never very friendly; nevertheless from the language of these Dutch settlers American English gained *coleslaw*, *cooky*, *cruller*, *boss*, *dope*, *hay barrack*, *spook*, *stoop* "porch," *poppycock* (from *pappekak* "soft dung"), *patroon* (which the Dutch had in turn taken from Latin *patronus*), *sleigh*, *scow*, *to snoop*, *bowery* "a farm" (but now more famous as the street name), *pit* "fruit stone," *boodle*, *Santa Claus*, *waffle*, and probably *Yankee*. In addition American English incorporated a number of geographical terms used in the region of the Hudson: *kill* "creek, stream, river," *dorp* "village," and *clove* "valley," which also appear in place names. Many of these Dutch words were not used by writers until well into the nineteenth century, but we may be fairly sure that they occurred in English contexts much earlier; and we may be equally sure that many more Dutch words than are recorded were once in use. *Hay barrack* represents what English-speaking people did to Dutch *hooi-berg*. *Coleslaw* is from Dutch *koolsla* "cabbage salad"; folk etymology frequently converts it to *cold slaw*. *Dope* has acquired a good many slang uses, as in *to dope out*, *to get the dope on*, and *he's a dope* (i.e., a dolt). It seems to have begun its career in American English meaning simply a drug, later adding the connotation "narcotic." *Boss*, from *baas* "master," was a very useful word, for it allowed the American working man to enjoy the satisfying if purely verbal illusion that he had no master; only slaves had masters in early American democracy. *Father Christmas*, not *Santa Claus*, visits good English children on Christmas Eve. Our name for the jolly saint is from *Sante Klaas*, a Dutch dialect form of *Sant Nikolaas*, that is, "St. Nicholas"; it seems to have taken a long time catching on, and was probably not very common until the nineteenth century. In my childhood *Santa* was always pronounced *Santy* even by the most highly cultured; people nowadays have become much more conscious of spelling and many use a pronunciation which the spelling *Santa* seems to indicate to them.

The source of *Yankee* is uncertain, but the word is most probably from *Jan Kees* (a variant of *Jan Kaas,* which has been in Germany and Flanders a nickname of long standing for a Hollander), used by the English to designate a Dutch pirate, a sense in which it apparently came also to be used in New York as an expression of the contempt in which the English held the Dutch. Because of the final *-s,* the name seems to have been misunderstood to be a plural; the form *Yankee* is thus what is known to linguists as a back formation, like *shay* from *chaise.*[3] It should also be noted that *j* in Dutch has the sound of English *y;* hence the initial sound of the English form of the word. It is a little difficult to understand why the word was transferred from Dutchmen to people of English descent. Perhaps the shift in application was the result of the same type of humor involved in nicknaming the fattest boy in school "Skinny"—the *lucus a non lucendo* principle. . . .

The meaning of *Yankee* has been anything but static. By the mid-eighteenth century its use in this country to designate a New Englander seems to have been well established. During the Civil War Southerners were employing the term, usually derogatorily, for any Northerner, and it was not long before it acquired what was in the usage of many Southerners the inseparable prefix *dam,* as in *dam-yankee.*

Since the Revolutionary War the British have used the word to designate any American, with connotations no more derogatory than those of the word *American* itself as it is used by them. It is difficult to imagine any experience more painful to most deep Southerners than to be called *Yankees;* yet there is only sporadic evidence that G.I.'s of Southern origin stationed in England during either World War ever objected very vigorously to the appellation. *Yank* is about as common in British colloquial usage as the unabbreviated form; the clipped form has never been very frequent in American use, though it was the title of a magazine distributed to American soldiers and occurs in a line of the World War I song *Over There* ("The Yanks are coming").

Despite the large number of Germans in this country long before

[3] For back-formation, see page 77. [eds.]

the outbreak of the Revolution, few German words entered the American vocabulary until about the middle of the nineteenth century, when many new immigrants from Germany arrived. The first large groups of Germans came from the Palatinate; they arrived on Delaware Bay in the early years of the eighteenth century, and, finding that the good lands around Philadelphia were already taken by descendants of Penn's colonists, proceeded to settle the back country. Those who subsequently moved on to other parts with the Scotch-Irish soon abandoned their native language. Those who stayed on in Pennsylvania kept pretty much to themselves—on farms and in villages where they continued speaking their dialect of German, which was in time considerably influenced by English but which had no appreciable effect upon English outside the areas in which they were settled. *Sauerkraut* appears in British English as early as 1617, though neither the word nor the food it designates ever really caught on in England. It is most likely that it was borrowed independently in this country. Similarly, *noodle* is recorded in England before its first known appearance in America, but was probably reborrowed here.

It is not improbable that other words which entered American English through Pennsylvania German were known outside the immediate German settlement area before the nineteenth century, but most of them are of such a nature that we should not expect to find them recorded as early as the eighteenth century. Some of them, like *ponhaus* "scrapple," are not listed in modern abridged dictionaries, probably because lexicographers do not consider them "standard," despite the fact that they are known and used by many speakers of standard American English at the present day. *Rainworm* "earthworm" is used in settlements of German origin and is probably a translation of *Regenwurm*. It occurs in the Pennsylvania German area and in the German settlements on the Yadkin in North Carolina, as well as in Nobleboro, Maine, which was settled from the Palatinate. Old English *regenwyrm* is doubtless the ancestor of the term as it occurs elsewhere, for instance, on Buzzards Bay in Massachusetts. *Sawbuck* is now widely disseminated but it originated in German and Dutch settlements from, respectively, *Sägebock* and *zaagbock*. The fact that each end of the rack on which wood is sawed is shaped like the letter X—the Roman symbol for ten—has given rise to the slang use of the term for a ten-dollar bill. *Woodbuck* is also heard over the entire German settlement area, obviously a partial translation of German *Holzbock*. *Hex* "a witch or the spell cast by a witch" and *to hex* "to cast a spell on" are fairly well known all over the country nowadays. *Ponhaus* (also occurring as *ponhoss, ponhorse, ponehoss,* and *pondhorse*) corresponds to standard German *Pfannhase;* it is current from the Pennsylvania German area proper westward to Ohio and is also well known in northwestern Maryland and northeastern West Virginia. Other gastronomical and culinary terms of Pennsylvania German origin are *sots* "yeast"; *snits* (also *schnitz*) "dried apples, pieces of fruit cut for drying" (also used as a verb "to cut into pieces"); *fat-cakes* "doughnuts" (*fettkuche*), *fossnocks* (*fasnachskuche* "Shrovetide cakes"); *thick-milk* "curdled milk" (*dickemilich); smearcase* "cottage cheese" *(schmierkäs*); and possibly, but by no means certainly, *applebutter. Clook* "setting hen," with its less frequent variant *cluck,* is from Pennsylvania German *kluck* (standard German *Klucke*). According to Hans Kurath's *Word Geography of the Eastern United States* (Ann Arbor, 1949), "the derogatory phrase *dumb cluck* obviously contains this word." *Belsnickel* (or *Belschnickel*) was, and still is, the southern Pennsylvania equivalent of *Santa Claus;* the last part of the name is an affectionate diminutive form of German *Nikolaus.* Another name of long standing for the unhappily commercialized saint who rewards good children at Christmas is *Kriss Kingle* (or *Kriss Kringle*); it is a modification of *Christkindl* "Christ child." *To dunk* "to dip (doughnuts usually) into coffee or milk" is from Pennsylvania German *dunken* "to dip," corresponding to standard German *tunken.* It has not really been widely current for more than about twenty years, although it spread very rapidly once it caught on. There is no usage label for the word in the *American College Dictionary,* so that it is apparently considered standard American English nowadays. *Dunker* (or *Dunkard*) is the popular name of a member of the German Baptist Brethren, a pietistic sect which practices baptism by immersion, that is, by dunking.

From French explorers and colonizers American English acquired, usually by way of the Canadian border, such words as *prairie, bateau, voyageur, chowder, buccaneer, carryall* (vehicle), *levee, calumet,* and perhaps *gopher. Chowder* is a modification of *chaudière* "caldron." Although it is recorded first in England, *buccaneer* should probably be regarded as an Americanism by virtue of its many American historical associations; it is ultimately a Carib word, but comes to English by way of French *boucanier. Carryall* is a folk-etymologizing of *cariole*. *Gopher* is most likely from *gaufre* "honeycomb," in reference to the animal's burrowing habits. *Prairie* is of frequent occurrence in American English, alone and in a number of compounds such as *prairie dog*, *prairie wolf* "coyote," and *prairie schooner* "small covered wagon." The word is now perfectly familiar in British English also. *Levee* is a derivative of French *lever* "to raise." Its use to designate an embankment for preventing the overflow of a river is largely confined to the South, as is also its later sense "landing place for vessels." *Calumet*, ultimately a derivative of Latin *calamus* "reed," was the word used by the French explorers for the ceremonial tobacco pipe of the Indians.

A number of Spanish words, such as *mosquito* "little fly," *negro* "black" (an adjective which was soon converted into a noun), *pecadillo* "little sin," *armada* "armed (naval) forces" (originally a past participle), and *alligator* (from *el lagarto* "the lizard"), along with Nahuatl words adopted by the Spanish, such as those cited at the beginning of this chapter, entered the English language as early as the sixteenth century. These words, though some of them are more frequently used in this country than in England, should be distinguished from words taken from Spanish by English-speaking people settled on this continent. Such words are very numerous at a later date but very rare before the nineteenth century. *Calaboose* "jail" is a modification of Spanish *calabozo*, used chiefly in the southern states; it is recorded first in the latter years of the eighteenth century. *Cockroach* (as *cacarootch*) first appears in the *General Historie* of Captain John Smith, who refers to it in a somewhat ambiguous passage as "a certaine India Bug, called by the Spaniards a *Cacarootch*, the which creeping into Chests they [that is, the "cacarootches"] eat and defile with their ill-sented dung." The word used by Smith is a modification of Spanish *cucaracha* "wood louse," or possibly a variant form of it. It was later folk-etymologized to *cockroach* (just as Latin *asparagus* is converted by some speakers into *sparrow grass*) and subsequently clipped to *roach* in this country, American verbal prudery perhaps playing some part in the elimination of the first element of what deceptively appeared to be a compound of *cock* and *roach*. *Key* "reef or low island" from Spanish *cayo* was in English use before it was recorded in America, but its use is now mainly confined to this country, particularly to Florida. *Key West* is a modification of *Cayo Hueso* "bone key." The form *cay*, riming with *day*, is now more usual in British English than *key*. *Stevedore*, from Spanish *estivador*, occurs first in the form *stowadore* by association with English *to stow*.

SUGGESTED ASSIGNMENTS

1. Using a detailed map and, if necessary, the aid of a foreign-language student for data, write a composition on one of these subjects:
   a. Spanish place names in the Southwest
   b. French place names in the Mississippi Valley
   c. French place names in Louisiana
   d. Dutch place names in the Hudson Valley
   e. German place names in Pennsylvania
2. If you live in a town that retains some Old World flavor derived from its early foreign settlers, write a theme about the words of foreign origin that are generally known to the community. You might consider such questions as these: Have their pronunciations changed? Have their referents changed? What areas of life do they represent? Why are they used instead of American words? Have they become naturalized, e.g., do they take *-s* plurals or verb endings in *-ed* and *-ing?*
3. Using library sources, write a composition on the influence of one language upon either American English or British English.
4. If you have studied Latin, write a composition on Latin words and phrases in English. Consider such matters as these: How have the meanings changed? Is the pronunciation Latin, English, or a combination of the two? Do the words fulfill a useful purpose? Among useful references for this assignment are these: Edwin Lee Johnson, *Latin Words of Common English;* E. E. Burriss and Lionel Casson, *Latin and Greek in Common Use;* and Jerome C. Hixson and I. Colodny, *Word Ways.*
5. Two historical dictionaries devoted to American English are *A Dictionary of American English*, edited by Sir W. A. Craigie and J. R. Hulbert, and *Dictionary of Americanisms*, edited by Mitford Mathews. Use these dictionaries to look up the following words to see when they are first recorded in American English and where they came from: *raccoon, skunk, moccasin, prairie, bureau, gopher, waffle, cockroach, mosquito.*
6. The following words are said to be examples of folk etymology: *country-dance, hoedown, primrose, woodchuck, cockroach, tweed, lark* (spree). Find their originals, using your desk dictionary and larger dictionaries if needed.

ETYMOLOGY AND MEANING

Simeon Potter

In the first two essays of this section we saw how changes in words and word forms are brought about. In this selection we shall see how word meanings are also altered. Meanings, as subjective phenomena, are especially unstable and elusive, and have not yet been subjected to the scientific analysis that other aspects of language have undergone. However, as we look back into linguistic history and observe successive changes in word meanings, we can discern specific directions in which words change. These directions, or "semantic categories," as Professor Potter calls them, are the subject of the essay which follows. Professor Simeon Potter, who was educated at the University of London and Oxford University, has taught in European universities and is now Professor of English at the University of Liverpool.

Few words have fixed significations like the pure numbers of mathematics or the technical formulas of chemistry. The mathematical sign π denotes a constant, namely, the ratio of the circumference of a circle to its diameter, or 3.14159 . . . The chemical formula NaCl denotes a substance, sodium chloride, or salt, and it always means that substance and nothing else. These symbols π and NaCl cannot vary with time or circumstance, nor do they ever change with their contexts. Few expressions in daily use have such simple and direct denotations as these. Even words like *mother* and *father*, *sun* and *horse*, denoting primary human relationships or natural objects and creatures, are not quite so definite. All four words occur in Old English and their meanings have not changed in twelve centuries. But in such sayings as "Westminster is the mother of Parliaments,"

"The child is father of the man," "He seeks a place in the sun," and "He rides the high horse," the primary meanings of these words are manifestly transcended.

What is the *sun?* According to *The Oxford English Dictionary* it is "the brightest (as seen from the earth) of the heavenly bodies, the luminary or orb of day; the central body of the solar system, around which the earth and other planets revolve, being kept in their orbits by its attraction and supplied with light and heat by its radiation." And what is the *horse?* It is "a solid-hoofed perissodactyl quadruped (*Equus caballus*), having a flowing mane and tail, whose voice is a neigh." Now are these so-called "dictionary definitions" really definitions, or are they not descriptions? As long ago as 1891, when he was writing his magistral *Essai de Sémantique*, Michel Bréal demonstrated that the cause of shifting meaning in so many words lay in the impossibility of complete definition and in the varying complexity of the word-thing relationship. "Language," he wrote, "designates things in an incomplete and inaccurate manner: *incomplete*, since we have not exhausted all that can be said of the sun when we have declared it to be shining, or of the horse when we say that it trots; *inaccurate*, since we cannot say of the sun that it shines when it has set, or of the horse that it trots when it is at rest, or when it is wounded or dead."

Could the word or symbol *sun* ever alter its reference and come to mean "moon," or "star," or something else? That, surely, is inconceivable. *Sun* is an ancient word, indicating the same "heavenly body" as its ancestral equivalent in Indo-European five thousand and more years ago. Day by day during those five thousand years, man has observed it "coming forth as a bridegroom out of his chamber, and rejoicing as a giant to run his course." Nevertheless, it has happened that üλ, the etymological equivalent of *sun* in Albanian, has come to mean "star"; and *haul* and *súil*, its equivalents in Welsh and Erse respectively, have come to mean "eye." At some period in the history of each of these three languages that apparently simple and rigid relationship between word and thing, between *symbol* and *referent*, has been deflected and distorted. The meaning, we say, has been changed. The seemingly impossible has occurred and any notions that we may have entertained concerning the indissolubility of the links connecting *etymology* and *meaning* have been rudely dispelled. The shock is, to say the least, disconcerting. We should so much prefer to regard a "speech-form as a relatively permanent object to which the meaning is attached as a kind of changeable satellite" (Leonard Bloomfield, *Language*, p. 426). The study of language would be so much easier for us if we could be assured that the etymology of a word is not only something *real* and *true* (as, indeed, the Greek *etymon* implies) but also that it is something permanent; and that the basic form or *root* of a word has some inherent connexion with the thing, quality or action denoted. Primitive peoples still believe that word has power over thing, that somehow the word participates of the nature of the thing. The word, in fact, is the symbol and it has no direct or immediate relation with the referent except through the image in the mind of the speaker. As Henri Delacroix once said (in *Le Langage et la Pensée*), "All thought is symbolic. Thought first constructs symbols which it substitutes for things." The symbol *sun* has no connexion with the celestial luminary other than through the thoughts or images in the mind of the speaker and the hearer. Unless these two images are identical, there can be no complete understanding.

Latin grammarians sometimes taught wrong etymologies long ago and more recent writers, who should have known better, have occasionally had recourse to fictitious etymologies in order to buttress a theory or to point a moral. Carlyle liked to define *king* as "he who can," associating the word with German *können* "to be capable, to know how to"; and Ruskin found pleasure in reminding the married women in his audience that since *wife* meant "she who weaves," their place was in the home. On the other hand, a speaker may knowingly or unwittingly ignore an etymology. He may refer to a "dilapidated wooden shed," although *dilapidated* is strictly applicable only to a building of stone (Latin *lapis, lapidis*). He may say that "the battalion was well equipped," although *to equip* (French *équiper*, from Old Norse *skipa*) means historically "to fit out a ship." He may say that "the life-boat was manned by Wrens," "the ocean liner sailed," and "the cattle were shepherded into their stables."[1] A rediscovered etymology may be highly informative and may give pleasure. Those two attractive birds, the nuthatch and the redstart, have most interesting names. The nuthatch is that little creeping bird that breaks or *hacks* the nuts in order to feed on the kernel. For the alternation be-

[1] A Wren is a member of a British World War II organization, the Women's Royal Naval Service. [eds.]

tween final plosive and affricative in *back* and *batch*,[2] you may like to compare *bake* and *batch*, *dike* and *ditch*, *lyke*wake and *lich*gate, *mickle* and *much*, *wake* and *watch*. The redstart is still called the fire-tail in some dialects and *start* "tail" survives in *Start* Point "tail-shaped promontory" and *stark*-naked, older *start*-naked. It is interesting to recall that a *governor* is etymologically a "steersman," a *marshal* a "horse-servant," and a *constable* a "companion of the stable." A *companion* is "one who eats bread" with another, a *fellow* is "one who lays down money," a *comrade* a "chamber-fellow," and a *friend* "one who loves."

If the meanings of words are not fixed, if they are liable to flux and change, is there any way of predicting in which direction they are most likely to change? Do changes in meaning admit of empirical generalizations? It is the aim of students of *semantics* or *semasiology* to find the answers to these questions. So far there has been little coordination of semantic research and investigators have fallen into two groups according to their preoccupation with mental processes (Bronislaw Malinowski, C. K. Ogden, and I. A. Richards) or with mathematical symbols (Ludwig Wittgenstein, A. N. Whitehead, Bertrand Russell, and Rudolf Carnap). At present these two groups —the linguistic psychologists and the mathematical logicians—seem to be moving on different planes. The student of language sees many parallels, and he is able to distinguish certain semantic categories, but he inclines to the view that generalizations are dangerous and unprofitable.

The most obvious semantic category is that involving specialization or narrowing. When a speech-form is applied to a group of objects or ideas which resemble one another in some respect, it may naturally become restricted to just one object or idea, and if this particular restriction gains currency in a speech community, a specialized meaning prevails. *Meat*, as in *sweetmeat* and as in the archaic phrase "meat and drink," meant any kind of food. It now means "edible flesh," a sense formerly expressed by *flesh* and *flesh meat*. *Deer*, like Dutch *dier* and German *Tier*, used to mean "animal" in general, as in Shakespeare's "mice and rats and such small deer." Latin *animal* and French *beast* have taken its place as the general words and *deer* now means "wild ruminant of a particular (antlered) species." *Fowl*, like Dutch and German *Vogel*, denoted "bird" in general as in Chaucer's

[2] Here the plosive, also called a stop, is the *k* sound; the affricative, or affricate, is the *ch* sound, as in *church*. [eds.]

"Parlement of Foules" and Biblical "fowls of the air" and as in modern names of larger kinds of birds used with a qualifying adjective, such as *sea fowl*, *water fowl*, and *wild fowl*. Otherwise, of course, *fowl* normally means a domestic cock or hen, especially when full grown. *Hound* formerly meant a dog of any breed and not, as now, a hunting-dog in particular. *Disease* was still conceived in Chaucer's day as being dis-ease "absence of ease." It might point to any kind of temporary discomfort and not, as now, to "a morbid physical condition." To *starve*, like Dutch *sterven* and German *sterben*, meant "to die," not necessarily from lack of food. In modern Yorkshire dialect a body can still "starve of cold." A *wed* was a pledge of any kind. In conjunction with the suffix *-lock* forming nouns of action, it has come to be restricted to "the marriage vow or obligation." To the Elizabethans an *affection* was a feeling of any kind and both *lectures* and *lessons* were "readings" of any kind. *Doctrine* was still teaching in general and *science* was still knowledge in general.

Sometimes a word has become restricted in use because a qualifier has been omitted. *Undertaker*, like French *entrepreneur* and German *Unternehmer*, used to mean "contractor, one who *undertakes* to do a particular piece of work." It is now used exclusively in the sense of *funeral undertaker*, although *mortician* has already superseded it in the cities and towns of America. In daily conversation *doctor* "teacher" means "medical doctor" and normally refers to a "general practitioner." Many words have both wider and narrower senses in the living language and many others have varying senses according to the persons addressed. *Pipe*, for example, evokes different images in the mind of the smoker, the plumber, the civil engineer, the geologist, the organist, and the boatswain. The *line* means a clothes-line to the laundrywoman, a fishing line to the fisherman, the equator to the seaman (as in Joseph Conrad's *Crossing the Line*), a communication wire to the telephonist, a succession of descent to the genealogist, and a particular kind of article to the man of business. To the geographer *cataract* means a cascade or waterfall, to the engineer a hydraulic controller, but a disease of the crystalline lens to the oculist.

The processes of specialization and extension of meaning may take place in a language side by side. For instance, as we have just seen, *hound* has been restricted in the course of a thousand years from a dog in general to a hunting-dog in particular; contrariwise, *dog* . . . has been extended from "a dog of ancient breed" to include any sort of dog, ranging from a formidable Alsatian to a puny and insignificant lap-dog. *Bird* meant "young birdling," just as *pigeon* meant "young dove" and *pig* "young swine." *Place* has had a remarkable history in English, where it has largely superseded the older words *stead* and *stow*. It derives from the feminine form of the Greek adjective meaning "broad," as in *plateîa hodós* "broad way." In one of its senses it still means "a group of houses in a town or city, now or formerly possessing some of the characters (positive or negative) of a square," like its well-known cognate in French, as in *Place de la Concorde*, or like Italian *piazza*, Spanish *plaza*, and German *Platz*. Now, however, it is also used in a hundred ways. . . .

If we assume that the central meaning of *place* is still "square" and that these other diverse uses *radiate* from that centre, we might equally well put it into our third semantic category: radiation, polysemia, or multiplication. Another excellent example is the word *paper*. It is the same as *papyrus*, the paper-reed of the Nile from the thin strips of which writing-sheets were first made as a substitute for parchment. The name was naturally transferred to paper made of cotton and thence to paper of linen and other fibres. To-day a paper may mean a document of any kind, for instance, a Government White Paper; an essay, dissertation or article on some particular topic, especially a communication read or sent to a learned society; a set of questions in an examination; a journal or a daily newspaper. *Power* "ability to do, state of being able" may hold radiating meanings as diverse as "capacity for mental or bodily action" (power of intellect, power of movement); "mechanical or natural energy" (horse-power, candle-power, electric power-station); "political or national strength" (the balance of power); "possession of control or command over others, dominion, sway" (the power of the Cabinet); "a political state" (the four great powers); and "a mathematical conception" (5^4 or five to the fourth power). Because the *head* is that part of the human body containing the brain, it may be the top of anything, literally or metaphorically, whether it resembles the head in shape (the head of a nail, screw, pin, hammer, walking-stick, flower, or cabbage) or in position (the head of the page, the list, the bed, the table or the stairs); or it may signify the person who is the chief or leader (the head of the school, the business, the family, the house, the State, the Church). It may denote the head of a coin (that side of a coin bearing the sovereign's head); a headland or promontory (St. Bees Head, Great Ormes Head, or Beachy Head, from tautologous Beau Chef Head); a single person or beast (lunch at five shillings a head, fifty head of cattle); or one of the main points or logical divisions of a subject or discourse (dealing with a theme under several heads). These and other senses do not derive from one another. They radiate from a common centre and are therefore mutually independent. Some of these senses will be translated by German *Kopf*, by French *tête*, by Spanish *cabeza* or by the ordinary word for *head* in other languages, but many senses will not permit of such direct translation. Each sense must be considered separately and in the process of translating our linguistic knowledge may be severely put to the test. It is surprising that in ordinary conversation in English there is so little ambiguity.

It is surprising, too, that every day we use words in both literal and metaphorical senses and that there is little danger of being misapprehended. We may speak as we will of "bright sunshine" or "a bright boy"; "a sharp knife," "a sharp frost" or "a sharp rebuke"; "a cold morning" or "the cold war"; "the Black Country" or "the black market." A person who is slow-witted may be described metaphorically as "dull," "obtuse," or "dim," the latter term being associated with the German *dumm* meaning "stupid," although cognate with our *dumb*. "Dumb" in German is now *stumm*, which is related etymologically to our *stammer*. Many words are themselves old metaphors: *dependent* "hanging from" (Latin *dē-pendens*); *egregious* "selected from the herd" (Latin *ē* for *ex* + *grex, gregis* "herd"); *precocious* "too early ripe" (Latin *praecox* from *prae* "before" + *coquere* "to cook, ripen").

Our next category of semantic changes may be labelled concretization. The naming of abstract qualities, such as *whiteness, beauty*, and *justice*, comes late in the evolution of a language because it results from conscious or unconscious comparison in the mind of man. Does *beauty* really exist apart from beautiful things? On this question the medieval schoolmen argued for centuries. No sooner are abstract nouns formed than men tend to think of each appearance of a quality or action in the abstract as a separate entity and so, by concretization, they make abstractions tangible and visible once more. *Youth*, "youngness" in the abstract, becomes a "young man." In the form *geogoþ* this word occurs eleven times in *Beowulf*, five times with the abstract meaning "youth," but six times with the concrete and collective meaning "young men." In much the same way Latin *multitūdo* "maniness, the quality of being many" came to signify "a crowd" and *congregātio* "flocking together" came to mean "a body of people assembled." Barristers appointed counsel to the Crown are named *King's Counsel.* A judge is addressed as *Your Honour* and an archbishop as *Your Grace. Health* is the quality of being *hale* or *whole*, soundness of body and mind. Modern man seeks diligently to maintain physical, mental, and social health. It is Greek *hugíeia* (from the adjectival form of which comes our *hygiene*), Latin *salūs*, French *la santé*, and German *die Gesundheit.* Clearly these are all highly abstract forms. Nevertheless, even *health* becomes concrete in the sense of a toast drunk—"Here's a health unto His Majesty!" *Wealth* was primarily "weal," "welfare," or "well-being," the state of being "well." In the old assonantal formula "health and wealth" the two abstract substantives were practically synonymous. But side by side with this meaning of *wealth* the concretized sense of "worldly goods, riches, affluence" also developed. The expression *wealth of nations*, denoting "the collective riches of a people or country," was certainly current before it was adopted by Adam Smith in 1776 as the title of his epoch-making book. "Money," wrote John Stuart Mill in 1848, "being the instrument of an important public and private purpose, is rightly regarded as wealth." "Let us substitute welfare for wealth as our governing purpose," said Edward Hallett Carr in 1948, exhorting us, in fact, to restore to the word *wealth* its older meaning. *Kindness*, *mercy*, *opportunity*, and *propriety* are historically abstractions, but to-day we speak of *kindnesses* in the plural in the sense of "deeds of kindness," *mercies* as "instances or manifestations of mercy," *opportunities* as "favourable chances or occasions," and *proprieties* as "proper forms of conduct." Similarly *provision* "foreseeing, foresight" has come to be applied in the plural to "stores of food."

Sometimes words, like men, "fall away from their better selves" and show deterioration or catachresis. *Silly* once meant "happy, blissful, holy," as in the "sely child" of Chaucer's *Prioress's Tale.* Later it signified "helpless, defenceless," becoming a conventional epithet in the "silly sheep" of Milton, Cowper, and Matthew Arnold. Then it descended yet lower and came to imply "foolish, feeble-minded, imbecile." *Crafty* "strong" and *cunning* "knowing" were once attributes of unmingled praise. A crafty workman was one skilled in a handicraft; a cunning workman was one who knew his trade. *To counterfeit* meant simply "to copy, reproduce," conveying no suggestion of fraud. "What finde I here?" asked Bassanio, as he opened the leaden casket, "Faire Portias counterfeit." (*The Merchant of Venice*, III, ii, 115.) It was, in fact, no counterfeit in the modern sense, but a true and lifelike delineation that came "so near creation." A *villain* once meant "a slave serving in a country-house or *villa*," a man occupying a lowly station in life. Chaucer's *vileynye* already showed depreciation, for it connoted the opposite of *courteisye*, that comprehensive term for a noble and chivalrous way of life, implying high courtly elegance and politeness of manners. A *knave*, like German *ein Knabe*, was just "a boy"; later, as in "the kokes knave, thet wassheth the disshes" of the *Ancrene Riwle*, "a boy or lad employed as a servant"; later still, "a base and crafty rogue." Like *rogue* and *rascal*, *knave* may still be used jocularly without seriously implying bad qualities. *Varlet*, a variant of *valet*, has shown an almost identical catachresis. *Nice* has become just a pleasant verbal counter: anything or everything may be nice. But *nescius*, its Latin antecedent, had the precise meaning "ignorant, unaware," a meaning maintained in Chaucer side by side with that of "foolish." From "foolish" it developed the sense "foolishly particular about small things," and so "fastidious, precise," as in "nice in one's dress." Later it was made to refer to actions or qualities, as in "a nice discrimination" and "a nice sense of honour." Since then, as H. W. Fowler has sagaciously observed in *A Dictionary of Modern English Usage*, "it has been too great a favourite with the ladies, who have charmed out of it all its individuality and converted it into a mere diffuser of vague and mild agreeableness." It is a pleasant, lazy word which careful speakers are bound to avoid using in serious contexts. *Propaganda*, which now implies an organized and vicious distortion of facts for a particular purpose, has suffered sad depreciation in recent years. In 1622 Pope Gregory XV founded a special Committee or Congregation of Cardinals for the Propagation of the Faith, in Latin *Congregātio dē propāgandā fide*. That marked the beginning of the history of this word, which, you see, is the ablative singular feminine form of the gerundive of *propāgāre* "to fasten or peg down slips of plants for growth, to multiply plants by layering." Most appropriately the Latin metaphor is agricultural and botanical. *Propaganda* should mean, in its extended sense, the dissemination of news of any kind. Unfortunately, since the year 1880 the meaning of the word has been poisoned. Propaganda and trustworthy news are dissociated in our minds. We even hear of propaganda and counter-propaganda!

Now all these semantic categories—specialization, extension, radiation, metaphor, concretization, and deterioration—are very interesting. Others too might be added to show in yet greater detail how inconstant are the relationships between symbol, image, and referent (word, thought, and thing). Men have sometimes associated speech-forms wrongly and the meanings of words have thus been modified capriciously and unpredictably. Let us admit that there have been losses and gains. When we blunder and are forced to offer abject apologies, we talk of eating *humble pie* and not *umble pie*, one made of umbles or entrails. Vaguely and hazily we may associate the epithet with *humble bee*, which is the old *hummle bee*, the bee that continuously *hums*. Hazily and lazily we may associate an *insurance policy* with the Government's *foreign policy*, not pausing to recollect that these two *policies* are etymologically quite different words. We associate *touchy* with *to touch*, forgetting that *touchy*, *techy*, or *tetchy* derives from *tetch* "a fit of petulance or anger, a tantrum." We say *restive* "refusing to move or budge" when we are half thinking of *restless*. Pardonably, perhaps, we connect *uproar* with *roar* and *outrage* with *rage*.

Certain expressions, like *comity* and *fruition*, are frequently "used loosely," and, since they are correspondingly in danger of being "understood loosely" too, careful speakers are almost compelled to refrain from using them. *Comity* means "courtesy, urbanity," not "company, assembly." The *comity of nations* is "the obligation recognized by civilized nations to respect one another's laws and customs." *Fruition* signifies "enjoyment," not "bearing of fruit." "If we live by hope," said Bishop Hugh Latimer, "let us desire the end and fruition of our hope." Like Archbishop Thomas Cranmer in the Epiphany Collect, Latimer was here using the word correctly. Today we frequently hear of plans and projects "coming, or being brought, to fruition." *Definitive* "having the quality or character of finality" should not be used as a more imposing form of *definite* "clear, precise, unmistakable." Our conception of the Middle Ages may be given a rosy tinge by an over-optimistic misinterpretation of the phrase "merry England," echoed by Sir Walter Scott in the opening sentence of *Ivanhoe*. King Charles II was "the merry monarch" and fun-fairs have their "merry-go-rounds," but "merry England" implied a pleasant and delightful countryside rather than a gay and carefree people. It was in the Northern *Cursor Mundi* that this epithet was first applied specifically to England. Later medieval poets repeated it and Spenser gave it wide currency in the First Book of

The Fairie Queene (Canto X, Stanza 61) when he identified the Red Cross Knight with "Saint George of mery England." But Spenser's "mery England" in the sixteenth century meant much the same as Blake's "England's green and pleasant land" in the early nineteenth.

When Francis Bacon referred to various people in the course of his *Essays* as *indifferent*, *obnoxious*, and *officious*, he was describing them as "impartial," "submissive," and "ready to serve." When King James II observed that the new St Paul's Cathedral was *amusing*, *awful*, and *artificial*, he implied that Sir Christopher Wren's recent creation was "pleasing, awe-inspiring, and skillfully achieved." When Dr. Johnson averred that Milton's *Lycidas* was "*easy*, *vulgar* and therefore *disgusting*," he intended to say that it was "effortless, popular, and therefore not in good taste."

Men frequently find themselves at cross-purposes with one another because they persist in using words in different senses. Their long arguments emit more heat than light because their conceptions of the point at issue, whether Marxism, democracy, capitalism, the good life, western civilization, culture, art, internationalism, freedom of the individual, equality of opportunity, redistribution of wealth, social security, progress, or what not, are by no means identical. From heedlessness, sloth, or sheer lack of intelligence men do not trouble to clarify their conceptions. Symbols or counters remain unchanged, but as the argument proceeds images and referents (thoughts and things) vary without end. By the way, what do *you* mean by *progress?* To define your terms at every step may seem an intolerable burden, but it is a sobering and salutary discipline. It is, indeed, the only effective way to sharpen up a blunted word and to restore its cutting edge.

SUGGESTED ASSIGNMENTS

1. Write a theme on radiation, or polysemia, in relation to one of these words: *heart*, *root*, *run*. Use an unabridged dictionary to help you.
2. In the foregoing pages Professor Potter discusses degeneration in words but does not mention the opposite process, elevation, whereby word-meanings change in a more favorable direction. Using a large dictionary, find out how these words are examples of elevation: *knight*, *fond*, *steward*, *marshall*, *pastor*, *pluck*, *guts*.
3. Look up the derivation of the following words and indicate which process each exemplifies, specialization or extension: *dunce*, *minister*, *butcher*, *pocket*, *box*, *campus*, *colossal*, *poison*, *liquor*, *bootleg*.

4. Which semantic category is illustrated in these everyday expressions? He told a *suggestive* story. They say he *drinks*. Your examination *smells*.
5. Spend an hour poking around in your desk dictionary and collecting interesting etymologies. In some cases you may wish to refer to an unabridged dictionary for further information. Then write a theme on what you found, using some such title as "An Etymological Excursion through a Dictionary," or "Glimpses of the Past in a Dictionary."

PERSONAL NAMES

George H. McKnight

The study of names is a fascinating area of investigation. The origin of some of the personal names we bear, like John *and* Mary, *goes far back into pre-Christian times, and each succeeding era has contributed its share to our vast onomasticon. Names, like other words, undergo strange transformations of form and meaning. Who would suspect, from the form today, that* Doolittle *might be a later-day form of* de l'hôtel, *that the first syllable of* Alfred *once meant an elf, that* Jones *is merely the possessive of* John, *or that* Follett *once meant a little madman? In the essay below, Professor McKnight traces many of our common personal names from the Old English period to the present and classifies the main sources from which they come. George H. McKnight was Professor of English at Ohio State University.*

IN ENGLAND, as in other countries of Europe, the use of surnames did not become customary until late in the Middle Ages. Most Englishmen of the Anglo-Saxon period were content with a single name. A characteristic form for English names of the earliest period was a compound word. A frequently appearing first element in these compounds is *Ælf-*, meaning "elf" or "fairy," appearing in such common names as *Ælfgar*, *Ælfgifu*, *Ælfheah*, *Ælfhelm*, *Ælfhere*, *Ælflæd*, *Ælfred*, *Ælfric*, *Ælfstan*, *Ælfwin*, and *Ælfthryth*. The use of this word suggests an attempt to propitiate the supernatural beings of an earlier faith, an attempt which in later times is paralleled by the seeking of saintly protection through giving to children the names of protecting saints. More frequently, however, the compound word is made up of names of qualities which the parent name-giver, with a degree of not unnatural sentiment, hoped to see realized in the character of his offspring: *Æthel-*, in *Æthelbald*, *Æthelberht*, *Æthelflæd*, *Æthelgifu*, and their kind, means "noble," obviously a desirable quality. *Ead-*, in *Eadberht*, *Eadgar*, *Eadgifu*, *Eadgyth*, *Eadhild*, *Eadmund*, *Eadred*, *Eadric*, *Eadsige*, *Eadweard*, *Eadwine*, *Eadwulf*, *Eadwig*, is probably to be associated with the adjective *ēadig*, meaning "happy." Other common elements are *beald*, "bold"; *ecg*, "edge," "sword"; *gōd*, "good"; *wīg*, "battle"; *sige*, "victory"; *wulf*, "wolf"; and such frequent suffixes as *beorht*, "bright," "renowned"; *heard*, "strong"; *here*, "army"; *mund*, "hand," "protection"; *rǣd*, "counsel"; *wine*, "friend"; appearing in such compounds as *Ecgberht*, *Sigebeorht*, *Gōdmund*, *Wigheard*, and their like. Less grandiose are such uncompounded names as *Cytel*, "kettle"; *Brand*, "sword"; *Rēad*, "red"; *Wicga*, "horse," "warrior"; *Wulf*, *Bæda*, *Ceol*, *Cutha*, *Offa*, *Duda*, *Hild* (a), *Hengest*, *Horsa*, *Ine*, *Tucca*, *Wini*, *Hudda*, *Wada*, etc., many of them probably to be explained as shortened or pet forms of longer names.

As specimens of modern names, often greatly disguised, derived from this early stock, may be cited: *Baldwin* (Bealdwine), *Winbolt* (Winebeald), *Herald*, *Harold*, *Harod* (Hereweald), *Bardell* (Beorhtwulf), *Elmer* (Ælfmær), *Colvin* (Ceolwine), *Goddard* (Godheard), *Herbert* (Herebeorht), *Herrick* (Hereric), *Hubert*, *Hubbard*, *Hobart*, *Hibbert* (Hygebeorht), *Wyman* (Wigmund), *Willard* (Wilheard), *Read*, *Reid*, *Reed* (Rēad, "red"), *Kemp* (Cempa, "warrior"), *Cobb* (Cobba), *Froude* (Frōda "prudent"), *Tucker* (Tucca), *Dodd* (Dodda), etc., besides later compounds such as *Hudson* (Hudda), and *Edison*.

In English names, as in so many other things, a great change followed the Norman Conquest. Not only were law and education brought under new control, but in matters more directly subject to the sway of fashion, continental manners followed the conquering Normans into England. Fashion in dress underwent striking change under the influence of the newcomers, and the character of names, likewise, underwent change in the new social order. Many of the older stock of words, such as *Edwin*, *Edgar*, *Alfred* and *Ethel* were reintroduced into common use at periods considerably later. But for the time being, names of the Anglo-Saxon type were out of fashion. Henry I, who cultivated the support of the native English, and his queen Matilda, sister of Edgar Ætheling, were ridiculed by the Norman element under the Anglo-Saxon names *Godric* and *Godgifu*.

The names of the new kind which were most widely used are said to have been *John*, *William*, *Thomas*, *Richard*, *Robert*, in the order given. Of these *John* and *Thomas* are scriptural names, which in Anglo-Saxon England had in general only a literary use and had retained their full Latin form, but which among the Normans were early appropriated as personal names and in popular use underwent striking transformation in many instances. To this class belong *Andrew* (Lat. *Andreas*, O. E. *Andreas*), *Matthew* (Lat. *Mattheus*, O. E. *Mattheus*), *James* (Lat. *Jacobus*, O. E. *Jacobus*), names to whose common use as personal names we owe the origin of the expression "Christian name."

Of these Christian names probably the one most widely used is *John* (Lat. *Johannes*, O. E. *Johannes*). The familiarity with which it has been handled, since brought into popular use in various languages, is shown by the variety of forms that it has assumed: Italian *Giovanni* (derivative, *Zany*), modern French *Jean*, Welsh *Evan*, Scotch *Ian*, Breton *Yves*, Russian *Ivan*, Danish and Dutch *Hans*, Scotch-English *Shawn*. The derivatives of *John* and its feminine correspondent *Joan* are innumerable, including *Jane*, *Jones*, *Johnson*, *Jennings*, etc.

The name *Thomas* owes its wide vogue to the popularity of the shrine of St. Thomas of Canterbury, the goal of popular pilgrimages. Not only the first part of the name has yielded derivatives such as *Thoms*, *Thomson*, etc., but the ending, a French clipped form in popular use, yields *Macey*, *Massie*, *Machin*, and *Masson*.

The other three names of the five mentioned are of Teutonic origin. The Middle High German form of *William* is *Willehelm*, in which may be seen the original meaning, "helm of resolution." In France the name assumed two forms: *Guillaume*, which is still in French use, and the form with initial W-, used in the northeast of France, whence the English form is derived. The double form is paralleled in the double forms: *Gautier* and *Walter*, *Guy* and *Wyatt.* The widespread use of *William* in England in the centuries following 1066 A. D. is not hard to explain. Derived from *William* are such names as *Williams*, *Wills*, *Williamson*, *Wilson*, *Wilkin*, *Wilkins*, *Willett*, etc., as well as *Gilliam*, etc.

The Teutonic forms of *Robert* and *Richard* appear in the Old High German *Hruodbert*, "fame-bright," and *Richart*, "powerful," names which will recall the Anglo-Saxon mode of name formation. *Richard* and *Robert* in familiar use gave origin to *Rick*, *Hick*, and *Dick*, and *Rob*, *Hob*, *Bob*, and *Dob*, respectively, from which in turn are derived such forms as *Ricketts*, *Hicks*, *Hixon*, *Dix*, *Dixon*, *Rich*, *Ritchie*, *Hitch*, *Higgs*, *Ditch*, *Digg*, *Robb*, *Robbins*, *Robson*, *Robinson*, *Hobbs*, *Hobson*, *Dobbs*, *Dobson*, etc.

Almost as markworthy as the popularity of *John*, *Thomas*, *Robert*, *Richard*, and *William* was the relative infrequency of names like *Arthur*, *Charles*, and *George*. These names were familiar enough, the first two being the names of central figures in the two best known medieval cycles of romance and the third, *George* (Greek, *Georgos* "tiller of the soil"), the name of England's patron saint; but all three owe the favor in which they have now come to be held to later events,—*Charles* and *George*, it is said, to the influence of the royal houses of Stuart and Hanover, and *Arthur* to the fact that it was the name of the Duke of Wellington. *Frederick*, in the same way, is said to owe its popularity to the fame of Frederick the Great.

The period following the Conquest was marked by another innovation, the adoption of the use of surnames. The development of surnames was a practical necessity. With the widening of interests from interests involving only a local community, to interests involving a whole country, and in our own day, to a considerable extent, the whole world, new means of distinguishing names have become more and more indispensable. The use of a second element in a name, a surname, for a time satisfied needs, but in later times additional means have been found necessary. The use of a third, or middle, name which was adopted in England in the eighteenth century, but which did not become frequent much before the nineteenth, has now become a general practice. This, one may come to realize, if he will consider the names famous in the literature of England and America from William Shakespeare and John Milton to Robert Louis Stevenson and H. G. Wells. In recent times, added power of distinction has been gained by supplementing the relatively restricted stock of given, or

Christian, names by names drawn from the more widely varied list of surnames. The hyphenation of surnames in recent times has served the same purpose. It must be reckoned a remarkable achievement in language to have been able to supply names sufficient in variety for so long a time to serve the ever-expanding need of distinction.

In the period before the Conquest, individuals were not infrequently distinguished by the use of an epithet, as in the case of Edmund Ironsides, Æthelred the Unready, Edward the Confessor, etc. Such additional names, however, are not to be reckoned as surnames in the modern sense of the word, because they were not transmitted from generation to generation. Probably the earliest form of surname proper was the patronymic, the name derived from parent or ancestor. For instance, Alfred the Great was distinguished by the added name *Æthelwulfing*, "son of Æthewulf." In early Teutonic life this mode of naming was in use. Among the characters in the Beowulf story, Healfdene, Hrothgar, Heorogar, Halga, are designated as *Scyldings*, "descendants of Scyld"; Wægmund, Ecgtheow, Weohstan, Wiglaf, and Beowulf are designated as *Scylfings*, "descendants of Scylf." The last four are also referred to as *Wægmundings*, since Ecgtheow and Weohstan were sons, and Wiglaf and Beowulf grandsons, of Wægmund. The suffix *-ing*, therefore, served to denote not only the immediate parent, but a famous ancestor more or less remote. It served in the formation of tribal designations, and if the use of surnames in the Anglo-Saxon period had been prevalent, would doubtless have been the distinctive suffix for surnames.

The patronymic surname is common in most languages. In Slavic languages it is familiar in the characteristic names ending in *-vitch*. In the Norman period the French word *fitz* (Mod. Fr. *fils*, "son") served the same purpose and appears in such modern English names as *Fitzgerald*, *Fitzsimmons*, as well as *Fitz* and *Fitch*. Among Scotch and Irish the same function is accomplished by the familiar syllable, *Mac*, meaning "relative." Among the Welsh, *Map*, or the later forms, *Ap* or *Ab*, serve the same purpose. This element, in disguised form, enters into the composition of many common names of Welsh origin, such as *Pugh* (ap + Hugh), *Bowen* (ap + Owen), *Powell* (ap + Howell, Hoel), *Price* (ap + Rhys), *Pritchard* (ap + Richard), *Prothero* (ap + Roderick), *Blood* (ap + Lud), as well as in *Upjohn*, *Updike*, etc. The Irish *O'* serves practically the same fuunction as *Mac*.

Among Scandinavian peoples the patronymic suffix is *-son*. The surnames most used in Norway, Sweden, and Denmark are said to be respectively *Olson* (Olaf + son), *Anderson* (Andrew's son), and *Pedersen* (Peter's son). For the most part, to Norse source or to Norse influence are to be attributed the names in *-son* so frequent in northern England and lowland Scotland as well as in the American Northwest, where the Scandinavian element in the population is so strong.

In the South of England the older genitive ending, *-s*, accomplishes a similar function. This mode of distinction is well enough known in large families of our own time, where the numerous Johns or Marys in a large family are distinguished by the added name of the parent, for example Tom's Mary as distinguished from Herbert's Mary, etc. To it are to be attributed in great part the many surnames ending in *s* frequent among the Welsh, such as *Jones, Williams, Hughes, Evans, Roberts, Edwards, Rogers, Harris,* etc.

A second source of surnames is from the country or locality with which a man is associated. *Scott* is said to be an English name applied to Scotchman; the reverse is of course true of the name *English. Cornish* and *Cornwallis* are names for natives of Cornwall, said to have originated in neighboring Devonshire. Names of provinces and towns find a like use as surnames, though usually much disguised in form. *Champneys* is a name applied to a native of Champagne. Other names of the kind are *Brett, Britton* (native of Brittany), *Picard, Power* (Picardy), *Loring* (Lorraine), *Bullen* (Boulogne), *Bloss* (Blois), *Loving* (Louvain), *Sessions* (Soissons), *Turney* (Tournay), etc. Place-names more purely local, which, serving first as a distinguishing addition to a name, have developed into surnames with or without the genitive *'s*, are *Ford, Bridges, Field, Craig* ("crag"), *Lake, Rivers, Creek, Brooke, Cairnes, Glenn, Dunne* and *Dun* ("hill"), *Hill*, etc. From the Old English *burh* (dat. *byrig*), meaning "fortified place," come *Burrows, Burroughs, Borrow, Brough, Burke, Bury, Berry, Attlebury*, etc. Many place-names no longer familiar as common nouns in standard language, continue in use as proper names, such as *Peak, Pike, Peck* and *Pick*, variant forms of the name for "hill-top"; *Law, Low, Lynn, Shaw, Holt, Hurst* and *Barrows*, all of them from words familiar in dialect or in the archaic language of poetry. More definite are the place-names appearing in *Tuttle* (Toot + hill), *Tyndall* (Tyne + dale), *Haywood* (Hay, "hedge" + wood), *Radcliffe, Wycliffe, Doddridge, Bradshaw* ("broadwood"), *Crashaw* ("crowwood"), *Earnshaw* ("eaglewood"), *Renshaw* ("ravenwood"), *Schofield* ("schoolfield"), and the like. The older northern form *yett* for *gate*, appears in *Yeats* and *Yates. Hyatt* is disguised *High* + *yett*. Dialectal variants of *Hedge* appear in *Hay*, *Haig*, *Haigh*, *Haw*, and *Hey*. Plural forms are *Hayes* and *Hawes*. Countless instances of common place-names used as surnames will occur to any one. Some of the less obvious instances cited here will serve to show how many such names live under disguise.

A third principal source of modern surnames is to be found in names of occupations. The number of names from this source is even greater than appears at first sight. There are *Smith*, *Butcher*, *Carpenter*, *Miller*, *Taylor*, and their like, now applied utterly without relation to occupation, but forming the most widely used type of surname. Besides these obvious instances there are numerous surnames from old forms of names of occupations the meanings of which are no longer always evident. The name *Chaucer*, "shoemaker," is an obvious instance. In this class may be included such early forms of name as *Hunt*, "hunter"; *Day* "dairyman"; *Webb*, "weaver"; *Kemp*, "warrior"; *Frick*, "warrior"; *Wright* (originally "worker," O. E. *wyrhta; Brewster*, *Baxter* and *Webster*, names for the feminine *brewer*, *baker* and *weaver*, respectively; *Millard*, "millward"; *Plummer*, "plumber"; *Inman*, "landlord"; *Ward*, "guard"; *Firminger*, "cheesemaker"; *Barker*, "tanner"; *Chapman* "merchant"; *Clark*, "scholar."

Besides these more or less disguised occupational surnames, there are a large number of surnames derived from names of obsolete occupations, occupations which have gone out of use because there is no further use for the article produced or because modern methods of manufacture, based on the principle of division of labor, have proved too efficient to permit the survival of the early type of craftsman trained to the production of a single article. With the decline in the importance of archery has come about the disappearance of the arrowmaker whose name survives in the surnames, *Arrowsmith*, *Fletcher*, and *Flower* (O. E. *flā*, "arrow"), *Boulter*, "bolt maker," and of the maker of bows whose occupational name survives in the variant forms, *Bowyer*, *Bower*, *Boyer*. Connected with the earlier art of cloth manufacture were the occupations whose names survive in *Fuller*, *Tucker*, *Shearer*, *Sherman*, *Walker*. To the same class of names are to be assigned, among others, *Tyler* ("tile man"), *Chandler* ("candle maker"), *Hawker* ("itinerant salesman"), *Parmenter* ("tailor"), *Pilcher* ("maker of fur cloaks"), *Quiller* ("maker of quilted ruffs"), *Cutler* ("knife maker"), *Spooner* ("spoon maker"), *Collier* ("charcoal burner"), *Croker, Crocker* ("maker of crocks"), *Cooper, Cowper* ("maker of casks"), *Lorimer* ("bridle maker"), *Sellars* ("saddle maker"), *Parker* ("park custodian"), *Hayward* ("a guardian of the tilled fields," literally "hedge ward"), *Marshall* ("horse servant"), *Constable* ("stableman"), *Stuart, Stewart* ("steward"). In the name *Graves* two forms have coalesced: the O. E. *gerēfa* ("reeve") and *Greaves* from an earlier form for *Grove*. The same is true of *Howard*, which originates, on the one hand, as a variant form of *Hayward*, on the other hand, from *Harward*, a late form for earlier *Hereward*.

A fourth general source of surnames is to be found in epithets or nicknames, the word nickname itself, from earlier "an eke name," originally being the equivalent of surname. The use of epithets in the Anglo-Saxon period, in such names as *Æthelred the Unready* and *Edmund Ironsides*, has already been referred to. The use of epithets in the succeeding period may be illustrated by the names of the successive kings: *William the Bastard, William Rufus* ("the red"), *Henry Beauclerc* ("fine scholar"), *Henry Plantagenet, Richard the Lion-Hearted, John Lackland, Edward Longshanks*. Of these, *Plantagenet* ("sprig of broom"), which Henry II inherited from his father, Geoffrey, Count of Anjou, became the surname of a long royal line.

The subject of nicknames and epithets is a treacherous one to handle. Their application is subject to every kind of caprice. The unessential quality is as likely as the essential to be the one to give the name. *Wolf*, as an epithet expressive of character, is not hard to understand. *Lovell* and *Lovett* are similarly explained since they are diminutive forms of the early French word for "wolf." *Drinkwater* probably was expressive of idiosyncrasy and is paralleled by the French equivalent, *Boileau. Dolittle* belongs to the same class. *Larned* represents an earlier pronunciation of *learned. Fairfax* had the meaning "fair hair." *Eames* comes from the genitive form of the old word *eme*, "uncle." Features of dress are expressed by *Capron* ("hood"), *Burden* ("staff"), *Motley* ("fool's costume"), *Gildersleeve*. Manner of speech is conveyed by *Purdy* and *Pardee*, from the oath *pardee*, of French origin. *Shakespeare* belongs in a class with *Wagstaff, Hurlbutt, Benbow* ("bend bow"), *Makepiece* and *Lovejoy*, all of them imperative compounds. *Little* requires no comment, but *Stout* had a broader meaning, "valiant"; *Seeley* meant "happy," "blessed"; *Moody* meant "courageous"; *Crook* and *Crum* meant "crooked";

Bolt meant "bold"; *Leaf* meant "dear"; *Stow* meant "big," "stout"; *Bragg* meant "brave."

The original meaning of many names is hidden because of their French extraction, as in the case of *Burnett* (diminutive of *brun*, "brown"), *Blunt* and *Blount* ("blonde"), *Gaylord* (*gaillard*, "gay," "brisk"), *Prout* (*cf.* Fr. Prud'homme), *Power* ("poor"), *Follett* (diminutive of *fol*, "mad"), *Curtis* ("courteous").

Many of the names of Celtic origin are interesting because the original meaning is so completely lost sight of, as in the Welsh *Gough* and *Roe*, both meaning "red"; *Bain*, *Wynne* and *Gwynne*, "white"; *Glass* and *Lloyd* and *Floyd*, "gray"; *Sayce*, "Saxon"; *Vaughan*, "little"; and the Highland Scotch *Cameron*, "crooked nose"; *Campbell*, "wry mouth"; and the Irish *Kennedy*, "ugly head."

Probably no other kind of word is so subject to variation in form as personal names, due in part at least, to the fact that they have so little logical relation to the persons named, and hence drift in sound like a craft loose from its moorings. The variant forms of the name of *Shakespeare* are familiar enough. Dr. *Crown*, a writer of the seventeenth century, spelled his own name in six different ways: *Cron*, *Croon*, *Crown*, *Crone*, *Croone*, *Croune*. Such variant forms as *Pierce*, *Peirce*, *Pearce*, *Pearse* and *Pears* are familiar to every one, all derived through the French *Piers* from the name of the apostle *Peter*. In the same way *Lea*, *Lee*, *Ley*, *Leigh*, *Legh*, *Legge*, *Lay*, *Lye*, are all derived from one place-name, the Old English word meaning "meadow." The fashion of clipping names in familiar use, which has given rise to such a group of names as *Elspeth*, *Elsie*, *Eliza*, *Liza*, *Lisa*, *Lizzie*, *Beth*, *Bet*, *Bettie*, *Betsy*, etc., all from the name *Elizabeth*, is well known. When to full name or to shortened forms are added suffixes like the diminutives *-kin*, *-in*, *-ie*, *-ett*, etc., probably expressive of endearment, and the other suffixes *-son*, *-s*, *-man*, *-cock*, it is apparent that variation has practically no limits. To the variants of *Pierce* may be added *Perkins*, *Pierson*, etc. *Matthew* and its old French form, *Mahieu*, give rise to *Matthews*, *Mayhew*, *Mayo*, *May*, *Mee*, *Mayes*, *Mekins*, *Meeson*, and, sometimes, *Mason*. *Philip* gives rise to *Phillips*, *Philip*, *Phipps*, *Phelps*, *Filkins*, etc. From *Bartholomew* come *Batty*, *Batten*, *Bates*, *Bartle*, *Bartilson*, *Bartlett*, *Badcock*, *Badman*. From *Hugh* and its diminutive *Huggin* come *Hewett*, *Hewlett*, *Howitt*, *Howlett*, *Hutchins*.

The remarkable divergence in popular use from the original pronunciation of names gives rise to many new names hard to associate with the original forms. As examples of this class may be cited *Farrar* from *Farquhar*, *Mean* from *Meaghan*, *Meany* from *Mahoney*, *Calhoun* from *Colquhoun*, *Marshbanks* from *Marjoribanks*, *Mannering* from *Mainwaring*, *Beecham* from *Beauchamp*, *Warrick* from *Warwick*, *Beeton* from *Bethune*, *Car* from *Ker*, *Mills* from *Milnes*, *Marr* from *Meagher*.

The names of saints, due to familiar use, have been particularly subject to this kind of change. *Tolley* comes from *Bartholomew*, *Munn* from *Edmund*, *Tedman* from *St. Edmund*, *Tobin* from *St. Aubyn*, *Toosey* from *St. Osith*, *Toomer* from *St. Omer*, *Tooley* from *St. Olave*, *Selleger* and *Sellinger* from *St. Leger*, *Seymour* from *St. Maur*, *Sidney* from *St. Denis*, *Sinclair* from *St. Clair*, *Semark* from *St. Mark*, *Semple* from *St. Paul*, *Simper* from *St. Pierre*.

Along with the natural unconscious tendencies toward change in pronunciation, later registered in changed spelling, must be reckoned the frantic striving for novelty, distinction, individuality. This spirit finds expression in forms of names of girls, often adopted by the girls themselves, such as *Alys*, *Edythe*, *Evelyn*, *Carolyn*, *Marye*, *Emmajeane*, *Evajeane*, *Donna*, *Gladelen*, *Gladene*, *Aleen*, *Karleene*, *Eunice*, *Nelle*, *Lorna*, *Thelma*, *Elaine*, *Marion*.

In the pronunciation of the names of foreigners one finds oneself in a predicament much like that in the case of foreign place-names. Down to times comparatively recent, names of foreigners have been anglicized in pronunciation, frequently in spelling as well. The great names of antiquity, sacred and profane, from *Confucius* to *Cæsar*, have taken English pronunciation. The same is true of the historic names of later times: *Charlemagne*, *Dante*, *Petrarch*, *Raphael*, *Titian*, *Galileo*, *Luther*, *Huss*, *Columbus*, *Cervantes*, *Gustavus Adolphus*, *Napoleon*, *Frederick the Great*, *Ney*, *Blücher*, *Schiller*, *Hugo*, *Swedenborg*, *Handel*, *Haydn*, *Mendelssohn*, *Mozart*, *Talleyrand*, *Metternich*. Down to recent times, only a small number of foreign names, such as *Goethe*, *Medici*, *Beethoven*, and *Chopin*, have failed in English use to take an English pronunciation. In our own times the situation is different. Attempt is made, in words like *Wagner* and *Maupassant*, more or less successfully, to give the pronunciation of the language to which the name is native. Is this because English has reached the saturation point? Or is it a form of pedantry? Even now almost any name that gains popular circulation inevitably takes the English stamp. Occasionally a name, not entirely popular, such as *Maeterlinck*, is made at home. Would it not be an obvious gain if, as in the case of place-names, the learned should espouse the popular cause and apply English sounds to the pronunciation of foreign names? The reason for the hesitation and vacillation is doubtless to be found in the uncertain pronunciation of English letters, which prevents the arrival at agreement in the pronunctiation of names with foreign spelling.

In the United States the problem of dealing with names of foreign extraction is an alive one. In the solution of the problem, however, considerable progress has been made through the assimilation of the foreign names. The assimilation usually comes about in one of two ways. The foreign name is fitted in pronunciation and spelling into an Anglo-Saxon form. Dutch names thus transformed are: *Reiger* to *Riker*, *Van Huys* to *Vannice*, *Van Siegel* to *Van Sickle*, *Haerlen* to *Harlan*. French names thus handled are *Caillé* to *Kyle*, *De la Haye* to *Dillehay*, *Dejean* to *Dishong*, *Soule* to *Sewell*, *Gervaise* to *Jarvis*, *Bayle* to *Bailey*, *Pebaudière* to *Peabody*, *Bon Pas* to *Bumpus*, *de l'Hotel* to *Doolittle*. German shifts of this kind are *Blum* to *Bloom*, *Reuss* to *Royce*, *Kuehle* to *Keeley*, *Stehli* to *Staley*, *Bauman* to *Bowman*, *Oehm* to *Ames*, *Furth* to *Ford*, *Kuntz* to *Coons* or *Kuhns*, *Jung* to *Young*, etc.

In a great many cases, on the other hand, the foreign name is translated. German *Pfund* becomes *Pound; Schumacher*, *Shoemaker; König*, *King; Koch*, *Cook; Neuman*, *Newman; Steiner*, *Stoner; Schwartz*, *Black; Weber*, *Weaver; Sontag*, *Sunday*.

Jews have been particularly active in modifying their names, changing *Cohen* into *Cohn*, *Cahn*, *Kahn*, *Kann*, *Coyne*, and *Conn*, *Aaron* into *Aren* or *Ahren*, *Solomon* into *Salmon*, *Salomon* or *Solomsen*, shortening *Wolfsheimer* to *Wolf*, *Goldsmidt* to *Gold*, *Rosenblatt*, *Rosenthal*, etc., to *Rose*, translating *Schneider* into *Taylor*, *Schlachtfeld* into *Warfield*, *Reichman* into *Richman*.

What might happen to a foreign name in America may be illustrated by the following anecdote of a resident of New Orleans:

> When he moved from an American quarter into a German quarter his name of *Flint* became *Feuerstein*, which for convenience was shortened to *Stein*. Upon his removal to a French district, he was rechristened *Pierre*. Hence upon his return to an English neighborhood he was translated into *Peters*, and his first neighbors were surprised and puzzled to find *Flint* turned into *Peters*.

An examination of the proper names in the United States reveals some interesting facts regarding the race material that makes up the population. In New York City the fourth most common name is now *Murphy*, and the fifth most common is *Meyer*. *Cohen* and *Levy* come eighth and ninth in rank. Of the names *Smith*, *Jones*, *Williams*, and *Taylor*, which rank first to fourth in England, only *Smith* holds its place in the United States. Nine names come ahead of *Jones* in New York, and *Taylor* comes twenty-third. *Smith*, *Brown*, and *Miller*, which are the first three names, ranked by numbers, in New York, hold their places because their numbers have been recruited from German and Scandinavian sources, from the ranks of *Schmidts*, and *Brauns* and *Müllers*. Judging from proper names, the elements in the American melting pot are showing new proportions.

SUGGESTED ASSIGNMENTS

1. List the names of members of a particular group; for example, those in your English class, house, club, team, dormitory wing, academic department, floor. Classify as many as you can into these categories given by Professor McKnight: patronymics (*Mac Donald*), names from places (*Brook*), names of occupations (*Baker*), epithets (*Small*), names formed with genitive *-s* (*Richards*), imperatives (*Lovejoy*).
2. Write a theme on the names of your friends.
3. Using a telephone or college directory, find five examples of names for each of the categories mentioned in *one* above.
4. Find a dictionary or listing of first names in the reference room of the library. After perusing it a while, set up first-name classes that seem to have numerous members, such as flower (*Lily*), Biblical (*Mary*), mythological (*Diana*), descriptive (*Prudence*), feminine form of masculine name (*Josephine*). Your categories may be quite different from these. Fill in each category with five or more names.
5. Many common names have come from proper names. Look up the source of these words: *sandwich, hamburger, wiener, frankfurter, tabasco, bologna, tantalize, tuxedo, meander, jovial, mercurial, saturnine, cashmere, sherry, port, cognac, bourbon, shetland, vandal, guy*.
6. Write a theme on a topic like one of these:
   a. Names I Like
   b. Names I Dislike
   c. Sources of First Names
   d. Nicknames of Persons I Have Known

EUPHEMISMS

H. L. Mencken

A euphemism is a softened, indirect expression used instead of one that seems too harsh and direct. For example, he passed away *and* he is gone *are euphemisms for* he died *and* he is dead. *Circumlocutions like these may arise from the desire to avoid giving pain and in such cases must be accounted useful terms. At times, however, euphemisms are employed merely through hypersensitivity or excess of delicacy. The Victorian use of* white meat *to avoid saying* breast, *and the Ozark woman's use of* lay down *to avoid the indelicate suggestiveness of* go to bed *seem to us cases of overconcern hinting of prudery. There is still a third reason for the use of euphemistic terms: to enhance prestige. The job of a garbage collector, for example, seems more prestigious if he is called a* sanitary engineer.

Euphemisms are forthrightly dealt with by Henry L. Mencken in the pages below. Mr. Mencken was a journalist, essayist, and champion of the language of the United States, and he wrote with vigor and bite. His American Language, *from which the present selection is taken, was a landmark in the study of our native tongue. It was followed by* Supplement One *and* Supplement Two, *both large volumes. The three are a storehouse of information on American English.*

THE AMERICAN, probably more than any other man, is prone to be apologetic about the trade he follows. He seldom believes that it is quite worthy of his virtues and talents; almost always he thinks that he would have adorned something far gaudier. Unfortunately, it is not always possible for him to escape, or even for him to dream plausibly of escaping, so he soothes himself by assuring himself that he belongs to a superior section of his craft, and very often he invents a sonorous name to set himself off from the herd. Here we glimpse the origin of a multitude of characteristic American euphemisms, *e.g.*, *mortician* for *undertaker*, *realtor* for *real-estate agent*, *electragist* for *electrical contractor*, *aisle manager* for *floor-walker*, *beautician* for *hairdresser*, *exterminating engineer* for *rat-catcher*, and so on. *Realtor* was devised by a high-toned real-estate agent of Minneapolis, Charles N. Chadbourn by name. He thus describes its genesis:

> It was in November, 1915, on my way to a meeting of the Minneapolis Real Estate Board, that I was annoyed by the strident peddling of a scandal sheet: "All About the Robbery of a Poor Widow by a Real Estate Man." The "real estate man" thus exposed turned out to be an obscure hombre with desk-room in a back office in a rookery, but the incident set me to thinking. "Every member of our board," I thought, "is besmirched by this scandal article. Anyone, however unworthy or disreputable, may call himself a real estate man. Why do not the members of our board deserve a distinctive title? Each member is vouched for by the board, subscribes to its Code of Ethics, and must behave himself or get out." So the idea incubated for three or four weeks, and was then sprung on the local brethren.[1]

As to the etymology of the term, Mr. Chadbourn says:

> Real estate originally meant a royal grant. It is so connected with land in the public mind that *realtor* is easily understood, even at first hearing. The suffix *-or* means a doer, one who performs an act, as in *grantor*, *executor*, *sponsor*, *administrator*.

The Minneapolis brethren were so pleased with their new name that Mr. Chadbourn was moved to dedicate it to the whole profession. In March, 1916, he went to the convention of the National Association of Real Estate Boards at New Orleans, and made a formal offer of it. It was accepted gratefully, and is now defined by the association as follows:

> A person engaged in the real estate business who is an active member of a member board of the National Association of Real Estate Boards,

[1] Private communication, Sept. 28, 1935.

and as such, an affiliated member of the National Association, who is subject to its rules and regulations, who observes its standards of conduct, and is entitled to its benefits.[2]

In 1920 the Minneapolis Real Estate Board and the National Association of Real Estate Boards applied to Judge Joseph W. Molyneaux of Minneapolis for an injunction restraining the Northwestern Telephone Exchange Company from using *realtor* to designate some of its hirelings, and on September 10 the learned judge duly granted this relief. Since then the National Association has obtained similar injunctions in Virginia, Utah and other States. Its general counsel is heard from every time *realtor* is taken in vain, and when, in 1922, Sinclair Lewis applied it to George F. Babbitt, there was an uproar. But when Mr. Chadbourn was appealed to he decided that Babbitt was "fairly well described," for he was "a prominent member of the local board and of the State association," and one could scarcely look for anything better in "a book written in the ironic vein of the author of 'Main Street.'"[3] Mr. Chadbourn believes that *realtor* should be capitalized, "like *Methodist* or *American*,"[4] but so far it has not been generally done. In June, 1925, at a meeting of the National Association of Real Estate Boards in Detroit, the past presidents of the body presented him with a gold watch as a token of their gratitude for his contribution to the uplift of their profession. On May 30, 1934, the following letter from Nathan William MacChesney, general counsel of the National Association, appeared in the *New Republic:*

[*Realtor*] is not a word, but a trade right, coined and protected by law by the National Association of Real Estate Boards, and the term is a part of the trade-mark as registered in some forty-four States and Canada. Something over $200,000 has been spent in its protection by the National Association of Real Estate Boards in attempting to confine its use to those real estate men who are members of the National Association of Real Estate Boards, subject to its code for ethics and to its discipline for violation. It has been a factor in making the standards of the business generally during the past twenty years, and the exclusive right of the National Association of Real Estate Boards has been sustained in a series of court

[2] Realtor: Its Meaning and Use; Chicago (National Association of Real Estate Boards), 1925.

[3] Letter to W. A. Frisbie, editor of the Minneapolis *Daily News*. This was in 1922. The letter was subscribed "Yours *realtorially*." A copy was sent to Mr. Lewis, who preserves it in his archives.

[4] Private communication, Sept. 4, 1935.

decisions, a large number of injunctions having been issued, restraining its improper use.

In 1924 the *Realtors' Bulletin* of Baltimore reported that certain enemies of realtric science were trying to show that *realtor* was derived from the English word *real* and the Spanish word *toro*, a bull, and to argue that it thus meant *real bull*. But this obscenity apparently did not go far; probably a hint from the alert general counsel was enough to stop it. During the same year I was informed by Herbert U. Nelson, executive secretary of the National Association, that "the real-estate men of London, through the Institute of Estate Agents and Auctioneers, after studying our experience in this respect, are planning to coin the word *estator* and to protect it by legal steps." This plan, I believe, came to fruition, but *estator* never caught on, and I can't find it in the Supplement to the Oxford Dictionary. *Realtor*, however, is there—and the first illustrative quotation is from "Babbitt"! In March, 1927, J. Foster Hagan, of Ballston, Va., reported to *American Speech* that he had encountered *realtress* on the window of a real-estate office there, but this charming derivative seems to have died "a-bornin." In 1925 or thereabout certain ambitious insurance solicitors, inflamed by *realtor*, began to call themselves *insurors*, but it, too, failed to make any progress.

Electragist, like *realtor*, seems to be the monopoly of the lofty technicians who affect it: "it is copyrighted by the Association of Electragists International, whose members alone may use it."[5] But *mortician* is in the public domain. It was proposed by a writer in the *Embalmers' Monthly* for February, 1895, but the undertakers, who were then *funeral-directors*, did not rise to it until some years later. On September 16, 1916, some of the more eminent of them met at Columbus, O., to form a national association, on the lines of the American College of Surgeons, the American Association of University Professors, and the Society of the Cincinnati, and a year later they decided upon National Selected Morticians as its designation.[6] To this day the association remains so exclusive that, of the 24,000 undertakers in the United States, only 200 belong to it. But any one of the remaining 23,800 is free to call himself a *mortician*, and to use

[5] Electragist, by Corneil Ridderhof, *American Speech*, Aug., 1927, p. 477. It means, according to Mr. Ridderhof, "a combined electrical dealer and contractor."

[6] I am indebted here to Mr. W. M. Krieger, executive secretary of the organization, the headquarters of which are in Chicago.

all the other lovely words that the advance of human taxidermy has brought in. *Mortician*, of course, was suggested by *physician*, for undertakers naturally admire and like to pal with the resurrection men, and there was a time when some of them called themselves *embalming surgeons*. A *mortician* never handles a *corpse;* he *prepares* a *body* or *patient*. This business is carried on in a *preparation-room* or *operating-room*, and when it is achieved the patient is put into a *casket*[7] and stored in the *reposing-room* or *slumber-room* of a *funeral-home*. On the day of the funeral he is moved to the *chapel* therein for the last exorcism, and then hauled to the cemetery in a *funeral-car* or *casket-coach*.[8] The old-time shroud is now a *négligé* or *slumber-shirt* or *slumber-robe*, the mortician's work-truck is an *ambulance*, and the cemetery is fast becoming a *memorial-park*. In the West cemeteries are being supplanted by public mausoleums, which sometimes go under the names of *cloisters*, *burial-abbeys*, etc.[9] To be laid away in one runs into money. The vehicle that morticians use for their expectant hauling of the ill is no longer an ambulance, but an *invalid-coach*. *Mortician* has been a favorite butt of the national wits, but they seem to have made no impression on it. In January, 1932, it was barred from the columns of the Chicago *Tribune*. "This decree goes forth," announced the *Tribune*, "not for lack of sympathy with the ambition of undertakers to be well regarded, but because of it. If they haven't the sense to save themselves from their own lexicographers, we shall not be guilty of abetting them in their folly."[10] But *mortician* not only continues to flourish; it also begets progeny, *e.g.*, *beautician*, *cosmetician*, *radiotrician* and *bootician*.[11] The barbers, so far, have not devised a name for them-

[7] *Casket* seems to have come in during the Civil War period. In 1863 Nathaniel Hawthorne denounced it in Our Old Home as "a vile modern phrase, which compels a person . . . to shrink . . . from the idea of being buried at all." At the start it had a rival in *case*. The latter was used in the Richmond *Examiner's* report of the funeral of Gen. J. E. B. Stuart, May 13, 1864. But the *Examiner*, in the same report, used *corpse* and *hearse*.

[8] Mortuary Nomenclature, *Hygeia*, Nov., 1925, p. 651.

[9] The *Mortician*, by Elmer Davis, *American Mercury*, May, 1927.

[10] *Editor and Publisher*, Jan. 30, 1932.

[11] I proposed the use of *bootician* to designate a high-toned big-city bootlegger in the *American Mercury*, April, 1925, p. 450. The term met a crying need, and had considerable success. In March, 1927, the San José *Mercury-Herald* said: "Our bootleggers are now calling themeslves *booticians*. It seems that *bootlegger* has some trace of odium about it, while *bootician* has none." (Reprinted in the Baltimore *Evening Sun*, April 4, 1927.) On July 23, 1931, according to the Associated Press, a man arrested in Chicago, on being asked his profession, answered proudly that he was a *bootician*.

selves in *-ician*, but they may be trusted to do so anon. In my youth they were *tonsorial artists*, but in recent years some of them have been calling themselves *chirotonsors*.[12] Practically all American press-agents are now *public relations counsel*, *contact-managers* or *publicists*, all tree-trimmers are *tree-surgeons*, all milk-wagon and bakery-wagon drivers have become *salesmen*, nearly all janitors are *superintendents*, many gardeners have become *landscape-architects* (in England even the whales of the profession are simple *landscape-gardeners*), cobblers are beginning to call themselves *shoe-rebuilders*,[13] and the corn-doctors, after a generation as *chiropodists*, have burst forth as *podiatrists*. The American fondness for such sonorous appellations arrested the interest of W. L. George, the English novelist, when he visited the United States in 1920. He said:

Business titles are given in America more readily than in England. I know one *president* whose staff consists of two typists. Many firms have four *vice-presidents*. In the magazines you seldom find merely an *editor;* the others need their share of honor, so they are *associate* (not *assistant*) *editors*. A dentist is called a *doctor*. I wandered into a university, knowing nobody, and casually asked for the *dean*. I was asked, "Which *dean?*" In that building there were enough deans to stock all the English cathedrals. The master of a secret society is *royal supreme knight commander*. Perhaps I reached the extreme at a theatre in Boston, when I wanted something, I forgot what, and was told that I must apply to the *chief of the ushers*. He was a mild little man, who had something to do with people getting into their seats, rather a come-down from the pomp and circumstance of his title. Growing interested, I examined my programme, with the following result: It is not a large theatre, but it has a *press-representative*, a *treasurer* (box-office clerk), an *assistant treasurer* (box-office junior clerk), an *advertising-agent*, our old friend the *chief of the ushers*, a *stage-manager*, a *head-electrician*, a *master of properties* (in England called *props*), a *leader of the orchestra* (pity this—why not *president?*), and a *matron* (occupation unknown).[14]

George might have unearthed some even stranger magnificoes in other playhouses. I once knew an ancient bill-sticker, attached to a Baltimore theatre, who boasted the sonorous title of *chief lithographer*. Today, in all probability, he would be called a *lithographic-*

[12] In 1924 representatives of 3000 of them met in Chicago, and voted for *chirotonsor*. See the *Commonweal*, Nov. 26, 1924, p. 58.

[13] There is a *Shoe Rebuilders'* Association in Baltimore. See the Baltimore *Evening Sun*, Oct. 17, 1935.

[14] Hail, Columbia!; New York, 1921, pp. 92-93.

engineer. For a number of years the *Engineering News-Record*, the organ of the legitimate engineers, used to devote a column every week to just such uninvited invaders of the craft, and some of the species it unearthed were so fantastic that it was constrained to reproduce their business cards photographically in order to convince its readers that it was not spoofing. One of its favorite exhibits was a bedding manufacturer who first became a *mattress-engineer* and then promoted himself to the lofty dignity of *sleep-engineer*. No doubt he would have called himself a *morphician* if he had thought of it. Another exhilarating specimen was a tractor-driver who advertised for a job as a *caterpillar-engineer*. A third was a beautician who burst out as an *appearance-engineer*. In an Atlanta department-store the *News-Record* found an *engineer of good taste*—a young woman employed to advise newly-married couples patronizing the furniture department, and elsewhere it unearthed *display-engineers* who had been lowly window-dressers until some visionary among them made the great leap, *demolition-engineers* who were once content to be house-wreckers, and *sanitary-engineers* who had an earlier incarnation as garbage-men. The *wedding-engineer* is a technician employed by florists to dress churches for hymeneal orgies. The *commencement-e.* arranges college and high-school commencements; he has lists of clergymen who may be trusted to pray briefly, and some sort of fire-alarm connection, I suppose, with the office of Dr. John H. Finley, the champion commencement orator of this or any other age. . . . The *extermination-engineers* have a solemn national association and wear a distinguishing pin; whether or not they have tried to restrain non-member rat-catchers from calling themselves engineers I do not know. In 1923 the *Engineering News-Record* printed a final blast against all the pseudo-engineers then extant, and urged its engineer readers to boycott them. But this boycott apparently came to nothing, and soon thereafter it abated its indignation and resorted to laughter.[15] Next to *engineer*, *expert* seems to be the favorite talisman

[15] See the issue for Jan. 15, 1925. Also, Some "Engineers" I Have Known, by a Civil Engineer, *Engineering News-Record*, April 19, 1923, p. 701. The engineers themselves have grossly misused the term designating them. In The Structure of the Engineering Profession, by Theodore J. Hoover, dean of the School of Engineering at Stanford University, *Journal of Engineering Education*, Jan., 1935, appears an exhaustive report upon what the 10,542 listed in "Who's Who in Engineering" call themselves. Mr. Hoover finds 2518 different titles, including such absurdities as *sales-e.*, *sales-promotion-e.*, *promotion-e.*, *application-e.*, *college-e.*, *social-e.*, *technical-publicity-e.*, *bank-management-e.*, and *export-e.* He advocates a complete reform of professional nomenclature, but when I last

of Americans eager to augment their estate and dignity in this world. Very often it is hitched to an explanatory prefix, *e.g.*, *housing-*, *planning-*, *hog-*, *erosion-*, *marketing-*, *boll-weevil-*, or *sheep-dip-*, but sometimes the simple adjective *trained-* suffices. When the Brain Trust came into power in Washington, the town began to swarm with such quacks, most of them recent graduates of the far-flung colleges of the land. One day a humorous member of Congress printed an immense list of them in the *Congressional Record*, with their salaries and academic dignities. He found at least one whose expertness was acquired in a seminary for chiropractors. During the John Purroy Mitchel "reform" administration in New York City (1914-18) so many bogus *experts* were put upon the pay-roll that special designations for them ran out, and in prodding through the Mitchel records later on Bird S. Coler discovered that a number had been carried on the books as *general experts*.

Euphemisms for things are almost as common in the United States as euphemisms for avocations. Dozens of forlorn little fresh-water colleges are called *universities*, and almost all *pawn-shops* are *loan-offices*. When *movie-cathedral* came in a few scoffers snickered, but by the generality of fans it was received gravely. *City*, in England, used to be confined to the seats of bishops, and even today it is applied only to considerable places, but in the United States it is commonly assumed by any town with paved streets, and in the statistical publications of the Federal government it is applied to all places of 8000 or more population. The American use of *store* for *shop*, like that of *help* for *servant*, is probably the product of an early effort at magnification. Before Prohibition saloons used to be *sample-rooms*, *buffets*, *exchanges*, *cafés* and *restaurants;* now they are *taverns*, *cock-tail-rooms*, *taprooms*, *American-bars*, *stubes* and what not. Not long ago the *Furnished-Room Guide* undertook to substitute *hotelette* for *rooming-house*,[16] and in 1928 President E. L. Robins of the National *Fertilizer* Association proposed that the name of that organization be changed to the National Association of *Plant Food* manufacturers or

heard from him he didn't seem to have much hope. On Feb. 21, 1935 the Associated Press reported that the National Society of Professional Engineers was trying to induce the American railroads to call their locomotive-engineers *enginemen*. The New York Central and the Pennsylvania, it was said, were already doing so.

[16] See the *New Yorker*, Jan. 9, 1935, p. 74. The *New Yorker* expressed a waggish preference for *furnished-roomateria*.

the American *Plant Food* Association.[17] In Pasadena the public garbage-wagons bear the legend: *Table-Waste Disposal Department.* The word *studio* is heavily overworked; there are *billiard-studios, tonsorial-studios, candy-studios,* and even *shoe-studios.*[18] Nor is this reaching out for sweet and disarming words confined to the lowly. Some time ago, in the *Survey*, the trade journal of the American uplifters, Dr. Thomas Dawes Eliot, associate professor of sociology in Northwestern University, printed a solemn argument in favor of abandoning all such harsh terms as *reformatory, house of refuge, reform school* and *jail.* "Each time a new phrase is developed," he said, "it seems to bring with it, or at least to be accompanied by, some measure of permanent gain, in standards or in viewpoint, even though much of the old may continue to masquerade as the new. The series, *alms, philanthropy, relief, rehabilitation, case work, family welfare,* shows such a progression from cruder to more refined levels of charity." Among the substitutions proposed by the learned professor were *habit-disease* for *vice, psycho-neurosis* for *sin, failure to compensate* for *disease, treatment* for *punishment, delinquent* for *criminal, unmarried mother* for *illegitimate mother, out of wedlock* for *bastard, behavior problem* for *prostitute, colony* for *penitentiary, school* for *reformatory, psychopathic hospital* for *insane asylum,* and *house of detention* for *jail.*[19] Many of these terms (or others like them) have been actually adopted. Practically all American insane asylums are now simple *hospitals,* many reformatories and houses of correction have been converted into *homes* or *schools,* all *almshouses* are now *infirmaries, county-farms* or *county-homes,* and most of the more advanced American penologists now speak of criminals as *psychopathic personalities.* By a law of New York it is provided that "in any local law, ordinance or resolution, or in any public or judicial proceeding, or in any process, notice, order, decree, judgment, record or other public document or paper, the term *bastard* or *illegitimate child* shall not be used, but the term *child born out of wedlock* shall be used in substitution therefor, and with the same force and effect."[20] Meanwhile, such harsh terms as *second-hand* and *ready-made* disappear from the American vocabulary. For the former the

[17] United Press report, Nov. 13, 1928.
[18] See *Studio,* by John T. Krumpelmann, *American Speech,* Dec., 1926, p. 158.
[19] A Limbo for Cruel Words, *Survey,* June 15, 1922.
[20] Laws of 1925, Ch. 515, in force April 9, 1925. I have to thank Mr. Sylvan Baruch of the New York Bar for calling my attention to this statute.

automobile dealers, who are ardent euphemists, have substituted *re-conditioned*, *rebuilt*, *repossessed* and *used*, and for the latter department-stores offer *ready-tailored*, *ready-to-wear* and *ready-to-put-on*. For *shop-worn* two of the current euphemisms are *store-used* and *slightly-second*.

The English euphemism-of-all-work used to be *lady*. Back in the Seventeenth Century the court-poet Edmund Waller thought it quite proper to speak of actresses, then a novelty on the English stage, as *lady-actors*, and even today the English newspapers frequently refer to *lady-secretaries*, *lady-doctors*, *lady-inspectors*, *lady-golfers* and *lady-champions*. *Women's wear*, in most English shops, is *ladies' wear*. But this excessive use of lady seems to be going out, and I note *women's singles* and *women's ice hockey* on the sports pages of the London *Daily Telegraph*.[21] The *Times* inclines the same way, but I observe that it still uses *Ladies' International* to designate a golf tournament, *ladies' round* and *ladies' championship* (golf and fencing).[22] In the United States *lady* is definitely out of favor. The *salesladies* of yesteryear are now all *saleswomen* or *salesgirls*, and the female superintendent of a hospital is not the *lady-superintendent*, but simply the *superintendent*. When women were first elected to Congress, the question as to how they should be referred to in debate engaged the leaders of the House of Representatives. For a while the phrase used was "the *lady* from So-and-so," but soon "the *gentlewoman*" was substituted, and this is now employed almost invariably. Its invention is commonly ascribed to the late Nicholas Longworth; if he actually proposed it, it was probably jocosely, for *gentlewoman* is clumsy, and in some cases, as clearly inaccurate as *lady*. The English get round the difficulty by using *the hon. member* in speaking of women M.P.'s, though sometimes *the hon. lady* is used.[23] A member who happens to be a military or naval officer is

[21] March 29, 1935.

[22] April 12, 1935, p. 6.

[23] I am indebted for the following to Mr. James Bone, London editor of the Manchester *Guardian*: "When a Minister answers a question in the House he says *Yes, sir*, or *No, sir*, whether the question is asked by a man or a woman M.P. The reason is that he is supposed to be addressing the Speaker. There was some laughter among young members when a Minister replied *Yes, sir* to a question by Lady Astor, but elderly members wrote to the papers at once, rebuking them and explaining the procedure." Some time ago I heard the trial of a case in one of the London Law Courts, with the Lord Chief Justice of England, Lord Hewart, on the bench. There were two women on the jury, but when they finished their labors he said "Thank you, *gentlemen*."

always, by the way, *the hon. and gallant member*, and a legal officer, say the Attorney-General or Solicitor-General, or a lawyer member in active practise, is *the hon. and learned member*. The English use *gentleman* much more carefully than we do, and much more carefully than they themselves use *lady*. *Gentleman-author* or *gentleman-clerk* would make them howl, but they commonly employ *gentleman-rider* and *gentleman-player* in place of our *amateur*, though *amateur* seems to be gaining favor. Here the man referred to is always actually a gentleman by their standards. . . .

SUGGESTED ASSIGNMENTS

1. In everyday discourse the terms *insane*, *lunatic*, and *insane asylum* have given way to various euphemistic substitutes. List as many as you can for each term.
2. Read Evelyn Waugh's *The Loved One*, a delightful, satirical novel that you can finish in a few hours. List the euphemisms that are employed in the grisly trade depicted.
3. Euphemisms are frequently employed in our daily lives; e.g., *perspiration* for *sweat*, *dentures* for *false teeth*, *underprivileged* for *stupid*, *custodian* for *janitor*. Write a theme on the euphemisms that you hear in the course of a week.
4. Delineate a human situation in which you would find it advisable to use euphemisms and show how you would handle the situation.
5. Write a theme on euphemisms in the daily paper.
6. British English has its own euphemisms. Find out the relationship between the British intensives *bloody* and *ruddy*.

FURTHER READINGS

1. Bloomfield, Leonard. *Language*. New York: Holt, Rinehart and Winston, Inc., 1933. On euphemism see Section 22.7.
2. Bradley, Henry. *Making of English*. New York: The Macmillan Company, 1904. On word-making see Chapter 4; on meaning changes, Chapter 5.
3. Brook, G. L. *History of the English Language*. New York: Oxford University Press, 1958. On meaning and meaning changes see Chapter 8.
4. Bryant, Margaret M. *Modern English and its Heritage*. New York: The Macmillan Company, 1948. On meaning changes see Chapters 40 and 41. On other semantic changes as well as word-formation see Chapters 42 through 47.

5. Burriss, Eli E. and Lionel Casson. *Latin and Greek in Current Use.* Englewood Cliffs, New Jersey: Prentice-Hall, Inc., 1939.
6. Estrich, Robert M. and Hans Sperber. *Three Keys to Language.* New York: Holt, Rinehart and Winston, Inc., 1952. On word taboos see Chapters 1, 2, 3. On meaning and meaning changes see Chapters 9, 10, 11, 12.
7. Fraser, Sir James G. and Theodor H. Gaster. *New Golden Bough.* New York: Criterion Books, Inc., 1959. For tabooed words among primitive peoples see pages 187-196.
8. Greenough, James B. and George L. Kittredge. *Words and Their Ways in English Speech.* New York: The Macmillan Company, 1901. Although more than a half-century old, this book, which is both scholarly and popular, is still a valuable source of information about English words. For euphemism see Chapter 21. For slang see Chapter 6. For meaning changes see Chapters 17, 18, 19, 20.
9. Hargrave, Basil. *Origins and Meanings of Popular Phrases and Names.* London: T. W. Laurie, 1911.
10. Hixson, Jerome C. and I. Colodny. *Word Ways.* New York: American Book Company, 1946. On words borrowed from other languages into English see pages 27-91. On meaning changes see Chapters 12 and 13. On slang see Chapter 16.
11. Johnson, Edwin L. *Latin Words in Common Use.* Boston: D. C. Heath and Company, 1931.
12. Marchand, Hans. *Categories and Types of Present-Day English Word-Formation.* Wiesbaden: Otto Harrassowitz, 1960. On back-formation see Chapter 6. On clipping see Chapter 9. On blends see Chapter 10.
13. Marckwardt, Albert H. *American English.* New York: Oxford University Press, 1958. On the contributions of other languages to American English, see Chapter 3. On place names in the USA see Chapter 8.
14. Myers, Edward D. *Foundations of English.* New York: The Macmillan Company, 1940. For brief treatment of meaning changes and slang, see Chapters 16 and 17.
15. Partridge, Eric. *Name into Word.* New York: The Macmillan Company, 1949. Common words that have come from proper nouns.
16. Potter, Simeon. *Language in the Modern World.* Baltimore: Penguin Books, Inc., 1960. See especially Chapter 5 on the making of words.
17. Potter, Simeon. *Modern Linguistics.* London: Andre Deutsch, 1957. On word-making see Chapter 4. This discussion is more detailed and technical than the preceding book.
18. Serjeantson, Mary S. *History of Foreign Words in English.* New York: E. P. Dutton & Co., Inc., 1936.

19. Smith, Logan P. *English Language*. New York: Oxford University Press, 1912. On word-formation see Chapter 4.
20. Weekley, Ernest. *Romance of Names*. 4th ed. New York: E. P. Dutton & Co., Inc., 1922.

3. Metaphor

FIGURATIVE LANGUAGE

Monroe C. Beardsley

It is both strange and ironic that figurative language, one of the most important and fascinating aspects of language, should be so misunderstood. Many people associate figurative language solely with poetry; moreover, they regard it as a kind of poetic decoration, the frosting on the cake merely, sweet and pleasant tasting but not really necessary. Such a view of figurative language is wrong on both counts. Figures of speech, it is true, do play a prominent part in poetry, but they also play an important role in prose, not only in imaginative works such as novels and short stories but also in expository and persuasive works. Indeed, though you may not be highly conscious of it, figures of speech occur frequently in your everyday conversation. And in whatever form figurative language appears—in poetry, prose writing, or ordinary speech—it is an integral and vital part; it is not decorative but functional.

Professor Monroe Beardsley, of Swarthmore College, opens the discussion of figurative language with an examination of the simile and the metaphor.

TAKE UP A BOOK, or article, on education—or start yourself thinking about that subject by asking yourself some questions. What good is it? Should everyone go on to school to the limit of his capacities?

Should private and parochial schools be given financial help by the Government? . . . . The chances are that you won't read far, or think long, without comparing education, consciously or half-consciously, with something else. Is an education like other things that you believe everyone has a right to? Are the skills and talents of American citizens like natural resources, which ought to be conserved? Is knowledge like tools, or like money, or like a hobby?

This tendency to make comparisons is a fact worth noting about the way we think. Education, for example, is a complicated process, of which we know much less than we should like to know. And when we study a complicated process, we are apt to begin by setting aside some of its complexities. We try to see what light we can throw on it by comparing it with another process we think we understand better. We simplify. If we did not, it is hard to see how we could come to understand anything.

Moreover, such comparisons often fix themselves in the very language we use. Many of the words and phrases that come to mind when we think about education embody comparisons that were made long ago. We speak of education in a number of different ways: (1) eating and drinking: "the omnivorous reader," "undigested facts," "crumbs of information," "ruminating," "swallowing the story whole," "drinking of the Pierian spring"; (2) writing on blank paper or a tablet: "inscribed on the memory," "impressed on the mind," Locke's "*tabula rasa*"; (3) piling up goods in a warehouse or store: "his mind was well stocked," "taking inventory of his knowledge," "loads of learned lumber in his head"; (4) mining: "digging out information," "delving into philosophy"; (5) going on a journey: "adventures of ideas," "traveling in the realms of gold." And there are many others.

These terms are borrowed from simpler activities of human beings and applied to education. At first such a borrowed term may help us to focus upon an important aspect of the process. Thus we may say that one's personality is "molded" by his schooling, because we see that it makes him more of a definite person that he was: it "shapes" his personality, for good or ill. But once we use the term "molded," our thinking will be partly guided by the comparison of teacher with sculptor. And this can easily lead to a serious mistake, if it makes us think that the student is or should be as passive as the clay.

. . . therefore, we must reckon with an important characteristic of language: its power to evoke in our minds the vivid recollection of our sensory experience, the pictures, smells, tastes, sounds, and touch sensations of our waking life. Language does this when it is *concrete*, that is, when it is rich in images.

An *image* is a term that designates characteristics that we can experience by our senses. "Red," "dark cloud," and "pretty girl" are images, because some of the characteristics of these things we can know by direct perception. But "atom," "government," and "civil rights" are not images: these things are conceived, but they are not sensed.

Of course, we can think, and we can understand words, *abstractly*—that is, without imagining concrete things and happenings. And the actual memories that appear to the mind when a word is spoken or heard vary greatly from person to person. When you hear the word "horse," perhaps you imagine a white horse whereas the speaker imagines a brown one; but you won't get into trouble as long as the two horses both satisfy the designation of the term (in having four legs, for example), and as long as you both get the same connotations from the term in its context.[1] The difference in imagination will not hurt your thinking or hinder your communication, if you keep your thinking from being dominated and controlled by these private little pictures. But images can trip the unwary thinker, whether writer or reader, by leading him to wander into interesting but irrelevant thoughts. And so in this chapter we shall look over the principles that will help you manage them, in your ordinary reading and writing.

SIMILE AND METAPHOR

Images become involved in our thinking (for better or for worse) when they enter into what are commonly called "*figures of speech.*" A figure of speech consists in a comparison between two things, which we may label "X" and "Y." Generally one of the things, say X, is the one we are saying something about, and the X-term (or **primary term**) denotes the thing *to which* some other thing is compared. In a figure of speech we say something about X by comparing Y *to* it; the Y-term (or **secondary term**) denotes the thing which is

[1] *Designation,* as Beardsley uses the term, means the defining characteristics of a thing. For example, the term *widow* designates the characterstics of being human, being female, having been married, and being one whose husband is dead. *Connotation* means those characteristics which are not a part of *designation* and also the personal associations of a word. [eds.]

compared to X.[2] In "love is blind," "love" is the primary term and "blind (person)" is the secondary term. Or when H. G. Wells says that the brain of man is a "food-getting instrument, like the snout of a pig," "brain" is the primary term and "snout of a pig" is the secondary term. When the figurative statement is elliptical, we have to supply part of the terms ourselves.

All figures of speech are comparisons, but not all comparisons are figures of speech. To begin with a simple example, we may say that "James was as angry as a hornet" is figurative, but that "James was angry as John" is *not*. It is not hard to see that there is a difference here, but it is impossible to state the difference exactly without using highly technical language. James and John are evidently much more alike than James and the hornet, for James and John both belong to the same biological species. Thus James and John can *both* be angry, in the same sense of the word. But James and the hornet *cannot* both be angry in the same sense of the word: the hornet doesn't feel the same way, and he doesn't behave the same way. He can't get red in the face or stamp his feet with rage: he can only zoom, buzz, and sting.

Thus there is a distinction between a comparison that is figurative and one that is not figurative, but the distinction is one of degree. Suppose you compare the human heart with a goat's heart, a pump, and a television relay. There is a greater difference between a human heart and a pump than there is between a human heart and a goat's heart. And there is a greater difference between a human heart and a television relay than there is between a human heart and a pump. If the difference is great enough, in a particular case, we say that the comparison is figurative. But "The heart is a pump" is a borderline case: it is figurative in some contexts, but not in others.

It is not possible, or necessary, for ordinary purposes, to be very precise about this distinction. The important thing is the degree of difference between the two things compared. When you want to understand a comparison clearly, there are three things to do. First, identify clearly the two terms of the comparison. Second, consider the chief points of likeness and of unlikeness between the two things. And third, examine the context in which the characteristics of the things are stressed. If the two things are *unlike* in some important way that is indicated by the context, then it is reasonable to say that the comparison is figurative.

[2] The primary term is also referred to as the *tenor*, the secondary term as the *vehicle*, as in I. A. Richards' essay, p. 158. [eds.]

The teacher of literature, who is skilled in dealing with highly figurative language, must make a number of distinctions. There are, for example, similes, metaphors, analogies, parables, tropes, myths. And besides these there are various technical terms of rhetoric for more special kinds of figure: as when we speak of a thing as a person ("personification"), a part as a whole ("synecdoche"), or one thing as another that is associated with it ("metonymy"). These distinctions are useful for analyzing certain kinds of discourse, but . . . [here] we are concerned with more general features of discourse. Yet there is one fundamental distinction that any critical reader must make: that is the distinction between a *simile* and a *metaphor*.

A **simile** is an explicit figurative comparison: that is, it is a statement that one thing is like another. Thus it contains a comparative word: "like," "as," "similar," or "same." And we may distinguish further between two kinds of similes: *closed similes* and *open similes*. Compare these two excerpts from a description of international political developments in the summer of 1949:

(1) "The international situation was *as tense as* a ball-game tied up in the ninth inning." (*Closed simile.*)
(2) "The international situation was *like* a ball-game tied up in the ninth inning." (*Open simile.*)

In both of these figures we have a primary term ("the international situation") and a secondary term ("a ball-game tied up in the ninth inning"). But the first figure not only compares the two things; it specifies the *respect* in which they are compared (the one was "as tense as" the other). Similes that do this we shall call "**closed similes.**"

An **open simile** is one that makes no mention of the respect, or respects, in which the two things are to be compared. Thus an open simile, by itself, doesn't give any definite information. It puts us in a frame of mind to note the points of likeness, but it leaves us in suspension. We have to search the context of the simile for an indication of the points of likeness that are relevant to the subject under discussion. *Any* two things are alike in *some* respects: the question is, what are the important, and relevant, respects? Perhaps the writer means that in the international situation the watchers were divided into two hostile groups, or perhaps he means that most people were fearful of the outcome, or perhaps he means that the suspense was likely to continue for some time. The simile, *by itself*, is noncommittal; its specific reference must be supplied by the context.

Thus an open simile is likely to be vague if it is not carefully handled. It might mean a good deal, or it might mean very little. When a poet says that "the evening is spread out against the sky/ Like a patient etherized upon a table," we must hold the terms of this comparison in mind until the rest of his poem tells us *how* the two things are alike. The same principle applies to similes when they occur in ordinary discourse.

When the words "like" and "as" are dropped out of a figure, and the primary and secondary terms are jammed together, the figure becomes a *metaphor*. A metaphor does not *state* a comparison, but it *suggests* a comparison. The reporter quoted previously went on to say:

> The diplomats made errors, and a few hits, but neither side scored. Everybody muffed the ball, and the peoples of the world breathlessly watched their chosen leaders swinging at wild curves as the international struggle dragged on.

Here is a whole string of metaphors, but take just one: "their chosen leaders swinging at wild curves." Y (a batter vainly trying to hit a badly pitched curve) is compared to X (a national leader dealing with an international crisis). But when we put this situation in the form of a statement, "Their chosen leaders swung at wild curves," we see that the metaphor is elliptical, for part of the comparison is left out. . . .

The simplest sort of metaphor has the form "X is Y": "He is a wolf." The secondary term doesn't have to be a predicate, however. It may be an adjective ("He has a wolfish appetite"), or a verb ("He wolfs his food"). To get the terms of the metaphor straightened out, we can always restate the metaphor in the simple form. We can write: "His appetite is wolfish," "His manner of eating is that of a wolf." This restatement will do violence to the metaphor, and it is not an exact substitute for it; it is merely a device for being clear about the structure of the metaphor. The same device can be applied to those richer metaphors that have added so much to the clarity, and confusion, of recent history: "New Deal," "pump-priming," "maginot-line mentality," "brass hats," "bottlenecks," "fox holes," "underground," "reconversion," "the Iron Curtain," and "Fair Deal."

In figurative language of the richest sort, similes and metaphors are interwoven in a complicated way, and it may take considerable analysis to understand exactly what is being said.

> Life, like a dome of many-coloured glass,
> Stains the white radiance of Eternity,
> Until Death tramples it to fragments.

This remarkable figure has several parts, which can be artificially separated for examination. Ordinary discourse seldom poses such complicated problems. Still, figurative language, even outside poetry, can be quite puzzling. A figure of speech can confuse your thinking, if you are not clear about its primary term and its secondary term, and if you do not recognize what kind of figure it is. . . .

INTERPRETING A METAPHOR

Metaphor is a handy linguistic tool, because it crams so many meanings into a few words. But metaphor is difficult to use skillfully, and, in the hands of a careless or malicious workman, it often gives the reader or listener a good deal of trouble. Metaphor can be a very subtle aid to slanting. And the more meaning that is packed into a metaphor, the harder it is for the critical reader to think *through* it. Therefore, in this section, we shall take up the question of finding out just what a metaphor means.

We may begin by noting the common distinction between a "literal" sense and a "metaphorical" sense of a term. The *literal* meaning of "pig" is just its designation: that is, the characteristics of having four legs, having a snout, and so forth. If you say, "The animal in that pen is a pig," this statement *can* be literally true; an animal can have four legs. In this context, the connotations of "pig" are not stressed. But if you say, "That man over there is a pig," it is clear that this sentence *cannot* be literally true. For, if he is a man, he has *not* four legs. So, if this statement is to be true at all, it is not the designation, but only the *connotation*, of "pig" that is being ascribed to the man. In this case "pig" is used *metaphorically*. And this metaphorical statement is (or may be, depending on the context) equal to a number of literal statements: he is greedy, he is gross, he is dirty, he is lazy, he is fat.

We can now give a fairly clear definition of "metaphor." This term covers both statements ("The fire is dying") and noun-phrases ("a dying fire"). Let us consider statements first. We shall say that a statement is "metaphorical" if it has both of the following characteristics: First, it must be *literally* false. That is, the subject cannot possibly have the characteristics designated by the secondary term.

Take, for example, the architectural slogan of an earlier decade: "A house is a machine for living." In the ordinary sense of the term, a machine is something that does work; we apply some form of energy (muscular effort, coal, gasoline, falling water) to it, and by the motions of its parts it changes the energy into a different form. This capacity is one of the characteristics designated by the term "machine." But a house is *not* a machine in this sense. Second, a metaphorical sentence *may* be (it does not have to be) true on the level of connotation. That is, the subject *can* have the characteristics connotated by the secondary term. "Machine" connotes the characteristics of being useful, of being designed to fulfill certain specific functions, of not having parts it doesn't need to serve its ends. And (whether or not it ought to be) a house *can* be a machine in this sense.

A noun-phrase may be called a "metaphor" if it can be transformed into a metaphorical statement. In this way we speak of "pork-barrel legislation," "the voice of doom," "a living death" as metaphors.

It is important to keep "literal meaning" (that is, designation) distinct from *etymological* meaning. It is misleading to say, for example, that "budget" (from the French *bougette*) literally means *wallet.* The word "budget" literally means just what the dictionary gives as its *two* standard senses: (*a*) an accumulation, as a "budget of paradoxes" (this meaning seems to be on the way out), and (*b*) a financial statement for the ensuing period. There *is* on record the *obsolete* English sense (*c*) a bag with its contents; that once was one of the designations of "budget," but is not its "literal meaning" today.

This example reminds us of the constantly shifting character of the distinction between the literal and metaphorical senses of words (or between their designations and connotations). When we speak of "dead metaphor" we mean something that *was* a metaphor but is not any longer. "Spinster" is a "dead metaphor." Once it designated *a person who spins* (man or woman). Then, because most such people were unmarried women, it came to connote that characteristic. But when it began to be used very widely in contexts that emphasized this connotation, the connotation came to be so closely linked with the word that *unmarried woman* became the standard meaning, or designation. Today, in the proper context, it can *connote* the characteristic of being one who spins, but it does not now *designate* that characteristic.

When we speak of the "eye of a needle," we do not feel that we are comparing an eye to the aperture of the needle (even though there is more than one respect in which they are similar). This use of "eye" is just one of its designations; the metaphor has "died." But when we read of the "eyes of Night," the context and the personification of Night present a situation in which we *do* feel a comparison of the star to the eye. This is a genuine metaphor. Of course, in between, there will be "half-dead" metaphors, borderline cases, such as, perhaps, "seeing eye-to-eye," in which the comparative element is almost lost and the phrase has practically hardened into an idiom.

It follows that the term "metaphor" is vague; there is no sharp line to divide living metaphors from dead ones. But for a full grasp of any discourse, you must make a good estimate of the amount of life left in its metaphors, especially when you are dealing with material from the social studies or psychology, where the borderline cases are frequent. In these fields, the technical vocabulary is often created by putting a metaphor to death. This is legal, but metaphors sometimes die hard. Hence the vocabulary of Freudian psychiatry has many terms, such as "repression," "censor," "projection," which are not yet fully under control. They are not quite dead enough so that their connotations can be ignored, and they can confuse the writer and reader.

We cannot tell whether a metaphorical statement is true or false until we know its meaning. To *interpret*, or *expand*, a metaphorical statement is to give a list of literal statements which, taken in combination, are equal in meaning to the original statement. In the case of "He is a pig," it may be possible to give a *complete interpretation*, but it would be an almost endless task to list *all* the characteristics wound up together in the meaning of a very rich metaphor. For most purposes this need not trouble us: usually we don't have to know *all* the characteristics connoted—but we do want to know whether a certain *particular* characteristic is connoted or not. Thus we must be able to give at least a *partial interpretation* of the metaphor, to bring out its special bearing upon the point of an argument.

As an example of a partial interpretation, let's consider the sentence "Russia has drawn an iron curtain across Europe," as it turns up in a discussion of American foreign policy. The first thing to do is to get the *terms* of the metaphor straight. We see that this metaphor is a double one. In the *main* metaphor, drawing an iron curtain is compared to Russian diplomatic and military behavior toward Eastern and Western Europe. But within the secondary term of the main metaphor, the "curtain" is stated to be an "iron" one.

The second step is to consider the connotations of the terms, beginning with the smallest units. You think of the characteristics of curtains (the kind you draw): their tendency to shut out air and light, to billow in a wind, to get dusty. Next you think of the characteristics of iron: its hardness, its brittleness, its uses for war. When you put these two groups of connotations together, they cancel each other out, in part, and in part they coalesce into the image of something that is strong, guarded, hard to penetrate. When you add the characteristics of drawing a curtain (the secrecy and suspense), you have a complicated skein of characteristics that are all wound up together in the meaning of the metaphor. The sentence *says* (whether it is true or false) that Eastern and Western Europe are being prevented from communicating with each other; that this is keeping information from getting into and out of Eastern Europe; that the lack of communication is entirely the fault of the Russians; that the boundary line is manned by armed troops—and there are many other meanings.

Clearly, when you ask whether the metaphorical sentence is *true* or not, you find that it is, in fact, a bundle of different statements, some of which may be true and some false. When metaphors turn up in the course of an argument, it is not safe to take them as they appear and leave it at that. You must interpret them; that is, you must break them down a bit, in order to make explicit exactly what is, and what is not, being stated.

Since the essays in this section constitute such a tightly knit group about a single topic, the assignments have been placed at the end of the section, p. 175. [eds.]

THE COMMAND OF METAPHOR

I. A. Richards

For nearly forty years I. A. Richards' seminal mind has been a stimulative force in the field of language study. His pioneer work, The Meaning of Meaning, *written in*

From *The Philosophy of Rhetoric* by I. A. Richards. Reprinted by permission of the publisher, Oxford University Press, copyright 1936.

collaboration with C. K. Ogden and published in 1923, has influenced a whole generation of scholars in their thinking about language. Richards is especially interested in the psychological aspects of language and in literary theory. His book The Philosophy of Rhetoric, *a series of lectures given at Bryn Mawr College in 1936, contains a penetrating analysis of metaphor which goes far beyond the rather elementary treatment by Beardsley. In profundity and importance, Richards' discussion ranks with that of Aristotle and of Coleridge as a major contribution to our understanding of the nature of metaphor.*

LAST TIME[1] I generalized, or stretched, the sense of the term metaphor—almost, you may think, to breaking point. I used it to cover all cases where a word, in Johnson's phrase, "gives us two ideas for one," where we compound different uses of the word into one, and speak of something as though it were another.[2] And I took it further still to include, as metaphoric, those processes in which we perceive or think of or feel about one thing in terms of another—as when looking at a building it seems to have a face and to confront us with a peculiar expression. I want to insist that this sort of thing is normal in full perception and that study of the growth of our perceptions (the animistic world of the child and so on) shows that it must be so.

Let me begin now with the simplest, most familiar case of verbal metaphor—the *leg of a table* for example. We call it dead but it comes to life very readily. Now how does it differ from a plain or literal use of the word, in *the leg of a horse*, say? The obvious difference is that the leg of a table has only some of the characteristics of the leg of the horse. A table does not walk with its legs; they only hold it up and so on. In such a case we call the common characteristics the ground of the metaphor. Here we can easily find the ground, but

[1] This essay, the last in the series, was preceded by a résumé of previous ideas about metaphor and an introduction to Richards' theory of the interaction of tenor and vehicle, terms equivalent to Beardsley's "primary term" and "secondary term" (see p. 151). [eds.]

[2] Dr. Samuel Johnson, the eighteenth-century lexicographer and literary critic, had written: "As to metaphorical expression, that is a great excellence in style, when it is used with propriety, for it gives you two ideas for one." Richards had commented in the previous lecture that Johnson's statement represented "the limited traditional view of metaphor." [eds.]

very often we cannot. A metaphor may work admirably without our being able with any confidence to say how it works or what is the ground of the shift. Consider some of the metaphors of abuse and endearment. If we call some one a pig or a duck, for example, it is little use looking for some actual resemblance to a pig or a duck as the ground. We do not call someone a duck to imply that she has a bill and paddles or is good to eat. The ground of the shift is much more recondite. The *Oxford Dictionary* hints at it by defining a "duck" in this use as "a charming or delightful object." An extremely simplified account of the ground here would make it something like this: that some feeling, of "tender and amused regard," say, that it is possible to have towards ducks is being felt towards a person.

A very broad division can thus be made between metaphors which work through some direct resemblance between the two things, the tenor and vehicle, and those which work through some common attitude which we may (often through accidental and extraneous reasons) take up towards them both. The division is not final or irreducible, of course. *That we like them both* is, in one sense, a common property that two things share, though we may, at the same time, be willing to admit that they are utterly different. When I like tobacco and logic, that is no very obvious character that they have in common. But this division, though it does not go very deep, may at a certain level help us sometimes to avoid one of the worst snares of the study—the assumption that if we cannot see how a metaphor works, it does not work.

Let us go back to *leg* for a moment. We notice that even there the boundary between literal and metaphoric uses is not quite fixed or constant. To what do we apply it literally? A horse has legs literally, so has a spider, but how about a chimpanzee? Has it two legs or four? And how about a star-fish? Has it arms or legs or neither? And, when a man has a wooden leg, is it a metaphoric or a literal leg? The answer to this last is that it is both. It is literal in one set of respects, metaphoric in another. A word may be *simultaneously* both literal and metaphoric, just as it may simultaneously support many different metaphors, may serve to focus into one meaning many different meanings. This point is of some importance, since so much misinterpretation comes from supposing that if a word works one way it cannot simultaneously work in another and have simultaneously another meaning.

Whether, therefore, a word is being used literally or metaphorically is not always, or indeed as a rule, an easy matter to settle. We may provisionally settle it by deciding whether, in the given instance, the word gives us two ideas or one; whether, in the terms I suggested last time, it presents both a tenor and a vehicle which co-operate in an inclusive meaning. If we cannot distinguish tenor from vehicle then we may provisionally take the word to be literal; if we can distinguish at least two co-operating uses, then we have metaphor.

For example, when Hamlet says:

"What should such fellows as I do crawling between earth and heaven?" Or when Swift makes the Brobdingnagian King say to Gulliver: "The bulk of your natives appear to me to be the most pernicious race of little odious vermin that nature ever suffered to crawl upon the face of the earth," are *crawling* and *crawl* to be regarded as literal or metaphoric?

My answer is that they are metaphoric. Hamlet or man may crawl literally—as babies and big-game hunters undoubtedly do at times—but in both passages there is an unmistakable reference to other things that crawl, to the motions of foul insects, to vermin, and this reference is the vehicle as Hamlet, or man and his ways, are the tenor. By this test, of course, most sentences in free or fluid discourse turn out to be metaphoric. Literal language is rare outside the central parts of the sciences. We think it more frequent than it is through the influence of that form of the usage doctrine which ascribes single fixed meanings to words and that is why I have spent so much time in these lectures inveighing against that doctrine.

Let us consider, now, some of the varying relations between tenor and vehicle. It is convenient to begin with the remark, which you will meet with everywhere, that a metaphor involves a comparison. What is a comparison? It may be several different things: it may be just a putting together of two things to let them work together; it may be a study of them both to see how they are like and how unlike one another; or it may be a process of calling attention to their likenesses or a method of drawing attention to certain aspects of the one through the co-presence of the other. As we mean by comparison these different things we get different conceptions of metaphor. If we mean calling attention to likenesses, we get a main 18th Century doctrine of metaphor. Dr. Johnson, for example, praises Denham's[3]

[3] Sir John Denham (1615-1669), the author of the famous poem "Cooper's Hill," which contains the lines on the Thames. [eds.]

lines on the Thames because "the particulars of resemblance are so perspicaciously collected." These are the lines,

> O could I flow like thee, and make thy stream
> My great exemplar as it is my theme!
> Though deep, yet clear; though gentle, yet not dull;
> Strong without rage; without o'erflowing, full.

Here the flow of the poet's mind, we may say, is the tenor, and the river the vehicle; and it is worth noting, as an exercise in analysis, that in the last two lines there is a repeated alternation of the relative positions of tenor and vehicle and of the direction of the shift between them. "Though deep, yet clear": the words are literally descriptive of the vehicle, the river; derivatively or metaphorically descriptive of the mind. "Though gentle yet not dull": "gentle" certainly is literally descriptive of the mind, the tenor, derivatively of the river, the other way about; but "dull," I suppose, goes from the river to the mind again. "Strong without rage" goes, for me, unquestionably from mind to river, and "without o'erflowing, full" goes back again from river, does it not? to mind. All through, of course, it is not etymology but how *we* take the words which settles these questions.

These details of order are not important to notice in themselves—though to do so gives practice in the peculiar sort of attention which is the method of the whole study. Still, this alternating movement in the shifts may have not a little to do with the rather mysterious power of the couplet, the way it exemplifies what it is describing:

> Though deep yet clear; though gentle, yet not dull;
> Strong without rage; without o'erflowing, full.

And also it may have something to do with what Johnson is rightly remarking when he says that "the flow of the last couplet is so smooth and sweet that the lines have not been overpraised." [*sic*]

"The particulars of resemblance (between tenor and vehicle) are so perspicaciously collected," that is a typical 18th Century conception of the kind of comparison that metaphor should supply, the process of pointing out likenesses—perspicuously collecting particulars of resemblance. But it does not really apply as an account of how these lines work. The more carefully and attentively we go over the senses and implications of *deep*, *clear*, *gentle*, *strong* and *full* as they apply to a stream and to a mind, the less shall we find the resemblances between vehicle and tenor counting and the more will the vehicle, the river, come to seem an excuse for saying about the mind something which could not be said about the river. Take *deep*. Its main implications as regards a river are, "not easily crossed, dangerous, navigable, and suitable for swimming, perhaps." As applied to a mind, it suggests "mysterious, a lot going on, rich in knowledge and power, not easily accounted for, acting from serious and important reasons." What the lines say of the mind is something that does not come from the river. But the river is not a mere excuse, or a decoration only, a gilding of the moral pill. The vehicle is still controlling the mode in which the tenor forms. That appears at once if we try replacing the river with, say, a cup of tea!

> Though deep, yet clear; though gentle, yet not dull;
> Strong without rage; without o'erflowing, full.

Comparison, as a stressing of likenesses, is not the whole mode of this metaphor though it commonly is in 18th Century writing—where, too, the tenor is usually the most important partner in the metaphor. The opposed conception of comparison—as a mere putting together of two things to see what will happen—is a contemporary fashionable aberration, which takes an extreme case as the norm. Here it is, in a summary and exaggerated form. This is André Breton, the leader of the French Super-Realists, stating the doctrine very plainly:

"To compare two objects, as remote from one another in character as possible, or by any other method put them together in a sudden and striking fashion, this remains the highest task to which poetry can aspire." (*Les vases communicants.*)

" 'To put them together in a sudden and striking fashion' "—"*les mettre en presence d'une manière brusque et saisissante.*" That, as "the highest task to which poetry can aspire"! It is a doctrine well worth some examination. Like Mr. Max Eastman, with his insistence (in *The Literary Mind*) that metaphor works by attempting "impracticable identifications," M. Breton sees no need to consider what should be put with what—provided they are sufficiently remote from one another—nor does he distinguish between the very different effects of such collocations. This is the opposite position from Johnson's, for whereas Johnson objected to comparisons being, like

Cowley's,[4] "far fetched," it is the distance of the fetching here which is the merit. Mr. Eastman shares this indifference as to the precise effect of the encounter of disparates. For him the poet "communicates a kind of experience not elsewhere accessible" and, to do so, Mr. Eastman says, he "must arouse a reaction and yet impede it, creating a tension in our nervous system sufficient and rightly calculated to make us completely aware that we are living something—and no matter what." (*The Literary Mind*, p. 205.) "No matter what?" These last words are heroic certainly. Tie a man down and approach him with a red-hot poker; you will arouse a reaction and sufficiently impede it to make him completely aware, I believe, that he is living something. This same heroism haunts a good deal of current literary theory and practice—not only in the Super-Realists' cult of artificial paranoias. It comes, I think, from a crude conception of the mode of action of metaphors. . . .

Let us consider more closely what happens in the mind when we put together—in a sudden and striking fashion—two things belonging to very different orders of experience. The most important happenings—in addition to a general confused reverberation and strain—are the mind's efforts to connect them. The mind is a connecting organ, it works only by connecting and it can connect any two things in an indefinitely large number of different ways. Which of these it chooses is settled by reference to some larger whole or aim, and, though we may not discover its aim, the mind is never aimless. In all interpretation we are filling in connections, and for poetry, of course, our freedom to fill in—the absence of explicitly stated intermediate steps—is a main source of its powers. As Mr. Empson well says (in his *Seven Types of Ambiguity*, p. 32), "Statements are made as if they were connected, and the reader is forced to consider their relations for himself. The reason why these statements should have been selected is left for him to invent; he will invent a variety of reasons and order them in his own mind. This is the essential fact about the poetical use of language." The reader, I would say, will try out various connections, and this experimentation—with the simplest and the most complex, the most obvious and the most recondite collocations alike—is the movement which gives its meaning to all fluid language.

[4] Abraham Cowley (1618-1667), one of the "metaphysical poets," was condemned by Johnson for his penchant for "the unexpected and surprising." [eds.]

As the two things put together are more remote, the tension created is, of course, greater. That tension is the spring of the bow, the source of the energy of the shot, but we ought not to mistake the strength of the bow for the excellence of the shooting; or the strain for the aim. And bafflement is an experience of which we soon tire, and rightly. But, as we know, what seems an impossible connection, an "impracticable identification," can at once turn into an easy and powerful adjustment if the right hint comes from the rest of the discourse. Here is an instance.

An incautious recent writer on the general theory of language says: "In England the symbol *house* may symbolise a reference to many different kinds of houses; metaphorically its reference may be so generalised as to refer to many more other things; but it can hardly ever have the same reference as, let us say, *bread*."

That sets us a problem; find an occasion in which *bread* may be metaphorical for house, or *house* for bread. It would not be hard, I think, to find several—but here is a fairly obvious one, from Gerard Manley Hopkins. From that rather distressing and unhappy poem, *The Drummer Boy's Communion*, when Hopkins is speaking of the wafer as the dwelling of the Divine Presence. This is the line:

> Low-latched in leaf-light housel his too huge godhead.

There is no strain, surely, in speaking of the bread here as the little house, housel.

But it is the rest of the poem that makes the connection easy and obvious, which witnesses to a general truth. The mind will always try to find connections and will be guided in its search by the rest of the utterance and its occasion.

I conclude then that these contemporary exploiters of the crude "clash them together—no matter what" view of metaphor are beguiling themselves with by-products of the process of interpretation and neglecting the more important cares of critical theory. But still one point of importance emerges clearly from examining these exaggerations. We must not, with the 18th Century, suppose that the interactions of tenor and vehicle are to be confined to their resemblances. There is disparity action too. When Hamlet uses the word *crawling* its force comes not only from whatever resemblances to vermin it brings in but at least equally from the differences that resist and control the influences of their resemblances. The implication there is that man should not so crawl. Thus, talk about the identification or fusion that a metaphor effects is nearly always misleading and pernicious. In general, there are very few metaphors in which disparities between tenor and vehicle are not as much operative as the similarities. Some similarity will commonly be the ostensive ground of the shift, but the peculiar modification of the tenor which the vehicle brings about is even more the work of their unlikenesses than of their likenesses.

This has, I believe, very important consequences for literary practice and theory at innumerable points. Insufficient analysis here has led not only to false doctrine and crude reading but to attempts in writing to make words behave in fashions which conflict with the nature of language as a medium. To take the danger of false doctrine first. One of the most influential of modern critics has been T. E. Hulme. His death in the War was a very heavy loss for many reasons —not least, perhaps, because his doctrine of metaphor was left at a half-way stage from which, I believe, he would certainly have developed it. As it stands, in the interpretation in which it has been vigorously infective for the last nineteen years—and especially since his papers on "Modern Art" and on "Romanticism and Classicism" were published in 1924 in the volume called *Speculations*—it seems to me most deceiving.

It says (p. 137) "Plain speech is essentially inaccurate. It is only by new metaphors . . . that it can be made precise." This you will see is only Shelley's point again,[5] and we can accept it, with a demurrer as to some of the implications of "new" here—a demurrer that Hulme himself hints on an earlier page when he says, "Works of art aren't eggs," and so need not be fresh or new laid. But he added various points about the precision that he supposed metaphor to aim at, and it is these that give occasion for mistakes. "The great aim," he says, "is accurate, precise and definite description." Poetry, fluid discourse, as opposed to prose, "is not a language of counters, but," he holds, "a visual concrete one. It is a compromise for a language of intuition which would hand over sensations bodily. It always endeavours to

[5] Shelley's point was that "Language is vitally metaphorical; that is, it marks the before unapprehended relations of things and perpetuates their apprehension, until words, which represent them, become, through time, signs for portions or classes of thought instead of pictures of integral thoughts: and then, if no new poets should arise to create afresh the associations which have been thus disorganised, language will be dead to all the nobler purposes of human intercourse." [eds.]

arrest you, and make you continuously see a physical thing, to prevent you gliding through an abstract process."

I have three quarrels with this account. First with that *always*. Only remember Shakespeare and you will not say that the language of poetry *always* does anything of this sort. My second quarrel is with the words *visual* and *see:* "make you continuously see a physical thing and prevent you gliding through an abstract process." That is patently false.

> If thou didst ever hold me in thy heart
> Absent thee from felicity awhile
> And in this harsh world draw thy breath in pain
> To tell my story.

You need *see* nothing while reading that, and the words certainly do not work by making you see anything. Besides, you already have the actors to look at. My third quarrel is with this fear of the abstract. The language of the greatest poetry is frequently abstract in the extreme and its aim is precisely to send us "gliding through an abstract process."

> This she? No, this is Diomed's Cressida.
> If beauty have a soul, this is not she,
> If souls guide vows, if vows be sanctimony,
> If sanctimony be the gods' delight,
> If there be rule in unity itself,
> This is not she.

We are not asked by Shakespeare here to perceive beauty, but to understand it through a metaphoric argument as the "rule in unity itself" and to understand its place in the soul's growth.

What can have happened to make so shrewd and acute a writer as Hulme blunder in this gross fashion? I have two explanations, which combine. The first is that he is tricking himself with the word *see* into supposing that he means it literally when his doctrine would only be sanctioned if he were using it metaphorically. Obviously if, in an argument, we say "I see your point!" we are using *see* metaphorically. So when Hulme wrote *see* and *visual* here, the words are to be taken metaphorically too or the doctrine must be condemned at once. What discourse "always endeavours" to do is to make us apprehend, understand, gain a realizing sense of, take in, whatever it is that is being meant—which is not necessarily any physical thing.

But if we say "a realizing sense," we must remember that this is not any "sense" necessarily, such as sense-perception gives, but may be a feeling or a thought. What is essential is that we should really take in and become fully aware of—whatever it is.

This blunder with the word *see* may seem too crude to be likely. But the patient toil of scores of teachers is going every day, in courses about the appreciation of poetry, into the effort to make children (and adults) visualize where visualization is a mere distraction and of no service. And little books appear every few months encouraging just this gross misconception of language. For words cannot, and should not attempt to "hand over sensations bodily"; they have very much more important work to do. So far from verbal language being a "compromise for a language of intuition"—a thin, but better-than-nothing, substitute for real experience,—language, well used, is a *completion* and does what the intuitions of sensation by themselves cannot do. Words are the meeting points at which regions of experience which can never combine in sensation or intuition, come together. They are the occasion and the means of that growth which is the mind's endless endeavour to order itself. That is why we have language. It is no mere signalling system. It is the instrument of all our distinctively human development, of everything in which we go beyond the other animals.

Thus, to present language as working only through the sensations it reinstates, is to turn the whole process upside down. It overlooks what is important in Mallarmé's[6] *dictum* that the poet does not write with thoughts (or with ideas or sensations or beliefs or desires or feelings, we may add) but with words. "Are not words," so Coleridge asked, "parts and germinations of the plant? And what is the law of their growth? In something of this sort," he wrote, "I would endeavour to destroy the old antithesis of Words and Things: elevating, as it were, Words into Things and living things too." We must do so if we are to study metaphor profitably. Hulme and the school teachers are forgetting everything that matters most about language in treating it as just a stimulus to visualization. They think the image fills in the meaning of the word; it is rather the other way about and it is the word which brings in the meaning which the image and its original perception lack.

That is one part, I think, of the explanation of these disorders of

[6] Etienne Stéphane Mallarmé (1842-1898), French Symbolist poet. [eds.]

thought—the mistaking of *see* and *perceive* in the literal sense instead of a wide and open metaphoric sense. But the other part of the explanation goes deeper: it is the mistaking of what I have been calling the tenor-vehicle antithesis for that between the metaphor (the double unit including tenor and vehicle) and its meaning. These two antitheses are easy to confuse, indeed, it is hard to keep them steadily distinct—especially when *metaphor* (and its synonyms), . . . sometimes means "vehicle," sometimes means "vehicle and tenor together." Nothing but habituation makes this shift manageable and keeps it from deceiving us. I think it deceived Hulme here—and I know it deceives others. When he says, "The great aim is accurate, precise and definite description" we can agree, if that is saying no more than "the words somehow must make us fully and rightly aware of whatever it is, the language must really utter its meaning." That is, the metaphor (the whole thing, tenor and vehicle together) should mean what it should. But Hulme turns his remark into something about a supposedly needful accuracy of correspondence between vehicle and tenor, and so into something which is false. "Plain speech is essentially inaccurate. It is only by . . . metaphors . . . that it can be made precise. When the analogy has not enough connection with the thing described to be quite parallel with it, when it overlays the thing it describes and there is a certain excess" it is inferior. "But where the analogy is every bit of it necessary for accurate description . . . If it is sincere, in the accurate sense, when the whole of the analogy is necessary to get out the exact curve of the feeling or thing you want to express—there you seem to me (he says) to have the highest verse." In part of this, Hulme is thinking of the whole metaphor and its meaning; in other parts he is thinking of the vehicle and tenor. Something which is obvious and true of the whole metaphor and its meaning thus lends an illusory plausibility to a false view of the correspondence of vehicle to tenor. Hulme seems not to be distinguishing these two couples and it is as fatal to confuse them as it would be in chemistry to mistake the order of complexity of a molecule and an electron, or in algebra, to ignore the brackets. His confidence in a truism—that speech should mean what it should mean—makes him (as I read his pages) certain that vehicle must correspond to tenor—the whole of the analogy be necessary to get out the exact curve—and that, in the sense in which I read him, is not a truism, but an easily demonstrable error, a misdescription of all our current practice.

For one thing, there is no whole to any analogy, we use as much of it as we need; and, if we tactlessly take any analogy too far, we break it down. There are no such limits to the relations of tenor and vehicle as this account puts. The result of the doctrine may be seen in those anxious, over-careful attempts to *copy* perceptions and feelings *in words*, to "hand over sensations bodily," of which modern prose at its most distinguished too often consists. Words are not a medium in which to copy life. Their true work is to restore life itself to order.

The error of mistaking the tenor-vehicle relation for the relation between tenor plus vehicle together and what they mean, has consequences which go far beyond what we are apt to regard (on a limited view) as literary matters. They enter into the ways we envisage all our most important problems. For example, into the question of belief. Must we believe what an utterance says if we are to understand it fully? Does the Divine Comedy, or the Bible tell us something which we must accept as true if we are to read it aright? These are questions that we cannot possibly answer satisfactorily unless we are clear as to the ways in which metaphoric utterances may say or tell us something. Mr. Eliot remarks somewhere of the Divine Comedy that the whole poem is one vast metaphor.[7] It is. And, if so, what is it that we might believe in it? Is it the tenor or the vehicle or their joint presentation; or is it "that tenor and vehicle are thus and thus related there"? Or is the belief required no more than a readiness to feel and will and live, in certain respects, in accordance with the resultant meaning in so far as we apprehend that meaning—or rather in so far as that meaning apprehends, grasps, takes control of, us? We are accustomed to distinguish between taking an utterance literally and taking it metaphorically or anagogically, but, at the simplest, there are at least four possible modes of interpretation to be considered, not two. And the kinds of believing that will be appropriate will as a rule be different. We can extract the tenor and believe that as a statement; or extract the vehicle; or, taking tenor and vehicle together, contemplate for acceptance or rejection some statement about their relations, or we can accept or refuse the direction which together they would give to our living. We need not go to the Alexandrian schools of early Christian interpretation, or to the similar exegetical developments of other religions, to find instances to show

[7] T. S. Eliot. The reference is to Eliot's essay "Dante," included in *Selected Essays 1917-1932* (New York: Harcourt, Brace & World, 1932), p. 206 [eds.]

how immense the consequences for belief of these choices may be. The varying possibilities of understanding of any metaphoric utterance will show them.

A "command of metaphor"—a command of the interpretation of metaphors—can go deeper still into the control of the world that we make for ourselves to live in. The psycho-analysts have shown us with their discussions of "transference"—another name for metaphor—how constantly modes of regarding, of loving, of acting, that have developed with one set of things or people, are shifted to another. They have shown us chiefly the pathology of these transferences, cases where the vehicle—the borrowed attitude, the parental fixation, say—tyrannizes over the new situation, the tenor, and behavior is inappropriate. The victim is unable to see the new person except in terms of the old passion and its accidents. He reads the situation only in terms of the figure, the archetypal image, the vehicle. But in healthy growth, tenor and vehicle—the new human relationship and the family constellation—co-operate freely; and the resultant behavior derives in due measure from both. Thus in happy living the same patterns are exemplified and the same risks of error are avoided as in tactful and discerning reading. The general form of the interpretative process is the same, with a small-scale instance—the right understanding of a figure of speech—or with a large scale instance—the conduct of a friendship.

But the literary instance is easier to discuss and more accessible to investigation. It is an old dream that in time psychology might be able to tell us so much about our minds that we would at last become able to discover with some certainty what we mean by our words and how we mean it. An opposite or complementary dream is that with enough improvement in Rhetoric we may in time learn so much about words that they will tell us how our minds work. It seems modest and reasonable to combine these dreams and hope that a patient persistence with the problems of Rhetoric may, while exposing the causes and modes of the misinterpretation of words, also throw light upon and suggest a remedial discipline for deeper and more grievous disorders; that, as the small and local errors in our everyday misunderstandings with language are models in miniature of the greater errors which disturb the development of our personalities, their study may also show us more about how these large scale disasters may be avoided. That at least was Plato's hope, as it was Spinoza's belief that there is but one end for the sciences. "Above all things, a method must be thought out of healing the understanding and purifying it at the beginning, that it may with the greatest success understand things correctly."

VOCABULARY IN MOTION

Margaret Schlauch

Margaret Schlauch, formerly Professor of English at New York University and now Professor of English Philology at the University of Warsaw, is a specialist in Chaucer, medieval literature, and language. She has translated from the Icelandic The Saga of the Volsungs, *and is the author of a number of other books and articles. Her most recent work is* The English Language in Modern Times. The Gift of Tongues, *from which the essay below is taken, is a highly readable account of many of the aspects of language with which we are concerned in this text. In "Vocabulary in Motion" she discusses the process of metaphorical extension and the vital part it plays in our everyday vocabulary.*

EXTENDING THE USE OF WORDS

AMONG THE WORDS first taught to children by their doting parents are the terms for the parts of the human body. Pressing down the diminutive button-like protuberance which shows signs of one day becoming a full-blown human nose, mama asks beguilingly: "What is this?" The child, shrewd and skilled already in the enormous task of humoring grown-ups, but nevertheless somewhat confused by the rain of new terminology about him, looks up co-operatively and suggests with hope but little conviction: "Baby's ear." "Oh, no!"

the mellifluous voice proceeds, while the pressure is still maintained, "Baby's nose. *Nose!*" And so the baffling epithet is learned, presumably for a lifetime.

Now "nose" is a concrete term which will cause the child little trouble once he learns it, especially so long as he limits it to this bodily member of himself and his fellow human beings. He can even apply it to the corresponding members of familiar animals without being involved in confusion of meaning. This is also true of other members, such as eyes, ears, hands, elbows, knees, feet, and the rest. These elementary physiological identifications must give him a comfortable sense that things mean what they say. If we wish to amuse ourselves by speculating on the kinds of words which originated first in human speech, there is some reason for surmising that names for our bodily parts were among them.

But very soon in the life of a child comes the experience of metaphoric use. He is watching his mother peeling potatoes, and begins to be aware of their shape and texture. Pointing to the buds visible on the surface of the brown tuber he asks: "Mama, what are these?" She replies: "The eyes of the potato." This designation is unhesitatingly accepted. In the first place, the elliptical depressions surrounding potato buds actually resemble human eye-sockets in shape. There is enough physical similarity to make the poetic image acceptable in place of a name. Besides, the child is in no position—as yet—to observe the difference in functioning between vegetables and animals which would cause him to challenge the existence of eyes in a potato: real eyes, that is, with a potential power of vision. He can hardly ask: "But has the potato a nervous system?!" He still lives in the mysterious, animistic world of fairy-tales, in which sticks and stones, knives and forks, tables and chairs possess souls. In such a world inanimate objects may confidently be expected to see and hear, to bless and curse, and in general to take definite attitudes of friendliness or hostility to little boys and girls. So it is not surprising if he pursues the subject of the potato-sprouts further and poses the (for him) quite logical question: "Then the Potato-man can *see* me?" This very plausible deduction is probably hailed by the mother with inner exultant glee. And aloud she may even go so far as to say: "Yes, if you're not good, the Potato-man will see you, *even in the dark* and at night he'll come for you, and *take you away. . . .*"

Thus metaphor is elevated into mythology. Fortunately for most children, these transparent lies are recognized at an early date. The slight change of tone that betrays them only complicates a bit more the day-long task of placating grown-ups. If the demonology of potatoes is taken too seriously, however, the results may be very serious. Those who have dealt with nervously maladjusted children are no doubt aware of the precise dangers involved. Considering the crude animism of the language surrounding children, it is a wonder that any of us escape undamaged!

METAPHORIC EXTENSION

When the bud of a potato is called an "eye," the designation is a metaphor. Physical similarity causes a transfer of an epithet originally clear, limited, and concrete in its application. A *semantic shift* has occurred, known as a simple transfer of meaning. It is useless to debate whether "eye" in the new context is a *new* word . . . or not. In any event the application of the physical sound-symbol [ai] has widened. This is the extension of words to include new referents somehow resembling the original ones. Metaphor implies the perception of such resemblances. By means of this process meanings of words are constantly broadening and shifting. Here are some everyday examples:

Parts of the body are further used in references to many things which are themselves concrete and familiar. We speak of the "lip" and the "ears" of a cup, the "teeth" of a saw or a comb, the "legs" of tables and other immobile articles of furniture, the "elbows" of pipes and macaroni, the "hands" of a clock, the "tongue" of a balance or a bell, the "eye" of a needle, and the "head" of a hammer. When we travel we encounter the "foot" of a mountain, the "mouth" of a river, a "head"-land, the "shoulders"—even the "soft shoulders"—of a road, the "brow" of a hill, and the "neck" of the woods. The German speaks eloquently of a *Meeresbusen* ("bosom" of the sea or gulf). Slightly disguised from us today are the "core" (heart) of an apple—a Romance word; and "axle" (shoulder) of a wheel—cognate with German *Achsel.* In politics we hear of a "rump" session of parliament and a "head" of the state. Perhaps "ward-heeler" may be included here, though it is actually a compound.

Animal names and animal members appear in many of the least regarded units of our discourse. We have "wing" chairs and collars, clothes "horses," darning "eggs" and also "egg"-plants, the "fangs" of a machine, "goose-neck" lamps, "hare" lips, "rats" of hair. The last is, to be sure, dated; it was current only in the days when women wore pads of artificial hair to eke out what nature had given them. We refer ambiguously enough to the "cock" of a water-tap, the "beak" of a vessel, and the "crest" of a hill or wave. "Catspaw" is more than a descriptive designation of an object similar to something else, and so presumably is "monkey wrench." Value judgments are tied up with both of these.

Plants and their parts give us the "nut" of a screw, a shoe "tree," the "stem" of a glass, and the "root" of a tooth or a cancerous growth. When we talk of the "root of the matter" we are already moving on a higher level of abstraction.

Tools and simple inventions have long supplied names for similar objects elsewhere. Carpentry and engineering use "pin" for very solid joiners; "table"-land (Spanish *mesa*) refers to plateaus; valleys have "cups"; roads and trees have "forks"; the arid section of the United States is called the "Dust Bowl." The parts of the human body are often described by simple figures taken from engineering. Thus we have the "bridge" of the nose, the "arch" of the foot, the "roof" of the mouth, the "canal" of a tooth. In addition there are vocal "cords," eye "lids," and "club" feet. Simple metaphor even furnished the names of three small bones in the middle ear: "hammer," "anvil," and "stirrup," and the ear "drum" itself. Parts of musical instruments are described in terms of simpler tools: pianos have "hammers" and "keys," violins have "bridges" and "bows" in a sense unknown to primitive warriors.

All workers in special crafts can surely augment this list. What has happened is of course that an elementary similarity in external aspect has caused a shift of the word to a new function.

Other shifts occur when words having to do with time relations are applied to space, or the reverse. Sometimes it is hard to tell which came first. We say "The tree stands *before* my house" and also "I did this *before* the spring house cleaning." Presumably one is a metaphoric application of the other. We transfer words describing impressions from one of the five senses, to make them apply to others. So it is quite usual to talk of a "sharp" tone, a "flat" taste, a "shrill" color, a "smooth" sensation of any sort. Finally, any of these physical terms can readily be applied to psychological states. "Bitter" grief is the kind that *bites* ("how sharper than a serpent's tooth . . ."); "anguish" is the kind that strangles, for the word is cognate with German *eng* and Latin *angustus* meaning "narrow, constricted." "Dreary" once meant "falling" or "dripping." Colors are taken to designate attributes of character: "He's *yellow*," or "That's mighty *white* of you" (regional U.S.A. dialect) in English. German has *einem grün sein* (with negatives), meaning to be devoted to someone; and Russian uses derivatives of the word *krasnyi* (red) for adjectives to express pleasure and approbation. (This, by the way, has nothing to do with politics. It is an old semantic shift no doubt connected with that preference for bright colors evinced in peasant embroideries and woodwork.)

SUGGESTED ASSIGNMENTS

1. Here are some simple metaphors from Melanesian Pidgin English, a language of the southwest Pacific:

rope he-got blut	vein, artery
he-got bone all-same water	cowardly
grass belong head (belong = of)	hair
eye belong musket	gun mouth
smoke belong bush	mist
smoke belong ground	dust

   Identify the primary and secondary terms in these metaphors and indicate the points of likeness and unlikeness.

2. Robert Burns begins a well-known poem with two open similes:

   My love is like a red, red rose
   That's newly sprung in June:
   My love is like the melodie
   That's sweetly played in tune.

   Does *love* refer to his beloved or to the feeling in his heart? Jot down all the points of likeness for each simile and bring them to class for discussion. What do these many points of likeness suggest to you about the role of the reader in interpreting figurative language?

3. A metaphor can say a great deal in little space. Let us suppose that you hear a student say as he comes out of class, "Well, Professor X certainly spun his wheels today." Write a literal statement of all that is suggested by this metaphor.

4. The area of animal life is a rich source of metaphor. Write ten sentences, each containing a metaphor or simile relating to one of these animals: chicken, duck, goose, horse, mule, weasel, ferret, wolf, fox, ox, cat, dog, monkey, hawk, sheep, cattle, lion, gopher, bear, deer, antelope, shark, butterfly, rooster, pigeon.

5. Students make considerable use of metaphors drawn from sports: I didn't get to first base with him; I got thrown for a loss in that exam.

Choose one sport with which you are familiar and in ten minutes write as many metaphors as you can which are derived from it.

6. Many proverbs and folk sayings are metaphors: Don't put all your eggs in one basket; Too many cooks spoil the broth. Find a good metaphorical proverb from a book of proverbs in the library. Then write a paragraph in which you give a complete interpretation of all the metaphor implies.
7. Language, it has been said, is a graveyard of dead metaphors. Using an unabridged or an etymological dictionary, look up the etymology of ten of the following words and report the live metaphors that they once embodied: *examine, stimulate, ponder, calculate, deliberate* (verb), *daisy, easel, stagnate, caper* (verb), *pavilion, dandelion, grenade, cocoanut, thrilling, cocky, window.*
8. A "mixed metaphor" occurs when two or more metaphors are used together, the secondary terms of which are incongruent. The effect is often ludicrous to the alert reader. Point out the mixed metaphors in the following examples:
   a. The British Lion will never pull in its horns or crawl back into its shell.
   b. His was the task—with his staff—to go over the state's school system with a fine-tooth comb, ferreting out the facts that will apply a yardstick to the system.
   c. Crisis, complications, and a whole series of vicious cycles are the fare upon which he and his revolutionary regime thrive. Unfortunately for him and for the whole Arab world, it is upon these same elements that the tentacles of the Soviet Union are feeding, blossoming and bearing fruit in the Middle East.
   d. The Indians had a chance in mid-May to put open water between themselves and the Yanks, who still were trying to find themselves. Instead, Cleveland went into a tailspin of its own, stalling badly and giving the Yanks a chance to catch their breath. And now the shoe is on the other foot. The Yanks are in front again, with the throttle open and the gas pedal on the floor.
9. Skillful speakers often employ metaphors that are drawn from the occupations of their listeners. For example, a political speaker might want to say that the promises of the other party sound fair but are not to be trusted. Here is the way he might express this idea metaphorically to different audiences:
   a. (To bankers) The Republicratic promises are nothing but watered stock.
   b. (To airplane pilots) The Republicratic promises are nothing but bent beams that will lead you to a crash on a mountain side.
   c. (To Texas ranchers) The Republicratic promises are nothing but

loco weeds. They look edible and nourishing, but if your stock eats them, you will lose your herd.

d. (To housewives) The Republicratic promises are the good berries on top of the basket.

Imagine yourself as an educational speaker touring the country. One idea you wish to express forcefully is this: The higher one advances in his education, the more difficult the work becomes. If you were speaking in a mountain area you might use this metaphor: The higher one climbs up the peak of education, the rockier the way becomes. Now, describe three other groups whom you might address and write metaphors fitting the background of each to express your idea.

10. One of the differences between dull, pedestrian prose and lively, pungent writing is the presence or absence of effective metaphors. Read an article or two in a quality magazine such as the *Atlantic*, *Harper's*, *Reporter*, *Saturday Review*, *New Yorker* (note especially its "Talk of the Town."). Collect a few of the effective metaphors and be prepared to discuss their effectiveness in class.

11. The metaphors that we accept, consciously or unconsciously, can become a strong influence in our thinking and on our actions. If, for instance, a college president or dean or professor accepts the metaphor that a college is a brain *factory*, the implications can be something like these:

    a. Every student, like an object on the assembly line, should receive exactly the same educational treatment: take the same standardized courses taught in the same way. And when a given number of operations have been performed on a student (as shown by his credit hours earned), he is a finished product, identical with the others.

    b. Every instructor, like an assembly-line worker, has one special job to do, and does it the same on every student.

    c. In time of haste, as in war, or of overcrowding, the assembly-line can be moved faster. Thus we can get more of the same products in less time, e.g., doctors in six years instead of eight years.

    Assume that the dean of instruction in your college accepts this metaphor: A college is a nursery which grows many kinds of trees, shrubs, flowers, and plants. Write out the implications that this metaphor might have on your educational life.

FURTHER READINGS

1. Brooks, Cleanth and Robert Penn Warren. *Modern Rhetoric* (With Readings). New York: Harcourt, Brace & World, Inc., 1949, pp. 403-441.

2. Estrich, Robert M. and Hans Sperber. *Three Keys to Language*. New York: Holt, Rinehart & Winston, Inc., 1952, pp. 174ff.
3. Perrin, Porter G. *Writer's Guide and Index to English* (Third Edition). Chicago: Scott, Foresman and Company, 1959, pp. 232-239.
4. Smith, Logan Pearsall. *English Idioms* (S. P. E. Tract No. XII). Oxford: Clarendon Press, 1923, pp. 14-54.
5. Stebbing, Susan. *Thinking to Some Purpose*. Baltimore: Penguin Books, Inc., 1939, pp. 106ff.
6. Walpole, Hugh R. *Semantics*. New York: W. W. Norton & Company, Inc., 1941, Ch. 7.

4. Semantics

CLASSIFICATION

S. I. Hayakawa

Whenever you open your mouth you are likely to make classifications. If you should say, "Today I saw President Kennedy," you would of course be referring to a single, unique individual; this would not be a classification. But think of all the other words you can use to refer to him: humanitarian, Catholic, Irishman, Christian, reformer, millionaire, national leader, World War II veteran, politician, writer, Harvard man. *In using any of these words to refer to Mr. Kennedy, you are classifying him, that is, you are putting him into a class or group, the members of which possess certain common characteristics. All such nouns are class-words. The class-word we choose to label any specific person or object depends on our purpose. Some such words express and evoke approval; others, disapproval. And the consequences of such classifications can be far-reaching, as you will soon see. Thus it is an important subject that S. I. Hayakawa deals with in this selection from his well-known book. Dr. Hayakawa is the editor of* ETC.: A Review of General Semantics.

GIVING THINGS NAMES

THE FIGURE BELOW shows eight objects, let us say animals, four large and four small, a different four with round heads and another four with square heads, and still another four with curly tails and another four with straight tails. These animals, let us say, are scampering about your village, but since at first they are of no importance to you, you ignore them. You do not even give them a name.

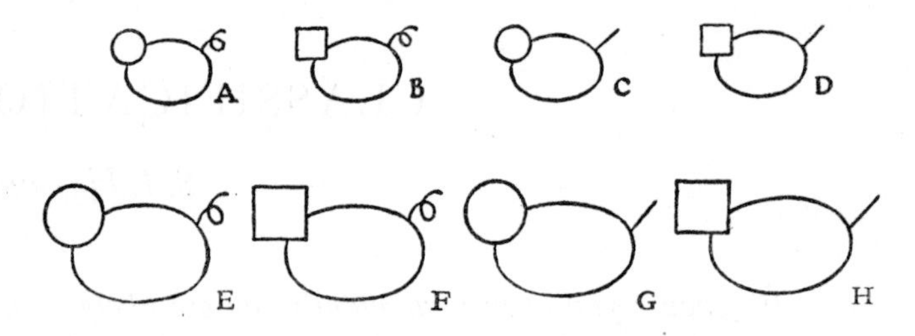

One day, however, you discover that the little ones eat up your grain, while the big ones do not. A differentiation sets itself up, and abstracting the common characteristics of A, B, C, and D, you decide to call these *gogo;* E, F, G, and H you decide to call *gigi*. You chase away the *gogo*, but leave the *gigi* alone. Your neighbor, however, has had a different experience; he finds that those with square heads bite, while those with round heads do not. Abstracting the common characteristics of B, D, F, and H, he calls them *daba*, and A, C, E, and G he calls *dobo*. Still another neighbor discovers, on the other hand, that those with curly tails kill snakes, while those with straight tails do not. He differentiates them, abstracting still another set of common characteristics: A, B, E, and F are *busa*, while C, D, G, and H are *busana*.

Now imagine that the three of you are together when E runs by. You say, "There goes the *gigi*"; your first neighbor says, "There goes the *dobo*"; your other neighbor says, "There goes the *busa*." Here immediately a great controversy arises. What is it really, a *gigi*, a *dobo*, or a *busa?* What is its *right name?* You are quarreling violently when along comes a fourth person from another village who calls it a *muglock*, an edible animal, as opposed to *uglock*, an inedible animal —which doesn't help matters a bit.

Of course the question, "What is it *really?* What is its *right name?*" is a nonsense question. By a nonsense question is meant one that is not capable of being answered. Things can have "right names" only if there is a necessary connection between symbols and things symbolized. . . . That is to say, in the light of your interest in protecting your grain, it may be necessary for you to distinguish the animal E as a *gigi;* your neighbor, who doesn't like to be bitten, finds it practical to distinguish it as a *dobo;* your other neighbor, who likes to see snakes killed, distinguishes it as a *busa.* What we call things and where we draw the line between one class of things and another depend upon the interests we have and the purposes of the classification. For example, animals are classified in one way by the meat industry, in a different way by the leather industry, in another different way by the fur industry, and in a still different way by the biologist. None of these classifications is any more final than any of the others; each of them is useful for its purpose.

This holds, of course, regarding everything we perceive. A table "is" a table to us, because we can understand its relationship to our conduct and interests; we eat at it, work on it, lay things on it. But to a person living in a culture where no tables are used, it may be a very big stool, a small platform, or a meaningless structure. If our culture and upbringing were different, that is to say, our world would not even look the same to us.

Many of us, for example, cannot distinguish between pickerel, pike, salmon, smelts, perch, crappies, halibut, and mackerel; we say that they are "just fish, and I don't like fish." To a seafood connoisseur, however, these distinctions are real, since they mean the difference to him between one kind of good meal, a very different kind of good meal, or a poor meal. To a zoologist, even finer distinctions become of great importance, since he has other and more general ends in view. When we hear the statement, then, "This fish is a specimen of the pompano, *Trachinotus carolinus,*" we accept this as being "true," even if we don't care, not because that is its "right name," but because that is how it is *classified* in the most complete and most general system of classification which people most deeply interested in fish have evolved.

When we name something, then, we are classifying. *The individual object or event we are naming, of course, has no name and belongs to no class until we put it in one.* To illustrate again, suppose that we were to give the *extensional* meaning of the word "Korean."[1] We would have to point to all "Koreans" living at a particular moment and say, "The word 'Korean' denotes at the present moment these

[1] By the extensional meaning of a word Mr. Hayakawa means "that which it points to . . . in the extensional world," i.e., in the world outside your skin. For example, the extensional meaning of "my dog" is the little creature himself that leaps and barks and wags his tail. It is the *thing* referred to in the world you observe. [eds.]

persons: A_1, A_2, A_3 . . . A_n." Now, let us say, a child, whom we shall designate as Z, is born among these "Koreans." *The extensional meaning of the word "Korean," determined prior to the existence of Z, does not include* Z. Z is a new individual belonging to no classification, since all classifications were made without taking Z into account. Why, then, is Z also a "Korean"? *Because we say so.* And, saying so —fixing the classification—we have determined to a considerable extent future attitudes toward Z. For example, Z will always have certain rights in Korea; he will always be regarded in other nations as an "alien" and will be subject to laws applicable to "aliens."

In matters of "race" and "nationality," the way in which classifications work is especially apparent. For example, the present writer is by "race" a "Japanese," by "nationality" a "Canadian," but, his friends say, "essentially" an "American," since he thinks, talks, behaves, and dresses much like other Americans. Because he is "Japanese," he is excluded by law from becoming a citizen of the United States; because he is "Canadian," he has certain rights in all parts of the British Commonwealth; because he is "American," he gets along with his friends and teaches in an American institution of higher learning without any noticeable special difficulties. Are these classifications "real"? Of course they are, and *the effect that each of them has upon what he may and may not do constitutes their "reality."*

There was, again, the story some years ago of the immigrant baby whose parents were "Czechs" and eligible to enter the United States by quota. The child, however, because it was born on what happened to be a "British" ship, was a "British subject." The quota for Britishers was full for that year, with the result that the newborn infant was regarded by immigration authorities as "not admissible to the United States." How they straightened out this matter, the writer does not know. The reader can multiply instances of this kind at will. When, to take another example, is a person a "Negro"? By the definition accepted in the United States, any person with even a small amount of "Negro blood"—that is, whose parents or ancestors were classified as "Negroes"—is a "Negro." *It would be exactly as justifiable to say that any person with even a small amount of "white blood" is "white."* Why do they say one rather than the other? Because the former system of classification *suits the convenience of those making the classification.*

There are few complexities about classifications at the level of dogs and cats, knives and forks, cigarettes and candy, but when it comes to classifications at high levels of abstraction,[2] for example, those describing conduct, social institutions, philosophical and moral problems, serious difficulties occur. When one person kills another, is it an act of murder, an act of temporary insanity, an act of homicide, an accident, or an act of heroism? As soon as the process of classification is completed, our attitudes and our conduct are to a considerable degree determined. We hang the murderer, we lock up the insane man, we free the victim of circumstances, we pin a medal on the hero.

THE BLOCKED MIND

Unfortunately, people are not always aware of the way in which they arrive at their classifications. Unaware of the characteristics of the extensional Mr. Miller not covered by classifying him as "a Jew" and attributing to Mr. Miller all the characteristics *suggested* by the affective connotations of the term with which he has been classified, they pass final judgment on Mr. Miller by saying, "Well, a Jew's a Jew.[3] There's no getting around that!"

We need not concern ourselves here with the injustices done to "Jews," "Roman Catholics," "Republicans," "red-heads," "chorus girls," "sailors," "brass-hats," "Southerners," "Yankees," "school teachers," "government regulations," "socialistic proposals," and so on, by such hasty judgments or, as it is better to call them, fixed

[2] The level of abstraction refers to the degree of generality of a word. For example, your dog, Duke, might be classified as a *bull terrier*, a *terrier*, a *dog*, an *animal*, a *pet*, or a *creature*. Here each successive term is more general than the preceding one; that is to say, each is on a higher level of abstraction than the one before it. Classifications at high levels of abstracton are extremely general words like *liberty*, *justice*, *democracy*, *officialdom*, *the American way*. Such words are hard to communicate with because they can mean so many different things. What, for example, does *the American way* mean? To a Russian, fed upon anti-American propaganda, it might mean all the objectionable things that he believes Americans do; it would include lynchings, acts of government corruption, illegal price fixing by large corporations, lavish living, gangster activities, oppression of the working man, denial of civil rights to Negroes, and many others. But to an American it might mean all of the good things we do: voting at the polls in secret, giving free education to all, allowing private citizens to speak their minds in public, giving voluntarily to charitable organizations, aiding underprivileged nations, and so on. Because the term can include so many thousands of specific acts, it is extremely vague. It is meaningless because it is so meaningful. [eds.]

[3] The affective connotations of a word are the feelings that it arouses. [eds.]

reactions. "Hasty judgments" suggests that such errors can be avoided by thinking more slowly; this, of course, is not the case, for some people think very slowly with no better results. What we are concerned with is the way in which we block the development of our own minds by such automatic reactions.

To continue with our example of the people who say, "A Jew's a Jew. There's no getting around that!"—they are, as we have seen, confusing the denoted, extensional Jew with the fictitious "Jew" inside their heads. Such persons, the reader will have observed, can usually be made to admit, on being reminded of certain "Jews" whom they admire—perhaps Albert Einstein, perhaps Hank Greenberg, perhaps Jascha Heifetz, perhaps Benny Goodman—that "there are exceptions, of course." They have been compelled by experience, that is to say, to take cognizance of at least a few of the multitude of "Jews" who do not fit their preconceptions. At this point, however, they continue triumphantly, "But exceptions only prove the rule!"[4] —which is another way of saying, "Facts don't count." In extremely serious cases of people who "think" in this way, it can sometimes be observed that the best friends they have may be Isaac Cohens, Isidor Ginsbergs, and Abe Sinaikos; nevertheless, in explaining this, they will say, "I don't think of them as Jews at all. They're just friends." In other words, the fictitious "Jew" inside their heads remains unchanged *in spite of their experience.*

People like this *cannot learn from experience.* They continue to vote "Republican" or "Democratic," no matter what the Republicans or Democrats do. They continue to object to "socialists," no matter what the socialists propose. They continue to regard "mothers" as sacred, no matter which mother. A woman who had been given up both by physicians and psychiatrists as hopelessly insane was being considered by a committee whose task it was to decide whether or not she should be committed to an asylum. One member of the committee doggedly refused to vote for commitment. "Gentlemen," he said in tones of deepest reverence, "you must remember that this woman is, after all, a mother." Similarly such people continue to hate "Protestants," no matter which Protestant. Unaware of characteristics left out in the process of classification, they overlook, when the term "Republican" is applied to both the

[4] This extraordinarily fatuous saying originally meant, "The exception *tests* the rule"—*Exceptio probat regulam.* This older meaning of the word "prove" survives in such an expression as "automobile proving ground."

party of Abraham Lincoln and the party of Warren Harding, the rather important differences between them: "If the Republican party was good enough for Abe Lincoln, it's good enough for me!"

COW_1 IS NOT COW_2

How do we prevent ourselves from getting into such intellectual blind alleys, or, finding we are in one, how do we get out again? One way is to remember that practically all statements in ordinary conversation, debate, and public controversy taking the form, "Republicans are Republicans," "Business is business," "Boys will be boys," "Women drivers are women drivers," and so on, are *not true*. Let us put one of these back into a context in life.

"I don't think we should go through with this deal, Bill. Is it altogether fair to the railroad company?"

"Aw, forget it! *Business is business*, after all."[5]

Such an assertion, although it looks like a "simple statement of fact," is not simple and is not a statement of fact. The first "business" *denotes* transaction under discussion; the second "business" invokes the *connotations* of the word. The sentence is a *directive*, saying, "Let us treat this transaction with complete disregard for considerations other than profit, as the word 'business' suggests." Similarly, when a father tries to excuse the mischief done by his sons, he says, "Boys will be boys";[6] in other words, "Let us regard the actions of my sons with that indulgent amusement customarily extended toward those whom we call 'boys' " though the angry neighbor will say, of course, "Boys, my eye! They're little hoodlums; that's what they are!" These too are not informative statements but *directives, directing us to classify the object or event under discussion in given ways, in order that we may feel or act in the ways suggested by the terms of the classification.*

There is a simple technique for preventing such directives from having their harmful effect on our thinking. It is the suggestion made by Korzybski that we add "index numbers" to our terms, thus: Englishman $_1$, Englishman $_2$, . . . ; cow $_1$, cow $_2$, cow $_3$, . . . ; Frenchman $_1$,

[5] In "Business is business" the word *business* shifts its meaning. This expression may be translated "Commercial transactions are matters concerned with profits, not ethics." [eds.]

[6] The word *boy* shifts meaning here, as a translation will show: "Young males of the human species will be mischievous creatures." [eds.]

Frenchman $_2$, *Frenchman* $_3$, . . . ; *communist* $_1$, *communist* $_2$, *communist* $_3$, . . . *The terms of the classification tell us what the indi-individuals in that class have in common;* THE INDEX NUMBERS REMIND US OF THE CHARACTERISTICS LEFT OUT. *A rule can then be formulated as a general guide in all our thinking and reading: Cow* $_1$ *is* NOT *cow* $_2$; *Jew* $_1$ *is* NOT *Jew* $_2$; *politician* $_1$ *is* NOT *politician* $_2$, *and so on. This rule, if remembered, prevents us from confusing levels of abstraction and forces us to consider the facts on those occasions when we might otherwise find ourselves leaping to conclusions which we may later have cause to regret.*

"TRUTH"

Most intellectual problems are, ultimately, problems of classification and nomenclature. Some years ago there was a dispute between the American Medical Association and the Antitrust Division of the Department of Justice as to whether the practice of medicine was a "profession" or "trade." The American Medical Association *wanted* immunity from laws prohibiting "restraint of trade"; therefore, it insisted that medicine *is* a "profession." The Antitrust Division *wanted* to stop certain economic practices connected with medicine, and therefore it insisted that medicine *is* a "trade." Partisans of either side accused the other of perverting the meanings of words and of not being able to understand plain English.

Can farmers operate oil wells and still be "farmers"? In 1947 the attorney general of the state of Kansas sued to dissolve a large agricultural co-operative, Consumers Co-operative Association, charging that the corporation, in owning oil wells, refineries, and pipe-lines, was exceeding the statutory privileges of purchasing co-operatives under the Co-operative Marketing Act, which permits such organizations to "engage in any activity in connection with manufacturing, selling, or supplying to its members machinery, equipment or supplies." The attorney general held that the co-operative, under the Act, could not handle, let alone process and manufacture, general farm supplies, but only those supplies used in the marketing operation. The Kansas Supreme Court decided unanimously in favor of the defendant (CCA). In so deciding, the court held that gasoline and oil *are* "farm supplies," and producing crude oil *is* "part of the business of farming."

"This court," said the decision, "will take judicial notice of the fact that in the present state of the art of farming, gasoline . . . is one of the costliest items in the production of agricultural commodities. . . . Anyway, gasoline and tractors are here, and this court is not going to say that motor fuel is not a supply necessary to carrying on of farm operations. . . . Indeed it is about as well put as can be on Page 18 of the state's Exhibit C where the defendant (CCA) says: '*Producing crude oil, operating pipe-lines and refineries, are also part of the business of farming. It is merely producing synthetic hay for iron horses. It is "off-the-farm farming" which the farmer, in concert with his neighbors, is carrying on.* . . . Production of power farming equipment, then, is logically an extension of the farmers' own farming operations.' " (Italics supplied.)

Is a harmonica player a "musician"? Until 1948, the American Federation of Musicians had ruled that the harmonnica was a "toy." Professional harmonica players usually belonged, therefore, to the American Guild of Variety Artists. Even as distinguished a musician as Larry Adler, who has often played the harmonica as a solo instrument with symphony orchestras, was by the union's definition "not a musician." In 1948, however, the AFM, finding that harmonica players were getting popular and competing with members of the union, decided that they were "musicians" after all—a decision that did not sit well with the president of AGVA, who promptly declared jurisdictional war on the AFM.

Is aspirin a "drug" or not? In some states, it is legally classified as a "drug," and therefore can be sold only by licensed pharmacists. If people want to be able to buy aspirin in groceries, lunchrooms, and pool halls (as they can in other states), they must have it reclassified as "not a drug."

Is medicine a "profession" or a "trade"? Is the production of crude oil "a part of farming"? Is a harmonica player a "musician"? Is aspirin a "drug"? The way in which such questions are commonly settled is by appeals to dictionaries to discover the "real meanings" of the words involved. It is also common practice to consult past legal decisions and all kinds of learned treatises bearing on the subject. The decision finally rests, however, not upon appeals to past authority, but upon *what people want*. If they want the AMA to be immune from antitrust action, they will go to the Supreme Court if necessary to get medicine "defined" as a "profession." If they want the AMA prosecuted, they will get a decision that it is a "trade." (They got, in this case, a decision from the Court that it did not matter whether the practice of medicine was a "trade" or not; what mattered was that the AMA had, as charged, *restrained* the trade of Group Health Association, Inc., a co-operative to *procure* medical services for its members. The antitrust action was upheld.)

If people want agricultural co-operatives to operate oil wells, they will get the courts to define the activity in such a way as to make it possible. If the public at large doesn't care, the decision whether a harmonica player is or is not a "musician" will be made by the stronger trade union. The question whether aspirin is or is not a "drug" will be decided neither by finding the dictionary definition of "drug" nor by staring long and hard at an aspirin tablet. It will be decided on the basis of where and under what conditions people want to buy their aspirins.

In any case, society as a whole ultimately gets, on all issues of wide public importance, the classifications it wants, even if it has to wait until all the members of the Supreme Court are dead and an entirely new court is appointed. When the desired decision is handed down, people say, "Truth has triumphed." *In short, society regards as "true" those systems of classification that produce the desired results.*

The scientific test of "truth," like the social test, is strictly practical, except for the fact that the "desired results" are more severely limited. The results desired by society may be irrational, superstitious, selfish, or humane, but the results desired by scientists are only that our systems of classification produce predictable results. Classifications, as amply indicated already, determine our attitudes and behavior toward the object or event classified. When lightning was classified as "evidence of divine wrath," no courses of action other than prayer were suggested to prevent one's being struck by lightning. As soon, however, as it was classified as "electricity," Benjamin Franklin achieved a measure of control over it by his invention of the lightning rod. Certain physical disorders were formerly classified as "demonic possession," and this suggested that we "drive the demons out" by whatever spells or incantations we could think of. The results were uncertain. But when those disorders were classified as "bacillus infections," courses of action were suggested that led to more predictable results. Science seeks only the *most generally useful* systems of classification; these it regards for the time being, until more useful classifications are invented, as "true."

SUGGESTED ASSIGNMENTS

1. A class-word, or classification, is sometimes accompanied in our minds by a mental picture, which is known as a stereotype. The following experiment will illustrate. Picture in your mind for a moment your idea of a little boy going fishing. Now answer these questions.
   a. Does he wear shoes or is he barefoot?
   b. If he has a hat, what is it made off?
   c. What is he carrying over his shoulder?
   d. What is it made of?
   e. Is his nose freckled or not?
   f. What is walking at his side?
   g. Are his clothes tidy or ragged?
   Here are the answers: a. barefoot b. straw c. a fishing pole d. of cane or of a branch e. freckled f. a dog g. ragged. If you passed the test you have in mind the usual little-boy-going-fishing stereotype. What do you think is the source of this stereotype?
2. Write a short description of a common stereotype, such as a grandmother, a traffic policeman, an old-maid school teacher, an army sergeant, a truck driver, a college professor. Now, write a second description of a real person you know who belongs in the same classification but who does not fit the stereotype.
3. Write a short theme describing a situation you are acquainted with in which a classification makes a real difference. You might consider such classifications as these: resident-nonresident, amateur-professional, junior-senior, drunk-sober, speeding-reckless driving, weed-flower, sane-insane, war-police action, borrowing-stealing.
4. A newspaper actually reported the following incident. An Oxford University student had a bass viol that was too large for taxis and too heavy to be carried. He solved the problem of moving it from place to place by providing it with a wheel on which he rolled it. But the police stepped in and classified it as a vehicle. The result was that he could wheel it only in the street, had to keep it off the sidewalk, and had to put head lights and a tail light on it. Whether he had to buy a license was not mentioned. What was the viol REALLY?
5. Try this experiment on several friends. Tell them that you are going to read them a short list of words and ask them to indicate the affective connotation that each word arouses, using these responses: F (favorable), U (unfavorable), and N (neutral). Then read these numbered words: 1. opera singer, 2. Shakespearean actor, 3. Communist, 4. lawyer, 5. star football player, 6. Negro. Now check the responses. The point is that each of these class-words may be applied to one particular in-

dividual, Paul Robeson. What does this suggest to you about the power of words to affect one's feeling about a given person or object?

6. The following letter appeared in a popular syndicated newspaper column:

> Dear ———: Please settle an argument. Where I work there is this woman who has silver-gray hair but a young face and a good figure. She must be about 50 but looks younger. She has 12 grandchildren, but she goes swimming with them, rides a bicycle with them, and she belongs to three bowling leagues. She says she never baby-sits with her grandchildren unless there is an emergency. Everyone says I am all wet with my ideas but I think a grandmother should ACT like a grandmother and should be proud of her grandchildren and not of her bowling score.

What do you think is the cause of the writer's attitude?

BIAS WORDS

F. A. Philbrick

A bias is literally a slant, from the French biais. *In English we use the word metaphorically to mean a slant in one's judgment. Bias words, then, are those which show a slanted judgment, either in favor of or against, in varying degrees of intensity. For example, you may be* thrifty, *but a person with the same characteristic whom you dislike is* stingy. *Bias words tend to creep into our speech and writing when we feel strongly about a subject. Though they have their place in certain kinds of discourse—eulogy, invective, satire, poetry—they are to be avoided in writing that purports to be objective and considered. Several methods of indicating bias are considered below by F. A. Philbrick. Mr. Philbrick, a graduate of Balliol College, Oxford, where he took a "first" in science, taught*

English at the University of Chicago and at top-flight preparatory schools in England and the United States. He was a keen observer of language and wrote about it clearly and intelligibly.

There are three classes into which all the women past seventy that ever I knew were to be divided: 1. That dear old soul; 2. That old woman; 3. That old witch.

Samuel Taylor Coleridge

NEUTRAL, FAVORABLE, AND UNFAVORABLE WORDS. Languages differ in the extent to which they allow a writer a choice of different words with the same referent. In Spanish this variation can often be achieved by different endings, such as *-ico*, *-ito*, *-uelo*, *-on*, *-ezo*, or *-acho*. For example, the Spanish words for "dog" include *perro*, *perrazo*, *perrillo*, *perrito*, *perrezno*, and *perrico*, each with a different reference. The first is the plain neutral word; the second implies large size and grotesqueness ("ugly" or "hulking"); the third, small size and pity ("poor little wretch"); the fourth, small size and fondness ("darling little"); the fifth, immaturity ("puppy"); and the sixth, what the dictionary, with rare candor, calls "sprightly humor impossible to characterize." The twist given by these endings to a neutral word, such as *perro*, is different for each word and is so subtle that all the manuals on the Spanish language advise the foreigner to be cautious in using such terminations or even not to use them at all. If he neglects this advice, a foreigner is apt to make awkward mistakes, and when wishing to compliment a Spanish lady on her "dear little baby," he may inadvertently suggest that the infant is undersized, contemptible, and of a disagreeable shape.

In English the possibilities are more limited, and the writer often has to choose from such a set as *dog*, *cur*, and *hound*. With fewer words available, each has to cover a wider range, so that while *cur* is always derogatory, *hound* sometimes implies grandeur ("majestic hound," "The Hound of the Baskervilles," "The Hound of Heaven") but sometimes the opposite ("mean hound," "wretched hound"). This variability does not make the word less effective, and "The Dog of the Baskervilles" or "The Dog of Heaven" are plainly less satisfactory than the actual titles. It is true that *hound*, like *perrazo*, implies large size, but even "The Large Dog of the Baskervilles" fails to come quite up to the original.

Words such as *cur* and *hound,* which have the same referent, but different references expressing different attitudes on the part of the user, will here be called *bias words.* Matthew Arnold called them words "touched by emotion," and Coleridge, calling them "watch-words," warned his readers against them, recommending "the beneficial after-effects of verbal precision in the preclusion of fanaticism, which masters the feelings more especially by indistinct watch-words."[1]

SOME BIAS WORDS EXAMINED. While it must never be forgotten that a word owes much of its meaning to its setting, yet it is still possible to estimate the kind of bias that certain words have acquired. The writer's attitude can also be expressed by phrases. "John did not come" and "John failed to come" refer to the same fact, but the second phrase suggests, without clearly saying so, that John was at fault. Writers use such phrases because of the possibility of hinting at a meaning without committing themselves.

As a first example of a pair of bias words *liberty* and *license* may be considered in the phrase "liberty not license." In the referents of the two words there is no difference; each word suggests the absence of restrictions on the doing of something, but *license* implies the liberty to do something of which the writer does not approve. Thus, writers wishing to restrict someone else's liberty often refer to that liberty as *license,* and sometimes draw attention to their own use of bias words as a substitute for reasoning by quoting the phrase itself. To call liberty *license* is not to advance an argument against it, but simply to say that we do not like it, and it tells the reader nothing about the thing referred to except that it is unwelcome to the writer. Again, the word *fad* may refer to any belief or practice that the writer disapproves of, with the implications that the person adhering to it (called the *faddist*) attaches too much importance to it, and that few others share his opinions. *Crank* is similar to *faddist,* with perhaps a deeper tinge of dislike and contempt.

Politics, as one of the great fields of controversy, is an abundant source of bias words. *Statesman* and *statesmanlike* are favorable words, *politician* and *political* often unfavorable. Here are two extracts from a recent account of the political situation in Washington:

[1] *Biographia Literaria,* Ch. 22.

Last week he was a great President, or a potentially great President, working in his study on great affairs of state. But all around him in the White House could be heard the ratlike sounds of politics, the scurrying and whispers . . .

Some of the truth about the incredibly tangled situation leaked out from Washington last week in little whiffs of rumor, in planted "true stories" circulated by each interested faction.[2]

The force of these sentences is chiefly derived from the bias words used in them. . . . *affairs of state* and *politics* are favorable and unfavorable words respectively, though with similar referents. *Faction* is also a bias word (compare the stronger word *pressure group*) and has no favorable word with the same referent; *party* is more nearly neutral, but in some settings is unfavorable, as in "And to party gave up what was meant for mankind." The quotation marks around *true stories* are to suggest that the stories were not true. *Whiff* is one of several words in the *odor* group; it has an unfavorable bias. Still more unfavorable words in the same group are the words *stink* and *stench; odor* and *smell* have a wide range of bias according to setting, but the middle of this range is perhaps almost neutral; *savor*, *aroma*, *perfume*, and *bouquet* (of wines) are all favorable. (Thus, an advertisement for cigars will refer to the *aroma* of the smoke, not to its *odor* or *smell*, still less to its *stench* or *stink.*) Finally, to revert to the quoted passages from *Time*, *scurrying* is an unfavorable word, and so are *rat* and *rat-like*. Zoological metaphors, as applied to people, are deservedly popular as being obvious and usually insulting. *Brute*, *animal*, and *creature* are unfavorable. *Lion*, *eagle*, and sometimes *tiger* are usually favorable; whereas unfavorable attitudes are suggested by *pig*, *donkey*, *mule*, *jackass*, *rat*, *monkey*, *ape*, *vulture*, *cat*, *bitch*, *fox*, *vixen*, *jackal*, *hyena*, *snake*, *reptile*, *worm*, *toad*, *skunk*, and *polecat*.

Metaphors and bias words drawn from family life are all favorable. To speak of *Mother Nature* is to emphasize the pleasanter features of our environment; consider too *alma mater* or *the father of his people*. To call a man *a son of Texas* (or South Dakota or any other place) is always to refer favorably to him—"one of Missouri's most loyal sons." Machine metaphors as applied to a person are also usually favorable as in *dynamo*, *steam engine*, or *steam roller*, but *machine politics* and *sausage machine* are unfavorable.

[2] *Time*, March 10, 1941.

Our study of the language of persuasion may now be continued in tabular form, though a complete list would fill a small dictionary. Political words will be found near the beginning.

FAVORABLE	NEUTRAL	UNFAVORABLE
leader of the people	party leader	demagogue
tribune of the people		ringmaster rabble-rouser political boss
strong man (*e.g.*, "the strong man of Ruritania")	absolute ruler	dictator
community	people	mob[3] the many-headed
patriot[4]	nationalist	jingo chauvinist
rights[5]		privileges
	socialist communist	red
	liberal	pink
social reformer		revolutionary
	conservative (adj.)	reactionary backward
With reference to the Spanish War:		
loyalist	supporter of the Spanish Republic	red
anti-red	supporter of General Franco	rebel
to develop the re-		to exploit the re-

[3] "Democracy dissolves communities into individuals and collects them again into mobs." Dean Inge, *Outspoken Essays, First Series*, Longmans, Green.

[4] "The controversy quickly got into the newspapers, and was carried on for months, with American patriots on one side and Englishmen and Anglomaniacs on the other." H. L. Mencken, *The American Language*, Knopf.

[5] We are apt to contrast our own rights with people's privileges.

FAVORABLE	NEUTRAL	UNFAVORABLE
sources of		sources of
a go-getter salesman	an energetic salesman	a high-pressure salesman
time-tested old-established well-tried	old (has wide range)	out-of-date outmoded obsolete antiquated old-fashioned (has wide range)
up-to-date	new	newfangled
progressive advanced	modern (has wide range)	cranky crackpot
thinking men	those who agree with me	
right-minded		wrong-headed
devout		bigoted
freethinker	atheist	infidel
esprit fort	unbeliever	pagan heathen
	to compel	to dragoon
A modern theory would suggest that	I think	
confidence		complacency
self-confidence		conceit arrogance

Many of the words in this list, and other words like them, are a valuable part of the English language, but a writer who uses them, or a reader who encounters them in the writing of others, should understand what is being done. Instead of giving information about the referent, these words give information about the writer; they express his attitudes and feelings and are chosen by him to convey, if possible, these attitudes and feelings to the reader. Such words are dangerous if they lead the writer or the reader to confuse the exposure of an attitude with the statement of an argument.

OTHER METHODS OF INDICATING BIAS. Direct statements of opinion, the selection of material, and the use of bias words by no means exhaust the means available to the writer who wishes to communicate his prejudices. The exploitation of words with multiple meaning is not a very common device, because it requires more skill than plain lying or calling names, but it is dangerous because less easily detected. *Progressive* is a word with multiple meaning, and as applied to a school it may mean either of two things—namely, that the school is devoted to certain theories of education, most concisely described as those of Dewey, Froebel, and Montessori, or alternatively, that the school makes progress along the scale from bad to good. Everybody must approve of progress of this second kind, because each person can put his own interpretation on *good* and *bad*, but it is not everyone who thinks that schools of the "progressive school" type are the best. Since many people are by no means well informed about multiple meaning, and believe, in a muddled kind of way, that things with the same name must be the same thing, it is possible for a dishonest writer (and easy for a speaker) to use the word *progressive* in two senses in the same passage, thereby convincing the thoughtless that a school "progressive" in one way must be "progressive" in the other.

The suggestion of inferences is a favorable method of persuasion, because readers are likely to hold more tenaciously to opinions supposedly their own than to those handed them ready-made by the author.[6] Rhetorical questions—"Should the American people entrust its destiny to unscrupulous politicians?"—are crude exploitations of the same theory, for it is supposed that the mental effort of discovering the answer will make the reader familiar with the line of reasoning employed, thereby convincing him that the conclusion must be true. But to achieve more lasting impressions the writer must use a less direct approach. "The scandal of Bishop X's connection with the Organ Fund," we read, "is now a thing of the past." The incautious

[6] An inference is a conclusion that one draws from observed facts. "Every inference," says John Dewey, "just because it goes beyond ascertained and known facts . . . involves *a jump from the known to the unknown.*" *How We Think* (New York: D. C. Heath, 1933), p. 96.

The unintended humor of the following news item, for example, rests not on the facts related for the reader but upon the inference that he may make: "Daniel Bertrand of Washington, D. C., who has been visiting relatives in Montpelier and Barre, is at Heaton hospital for care and treatment." [eds.]

reader will conclude, as is intended, that Bishop X stole the money out of the Organ Fund, or perhaps just borrowed it without meaning to pay it back. Yet this is nowhere asserted by the writer, and if he were accused of suggesting it, he would reply that the scandal arose because the bishop refused to have anything to do with the Organ Fund and wanted the money to be devoted to foreign missions instead. . . .

Certain words, of which *real*, *true*, *genuine*, and *good* are examples, are used in conjunction with bias words as intensifiers, or as appeals to the reader not to ignore the bias intended by the writer. "No Real Sportsman"[7] means "No Sportsman (as I understand the word)," and "All really modern theories" means "All theories now current that I approve of." When so used, these words are mere admissions of failure by the writer.

BIAS AND SETTING. The writer who uses bias words will do well to consider what readers his work is likely to find, because the references of these words may change in different times and places. *Socialist* is almost a term of abuse in some circles but a term of praise in others. Again, *Uncle Sam* is a term sure of a favorable reception in the United States (except perhaps in penitentiaries), and a political cartoon would miss its mark if it showed this figure doing anything base, but in some foreign countries the opposite is true, and an allusion to Uncle Sam would be likely to arouse feelings of anger and dislike.

SUGGESTED ASSIGNMENTS

1. Give one unfavorably biased word to contrast with each of these favorable words: *slender*, *generous*, *self-confident*, *daring*, *statesman*, *public medicine*, *chatty*, *meticulous*, *trusting*.
2. In 1948 Bertrand Russell, the eminent British philosopher, appeared on a BBC program during which he humorously conjugated an "irregular verb" as "I am firm, you are obstinate, he is pig-headed." These are bias words, of course, shifting from favorable to unfavorable. Try writing five such conjugations.
3. The following illustration of bias words is taken, with permission, from the *American Bar Association Journal*, July, 1949, p. 559. Underline the favorable words:

[7] "No Real Sportsman Takes Black Salmon"—headline in *The Boston Herald*, April 24, 1941.

The President achieved (notoriety fame) by (tenaciously stubbornly), (bitterly vigorously), (zealously fanatically) asserting his (bold claims impudent pretensions) even in legislative councils through his (tools agents) who (skillfully cunningly) (insinuated introduced) themselves into those councils. The Senate being in accord with his (prejudices principles) (succumbed yielded) to his (domination leadership). He was a man of (faith superstition) and of (obstinacy strength of purpose) whose policy combined (firmness and courage bigotry and arrogance) with (cowardice caution).

He was a (man creature) of strong (biases convictions) and belonged in the camp of the (reactionaries conservatives). His conduct of the Presidency (portended foreshadowed) a (change degeneration) of that office into one of (dictatorship leadership).

4. Think of a campus problem about which you have strong feelings. Then write a letter to the editor of your college paper expressing your point of view in objective and impersonal language. Next, write a second letter conveying the same ideas with a vigorous use of bias words. Underline the bias words and expressions. What kind of reader do you think each letter would appeal to the most?
5. Choose a newspaper from your area and read all the letters to the editor, underlining the bias expressions. Then read all the letters to the editor in the Sunday *New York Times*. If you notice any difference in the number of bias words used, how do you account for it?
6. In the reading from Mr. Philbrick you learned that bias can be indicated by the selection of material. Write an objective and accurate description of an acquaintance of yours in such a way that, by your selection of details and facts, you give a favorable bias. Now describe the same person, again accurately, selecting facts that will create an unfavorable bias.
7. Write a news item or a short narrative which conveys an inference even though you present only factual data. Here is a sample from a Cornell University publication:

> Dr. Stewart G. Wolf, associate professor of medicine, spoke at the annual meeting of the Washington State Medical Association on "Practical Aspects of the Treatment of Headache." Dr. Wolf had a second child, Angelina, born September 29.

CONTEXTS

Robert H. Moore

The word context *means associated surroundings, material or mental. One key idea in language study, succinctly stated, is this: Context determines meaning. Consider, for example, the statement "Indians Scalp Yankees" in the place context of an American history book and in that of the sports page, and you get two different meanings. Or put the sentence "Russia fights with U. S." in the time contexts of 1945 and 1960 and again two meanings emerge. In this essay and the assignments that follow, the idea that context determines meaning is developed and its various implications are shown. The author first explains briefly the well-known Ogden-Richards contextual theory of meaning and then discusses three kinds of context.*

SIGNS AND SYMBOLS

AN UNDERSTANDING of *why* one person will interpret a word differently from another person is necessary if we are to . . . [improve our] interpretative abilities. The following quotation from *The Meaning of Meaning* gives us one explanation of why an individual interprets a sign in a certain way:

The effects upon the organism due to any sign, which may be any stimulus from without, or any process taking place within, depend upon the past history of the organism, both generally and in a more precise fashion. In a sense no doubt, the whole past history is relevant; but there will be some among the past events in that history which more directly determine the nature of the present agitation than others.

. . . .

. . . when a context has affected us in the past the recurrence of merely a part of the context will cause us to react in the way in which we reacted before. A sign is always a stimulus similar to some part of an original stimulus and sufficient to call up the engram formed by that stimulus.

An engram is the residual trace of an adaption made by the organism to a stimulus.[1]

A sign, according to Ogden and Richards, is not necessarily formed for the purpose of communicating meanings. A symbol, however, is a stimulus provided for the purpose of conveying one person's thoughts or feelings to another person.

When for the first time we see a flash of lightning and hear almost immediately a clap of thunder, we do not perceive a sign! The lightning flash does not lead us to expect a clap of thunder. However, after we have experienced several thunder storms, a flash of lightning (part of an original stimulus) calls up other details which accompanied flashes of lightning we have seen earlier and leads us to react as we did previously to the entire stimulus. A lightning flash then becomes a sign to us.

The lightning is not, though, a symbol, for it is not formed for the purpose of conveying meanings to anyone. If, however, a small child has heard his parents say, "A thunderstorm is coming," before a storm occurs and "That was the worst thunderstorm we've had all summer," after the storm is over, the word *thunderstorm*, when later spoken by the mother to the child, becomes a symbol to him, since the word is used for the purpose of communicating meaning.

Words, which are verbal symbols, are normally learned by the individual as the child mentioned in the preceding paragraph learned the meaning of *thunderstorm*. That is, they are heard by the individual as part of an actual experience. When heard again they recall to the mind of the hearer the parts of the original experience which accompanied the word.

. . . it is actually through their occurrence together with things, their linkage with them in a "context" that Symbols come to play that important part in our life which has rendered them not only a legitimate object of wonder but the source of all our power over the external world.[2]

[1] C. K. Ogden and I. A. Richards, *The Meaning of Meaning*, pp. 52-53.
[2] *Ibid.*, p. 47.

We learn the meanings of some words, of course, without actually hearing them spoken at a time when we are experiencing that to which the words refer. For instance, few of us have heard or seen or participated in a battle in time of war. Yet the word has meaning for us when used in combination with other words. We have, though, seen guns and heard them fired; we have seen soldiers, airplanes, and perhaps ships and tanks; we have heard the roar of explosions; and we have seen blinded or crippled war veterans. The word *battle* is merely an abbreviated form to indicate a certain relationship among objects which we have experienced with our senses and the names of which we have learned in connection with our experiencing them. If we had not seen and heard and learned the names of the implements of warfare before reading and hearing of battles, we would have but the faintest idea of the meaning of the word *battle*.

Because most civilians have learned the word *battle* from reading and hearing spoken sentences containing it while surrounded by comparative peace and quiet, they have but a limited understanding of the non-verbal event for which it stands. A veteran of one or more battles, on the other hand, has no doubt heard *battle* used before an engagement with the enemy began and at a time when the suspense was very great; he may have heard it spoken during the action; and almost certainly he has heard it used to refer to the engagement soon after it ended. If, as Ogden and Richards say, "Our interpretation of any sign is our psychological reaction to it, as determined by our past experience in similar situations, and by our present experience,"[3] it is plain to be seen that a civilian who has only read or heard of battles will interpret the word *battle* differently from a soldier who has lived through one or more battles. No two men who have gone through the same battle will respond to *battle* in exactly the same way, of course, since each engaged in different activities, saw events from different angles, and experienced different sensations; but these two men will interpret words pertaining to warfare much more nearly alike than will a civilian and a veteran of one or more battles.

For communication to take place, there must be a certain amount of experience common to writer and reader. It is in this common or overlapping experience that words get meanings in discourse. The fact that no two persons have any experience precisely identical makes full or perfect communication impossible, and creates the necessity for inter-

[3] *Ibid.*, p. 244.

pretation. In any discourse, then, the meaning of a word depends upon its total incidence in the past experiences of writer and reader; and upon the situation in which it is being used.[4]

Since the meaning a word has for a person is determined by his past experiences and the present situation, the reader or hearer of any expression can better understand what he hears or reads by taking into consideration the experiential background of the writer or speaker and the conditions under which the words are written or spoken. If the reader of a communication issued by Joseph Stalin from Moscow thinks of the difference between the Russian Dictator's past experiences and his own, he will be acutely aware of the fact that what Stalin means by *freedom* may not be similar to what he (the reader) means by the same word.

Similarly, the reader of the following statement issued by Alexander F. Gorkin, Secretary of the Presidium of the Supreme Soviet, should recognize that the words used in the statement may not mean what he assumes they mean:

> The Red army has no aim of seizure of foreign countries or subjugation of other peoples.
>
> We have not and cannot have any such war aims as that of imposing our will and our regime upon the Slavic or other enslaved nations of Europe who are expecting our help. Our aim is to help these nations in their struggle for liberation from Hitler's tyranny, and then to leave them to organize their lives on their own land as they think fit.
>
> There must be no interference whatsoever in the internal affairs of other nations. The strength of the Red army consists in the fact that it is waging a just war, a war of liberation.[5]

Foreign countries or *other nations* in this quotation may denote nations as constituted before the outbreak of the European war. If so, the statement would mean that the boundaries of pre-war Poland and of the Baltic countries would be restored. On the other hand, the expression may refer to areas not under Russian control at the time of the beginning of the hostilities between Germany and Russia in 1941. Only part of what was once Poland and none of the Baltic countries would then be regarded as having the right to self-government.

[4] Progressive Education Association, *Language in General Education*, p. 96.

[5] From an International News Service Bulletin, *The Columbus Dispatch*, March 4, 1943, Section A, p. 2.

CONTEXTS: PHYSICAL, PSYCHOLOGICAL, VERBAL

Since the same word may have different meanings for different people and different meanings in different situations for the same person, it is evident that a reader or listener must make use of all possible means of determining the meaning intended to be conveyed by the writer or speaker. A clue as to how to go about devising methods for accurately interpreting spoken or written words is given by Bronislaw Malinowski in a supplement to *The Meaning of Meaning*.

> A statement, spoken in real life, is never detached from the situation in which it has been uttered. For each verbal statement by a human being has the aim and function of expressing some thought or feeling actual at that moment and in that situation, and necessary for some reason or other to be made known to another person or persons—in order either to serve purposes of common action, or to establish ties of purely social communion, or else to deliver the speaker of violent feelings or passions. Without some imperative stimulus of the moment, there can be no spoken statement. In each case, therefore, utterance and situation are bound up inextricably with each other and the context of situation is indispensable for the understanding of the words. Exactly as in the reality of spoken or written languages, a word without *linguistic context* is a mere figment and stands for nothing by itself, so in the reality of a spoken living tongue, the utterance has no meaning except in the context of situation.[6]

If "utterance and situation are bound up inextricably with each other," it would be hopeless to attempt to understand words without understanding the conditions under which they are spoken and written. The term *context* is often employed to refer both to the conditions surrounding the utterance of a word and to the other words which precede and follow a word in discourse. For purposes of discussion, the different types of context may be classified as physical, psychological, and verbal. The place where words are spoken or written, the time when they are spoken or written, and the activities going on around the speaker or writer make up the physical context. The experiential background and the present mood of the speaker or writer constitute the psychological context. The words which are used with any one word or group of words make up the verbal context.

Usually, of course, all the factors discussed in the preceding para-

[6] Bronislaw Malinowski, "The Problem of Meaning in Primitive Languages," Supplement I in *The Meaning of Meaning*, p. 307.

graph are involved whenever a word is spoken. Depending on the particular situation, however, one type of context may give more of a clue to the meaning of an expression than another.

If a passer-by sees a man walk through the gate of a penitentiary and hears him say, "It certainly feels good to be free again," he is able to interpret the word *free* from an understanding of what the man is doing and where he is doing it. In other words, he studies the physical context of the utterance in his effort to interpret it.

If this same passer-by should overhear a man who he knows has been in prison say, "I'm glad to be free again," he would know, regardless of where or under what conditions the words were uttered, that *free* should be understood to mean "out of prison" or "without physical restraint." The psychological context would then provide the clue for correct interpretation of the words.

Next, let us suppose that a person who has recently been released from prison is overheard by a stranger to say, "After three years in prison, I certainly am glad to be free again." The hearer of this remark is able to interpret the word *free* without any previous knowledge of the case and wherever he hears it. A study of the verbal context of the word *free* has guided the hearer to an accurate interpretation of the word.

Under some conditions, of course, a single word has meaning for its hearers. When a girl in a crowded room in the Cocoanut Grove Night Club in Boston in 1942 screamed "Fire!" the occupants of the room knew almost instantly what she meant. Their understanding of the meaning of the word came almost entirely from the physical context of the utterance. Since the expression contained only one word, verbal context provided no help to the hearers in interpreting the word. Many people, because of real or vicarious experiences, have "in the back of their minds" a fear of fire when they enter tightly packed buildings. Perhaps this half-hidden fear of fire caused some persons to react almost instantly to the word *fire*. If so, the psychological context of the utterance helped them to interpret the one word which they heard and led them to act in a way which was partly responsible for the holocaust which followed the outbreak of the fire.

Although we are sometimes able to tell the meaning of a word when it is used alone, we usually employ words in groups and rely to some extent on the verbal context as an aid to our interpretation of any one word. In our everyday conversation, however, verbal context is incomplete; that is, the hearer must interpret words largely from a study of their physical and psychological contexts.

If, for example, we hear someone shout, "George passed," we can, if we are seated in a stadium on a Saturday afternoon in October or November, and if we are acquainted with the fact that a halfback on one football team is named *George*, determine that the words mean that George, the halfback, threw the ball to one of his team mates. We have been able to interpret through their physical and psychological contexts words which out of their context would be meaningless. The speaker in the situation is, because of our ability to interpret words through their physical and psychological contexts, spared the necessity of saying, "George Miller, the halfback on our team, threw the football to one of his team mates."

If the physical and psychological contexts of the sentence, "George passed," are changed, our interpretation of it will change accordingly. If George's partner in a bridge game says, "George passed," we realize at once that the words are used to convey the information that George, one of the players, declined to bid.

Although the words used in the two different settings are the same, their referents are different. Because, in each instance, we are aware of what is happening and where it is happening, and because we have an understanding of what has preceded the events which are now taking place, we are able to agree with the speaker on the referents of the words.

In the two examples we have given, it would be difficult for the hearer to misinterpret the speaker. And if he did misinterpret him the results would not be far reaching. The examples have been given merely to show that most spoken words have little meaning apart from the situation in which they are spoken and that accurately to interpret an utterance we must know under what circumstances it was spoken.

Individuals who immediately become angry at a friend or relative because someone has told them what the friend or relative has said about them without telling under what circumstances the remark in question was made and without indicating what else was said at the time are ignorant of or pay no heed to the principle stated in the preceding paragraph. As a result, untold unpleasantnesses arise and countless friendships are disrupted.

In written expression the reader must depend to a large extent on verbal context to interpret the meanings of words. It is usually difficult to determine the conditions surrounding the writer at the time of the writing. Usually, too, the speaker and the hearer have more knowledge of each other and have had more experiences in common than have the writer and reader. The writer must, then, supply through words as much information as is needed to enable the reader to interpret his meaning accurately. Nearly always, however, an acquaintanceship with the writer, with the events of his life, and with circumstances surrounding the writing will enable the reader to interpret written words more accurately than he could without such acquaintanceship. Verbal context, in short, cannot entirely take the place of physical and psychological contexts.

The writer must, if he really wishes to convey his ideas to a reader, supply a verbal context which will make as clear as possible the meaning of words the understanding of which is essential to accurate interpretation. In a discussion about the postwar world, for instance, the writer should endeavor to leave no doubts in the minds of his readers as to his intended meaning of *freedom*, *liberty*, and *justice* if he uses these terms, as he probably will.

The following letter, written to the letters-to-the-editor department of the *Columbus Dispatch* by an individual who terms himself "a working man," employs terms an understanding of the meaning of which is essential to accurate interpretation of the letter, without supplying a verbal context of such a nature as to make clear the meaning which he wishes to convey by these terms:

I wonder what the thoughts of the New Dealers and Roosevelt worshippers must be as they take their coupons to the stores and try to figure out what to buy. Indeed, this is the more abundant life, as promised.

None of our citizens object to doing without to give our soldiers more, but I certainly object to going hungry in order to feed the Russians and Pal Joey. If we had less Communist influence at Washington we wouldn't be rationed, regimented, and reduced to the status of serfs and slaves.

I am a working man who was foolish enough to believe in the New Deal. It has certainly turned out to be a raw deal.

We are sending our boys to all the outposts of the world to fight for freedom and losing it at home. It is time that all true Americans wake up and realize that only by supporting an independent congress and a free press and never missing an opportunity to talk for freedom, that we can preserve that freedom.

God grant, that in our next election, we shall be sufficiently alive to the dangers presented, and that we will elect an administration pledged to restore America to its former freedom. Wake up, America, before it is too late.[7]

The key word in this letter is obviously *freedom,* since the writer's chief purpose seems to be to influence his readers to elect an administration which will restore "freedom" to America. Yet the reader cannot possibly determine the meaning of this key word from a study of its physical, psychological, and verbal contexts. The fact that the letter was written in February, 1943, during a time when several rationing programs were in effect and just before the beginning of the rationing of certain canned and processed foods suggests the possibility that the writer may regard the right to buy products wheneven and in whatever quantities one wishes as one aspect of freedom. The fact that the writer is a working man might lead to the belief that he regards the placing of a ceiling on wages by the government as contrary to the principles of freedom. Since there were millions of working men in February, 1943, most of whom probably had altogether individual ideas as to the nature of freedom, it is apparent that the reader can gain but slight help in interpreting *freedom* from either its physical or psychological context.

When the verbal context is examined, we find that the reader is again provided with but little assistance in his attempts to interpret *freedom.* In the second paragraph, the writer insists that Americans "are rationed, regimented, and reduced to the status of serfs and slaves." *Freedom* obviously means, on the basis of these words, the absence of rationing and regimentation. The meaning of *rationing* is fairly clear to the reader; regimentation, however, needs further explanation, since some degree of regulation is necessary in all civilizations. The writer should indicate under what circumstances regulation becomes regimentation. In the final paragraph he expresses, by implication, the belief that Americans have lost their former freedom, since he hopes that an administration pledged to restore it will be elected. *Freedom* here, then, clearly does not involve the right of a people to select their own leaders, for if they have lost their freedom, yet still have the opportunity to elect their own rulers, it is evident that *freedom* does not mean the legal right of a people to govern themselves. In the fourth paragraph, the writer states that America is sending soldiers abroad to fight for freedom. On the basis of other

[7] "A Working Man Speaks," *The Columbus Dispatch,* February 26, 1943, Section B, p. 2.

sentences in the letter, it would be logical to assume that the writer means that America is sending soldiers abroad to fight against rationing and regimentation but not necessarily to secure the rights of peoples to govern themselves. If the writer does mean that American boys are fighting abroad for the right of people to elect their own leaders, then the meaning of *freedom* shifts throughout the letter without the reader's having been given any indication that any shift in meaning was occurring.

Because of his failure to define *freedom* and possibly to avoid an unmarked shift in the meaning of the word, the writer of the letter has failed to convey any information to the reader except that he dislikes the present administration and would like to see it replaced at the next election. Yet some readers will no doubt assume that *freedom* is used by the writer to mean what they themselves would use the word to mean, and will, in addition, be moved by such strongly connotative terms as *Communist influence*, *Pal Joey*, and *regimented*. As a result, they may be influenced to vote differently from the way they would have voted had they not read what is, in realtiy, an almost meaningless bit of writing.

An open letter sent in 1943 by Sewell Avery, president of Montgomery Ward and Company, to the National War Labor Board provides us with an example of a statement which makes clear to its reader what it means by terms which might well be misinterpreted.

The letter was written in response to a recommendation by a National War Labor Board panel that the Board issue an order imposing a form of closed shop called "maintenance of membership" and compulsory arbitration of questions raised by the union upon six Montgomery Ward stores in Denver, Detroit, and New York City. The eighth of nine reasons given by the company for objecting to the proposed order is as follows:

> The proposed order violates the fundamental principles of liberty. Liberty requires that an employee be free to join, to refuse to join, or to resign from a union without losing his job. Liberty requires that an employer be free to employ the person best suited for the work.[8]

In this statement the reader is left no doubt as to what the writer means by *liberty*. The reader may not believe, of course, that the principles mentioned in the quotation are fundamental principles of

[8] Sewell Avery, "Montgomery Ward's Statement to the National War Labor Board," *The Columbus Dispatch*, March 2, 1943, Section B, p. 9.

liberty as he himself would use the term. He would not, then, object to the proposed order of the Board on the grounds that it would violate the principles of liberty. If, on the other hand, the reader agrees with the company's assertion that the principles it mentions are fundamental principles of liberty, he would object to the proposal on the grounds that the employees and employer were, to some extent, being denied liberty. In either case, the reader's attention is centered more on the specific regulations and actions involved than on the meaning of the high order abstraction, *liberty*.

Suppose, on the other hand, the statment had merely asserted that the proposed order would violate the fundamental principles of liberty. A careless reader, then, not having been told what the writer considers "fundamental principles of liberty," and assuming that the expression has the same meaning for the writer as for himself, might, because of his reverence for *liberty*, object to the Board's order. A reader who responds in this way to what he reads reacts not to what words stand for but to words themselves. His actions, then, are not apt to be appropriate to conditions in the non-verbal world surrounding him.

In the statement issued by him in behalf of Montgomery Ward and Company, Sewell Avery expands the word *liberty* by listing in terms closer to reality (or in less abstract terms) certain acts which he feels may be summarized by the word. As a result, most readers can, with a reasonable degree of accuracy, understand the position taken by the Company on the proposed order of the National War Labor Board.

Had the writer of the first letter followed a plan similar to Avery's and mentioned some restrictions or actions which he considered as opposed to the principles of freedom and some privileges or rights which he considered as fundamental principles of freedom, he would have succeeded in conveying his meaning to many more people than he did.

If students become aware of the fact that one word may have many different meanings at different times, or different meanings for different people at the same time, they will realize that they must not take for granted that they can always tell what a writer or speaker intends a word to mean.

By being led to observe that the meaning of a word usually depends upon who speaks it or writes it, upon the circumstances under which it is spoken or written, and upon the words which are spoken or written *with* it, students will come to realize that they can accurately interpret a word only by studying its physical, psychological, and verbal contexts. They will also come to understand that because of the nature of a word's contexts they may not be able to discover the meaning of the word at all.

SUGGESTED ASSIGNMENTS

1. Do you know what a *fleep* is? Not yet, but you soon will as you meet the word in a series of contexts that will narrow the meaning step by step and make it specific. The contexts are in this short paragraph:

   I have a fleep with me nearly every day. This fleep goes with me everywhere, and I consider it an indispensible part of my life. In appearance it offers an attractive contrast: one part is bright and shiny, the other quietly dull. My fleep outlasts the other parts of my wardrobe, and I can often wear it for several years. Being unobtrusive, it seldom goes out of style. Some people like a stretchy fleep but I prefer the traditional kind. The leather of my fleep is soft and supple so that it gives with every movement of a part of my body. This fleep is very important to my well-being, for without it my trousers would come down. So every morning I buckle it around my waist and step forth to meet the world with a feeling of confidence.

   Write a similar paragraph to teach the meaning of *muggle* through a set of contexts. Try to sharpen the meaning with each step, but hold off the precise meaning through as many steps as possible.
2. Explain what the sentence "Make mine black and white" might mean in each of these contexts: a coffee shop, the club car of a train, a college soda fountain, a pet shop.
3. Write a short phrase or sentence and then embed it in two short paragraphs so that the two contexts give it two different meanings.
4. An advertisement of a French film called "Portrait of Innocence" reported that Bosley Crowther, movie critic of *The New York Times*, had described it as "sparkling and penetrating." What Crowther had actually written was "While sparkling and penetrating in flashes, it is rather laboriously contrived." To show that quotations out of context can be misleading and even dishonest, find a quotation on a book jacket or in an advertisement and then write a context for it in which its meaning is different from that of the quotation by itself.
5. Choose a common word like *run*, *light*, *go* and put it into ten different sentences to give it ten different meanings. Try to get one sentence in which it has a meaning not recorded in the dictionary. For example, in the following sentence the word *day* means hunting: "When the

hunters returned from tramping in the fields for pheasants, Joe asked, 'What kind of day did you have?' "

6. At times a word is normally used in certain contexts which give it a special nuance. For instance, one *commits* murder, perjury, adultery, a crime, a sin. When such a word is used in a different kind of context, such as "He committed matrimony," a peculiar effect results. Find such a word (e.g., brink, to harbor, aroma), write out the usual contexts, and then use it in an unusual context for special effect.
7. Often a single context is sufficient to explain an unknown word. Here are some examples:

   a. "At closing they came out, stepping from the *fugginess* of tobacco and bright lights into the fresh night air."

   Daphne Du Maurier

   b. ". . . yet when they begin to be well *whittled* with nectar, and cannot think of anything serious . . ."

   Erasmus

   c. [About a rooster and his hens]
   "And with a *chuk* he then began to call."

   Chaucer

   Find five words that your classmates probably do not know and put each one in a context so clear that the meaning is immediately apparent.

INTERPRETATION

F. A. Philbrick

In the preceding essay we learned how words acquire meaning in numerous contexts and how the three different kinds of context enable us to interpret words. In the essay that follows, F. A. Philbrick, after summarizing several language concepts, shows us the context theory at work in the law courts. Mr. Philbrick is identified in the headnote to "Bias Words," page 190.

From *Language and The Law* by F. A. Philbrick. Reprinted by permission of Mrs. Sybil Philbrick. Published by The Macmillan Company, 1951.

WORDS, WHETHER WRITTEN OR SPOKEN, are symbols. They stand for or represent something in such a way that when we notice the word, whether by seeing it or hearing it, the thought of that something comes into our minds. Words, that is, are symbols for thoughts. There are many other possible symbols for thoughts. A bunch of flowers sent to a friend on her birthday is such a symbol; so is the bow that we make to her when we meet her; and so are the gestures that many people make when they speak. This is not mere linguistic theory. It has for long been recognized in the courts, and a libel action can be as well grounded on symbolical behavior as on words. The courts have held that it is libellous to burn a man in effigy, and a gallows placed over a man's door is likewise a libel on him. An English litigant once brought an action because a wax figure of him had been placed on the threshold of the Chamber of Horrors in Madame Tussaud's well-known exhibition in Baker Street, London, and it was held that an action lay. Even a dash representing a name, or a row of asterisks, can be libellous, and if the identity of the plaintiff can be plausibly guessed by a reader, it is no defence to say that his name was not mentioned in the libel.

Like other symbols, words do not maintain a strict one-to-one relation with the things symbolized. They seem to grow roots in the mind, and there they get tangled with other growing things, so that all the words standing for thoughts that are important to the thinker have associations for him. These associations are called the *connotation* of the word, and are different for every person, though the various connotations that the same word has for different people are likely to have much in common. The so-called "actual" or "dictionary" meaning of a word is sometimes described as its *denotation*, though many writers avoid this term because it suggests that a word has a fixed and ascertainable meaning common to all persons who use or encounter it—an idea which as applied to many words (i.e., the abstract words) is dangerously false.

Words not only have associations that a user could enumerate if he had the necessary memory and application, but also form secret or hidden connections in the unconscious levels of the mind. A man may find, for instance, that the apparently inexplicable dislike which he feels for a person or a place originates in a name with unpleasant associations for him. Most such connections, however, are less obvious, and can be restored to consciousness only with the help of psychoanalysis. For this reason, it is seldom possible for a lawyer to know what word-associations are likely to be favorable or unfavorable for members of a jury, though he should certainly try to exclude any prospective juryman whose name is the same as that of any of the parties, or even the counsel, on the other side.

The study of the connection between a word and what it stands for is called the theory of definition. It is the beginning of any study of the working of language, and is of practical importance in some branches of the law; for instance, the law of libel and slander. Fortunately an elementary study offers no difficulty.

First we had better dispose of some superstitions. A primitive notion survives in many parts of the world—it is perhaps hardly rational enough to be called a belief—that the connection between a word and the thing it stands for is closer than the merely mental connection between symbol and object. Most primitive peoples imagine that the word not only stands for but in some sense *is* the thing. Such a notion leads them to incantations and other manifestations of word-magic, and is responsible for the ancient horror of blasphemy. The true names of the old gods, including Yahweh, the god of the Hebrews, were often secret, and since to mention one of these names aloud was to bring down the god himself (the name being identified with the deity), the utterance was regarded as an act endangering the public safety. The blasphemy laws enforced in recent times protected the names of religious veneration only from public disrespect, and could no doubt be justified as tending to prevent breaches of the peace, but in this they were typical of primitive customs that survive in modern times in disguise. Such Christian anniversaries as Easter, Christmas, and All Souls' Eve are the modern representatives of primitive festivals celebrated at corresponding seasons, and the pre-Christian archetypes of the Holy Communion are well known to students of the history of religion. When a witness in our courts lifts his right hand as he takes the oath, he no longer expects his god to strike him dead if he tells lies, but there are many plausible reasons for continuing the custom after the belief that it was based on has passed away.

The rational connections between words and thoughts are not difficult to follow. Words may stand for thoughts of three kinds. First come thoughts of picturable things that can be seen and touched. Words referring to these things are defined by pointing. If there is any doubt as to the meaning of the word *coal*, some specimens of coal are procured and doubt is at an end. Second come thoughts of actions. Words referring to these actions are defined by pantomime: the verb *to kick*, for example, is defined by performing the action. These pantomime definitions are called *operational definitions* by physical scientists. All physical units, such as the *yard* or the *centigrade degree* or the *ampere*, are defined in this way, and many of the definitions are embodied in statute law.

Words that can be defined by pointing or by pantomime may be called *concrete* words. Words of the third type, called *abstract* words, stand for thoughts of relations, whether these relations are between picturable things or between actions or between thoughts. An abstract word has to be defined by a metaphor—by an *as though* or *as if* process—and for this reason abstract words have no fixed or "correct" or "accepted" meanings, nor can their definitions be incorporated into statutes. Controversies about the "correct" definitions of words are usually about abstract words. *Democracy* and *beauty* are examples, and of special interest to lawyers are *freedom*, *justice*, *law*, and *rights*. . . .

Many years before writers on language had clearly formulated their opinions about meaning . . . , necessity had driven advocates and judges to similar conclusions—especially those lawyers concerned with actions for libel and slander. In such actions two important semantic principles have been thoroughly established in American and English courts: the first, that meaning is in the mind of the hearer or reader; the second, that meaning depends on context.

In actions for libel or slander, it has long been laid down that the meaning of the words is not the thought in the mind of the utterer. "The question is not what the writer of an alleged libel means, but what is the meaning of the words he has used." (Lord Bramwell in *Henty's Case*). And Gatley, in his *Libel and Slander*, from which this quotation is taken, continues, "the meaning of the writer is quite immaterial. The question is, not what the writer meant, but what he conveyed to those who heard or read." A slander spoken in a foreign language is not actionable if no one present understands the language. And again, it is no defence to say that words were spoken in jest unless they were also understood in jest. "The whole question is," says Gatley, "whether the jocularity was in the mind of the defendant alone, or was shared by the bystanders." Ironic praise is actionable, if the irony is understood by the hearers, and there was a successful action against a defendant who said the plaintiff had done something "God only knows whether honestly or otherwise."

It seems to have been I. A. Richards who first explicitly declared that the meaning of a word is the missing part of its context. Because this is so, we are able to understand without referring to a dictionary words that we meet for the first time, thus adding to our vocabularies by the process that children use. When a boy reads in an advertisement that something is the *acme* of perfection, it is easy for him to guess that *acme* means summit, since that meaning is the only one that makes sense of the context. The meaning that a hearer attributes to a familiar abstract word heard in a speech is therefore made up of two elements: the meaning that he already has for it in his mind, made up of the missing parts of the previous contexts in which he has heard or read it; and the meaning that he thinks is required by the word in its present context. Here *context* includes not only the other words in the speech, but everything else that has any bearing on the speaker's intention: his gestures, tone, and actions, and the circumstances in which he finds himself. To give a simple example of what may be highly complicated, the word *hell* has different meanings when pronounced in a sermon in church and when used as an expletive on the golf links.

All this has been known for many years to lawyers engaged in libel suits. This is what Gatley says (*op. cit.*):

"If the words in their natural and ordinary sense are innocent or meaningless, still a further question may arise: Were there any facts known to those to whom the words were published which would lead them to understand them in a secondary and defamatory sense? Words in themselves apparently innocent may be shown to have a defamatory meaning when they are read with reference to the circumstances in which they were uttered or written, and with reference to the context in which they appear.

"The manner of publication, and the things relative to which the words were published and which the person knew or ought to have known would influence those to whom it was published in putting a meaning on the words, are all material in determining whether the writing is calculated to convey a libellous imputation. There are no words so plain that they may not be published with reference to such circumstances and to such persons knowing those circumstances as to convey a meaning very different from that which would be understood from the same words used under different circumstances."

"The words must be construed as a whole. It is necessary to take into consideration, not only the actual words used, but the context of the words. It would be unfair to the defendant to pick out this or that sentence which may be considered defamatory, for there may be other passages which take away their sting. If in one part of the publication something disreputable to the plaintiff is stated, but that is removed by the conclusion, the bane and the antidote must be taken together. The defendant is entitled to have read as part of the plaintiff's case the whole of the publication from which the alleged libel is extracted, and also any other document referred to which qualifies or explains its meaning."

"Where nothing is alleged to give them an extended meaning, the words must be construed in their natural and ordinary meaning, i.e., in the meaning in which reasonable men of ordinary intelligence would be likely to understand them." It should be noted that Gatley does not say that the meaning of a word is its dictionary meaning; on the contrary, he says that meaning resides in the mind of the hearer. This is illustrated in the following case quoted from his book:

"The defendant, a tax collector, having applied to the plaintiff for payment of certain taxes, was told by him that J. S. would pay them. He subsequently wrote and mailed to the plaintiff a postcard containing these words: 'I saw J. S. this morning: he said, "Make the S. B. pay it."' The plaintiff brought an action for libel, alleging in his innuendo that the letters S. B. meant 'Son of a bitch.' It was held by the Court of Appeal in Ontario, affirming Britton, J., that the postcard was harmless in its primary meaning, and that the letters S. B. not having acquired in the vernacular any meaning as a customary abbreviation of any particular phrase or expression, and the plaintiff having given no evidence that they conveyed the defamatory meaning alleged in the innuendo, the defendant was entitled to judgment."

Two examples may be given of words that have been defined by statute. In England the Anglo-Portuguese Commercial Treaty Act of 1914 states that

> The description "Port" or "Madeira" applied to any wine or other liquor other than wine the produce of Portugal and the island of Madeira respectively shall be deemed to be a false trade description within the meaning of the Merchandise Marks Act, 1887, and that Act shall have effect accordingly.

In 1923 a company which had been selling a liquor labelled "Tarragona port" claimed that "Tarragona" was a well-known article of commerce before the Treaties, and that "Tarragona port" was not a false description provided the liquor contained a reasonable proportion of Tarragona. The English courts found against them. A more significant example is afforded by the word *Negro*. In some Southern states, statutory definitions lay down that a Negro is anyone with one quarter (in some states one eighth) African blood. A. G. Hays, in his book *City Lawyer*, tells of a couple from the Bahamas who after building a house in Scarsdale, New York, found that the property was included in a covenant prohibiting tenancy by Negroes. There is no statutory definition of a Negro in New York, and Mr. Hays was able to obtain an affidavit from Professor Franz Boas, the celebrated head of the Anthropology Department at Columbia University, that a Negro is "a human being with one hundred per cent African blood."

The words whose definitions have been fixed by statute are naturally few. Unreflecting persons are often inclined to suppose that the definition of any word is fixed by the dictionary, but this, as has already been hinted, is an illusion. There is death in the dictionary, said Lowell. Definitions are fixed by usage, and meanings by usage and context. Dictionaries follow usage; they do not decide or lead it. If there were no dictionaries (and many of the cultivated people whose preferences determine usage never consult one), meanings would be unchanged. But though dictionaries do not settle meanings, they act as anchors or stabilisers in restricting changes in meaning.

It is important in many fields of study, and not least in the law, to get a firm grasp of the fact that abstract words have no fixed or "correct" meanings. The theory, for example, that there is such a thing as *justice* that exists independently of human minds, and that the business of the law is to find out what it is, will not stand examination. The theory is a modern representative of Plato's philosophical concept of universals, and survives partly as a naïve idea that if there is a name for a thing the thing must exist, and partly (as is persuasively argued in Jerome Frank's *Law and the Modern Mind*) as a relic in adults of the childish desire for certainty and fixity in a changeable and difficult world.

Much the same may be said about the abstract word *democracy*. The relationships represented by this word are those which the citizens of a country bear to each other and to their government. These relationships distinguish an autocratic country from a democratic one. It must however be admitted that one man's thoughts on these relationships will certainly not be the same as another man's. The resemblance between A's thoughts and B's thoughts is close enough to make the word *democracy* useful in discussion, though not close enough for them always to avoid controversies about what it "really means." An abstract word has no "correct meaning," never has had one, never will have one, and in the nature of things never can have one. For the lawyer, semantics has no more useful lesson.

It is a lesson that is very far from being universally understood, by lawyers or anyone else. . . . One fallacy prevalent among the learned is that the "true" meaning of a word can be discovered from the derivation, and that the word *radical*, for instance, "really means" someone who wants to get to the root of things. An amusing exploitation of the fallacy is quoted by Wellman in *The Art of Cross-Examination.* A young man who had been injured in a railroad accident was examined by the railroad doctor, who declared that the injury to his nervous system was merely hysterical, and would probably disappear in a short time. The cross-examination of the doctor by the patient's counsel, Benjamin F. Butler, is recorded as follows in Butler's autobiography:

Mr. Butler: Do I understand that you think this condition of my client wholly hysterical?

Witness: Yes, sir; undoubtedly.

And therefore won't last long?

No, sir; not likely to.

Well, doctor, let us see; is not the disease called hysteria and its effects hysterics; and isn't it true that hysteria, hysterics, hysterical, all come from the Greek word 'υστερα?

It may be.

Don't say it may, doctor; isn't it? Isn't an exact translation of the Greek word 'υστερα the English word "womb"?

You are right, sir.

Well, doctor, this morning when you examined this young man here, did you find that he had a womb? I was not aware of it before, but I will have him examined over again and see if I can find it. That is all, doctor; you may step down.

Since, however, language has to be put to practical use, and since the interpretation of the laws is the duty of the courts, lawyers and judges are frequently obliged to make estimates, which may afterwards have the force of law, as to the "true" meaning of certain words and phrases. Unfortunately, the situation to which the law has to be applied is seldom one that could have been in the minds of the legislators who framed it. In the eighteenth century, for example, lawmaking bodies could not have foreseen that their laws would have to be applied to the distribution of electric power. The court has then to decide how they would have intended the law to apply if they had been acquainted with the situation. The task of making such decisions may be one to exercise the keenest intellects in the profession. Before giving examples of the efforts of advocates to interpret words in some desired sense, we may quote passages from two masterly judicial interpretations, made by Justice Holmes, of phrases in the Constitution of the United States.

The first, delivered when Holmes was a justice of the Supreme Court, deals with the constitutional guarantee of "the equal protection of the laws." The question to be settled was, whether the state of Virginia had the right to sterilise mentally defective patients in an asylum. The court decided that it had. *Buck v. Bell*, 274 U.S. 200 (1927); Holmes, J., for the Court.

We have seen more than once that the public welfare may call upon the best citizens for their lives. It would be strange if it could not call upon those who already sap the strength of the state for these lesser sacrifices, often not felt to be such by those concerned, in order to prevent our being swamped by incompetence. It is better for all the world, if instead of waiting to execute degenerate offspring for crime, or to let them starve for their imbecility, society can prevent those who are manifestly unfit from continuing their kind. The principle that sustains compulsory vaccination is broad enough to cover cutting the Fallopian tubes. *Jacobson v. Massachusetts*, 197 U.S. 11. Three generations of imbeciles are enough.

But, it is said, however it might be if this reasoning were applied generally, it fails when it is confined to the small number who are in the institutions named and is not applied to the multitudes outside. It is the usual last resort of constitutional arguments to point out shortcomings of this sort. But the answer is that the law does all that is needed when it does all that it can, indicates a policy, applies to all within the lines, and seeks to bring within the lines all similarly situated so far and so fast as its means allow. Of course so far as the operations enable those who otherwise must be kept confined to be returned to the world, and thus open the asylum to others, the equality aimed at will be more nearly reached.

A careful reader will not fail to note the sarcasm in the final sentence of this opinion.

The second specimen of Holmes's interpretations of the Constitution dates from 1901, when he was Chief Justice of the Supreme Court of Massachusetts. In 1898 a statute had been passed in Massachusetts which replaced hanging by electrocution. The first criminal to be sentenced to death after the enactment of the statute appealed, on the ground that the Constitution of the United States forbad "cruel and unusual punishments" and that electrocution was unusual. Penal electrocution, as a novelty in Massachusetts, incontestably was unusual, but the Court held that *unusual* must be taken with *cruel*—an excellent example of the principle that meaning depends on context. *Storti v. Commonwealth,* 178 Mass. 549 (1901); Holmes, C. J., for the Court:

The answer to the whole argument which has been presented is that there is but a single punishment, death. It is not contended that if this is true the statute is invalid, but it is said that it is not true, and that you cannot separate the means from the end in considering what the punishment is, any more when the means is a current of electricity than when it is a slow fire. We should have thought that the distinction was plain. In the latter case the means is adopted not solely for the purpose of accomplishing the end of death but for the purpose of causing other pain to the person concerned. The so-called means is also an end of the same kind as the death itself, or in other words is intended to be a part of the punishment. But when, as here, the means adopted are chosen with just the contrary intent, and are devised for the purpose of reaching the end proposed as swiftly and painlessly as possible, we are of opinion that they are not forbidden by the Constitution although they should be discoveries of recent science and never should have been heard of before. Not only is the prohibition addressed to what in a proper sense may be called the punishment but, further, the word *unusual* must be construed with the word *cruel* and cannot be taken so broadly as to prohibit every humane improvement not previously known in Massachusetts.

Forensic ingenuity of the same type, though applied to a less tragic situation, appeared in the *New Yorker* of December 7, 1946, in an account of the well-known New York law firm of Howe and Hummel. The firm was retained to defend three Philadelphia gypsies who had been arrested for performing a *danse de ventre*, described as a "lewd and lascivious contortion of the stomach." The stomach, however, said Hummel, was merely a small sac in the abdominal region, whose contortions, if any, could not be perceived except from inside the body. The case was dismissed.

The meaning of a word may be completely altered by differences in tone and emphasis, and these differences, if made clear by an able lawyer, can sometimes change the whole complexion of a case. Sir Edward Marshall Hall delivered some wonderfully acute expositions of this sort, recorded in the biography by Edward Marjoribanks, *For the Defence*. In 1900 he appeared at the Assizes at Guildford, near London, to defend a young unmarried woman on the charge of murdering her baby. She had been seduced by a married man, and before the birth of her child she left her home and found work as a laundress in another part of England. The child died ten days after birth, probably from being accidentally overlaid by the mother. She put the body in a box and left the neighborhood, but she was traced, and to the detective who questioned her she said, "I will tell you the truth. I killed it—I did not know what to do with it—I put it in a box; you will find it there." The body was found, and the mother was charged with willful murder, which she confessed to the police inspector who charged her—or so said the prosecution. Under cross-examination, however, the inspector admitted that he had never charged her with the willful murder of the child, but merely with causing its death. But the prisoner had to explain still another, and a more serious, admission. Shortly before taking the child up to bed with her on the last night of its existence, she said to the nurse who was sitting with them, "How can anyone get rid of a baby?" Marshall Hall's virtuosity in presenting the true meaning of these two admissions is a beautiful example of what can be done by a lawyer sensitive to the possibilities of the spoken language.

By cross-examination of the nurse he showed that the actual words used by the prisoner were "How can anyone get rid of a little baby like this!," and that the stress fell on the word *can*. The nurse also agreed that when the words were spoken the mother was kissing and fondling and actually feeding the child, behavior which, when taken with the altered stress of the sentence, made it seem most improbable that she was asking for advice as to how to murder it. The meaning of the admission to the detective is altered by a change in punctuation: "I killed it. I did not know what to do with it; I put it in a box." If the sentence "I did not know what to do with it" goes with "I put it in a box," the admission is much less detrimental than if it goes with "I killed it."

Marshall Hall's defence convinced the judge. "There is no doubt," said the judge, "that the prisoner was fond of her child. In the whole of my experience I have never known a case where accent had greater significance. I confess that when I read the depositions taken at the inquest I thought the girl's words were meant as an enquiry, but what Mrs. Deaker said before the magistrates was exactly consistent with what she said this morning, namely, 'How *can* anyone get rid of a baby like this!' with the accent on the 'can.' This puts an entirely different complexion on the matter. With regard to the prisoner's admission to the police-inspector, that is a very serious illustration of the difference punctuation may make to the meaning of words. 'I killed it—I did not know what to do with it.' If you make a pause there, and then go on, 'I put it in a box,' the phrase is an ugly one, inasmuch as it is perfectly consistent with, 'I killed it *because* I did not know what to do with it.' If, however, you pause after 'I killed it,' and proceed, 'I did not know what to do with it, and I put it in a box,' the import of the phrase is not nearly so serious." The jury found the prisoner not guilty without leaving the box.

SUGGESTED ASSIGNMENTS

1. A footnote in the book *Is Anybody Listening?* by William H. Whyte, Jr. and the editors of *Fortune* describes a revealing experience of Stanley Talbott, vice-president of the shoe-manufacturing firm of Joyce, Inc. For two months Mr. Talbott questioned women in Laundromats about the words that provoked in them the most intense reactions. The most "repulsive" word, he discovered, was *habit.* In the light of what you have learned about context, how would you explain this choice? For the other words, with both favorable and unfavorable connotations, see page 35 of Whyte's book.
2. A word receives its connotation as well as its denotation through the past contexts in which one has experienced it, or its referent, or both together. One powerful emotional experience may be enough to load a word with a specific connotation. The child, for example, who is badly frightened by a dog, may ever after carry the psychic scar of this traumatic experience and always feel a fearsome connotation in the word *dog.* Or a series of experiences may build up a connotation. Another child who has had a friendly and playful little dog as a pet may, as a result of repeated pleasant experiences, attach a happy connotation to the same word. Connotations seem to be much more variable than denotations. Select a word which has a strong connotation for you and write an explanation of how it acquired its connotative flavor.

FURTHER READINGS

1. Black, Max. *Critical Thinking*. Englewood Cliffs, New Jersey: Prentice-Hall, Inc., 1955. On context, see pages 190-192.
2. Fearnside, W. Ward and William B. Holther. *Fallacy, the Counterfeit of Argument*. Englewood Cliffs, New Jersey: Prentice-Hall, Inc., 1959. For a further treatment of classification, see pages 33-53.
3. *Language in General Education*. New York: Appleton-Century-Crofts, Inc., 1940. On meaning and context, see pages 94-104.
4. Lee, Irving J. *Language Habits in Human Affairs*. New York: Harper & Brothers, 1941. A highly readable introduction to general semantics.
5. Rapoport, Anatol. *Science and the Goals of Man*. New York: Harper & Brothers, 1950. On classification, see pages 70-81.
6. Whyte, William H., Jr. and the editors of *Fortune*. *Is Anybody Listening?* New York: Simon and Schuster, Inc., 1952.

5. The Sounds of Language

THE GODS WHO TROUBLE THE WATERS OF OUR VOICE STREAM

Charlton Laird

In defining language, Edward Sapir, you will remember, stressed the primacy of speech, and made the point that writing is a derived form composed of symbols once removed from the original speech sounds. Important as the written symbols are in fastening down and making more or less permanent what otherwise would be gone with the wind, they nonetheless limit our perception of the nature of language. Indeed they may actually distort our perception of it. Such basic matters as vowels and consonants, for example, are misunderstood by those who think of them in terms of the letters of the alphabet rather than in terms of the sounds themselves.

In the next essay, Charlton Laird, Professor of English at the University of Nevada, deals with matters of fundamental importance in understanding language as a system of sounds, especially with the production and classification of speech sounds. As is true in all sciences, technical terms with precise definitions are used. Though these terms may be new to you, they should not be regarded as barriers to understanding. They are necessary, and they are no more difficult than terms used in sociology or in elementary physics. The gods referred to in the title go back to the first sentence of Professor Laird's essay, the introductory sections of which have been omitted in this selection: "Whatever whimsical gods there be, not the least of their ironies is this, that language, which is often durable as the granite-ribbed hills, is built with air."

ALTHOUGH SPEECH is possible employing a stream of air which goes either in or out, and a few languages make some use of intaken breath, practically, speech relies upon an outward stream. The diaphragm thrusts upward, and the intercostal muscles contract the chest. The lungs, being compressed, expel air, which can escape only through the trachea, or windpipe. Obviously, several things can be done to this stream of air. It can be allowed to flow freely, or it can be disturbed. If disturbed, it can be disturbed in three ways: it can be stopped completely; it can be constricted; it can be made to vibrate as a column. Freely flowing air becomes normal breath; asthma and snoring, from a physical point of view, approach language, because they involve interference with the breath stream. True, snoring has little meaning, but some conversation has little meaning anyhow, so that if one wished to, he might call snoring a sort of subconscious sub-language.

The three means of disturbing the breath stream are the means by which we speak. These three are used in varying combinations, varying degrees, and are contrived by various instruments, but all speech is created by this vocal trinity. A speaker can stop the flow of air completely and then let it go, as in the letter *t*. He can constrict it so that it whistles, as in the letter *s*. He can make it vibrate while he relaxes, as in any pronunciation of the letter *a;* the pronunciation of this letter known as Italian *a* is so beloved of opera singers because it is made by the most uninhibited use of air for language. The singer has only to start his vibrating mechanism, relax, open his mouth, and having thus made himself into a sort of human saxophone, let himself go.

But how does one become a human saxophone? The key organ is the larynx, which is commonly known as the Adam's apple, just as though, deep in our subconscious, we were aware that the original sin was too much talking. This organ constitutes the upper end of the windpipe, and is made of various pieces of cartilage, elastic tissue, and mucous membrane called vocal cords, all so articulated that the membranes can be relaxed completely during normal breathing but can be contracted so that they will vibrate in pitch. The result of this vibration we call *voice*, and any sound made with the aid of these vocal cords is said to be *voiced*. You can feel the vibration by putting the tips of your fingers in the hollow of your throat and pronouncing any vowel.

Now to the sounds which we produce in speech. Roughly they may be divided into two sorts, *vowels*, in which the breath is but little constricted, and *consonants*, in which it is more emphatically constricted. Actually, there is no dividing line between the two. Some sounds are restricted so little that they cannot be very confidently called either a vowel or a consonant. For instance, of the various sounds indicated by the letter *r* in *rarer*, which are vowels and which consonants? The answer is not easy, but the distinction between consonants and vowels is traditional and familiar, and has enough reality to be useful in understanding what happens when we speak.

First, then, to the vowels. Since they are made with an almost unrestricted column of air, they must be voiced or somehow disturbed; otherwise we would not hear them. They all are voiced in English and in most other languages. Since the sound of the vowels depends upon a vibrating column of air, the differences in sound must depend upon the various ways in which the air can be made to vibrate. Here we should perhaps think of ourselves not as saxophones, but as instruments resembling a bagpipe, a slide trombone, a cornet, and a cat-tail fiddle. We can vary the stress by varying the pressure of air, as in a bagpipe. We can alter the center of vibration and the character of the vibrating column, as in a slide trombone. We can direct a column of air into different passages, as in a cornet. And we can alter the vibrations by changing the tension of the vibrating instrument, as in the cat-tail fiddle—the cat-tail fiddle being a somewhat legendary device said to have been played by grasping a tomcat by the neck and the tail, and sawing upon it as though it were a violin, increasing the tension on the tail to increase the pitch of the cat.

Of the methods of creating sounds, the most useful for our present discussion is that which permits shifting the point at which the vibration centers. In all true vowels, the vibration takes place in the mouth. If you will now pronounce slowly the words *sleek hawk*, you will notice that the vowel in *sleek* is made far forward and high up, about at the roots of the upper front teeth, and that the vowel in *hawk* is made so far back in the throat that you are almost in danger of swallowing it. Similarly, each of the other vowels has a distinctive place in the mouth at which the vibration centers. The resultant sound can be still further altered by the stress with which breath is expelled and by the shape of the oral cavity. This shape can be altered in many ways, but most noticeably by movements of the tongue, by rounding and unrounding the lips, and by the tenseness or slackness of the tongue and other muscles. Accordingly vowels can be described by the position of the vibration, the degree of stress, the degree of rounding, the degree of tenseness, and the action of the tongue.

At this point, we must become technical. Before we can go further in describing sounds, we must find out, one by one, how they are made. Furthermore, we shall need a vocabulary with which we can talk about sounds, symbols which will permit me to know what I mean to say, and you to guess what I am trying to say. We cannot very well go on with me talking about "the sound of *a* in *aunt*." That is too clumsy, and there are a variety of ways of saying *aunt*. We need symbols for sounds, and then we need an understanding of how the sounds are made which are represented by the symbols.

Both are provided by what is known as IPA, the International Phonetic Alphabet. It runs to hundreds of symbols, and with it one can transcribe phonetically, at least roughly, any language on earth, and it is used by all serious students of language the world over. Fortunately, we shall need only a small part of it. After all, we are not transcribing a tonal language like Chinese or Zapotec. A few dozen symbols will represent most sounds in English, and learning to identify them can be quite a lot of fun.

Besides, doing so is economical. After all, you have been provided with an excellent linguistic laboratory, equipped with all instruments necessary for basic linguistic research, and if you insist on leaving this laboratory locked within you unused, you are guilty of shocking waste. At worst, you ought to run a few simple experiments, just to feel you are getting some return on your anatomical investment.

Seriously, a little attention to the manner in which sounds are made is likely to open vast new understandings of language. In the following discussion, you will do well to try each of the suggestions, using your own vocal laboratory, before you go on to read the discussion of it. For instance, if you are asked to say *cat* slowly, do so, before you find out why.

So now we are ready to begin our experiments. You will recall that a page or two back we pronounced the combination *sleek hawk*,

ENGLISH VOWEL CHART

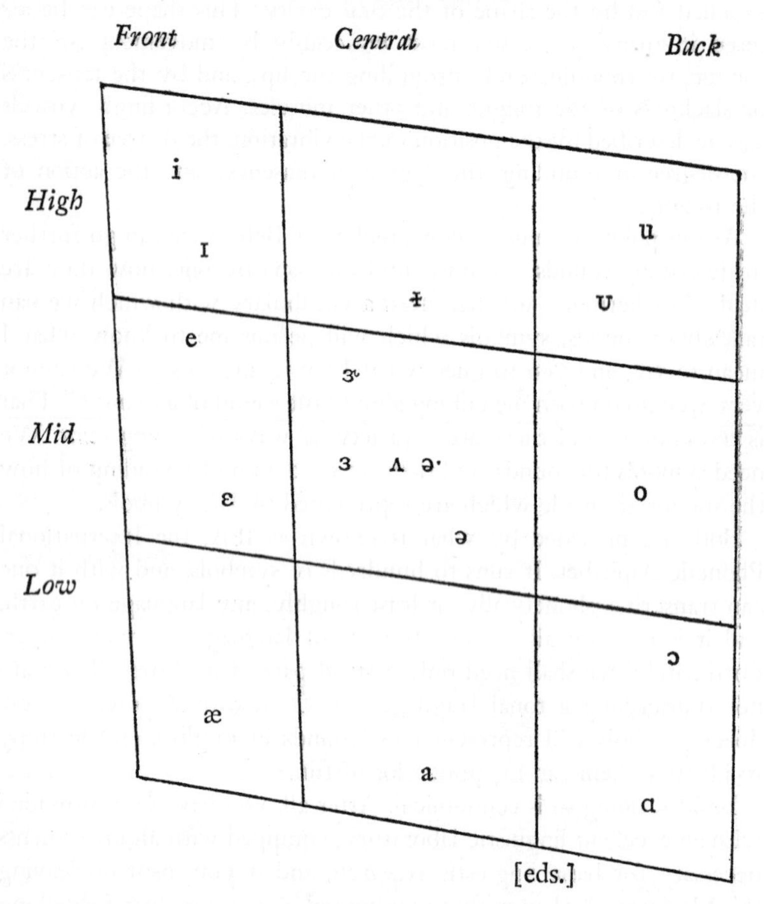

Note: Three vowels have been added which are not included in Laird's discussion: [ɨ] lower high-central unround. Called "barred i," it is often heard in unstressed positions, as in the adverb *just* (He was just here), and the first syllable of *bereave,* and the last syllable of *started.* In some dialects it occurs in stressed positions in such words as *sister, children, dinner.* [a] low-central slack. It is sometimes heard in Boston and other parts of New England, as in *ask* and *path.* It is not the [ɑ] usually heard in *father.* It is midway between [æ] and [ɑ]. [ɜ] mid-central unround. This is the vowel of *burn, first, third* as heard in parts of the South, New York City, and eastern New England; it is used by those speakers who do not use [ɝ]. [eds.]

and observed that the first vowel is pronounced just back of the upper teeth. It is tense; it cannot be pronounced without relatively strong tension in the tongue and the oral muscles. Try, for instance, to pronounce *eat* without some tenseness; it will inevitably become *it*, *et*, or *ut*. For this sound in *sleek*, the lips are unrounded. Therefore, we may describe it by calling it a high front tense unround vowel. The IPA symbol for it is [i], and you will find it appropriately placed in the diagram on the following page, which is intended to represent the oral cavity. The vowel in *hawk*, on the other hand, is a low back tense round vowel; the symbol for this sound is [ɔ]—the one my students nicknamed "the little shrimp." (To distinguish phonetic symbols from letters, they are put within brackets.)

Now try a few more sounds on your vocal laboratory. Repeat slowly the following words: *sought*, *sot*, *sat*, *set*, *sate*, *sit*, *seat*. If your pronunciation is roughly normal, you should produce a series of vowels that proceed in an orderly row along the lower side of your oral cavity, from [ɔ] to [i]. As you will observe in the diagram, the second of these vowels, the so-called Italian *a*, is written [ɑ]. The others follow in order [æ], [ɛ], [e], [ɪ], and [i]. Now pronounce consecutively, *foal*, *full*, and *fool*. This time you should produce a series of vowels that go upward along the back of your mouth; you will find them written as [o], [ʊ], and [u] in the diagram. Now say *cutaway*. In this word the first vowel is stressed, the second unstressed. As a result, the stressed sound appears a little higher than the unstressed sound, but the main difference between them is the difference in stress. They are written [ʌ] and [ə]; the latter is often called *schwa*. It is the most common sound in modern American speech, for all American unstressed vowels tend to become *schwa* or [ɪ].

This list completes the pure vowels that occur commonly in American speech. There are two groups of vowels which have peculiarities. For the first of these, pronounce the word *Herbert*. The first syllable is stressed and somewhat tense, the second unstressed and slack, but for both sounds the tongue flicks back a little; that is, these are called *retroflex* vowels. The first, the tense vowel, is written [ɝ]; the second, the slack vowel, [ə·]. And now for the diphthongs. As their name indicates, they are composed of two sounds; in Greek the word *diphthong* means "two-sounds." To observe them, pronounce slowly the words, *white house*, several times, while you listen. In each of these words a keen ear will detect that the vowel starts out as one sound and shifts to another. Almost universally, the diphthong

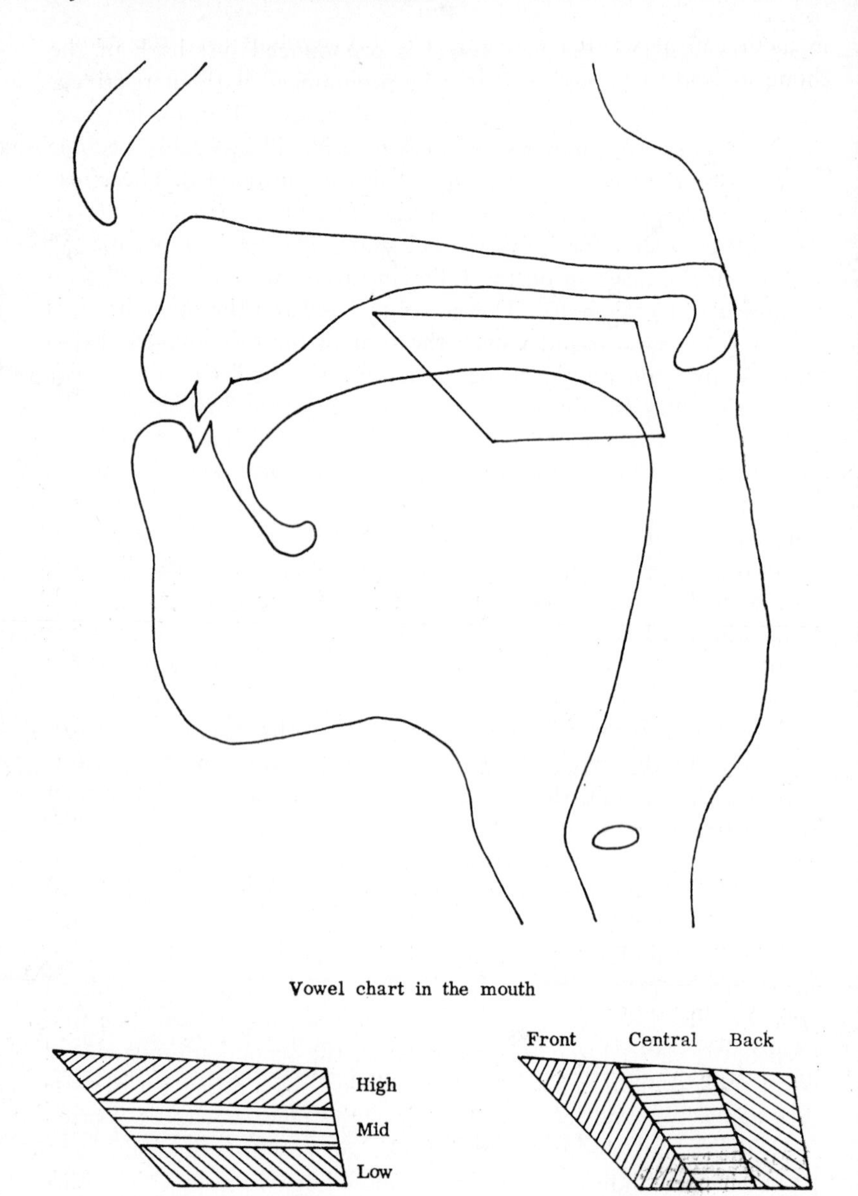

Vowel chart in the mouth

From Yao Shen, *Articulation Diagrams of English Vowels and English Consonants* (Ann Arbor, Michigan: University of Michigan, 1958). Reprinted by permission of the author, copyright 1958. [eds.]

in *white* can be written with the two IPA symbols [aɪ]; the diphthong in *house* will appear in IPA symbols either as [ɑʊ] or [æʊ].

ENGLISH CONSONANT CHART

		Bilabial	*Labio-dental*	*Inter-dental*	*Alveolar*	*Alveolopalatal*	*Velar*	*Glottal*
Stops	vl	p			t		k	
	vd	b			d		g	
Frictatives	vl		f	θ	s	ʃ		h
	vd		v	ð	z	ʒ		ʍ
Affricates	vl					tʃ		
	vd					dʒ		
Nasal continuants	vd	m			n		ŋ	
Lateral continuant	vd				l			

Note: The three glides, [w], [r], and [j], are not included in the charts since they partake of the nature of both consonants and vowels. [eds.]

So much for the vowel. Later we shall need to observe that these vowels can be classified. They vary in stress, in tenseness, in position, and in the degree of their rounding, but let us pass that for the moment, and go on to the consonants.

Returning to our earlier analysis, we can observe that consonants can be made either by stopping the breath or by disturbing it, making it explode, or making it buzz or hum. Since stopping is simpler than disturbing, let us start with breath stoppages.

We have various instruments with which we can stop the breath, but let us start with the lips. Expel a column of air, stop it with the lips, and then let it go. If you have now done this, you have produced a sound like the first part of the word *putt* or the first part of the word *but*. These are the conventional sounds of *p* and *b* in English, and of [p] and [b] in IPA.

You must distinguish here between the name of the letter *p* in spelling and the sound of the symbol [p] in speaking. If I as writer could appear for even a few seconds before you as reader, I could make this sound [p], and thenceforth you would have no difficulty understanding what is meant by a phonetic symbol. But since obviously I cannot, you will have to make the sound. It is not anything I can describe, except that I can tell you how to make it. Purse your lips as though you were to say *put;* let some air pressure build up behind the lips. Then let the air go with a slight puff, but do not say any more of the word *put* except so much as is involved in the explosion when you suddenly open your lips. This much, and no more, is embodied in [p]. It is the transcription of a sound; it is not the name of a letter in spelling.

Now for the next sound, place your tongue against the roof of your mouth, just back of the upper teeth, stop the breath column with your tongue, and let the air go in a small explosion. You should have produced either the first part of the word *tub* or the first part of *dub*, that is, the sounds [t] or [d]. Now try raising your tongue in the back part of your mouth, stopping the air, and then releasing it. You will produce either [k] as in *kick*, or [g] as in *gig*. A little girl of my acquaintance would understand this explanation. She brought home the first report card on which she had received grades more explicit than *S* for *Satisfactory* and *U* for its opposite. Her mother praised her for her good grades, saying, "I know that reading is hard for you, but I see you got *G* in it."

"Oh, Mother," the little girl replied impatiently, "that's not *gee*, that's [g]."

Here we might pause to notice a curious detail. Is it not surprising that all of these stops occur in pairs, that wherever and however you make the stop, you get two? It is curious. It is more: it is significant, and if you will use your vocal laboratory you can find out why. Put the tips of your fingers on the hollow of your throat and make consecutively the sounds represented by the IPA symbols [p] and [b]. You ought to feel a vibration in your throat with [b] that you do not feel with [p]; if you feel this vibration with [p], it means that you are not pronouncing [p] only, but are following it with a vowel.[1]

[1] You can make another test of the difference between an unvoiced (voiceless) sound and a voiced one by covering your ears with your hands and pronouncing the contrasting consonants; when you pronounce a voiced one, you will notice a buzzing sound. [eds.]

Now try the same thing with the other stops, the sounds associated with [t] and [d], with [k] and [g]. You should have vibrations with [d] and [g], very little with [t] and [k]. Now pronounce any of the vowels, several of them. You should feel vibration similar to that in [b], [d], and [g]. But the vowels, you will remember, are all voiced. Now you will suspect—if you have not suspected it already—that certain of the consonants are voiced and others are unvoiced, and this causes the difference between them. A stoppage of the air by the lips produces [p] if the sound is voiceless, [b] if the sound is voiced; a stoppage of air with the tongue at the roots of the teeth produces [t] if the sound is voiceless, [d] if the sound is voiced; farther back in the oral cavity [k] is voiceless, [g] is voiced.

Those are the stops in English, all the sounds that are made by a complete and simple stoppage of the air. Now for the sounds made by obstructing the air; since they are made by friction of air, we may call them *fricatives*. First, direct a column of air straight at your middle upper front teeth. Your mouth should be nearly closed, and the air should be channeled through your tongue, but your tongue will probably take care of itself if you just try to make the air hit your two upper central front teeth. Let the air whistle past them. You have produced either the sound of *s* or the sound of *z*, in IPA [s] and [z] respectively. You will not need to be told why these sounds appear in a pair; [s] is voiceless, [z] is voiced. Now direct a column of air at the roof of your mouth just back of the upper teeth. You have produced the central sound in either *fresher* or *measure*, the first voiceless, the second voiced. Since these sounds are not well represented in European languages by one letter, we have special symbols in IPA for them, [ʃ] for the sound of *sh*, [ʒ] for the corresponding voiced sound. Now, barely touch your upper teeth to your lower lip, and constrict air as it passes through. You have produced either the sound associated with *f* or the sound associated with *v*, the first voiceless, the second voiced, and written [f] and [v]. Now, put your tongue against your upper teeth, and constrict the air. You have produced the first consonant in either *thing* or *this*, the first voiceless and written in IPA with the Greek theta [θ], the second voiced and written with the Anglo-Saxon crossed *d* [ð]. And these are all of the fricatives common in English.

There are, however, a few more consonants. Repeat the sentence, "The *judge* went to *church*." A keen ear will detect that the consonants in *church* are neither exclusively stops nor fricatives. A very keen ear will detect that they are both, that the sounds begin with a [t], which shifts into a [ʃ]. That is, the word *church* sounds as though it should be written in English *tshurtsh*, and is written in IPA [tʃɝtʃ]. And as you will imagine, or find out by trying it on your vocal cords, the consonants in *judge* are only these same sounds voiced; that is, they sound like *dzh*, and are written [dʒ]. These sounds, which begin with a stop and continue with a fricative, are called *affricates*.

In the next set of consonants, you use your abilities as a cornet; that is, you stop your oral passage, and let the air out through your nose. Close your mouth completely, and make a sound through your nose. It was *m*, written [m]. Now stop the air by putting the forward part of your tongue against the roof of your mouth, and as before, make a sound in your nose. It was *n*, written [n]. Now stop the air farther back in your mouth, and again make a sound. It was the final consonant in *sing*, in IPA, [ŋ]. These are the common nasals in English. In French, there are more, but we manage with the three. All are made as a matter of course by voicing, and the sound you hear is the vibrating of the voiced column of air as it passes slowly through the nasal passages. This passage of air is so slow as to be almost imperceptible, but if you doubt that the air is moving, hold your nose, and then try to make the sound. If you tried it, you made no sound. This is, of course, the basis of the old joke about the man who delights in spring by saying, "Sprig is cub." His nose is stopped up, so that he cannot pronounce nasal sounds, and he makes the corresponding stops. These consonants are called *nasals*, or *nasal continuants*, or just *continuants*.

A few consonants will not be pinned down. For instance, say slowly the words *your*, *year*, and *loyal*. All the consonants here are said with so little restriction, that you may not be quite sure whether to call them vowels or consonants. You will probably notice, also, that they do not stay in one place in the mouth. There are many ways of pronouncing the sounds we indicate by the letter *y*, and perhaps even more ways of pronouncing the sounds indicated by *r* and *l*, but you will probably notice that they slip around, that they glide from one vowel to another, and, accordingly, they are called *glides*.[2] They are sometimes called semivowels, also, because they resemble vowels. The sound of *y* is written [j]; *r* and *l*, [r] and [l];

[2] Most phoneticians classify [l] as a lateral continuant. [eds.]

the semivowel *w*, [w], is little more than a rounded vowel. The sound of *h*, [h], is a voiceless breath—it is sometimes called an *aspirate*, Greek for *breath*—with enough friction far back in the mouth to make it audible. This sound is combined with [w] in words like *when*, which are spelled *wh*, but in prevailing usage pronounced (*hw*). In IPA this combination is often represented by the letter *w* inverted [ʍ]. The simplified pronunciation [w] is now heard in increasing frequency.

We have now examined the commonest sounds in English and noticed roughly how each is made. We have found that they can be classified on the basis of their production. Since we shall need names for these sounds, we had best name them, also, from the manner in which they are produced. To do so, we shall need a few terms, not many, but if you do not know them you had better fix them in mind now. We have already used the word *vowel*, and have defined *voice*, *stop*, *fricative*, *affricate*, *nasal*, and *glide*. Now we need to define a few points in the oral cavity. The ridge just back of the upper teeth is called the *alveolar ridge*. Back of this, the roof of the mouth is called the *hard palate*, referred to in the adjective *palatal*. Back of the hard palate is the soft palate, or *velum*, referred to by the adjective *velar*. Back toward the throat is the *glottis*, and this area is identified as *glottal*. These words can be combined; for instance, *alveolopalatal* would mean that the sound could be made in the vicinity of either the alevolar ridge or the hard palate. *Lateral* refers to sounds which are spread out across the width of the tongue. Other words are more familiar; *labial* refers to the lips, and *bilabial* to both lips; *dental* to the teeth, *lingual* to the tongue, and *nasal* to the nose. *Retroflex* means turned back.

With these definitions we are ready to name sounds by describing the manner in which they are made. The following list is intended for reference.

VOWELS

[i]	as in *sleek*	High-front unround tense
[ɪ]	as in *ill*	Lower high-front unround slack
[e]	as in *ate*	Mid-front unround tense
[ɛ]	as in *tell*	Lower mid-front unround slack
[æ]	as in *cat*	Low-front unround slack
[ɑ]	as in *not*	Low-back unround tense
[ɔ]	as in *hawk*	Higher low-back round tense

[o]	as in *road*	Mid-back round tense
[ʊ]	as in *full*	Lower high-back round slack, lowered and retracted
[u]	as in *mood*	High-back round tense
[ʌ]	as in *hull*	Lower mid-back unround
[ɝ]	as in *bird*	Mid-central unround retroflex
[ə·]	as in 2nd syllable of Al*bert*	Mid-central unround retroflex slack
[ə]	as in 1st syllable of *a*bove	Mid-central unround slack

CONSONANTS

[p]	as in *papa*	Voiceless bilabial stop
[b]	as in *baby*	Voiced bilabial stop
[t]	as in *tat*	Voiceless alveolar stop
[d]	as in *did*	Voiced alveolar stop
[k]	as in *kick*	Voiceless palatal or velar stop
[g]	as in *gag*	Voiced palatal or velar stop
[f]	as in *fife*	Voiceless labiodental fricative
[v]	as in *vivid*	Voiced labiodental fricative
[s]	as in *sissy*	Voiceless alveolar fricative
[z]	as in *dizzy*	Voiced alveolar fricative
[θ]	as in *think*	Voiceless interdental fricative
[ð]	as in *this*	Voiced interdental fricative
[ʃ]*	as in *she*	Voiceless alveolopalatal fricative
[ʒ]*	as in *pleasure*	Voiced alveolopalatal fricative
[h]	as in *how*	Voiceless glottal fricative (also called aspirate)
[ʍ]	as in *when*	Voiceless glottal fricative followed by voiced labiovelar glide
[tʃ]*	as in *church*	Voiceless alveolopalatal affricate
[dʒ]*	as in *judge*	Voiced alveolopalatal affricate
[m]	as in *mama*	Voiced bilabial nasal continuant
[n]	as in *nanny*	Voiced alveolar nasal continuant
[ŋ]	as in *song*	Voiced velar nasal continuant
[l]	as in *lull*	Voiced alveolar lateral continuant

* Some linguists, like C. C. Fries in the last reading of this section, use other phonetic symbols for these: [š] for [ʃ], [ž] for [ʒ], [č] for [tʃ], [ǰ] for[dʒ], [y] for [j]. [eds.]

[w]	as in *water*	Voiced labiovelar glide
[r]	as in *roar*	Voiced retroflex tongue glide
[j]*	as in *youth*	Voiced linguopalatal glide

Admittedly, the preceding discussion and this table are vastly simplified. . . . None of the characteristics mentioned here is a simple thing, and the characteristics are interreliant. Tenseness, for instance, is not one thing in all vowels which we have called tense; [i] is certainly more tense than [ɔ]. Tenseness itself is not a single thing. There is more tenseness in the tongue in [i], but perhaps more in some of the other muscles in [ɔ]. Similarly, tenseness tends to increase with stress. It tends to increase when the vowel is adjacent to certain consonants, before terminal stops, for instance. Note the difference between the vowels in *heat* and *stream.* Even the consonants are not so simple as we have made them seem. There is more than one sound for *t*, for instance, as you will see if you will say carefully, "take a step." The sound associated with the second *t* is made closer to the teeth than is the first; it uses a part of the tongue farther from the tip than does the first, and it has a little of the quality of a fricative. Even so, we should have to transcribe both sounds [t]. Similarly, the [z] in *freeze* is not identical with the [z] in *needs.* But for our purposes, the description here should be sufficiently detailed.

SUGGESTED ASSIGNMENTS

1. Make a list of words spelled with the letter *a* in which the *a* represents in each instance a different sound.
2. Many pairs of words in English are kept apart solely by the presence or absence of voicing, e. g., *bin* and *pin.* Make a list of contrasting words whose difference is solely a matter of a voiced or an unvoiced stop.
3. The letter-combination *th* in English spelling represents both a voiced and an unvoiced sound. Arrange the following words in two columns, one for the voiced *th*, the other for the unvoiced *th: heath, bathe, cloth, thing, then, thought, through, though, both, thermal, clothe, health, heathen, weather.*
4. Read aloud the following list of words written in IPA:
   ræŋ, pʊl, hoz, nɔ, ʃɝt, əlaɪv, θʌm, wɛðɚ, sit, lɔŋgɚ, hauzɪz, bam, hɪtʃ, nɔɪz, kedʒ, juθ, kwɪk, mædɚ, fɪks, but.
5. Count the different sounds in each of the following words, taking care

not to be misled by the spelling: *talk, called, judge, singer, moan, thing, latch, Lincoln, philosophy, pushed, box, finger, choose, cough.*

6. Since there are more sounds in English than letters in the alphabet, some letters represent more than one sound. Surprisingly, though, our alphabet has some excess letters. Which ones could we dispense with and why?
7. If asked to tell how the past tense of our regular verbs is formed, most people would say by the addition of *d* or *ed* to the base form, e. g., *love* plus *d* is *loved*, *walk* plus *ed* is *walked*. Such a description is based on spelling and does not accurately describe the different sounds involved. Classify the past-tense forms of the following verbs on the basis of the three different sounds used in forming the past tense: *love, walk, like, mill, hand, wash, mob, laugh, slug, mop, grant.* Examine carefully the final sound of the base form in relation to the added sound, and figure out for yourself what principle determines the classification.
8. As in the case of our regular past-tense forms, we do not accurately describe the pluralization of our regular nouns if we say that they are formed by the addition of *s* or *es*. Classify the plural forms of the following nouns on the basis of the three different sounds used in forming the plural: *move, broth, pick, smudge, path, chief, hiss, log, buzz, catch, cad, house, cat.* What principle determines the classification?

PHONETIC CHANGE: ASSIMILATION

Charles Kenneth Thomas

You probably have wondered why it is that the word cupboard, *which is obviously a compound of* cup *plus* board, *is not pronounced in accordance with its spelling. If you were to write* cubberd *for* cupboard, *you would be branded as an illiterate, even though* cubberd *represents the pronunciation, certainly as old as "Old Mother Hubbard," more accurately than the standard spelling.*

As a matter of fact, cubberd, *along with* cobbourd, cubboorde, cubbord *and others, was a common spelling during the sixteenth and seventeenth centuries. It was not until the eighteenth century that the spelling became standardized as* cupboard, *but people went right on saying* cubberd. *Clearly something interesting is at work in the spoken language that is not adequately reflected in writing.*

When we speak we do not utter a series of individuated units of sound. Rather, we speak in a continuous flow of sounds; vowels and consonants are constantly jostling each other, often blurring or wearing away the edges of adjoining sounds especially. In other words, under certain conditions phonetic changes take place. One type of phonetic change is assimilation, which Charles Thomas, Professor of Speech at the University of Florida, discusses in the following essay. An understanding of assimilation will let you in on the secret of some of the mysteries of English pronunciation.

VARIATIONS in pronunciation . . . should convince us that language is not static and uniform, but that it develops and changes. We notice this development even more if we read the literature of earlier periods. Shakespeare's English is noticeably different from our own, even though our present-day archaic spelling masks some of the differences. To understand Chaucer we must frequently refer to a glossary; to appreciate his rhythms and rhymes we must also know something about the language spoken in fourteenth-century London. To read Old English, of the time of King Alfred for instance, we must study it as we would a foreign language.

Changes in the language are usually imperceptible till afterward, and often seemingly capricious. Analysis of the historical changes shows, however, that the patterns of development are usually clear in retrospect, and that definite causes can be assigned to some of them. . . . we are going to examine one type of historical change, in order to throw light on the changeable nature of present-day speech.

ASSIMILATION

The usual pronunciation of *income* is [ˈɪnˌkʌm],[1] with primary stress on the first syllable, secondary stress on the second syllable, and a distinct syllabic division between [n] and [k]. When we use the word as an adjective, however, in the phrase *income tax*, the pronunciation may be [ˈɪnˌkʌm ˈtæks], but often it changes to [ˈɪŋkəm ˌtæks]. The reduced vowel represents reduced stress. The change from [n] to [ŋ] illustrates what is known as *assimilation*, a type of phonetic change which occurs frequently enough to warrant detailed examination.

When *income* becomes part of the larger unit, *income tax*, we scan the details more rapidly. The succession of three stressed syllables conflicts with our normal rhythmic patterns, and we weaken the second syllable from [ʌ] to [ə]. The phrase as a whole telescopes within itself, and the amount of time available for the shift from one syllable to the next is shortened. The tongue, however, requires an appreciable amount of time to shift from the alveolar contact of [n] to the velar contact of [k]. If the time is too short, the tongue anticipates the velar contact by shifting from [n] to [ŋ], since the sequence [ŋk] can be made with a single contact of the tongue, instead of the sequence of contacts required for [nk]. Furthermore, as Kent has pointed out,[2] thought constantly outstrips utterance, and this mental anticipation is closely associated with the mechanical adjustment just described.

Assimilation may therefore be defined as the process whereby one sound is changed to a second under the influence of a third;[3] in *income tax* the alveolar [n] changes to the velar [ŋ] under the influence of the velar [k]. Another useful definition is that of Bloomfield,[4] who points out that the position of the speech agents for the production of one sound is altered to a position more like that of a neighboring sound.

All assimilations start in a manner similar to that of *income tax*. The change may take place as soon as the two original sounds come

[1] For a table of phonetic symbols, see p. 235. [eds.]

[2] Roland G. Kent, "Assimilation and Dissimilation," *Language*, XII (1936), 245-58.

[3] Compare Daniel Jones, *An Outline of English Phonetics* (8th ed.; New York: E. P. Dutton & Co., 1956), pp. 217-18.

[4] Leonard Bloomfield, *Language* (New York: Holt, Rinehart and Winston, Inc., 1933), p. 372.

close together: we have every reason to suppose that the sequence [ŋk] formed as soon as the word *sank* was formed. On the other hand, the change may take place more slowly if, as in *income tax*, the sequence is brought gradually together in the act of compounding. That is, many assimilations start as accidental mispronunciations of an accepted sequence of sounds. Some never progress beyond this stage, for they may be noticeable enough to cause adverse criticism, and to induce speakers to avoid the assimilation.

A substandard pronunciation of *length* illustrates this accidental type of assimilation. The shift from the velar [ŋ] to the linguadental [θ] is apparently too great for some speakers' muscular control. Consequently the tongue anticipates the dental position, [ŋ] changes to [n] in anticipation of the following [θ], and we hear the new pronunciation [lɛnθ], rhyming with *tenth* [tɛnθ]. The pronunciation [lɛnθ] has never, however, risen to the standard level, because it has always been noticeable enough to provoke adverse criticism. Most people pronounce *length* as [lɛŋθ] or [lɛŋkθ], the added [k] serving as a kind of insulation against assimilation.

On the other hand, some assimilations are adopted so promptly and generally that adverse criticism is futile. For example, derivatives of the Latin preposition *cum* occur in English with all three nasal consonants. The original [m] of *cum* survives in such words as *combine* [kəmˈbaɪn], *compare* [kəmˈpɛr], and *comfort* [ˈkʌmfɚt]; but it has become [n] in such words as *contact* [ˈkɑnˌtækt], *condemn* [kənˈdɛm], and *constant* [ˈkɑnstənt]; and has become [ŋ] in such words as *congress* [ˈkɑŋgrəs] and *conquer* [ˈkɑŋkɚ]. A glance at the consonant which follows the nasal shows that in every word the nasal has approximated the position of the following consonant; [m] has assimilated to [n] before alveolar consonants, and to [ŋ] before velars. Many of these assimilations took place in the Latin period.

The assimilative process is essentially the same, whether in *length*, *income tax*, *condemn*, or *congress*, but the effect of adverse criticism has been selective. There was probably no appreciable criticism of the assimilations based on Latin *cum;* most of them were completely established and accepted before English adopted the words from Latin or French.

Between the extremes of accidental, substandard assimilations of the type of [lɛnθ] and established, standard assimilations of the type of [ˈkɑŋgrəs] lie a few instances on which a final verdict has not yet been made. Some people object to [ˈɪŋkəm ˌtæks]; others accept it, not only without objection, but often without even being aware that any change in pronunciation has taken place. Some people object to the assimilated [ˈhɔrʃɪʃu] for *horseshoe*; others accept it without noticing that they have lost the [s] of *horse* [hɔrs]. The fate of these and similar assimilations will be decided only in the future. In and of themselves, assimilations are neither good nor bad. General acceptance or rejection of a particular assimilation is completely irrelevant to the assimilative process.

When we consider the inherent nature of the assimilative process, we notice that in all the illustrations used thus far the preceding sound has been influenced in anticipation of the sound that follows. Though this is the most common type,[5] the direction of influence may be otherwise.

Americans who pronounce *tune* [tun] and *duty* [ˈduti] often wonder why British and Canadian speakers sometimes insert a seemingly gratuitous [ʃ] in *tune* [tʃun] and *duty* [ˈdʒutɪ]. Far from being gratuitous, these sounds represent the assimilations that sometimes develop from [tjun] and [ˈdjutɪ]. The sequences [tj] and [dj] are unstable, not because of the distance through which the tongue must move, but because of the delicacy of adjustment required. In [tʃun], the tongue has moved forward from the position of [j] to that of [ʃ], which blends more readily with [t]. In [ˈdʒutɪ], the tongue has moved forward from the position of [j] to that of [ʒ]. Thus [t] has assimilated [j] to [ʃ]; [d] has assimilated [j] to [ʒ]. The articulation of [t] and [d] is vigorous enough to move the place of articulation forward for the following sound, and the voiceless quality of [t] also carries over to the following sound. A more subtle illustration can be shown in the comparison of *rip*, *drip*, and *trip*. In *rip*, most Americans use the ordinary frictionless [r]. In *drip*, the tip of the tongue is so close to the gum ridge after [d], that a frictional allophone of [r] often results.[6] In *trip*, the allophone of [r] may be both frictional and

[5] See Roland G. Kent, "Assimilation and Dissimilation," *Language*, XII (1936), 246; Leonard Bloomfield, *Language* (New York: Henry Holt & Co., Inc., 1933), p. 372; E. H. Sturtevant, *Linguistic Change* (Chicago: University of Chicago Press, 1917), p. 49.

[6] The term *allophone* can be easily explained. The first consonant sound in *goose* is not exactly the same as the first consonant sound in *geese*. You can test this easily by whispering these sounds. Yet, though both are a *g* sound, the difference between the two never makes a difference in meaning in English. We call each of these *g* sounds an allophone of the *g*, which is called a phoneme. A phoneme is a speech sound, which may have allophonic variations, that makes a difference in meaning. Our *g* is a phoneme because it dis-

voiceless. In all these instances in which the preceding sound influences the sound that follows, classify the assimilation as *progressive.* When the second sound influences the first, as in *length* and *congress,* we call it *regressive.*

Finally, there is a third assimilative classification known as *reciprocal,* in which the two sounds influence each other and combine to produce a single sound which is a compromise between the two. The word *sure,* for instance, was formerly pronounced [sjʊr]; but the sequence [sj] required a more delicate adjustment than most speakers gave it. Consequently, the tongue slipped further back for [s] and further forward for [j], perhaps through some intermediate stage like [ʃj] or [sç], until the two sounds came together at the position for [ʃ] and gave us our present pronunciation [ʃʊr].

A similar reciprocal assimilation has taken place in *vision* [ˈvɪʒən], from earlier [ˈvɪzjən]. In *issue* and a few similar words, Americans habitually use the assimilated [ˈɪʃu]; the most frequent British pronunciation seems to be the unassimilated [ˈɪsju].[7] Similarly, the change from [hw] to [w̥] in such a word as *when* is a reciprocal assimilation in which [w̥] takes its adjustment of tongue and lips from [w] and its voiceless quality from [h].

ASSIMILATION AND VOICING

From the direction of influence in the assimilative process we now turn to the nature and varieties of the physical changes. First, assimilation may produce a change in the voicing of consonants. In *north* [nɔrθ] and *worth* [wɝθ], the final consonant is voiceless; but in *northern* [ˈnɔrðɚn] and *worthy* [ˈwɝði], the voiceless [θ] has been assimilated to the voiced [ð] by the voiced quality of the following vowels. In *thieves* [θivz], in comparison with *thief* [θif], [v] results from an earlier assimilation to a vowel which is now no longer pronounced.

Instances of the change from a voiced to a voiceless consonant are more numerous. The inflectional ending *-ed* . . . ends in [d] so long as the ending remains a separate syllable and [d] follows either of

tinguishes the meaning of *goose* from *loose, moose, noose,* and so on. A phoneme is usually written between slants, e.g., /g/, and an allophone is written between brackets, e.g., [g]. [eds.]

[7] See the 1956 edition of Daniel Jones, *An English Pronouncing Dictionary.*

the voiced sounds [ɪ] or [ə], as in *heated* [ˈhitɪd] or *heeded* [ˈhidɪd].[8] But when inflectional *-ed* becomes nonsyllabic, it remains [d] after voiced sounds, as in *begged* [bɛgd], but assimilates to the voiceless [t] after voiceless consonants, as in *baked* [bekt].

Similarly, inflectional *-es* continues to end in [z] when the ending is syllabic, as in *guesses* [ˈgɛsɪz]. When reduced to nonsyllabic status, inflectional *-es* and *-s* remain [z] after voiced sounds, as in *begs* [bɛgz], but assimilate to the voiceless [s] after voiceless consonants, as in *bakes* [beks].

A double assimilation takes place in the phrase *used to*. The verb *used* [juzd] has been assimilated to [just] by the following [t], and has acquired the meaning "formerly accustomed." The unassimilated pronunciation, with looser juncture, has been kept for the meaning "utilized." Thus, *the pen he used to* [ˈjustə] *write with* means the pen he was accustomed to write with; *the pen he used to* [juzd tə] *write with* means the pen he utilized for writing.

Something similar occurs in the phrases *have to* and *has to* when they denote compulsion. *That is all I have to* [ˈhæftə] *do* means that that is all I am compelled to do. *That is all I have to* [hæv tə] *do* means that that is all I have on hand at the moment to do. In the sentence, *That is all he has to do*, [ˈhæstə] and [ˈhæz tə] indicate the same distinction in meaning. The form [ˈjustə] is fully established in standard speech; the assimilated [ˈhæftə] and [ˈhæstə], despite their usefulness, still impress some conservatives as substandard.

A few minor instances, such as the occasional assimilation of *width* [wɪdθ] to [wɪtθ] and *breadth* [brɛdθ] to [brɛtθ], complete the list of changes from voiced to voiceless consonants. There is an element of unvoicing in the assimilation of [sj] to [ʃ] in *sure* and of [tj] to [tʃ] in *tune*, but these assimilations are primarily positional. . . .

ASSIMILATION OF NASAL CONSONANTS

Another class consists of those assimilations which involve a change in the place of articulation of nasal consonants. We have already seen this class illustrated in such derivatives of Latin *cum* as *compound* [ˈkɑmˌpaʊnd], *combine* [kəmˈbaɪn], and *comfort* [ˈkʌmfɚt], which retain the unassimilated [m] before labials and labio-

[8] The inflectional ending *-ed* is syllabic when it follows a base which ends in *t* or *d*. *Heated* and *heeded* are also pronounced [hitəd] and [hidəd]. [eds.]

dentals; and *content* [kənˈtɛnt], *condemn* [kənˈdɛm], *constant* [ˈkɑnstənt], *conquer* [ˈkɑŋkɚ], and *congress* [ˈkɑŋgrəs], which illustrate assimilation of the nasal to the place of articulation of the following consonant.

Other illustrations in this class usually depend on the loss of an "insulating" sound. After the loss, an instable sequence results, and assimilation is likely to take place. Thus if *open* [ˈopən] loses [ə] and becomes [ˈopn], it is likely to assimilate to [ˈopm], the alveolar [n] giving way to the labial [m] under the influence of the labial [p]. Similar assimilations may take place in *ribbon*, which may change from [ˈrɪbən] to [ˈrɪbn], and then assimilate to [ˈrɪbm]; in *bacon*, which may change from [ˈbekən] to [ˈbekn], and then assimilate to [ˈbekŋ]; in *wagon*, which may change from [ˈwægən] to [ˈwægn], and then assimilate to [ˈwægŋ]; in *grandpa*, which may change from [ˈgrændpɑ], to [ˈgrænpɑ], and then assimilate to [ˈgræmpɑ]; and in *pumpkin*, which may change from [ˈpʌmpkɪn] to [ˈpʌmkɪn], and then assimilate to [ˈpʌŋkɪn].

PARTIAL ASSIMILATIONS

Most of the assimilations discussed thus far are readily audible, even to speakers with little or no phonetic training. Most of them involve shifts from one phoneme to another. There remain some minor assimilations in which the change is slight enough not always to be audible to the untrained listener. Most of these changes involve only a shift from one allophone to another. Thus the [g] of *goose* has the normal contact of the back of the tongue with the soft palate. The [g] of *geese*, however, is a different allophone, partially assimilated to the front vowel [i] which follows it, and articulated farther forward in the mouth, sometimes as far forward as the back part of the hard palate. In *sing*, [ŋ] is similarly assimilated to a more forward allophone by the preceding front vowel [ɪ]; in *song*, a more backward allophone of [ŋ] follows the back vowel [ɔ]. The [t] of *eighth* [etθ], the [d] of *width* [wɪdθ], the [n] of *tenth* [tɛnθ], and the [l] of *health* [hɛlθ] are not ordinarily the usual alveolar allophones, but are usually assimilated to the dental position in anticipation of the dental [θ].

In initial sequences of voiceless consonants followed by voiced semivowels, the voicing of the semivowel may be slightly delayed by assimilation to the preceding voiceless consonant. This assimilation is most noticeable after voiceless fricatives. *Sweet* [swit] may become [sʍwit] or [sʍit]; *thwart* [θwɔrt] may become [θʍwɔrt] or [θʍɔrt]. *Sled, frame, flame, throw,* and *shred* may have voiceless or partly voiceless [l] and [r] instead of the usual voiced allophones.

After voiceless stops, the assimilative unvoicing is a little less noticeable, but *twice* [twaɪs] may become [tʍwaɪs] or [tʍaɪs]; *quart* [kwɔrt] may become [kʍwɔrt] or [kʍɔrt]; and *play, pray, tray, clay,* and *crane* may have partly or completely unvoiced allophones of [l] or [r]. *Smell* and *snail* may have partly unvoiced [m] or [n].

Except for the idiomatic phrases *used to, have to,* and *has to,* single words have been used to illustrate the assimilative process. But assimilation may also take place at the junction of words, whenever the words are spoken without a pause. Thus we may hear such assimilations as *Miss Shaw* [mɪʃ ˈʃɔ], *Miss Young* [mɪʃ ˈjʌŋ] or [mɪʃ ʃʌŋ], *did you?* [ˈdɪdʒə], *was sure* [wəʒ ˈʃur] or [wəʃ ˈʃur], and *in court* [ɪŋ ˈkɔrt]. Though the social status of some of these illustrations is not secure, it must be realized that they look stranger than they sound.

The question of standard speech is, as we have seen, quite distinct from that of assimilation. The latter is a phonetic process, continually taking place, and restricted at times by conservative opinions. Many of the results of the assimilative process have been accepted on the standard level, immediately or eventually. Some of the assimilated forms characterized in this chapter as substandard may come to be accepted as standard in the future. Others may continue indefinitely to carry the stigma of substandard usage. The classification of particular assimilations as standard or substandard is therefore but one aspect of the question of standard or substandard speech in general. Questions of standards involve the judgments of speakers and critics of the language; they must not be confused with the "natural history" of the language itself.

SUGGESTED ASSIGNMENTS

1. A device that writers use to characterize an illiterate person is to represent the way they talk, e.g., "I da wanna go!" or "I betcha can't." Often the result in print produces a humorous effect, as writers of humorous stories and comic strips well know. Examine a comic book that contains dialogue of this sort and see to what extent the distorted spelling represents assimilations that are normal in colloquial language.

Write a theme on your findings, identifying and explaining the assimilations you come across.

2. Many people have difficulty spelling words like *aggravate* and *alleviate.* If you find such words troublesome, here is where you can make your investment in the study of assimilation pay dividends. Examine carefully the following list: *accept, addict, admonish, affix, aggravate, alleviate, announce, appear, arrive, assimilate.* (a) How do you account for the double letters in all the words except *admonish?* (If you can't figure it out for yourself, consult a good college desk dictionary.) (b) What causes the spelling difficulty? (c) Arrange in columns as many words as you can that are patterned after each of the words in the list except *admonish.*
3. If you were to make a list of words patterned after *admonish,* you would probably include such words as *adapt, adhere, adjacent, adjective, adjourn, adjudicate, adjust, admire, adorn, adverb, advocate.* These words appear to be identical in structure, *ad* plus a base, yet five of them are often misspelled. Which ones are they, and what causes the difficulty?
4. In English the prefix *in-* has a double set of meanings; sometimes it means in or into, as in *inhale,* to breathe in, and at other times it has the negative sense of no, not, without, as in *incomplete,* not complete. As a result of assimilation *in-* appears in a number of other forms, e.g., *il-,* as in *illegal.* What are the other assimilated forms of *in-*? Make four lists of words, one for each of the prefix forms, and then formulate a statement that explains the conditions under which assimilation takes place.
5. One of the things we all had to learn as children was to say *feet* instead of *foots, geese* instead of *gooses.* Words like *feet* and *geese* are often referred to as irregular plurals. In comparison with words like *boys, cats, books,* and *stones,* they are irregular. But these "irregular" forms did not come about in a haphazard fashion; they are the result of a regular sound change that occurred centuries ago. With your knowledge of assimilation, and with a bit more information, you should be able to explain the presence of these peculiar plurals in English. The pattern *foot-feet, goose-geese,* you will note, reveals a contrast of back to front vowels. The problem is how to account for the fronting. In Old English the forms of *foot* looked like this:

	Singular	*Plural*
Nominative	fōt	fēt
Genitive	fōtes	fōta
Dative	fēt	fōtum
Accusative	fōt	fēt

Notice that in Old English the dative singular as well as the nominative and accusative plural contained a front vowel. If we go farther back in time to the Germanic ancestor of English, we find that the Primitive Germanic dative singular was **fōti* and that the nominative and accusative plural was **fōtiz*. Somewhere along the line **fōti* and **fōtiz* became *fēt*. Philologists speak of the change that occurred as "i-umlaut," which is just another instance of assimilation. Can you explain what assimilation took place? The same sort of thing happened with *man*, *tooth*, *mouse*, and *louse*.

SPELLING PRONUNCIATION

John Samuel Kenyon

If you pronounce the word victuals *as* vittles *and spell it as you pronounce it, your writing would be regarded as nonstandard. If you spell* victuals *and pronounce it in accordance with its spelling, your pronunciation would be nonstandard. Only if you spell it* victuals *but pronounce it* vittles *would you be using standard forms in both writing and speech. We are back once more, you see, to that knotty problem of the relationship between speech and writing. Why is it that with a word like* cupboard *you would never think of pronouncing it the way it is spelled but with* victuals, *for many people, there would be a strong tendency to do so? You can find the answer to this question in the following essay by John S. Kenyon. Professor of the English Language for many years at Hiram College, he made important contributions to the study of language, especially in the areas of speech and phonetics. He was co-editor, with Thomas A. Knott, of* A Pronouncing Dictionary of American English.

. . . PHONETIC CHANGE is concerned primarily with the spoken language, and not with the written or printed representation of it. Most phonetic change is unconscious, and some of it has begun with the illiterate and afterwards found its way into cultivated usage. As a rule the changes that have occurred have either never found their way permanently into the spelling—as seen in the word *use*, which has gained an initial j that has not appeared in the spelling; or if the spelling has been changed to express the new sound, as it was in the word *you* (formerly without *y* or j sound), this has always happened long after the new pronunciation has become firmly fixed in speech. Thus it was two or three hundred years after the final syllable ceased to be sounded on words like *sunne*, *runne*, *houre*, *seeme*, *heare*, and hundreds of others, before the spelling was changed to *sun*, *run*, *hour*, *seem*, *hear*, to correspond with the sound; and in numerous cases the spelling has not even yet conformed to changes in sound made hundreds of years ago, as in such words as *have*, *love*, *make*, *cause*, *tell*, *said*, etc. Reflection on this aspect of the development of English shows how entirely without foundation is the reasoning frequently heard when a question is raised about the pronunciation of a word: "It is spelt so and so; therefore it should be pronounced so and so." E.g., it is argued that *clerk* and *sergeant* cannot properly be pronounced **kla(r)k** and **sa(r)dʒənt** because they are spelt with *er*. Yet *clerk* is regularly so pronounced in England, and *sergeant* so generally. Such reasoning puts the cart before the horse. The logical reasoning would be, since *clerk* and *sergeant* are pronounced **kla(r)k** and **sa(r)dʒənt**, they should be spelt with *a* instead of *e*.

It happens that the spelling of most words like *star*, *carve*, *smart*, *hart*, *far*, *farm*, has, in fact, conformed to the pronunciation. These words, like *clerk* and *sergeant*, formerly were all spelt with *er*, and continued to be so written long after the sound had changed from **ɛr** to **ɑr**. . . .

Those who reason that words should be pronounced as they are spelt scarcely realize what a revolution would be wrought in present English if they carried out their rule to any extent. Transcribe the following words in a spelling-pronunciation; that is, with the pronunciation they would have if all the letters were sounded in what would seem to you their most usual way:

Among, *slough*, *brought*, *anxious*, *said*, *nothing*, *worst*, *people*, *pretty*, *brief*, *fiend*, *friend*, *money*, *could*, *bargain*, *road*, *abroad*, *scarce, farce, mouse, rouse, famous, where, here, hear, heard, beard, treat, great, leak, break, steak, ever, fever, done, gone, tone, none, whose, those, whole, whale, poor, moor, door, floor, seven, even, early, nearly, pearly, pear, fear, goer, doer, swear, answer, swore, sword, word, ford, form, worm, though, thought, tough, bough, through, home, some, mere, there, pays, says, gown, grown, down, mown, eight, height, caught, laughed, draught, evil, devil, double, doubtless, beeches, breeches, been, cloven, oven, bother, other, honor, honest, host, heir, weir, shelf, self, half,* Ralph, *revived, lived, power, mower, finger, singer, longer, anger, hanger, sorehead, forehead, hew, sew, county, country, grove, above, move, prove, over, cover, mover, all, shall, believe, sieve, wholly, jolly, surmise, promise, dully, gully, fully, pullet, mullet, goes, toes, does, shoes, frowned, owned, cross, gross, toward, coward, hearing, bearing, pouch, touch....*

The influence of spelling on standard pronunciation has been especially important since the middle of the 18th c., and especially owing to the influence of Dr. Johnson, who, though he recognized both a colloquial and a formal style of pronunciation, stated this principle: "For pronunciation, the best general rule is to consider those as the most elegant speakers who deviate least from the written words." This statement was made in apparent disregard of the utter impossibility of carrying it out in the state of English spelling then and since. His influence was strengthened by the prevailing idea of the time that the written form of the language was the language itself. This appears clearly in the dictionaries of John Walker (1791 and on), in which letters are treated as the elements of language, with "powers" of sound, as if they were a kind of seed from which the spoken language sprouted and grew, and therefore the original source to which all questions of correct pronunciation were to be referred back.

This point of view is still current and influential. Its adherents cry in triumph, "Isn't there a *t* in *often?* Why should we neglect to pronounce it?" As Dr. Fuhrken has aptly expressed it, they are willing to mispronounce words in order to show that they know how they are spelt. In addition to being fundamentally in error about the nature, origin, and growth of all language, they strangely ignore the fact that they neither do nor can carry out their own rule, as the exercise above is sufficient to show.

A spelling-pronunciation that departs from the traditional pronunciation (the one that is transmitted by word of mouth and learned by ear) is a blunder, of the same kind that it would be to pronounce *many* as **mænɪ** or **menɪ** instead of **mɛnɪ.** But when such a blunder is adopted into general good use, as was **swun,** formerly by regular sound-law pronounced **sun** (cf. *sword* **sord**), or **ˌæsɪgˈneʃən** (cf. *sign* **saɪn**), and a large number of others, it is accepted and supersedes the correct traditional form. So a very considerable number of words—though a very small proportion of all—have conformed in some respect to the spelling which happened to be current when the change was made. Such changes are, however, apt to be isolated ones, leaving unchanged many other words spelt in the same way. Thus the pronunciation **kɑnstəbl,** a spelling-pronunciation for the traditional **kʌnstəbl̩,** or **kɑmræd** for traditional **kʌmrœd,** have become isolated in pronunciation from the many other words in which **ʌ** is spelt with *o*, as *honey*, *love*, *above*, *some*, *come*, etc. In two groups, however, (1) words like *host*, *human*, *hospital*, etc., which all came into English from **OF** without a **h** sound . . . , and (2) words like *theater*, *author*, *apothecary*, etc., which came into English with **t** spelt *th*—spelling-pronunciation has changed nearly all the words to pronunciations with the **h** sound and the **θ** sound. . . .

On comparing *host*, *human*, *hospital*, with *hour*, *honest*, *honor*, and *theater*, *author*, *apothecary* with *Thomas*, *Thames*, *Esther*, an underlying principle of spelling-pronunciation is revealed. The **words that have resisted spelling-pronunciation** (*hour*, *Thomas*) **are more common words,** and therefore more likely to be thoroughly learned by children before they learn to read and write. On the other hand, if we first learn words from books, or if we see them in print oftener than we use them, we are more apt to guess at the pronunciation from the spelling. As a great many people are apt to do this, and many even cultivated and influential people unconsciously reason that words should be pronounced as they are spelt, many such spelling-pronunciations get into good use, and older traditional and phonetically natural pronunciations are gradually abandoned.

Spelling-pronunciation is especially apt to affect proper names—particularly names of places pronounced from the spelling by people who do not live in them and hence do not know the traditional pronunciation. So *Greenwich*, *Woolwich*, and *Norwich* in England are pronounced by the inhabitants of those towns **grɪnɪdʒ, wʊlɪdʒ, nɒrɪdʒ** (the latter riming with "cold pease porridge"). But people not personally familiar with the places themselves and seeing the names in print are likely to call them **grinwɪtʃ, wʊlwɪtʃ, nɔrwɪtʃ.** So *Ciren-*

cester **sɪsɪtɚ** is apt to be called elsewhere **saɪrənsɛstɚ**. *Concord* **kɒŋkəd** and *Chelmsford* **tʃɛmzfəd** are usually called **kɑnkɔrd** and **tʃɛlmzford** outside of New England. The student can easily find other examples of the same sort.

Evidence that the influence of spelling on pronunciation is increasing with the advance of popular education is seen in that in recent times in some of the places themselves the traditional pronunciation is giving way to the spelling-pronunciation. Thus the inhabitants of Cirencester and others in England are beginning to call the place **saɪrənsɛstə, -tɚ**. *Ravenna* (Ohio) is called by its old residents **rɪˈvænə**, but it is now commonly **rəˈvɛnə**. *Mantua* (Ohio) is locally **ˈmæntəˈwe**, but sometimes called **ˈmæntʊə** or **ˈmœntʃʊə** by those who depend on the spelling.[1]

The comparatively recent increase in the influence of spelling on pronunciation has resulted in the fact that certain places in England have the traditional name, often widely separated from the fixed spelling, while places in America with the same names have the more theoretical pronunciation according to the spelling. Thus we have **grɪnɪdʒ** in England, but **grinwɪtʃ** in Connecticut; the river **tɛmz** in England, but **θemz** in Connecticut, except as the English name is imitated; *Waltham* **wɒltəm** in England, but **wɒlθəm, wɔlθæm** in Massachusetts; *Edinburgh* **ɛdn̩bʌrə** in Scotland, and **ɛd(ɪ)nbɝg**, various American towns; *Marlborough* **mɔlbərə**, England, and *Marlboro* **ˈmɑ(r)lˌbɝo**, Massachusetts.

In some cases, compounding of names brings together certain letters so as to suggest sounds not found originally in the name. Thus the name *Waltham* is composed of *Walt+ham* ('home,' 'dwelling'), in the same way as *Windham* **wɪndəm**, Durham **dɝəm**; so we should expect **wɔltəm**, as we find in England. But the spelling *th* has suggested the sound **θ**, which is used in the American name **wɔlθæm**. *Chatham*, however, remains **tʃætəm**, and is often **ˈtʃœ́tˈhœ̀m** in the Ohio town and on Cape Cod, being also a spelling-pronunciation, but with a dif-

[1] Regarding the correctness of the different pronunciations, it should be remembered that a different law governs in personal and place names from that of speech in general. In the latter, general usage of the cultivated determines correctness. But in personal and place names, it is personal and local usage that determines the pronunciation. For example, all the rest of the country cannot properly change the name of Concord, Massachusetts, to **|kan|kɔrd** so long as the local inhabitants regularly call it **|kɑŋkəd**. The same principle holds in family names. See Allen W. Read. *Amer. Speech*, Feb. 1933, pp. 42-46. [The **ɒ** represents a sound between **ɑ** and **ɔ**. eds.]

ferent result. *Windham*, Vermont, is locally often **ˈwɪndˈhæm**. Similar to *Waltham* are *Eltham* in England **ɛltəm, ɛlθəm,** *Bentham* **bɛntəm, bɛnθəm,** *Walsham* **wɒlsəm, wɒlʃəm,** *Lewisham* **luɪsəm, luɪʃəm,** *Feversham* **fɛvəzəm, fɛvəʃəm.**

In personal names spelling-pronunciation is seen in *Leopold*, formerly **lɛpl̩d** (cf. *leopard*), now, from the spelling, **liəpold;** *Ralph*, formerly, and still in England **ref,** now **rælf;** *Theobald*, formerly **tɪbl̩d,** now **θiəbɔld;** *Walter*, formerly **wɔtɚ,** now **wɔltɚ.** Personal names, being applied to many individuals and families, often split up into several different forms. Thus the name *Theobald* is represented by the various forms of the older pronunciation **tɪbl̩d** in the names *Tibbits, Tibalt* (*Tybalt* in *Romeo & Juliet*), *Tibbals*, and the spelling-pronunciation **θiəbɔld.** *Walter* shows relics of its earlier pronunciation in the derivatives *Watt, Waters, Watson, Watkins.* . . .

Sometimes the spelling of a name has conformed to the earlier traditional pronunciation. So in the name *Ker, Kerr,* **kɑr,** changed in spelling to *Carr* to correspond to the sound; and vice versa, the pronunciation of other instances of the same name has conformed to the spelling *Kerr*, becoming **kɝ.** So with *Berkeley* and *Barclay*. *Berkeley* was formerly pronounced **bɑ(r)klɪ,** as still in England, and accordingly sometimes spelt *Barkley, Barclay*, while in other cases the pronunciation conformed by spelling-pronunciation to the form *Berkeley* and became **bɝklɪ.**

Of words other than names, spelling-pronunciation has changed some that have become less familiar than formerly. Often both pronunciations are used—the older traditional one, and the newer spelling-pronunciation. So it is, frequently, with a class of words having the sound **ʌ** spelt with *o*, such as *love, dove, above, come, shove*, etc. The commoner words have retained the **ʌ** sound. But the word *wont* **wʌnt,** "custom," "accustomed," is now often pronounced **wont** from the spelling. Words which formerly had **ʌ** but now have **ɒ, ɑ** from the spelling are *dromedary* **ˈdrʌməˌdɛrɪ, ˈdrɑməˌdɛrɪ,** *comrade, constable, bomb, groveling*. The old pronunciation with **ʌ** is still heard in these, and commonly in some of them.

A group of words like *fault, vault, falcon*, borrowed from French, in which the spelling with *l* is due to imitation of their Latin originals, had no **l** sound when they became English, and for long afterwards. But most of them have now conformed to the spelling; *fault* was **fɔt** in the 18th century. This accounts for the pronunciation of *Walter* mentioned above, . . .

Miscellaneous examples of spelling-pronunciation are: *steelyards,* formerly **stɪljɚdz,** now sometimes **ˈstilˌjɑrdz;** *registrar* formerly **rɛdʒɪstrɚ,** now **ˈrɛdʒɪsˌtrɑr;** *nephew* **nɛvju,** now mostly **nɛfju;** *apothecary,* formerly **əˈpɒtɪˈkɛrɪ,** now **əˈpɑθəˈkɛrɪ;** author, formerly **ɔtɚ,** now **ɔθɚ;** *soldier,* formerly **sodʒɚ,** now **soldʒɚ;** *Wandsworth,* formerly **wɒndzə,** now **wɒndzwəθ;** *Southwark* **sʌðək,** sometimes now **saʊθwək.**

SUGGESTED ASSIGNMENTS

1. The names of which states of the United States are likely to be mispronounced by foreigners because of the spelling?
2. Pronounce the following words: *blackguard, clapboard, breeches, calm, comptroller, provost marshall.* Now look up the pronunciations given in the dictionary. Which ones did you pronounce with a spelling-pronunciation?
3. Make a list of place names in your state that you think outsiders would be likely to mispronounce because of the spelling. Ask one of your college friends from a different state to pronounce the names on your list. Then tell him the correct pronunciation and note his reaction.
4. It is occasionally proposed that, because our English spelling is so wretched, the schools replace our present alphabet with a phonetic alphabet and that all publications convert to this system. Write a theme evaluating this proposal.

STANDARDS OF ACCEPTABLE ENGLISH: PRONUNCIATION

Charles Carpenter Fries

How often have you heard people criticize the pronunciaation of others? "He said abˈdōmen *when he should have said* ˈ*abdŏmen." "Did you hear that? Ac*ˈ*clīmate*! *Everybody knows it should be* ˈacclĭmate." *Or again, "He said*

From *The Teaching of English* by Charles C. Fries. Reprinted by permission of the publisher, George Wahr Publishing Company, copyright 1949.

toozdi *instead of* tiuzday." *Such self-appointed arbiters of the language are more often in error than those whom they criticize. Not because their pronunciation is wrong, but because they are under the false assumption that the pronunciation of Standard English is uniform, that there is only one acceptable pronunciation of a word. Actually the pronunciation of many words varies considerably among educated people; it varies from place to place, from group to group, and from individual to individual. A New Yorker does not speak like a Georgian, nor does a Texan speak like a Vermonter. Nor do all New Yorkers speak like each other. As a matter of fact, each individual has his own unique way of speaking. No one speaks like anyone else in every respect.*

Diversity of pronunciation is not, as was formerly thought, something to be deplored. Although linguists have long recognized diversity of pronunciation as natural and inevitable, it is only recently that their views have gained acceptance. This change in attitude is due in part to the work of Charles C. Fries, Professor of English, Emeritus, and former Director of the English Language Institute at the University of Michigan. The achievement of Professor Fries in helping to bring about a more realistic attitude toward our language as well as a more accurate description of it can not be underestimated. He is the author of numerous articles and books. Especially noteworthy are his American English Grammar *(1940) and* The Structure of English *(1952).*

"Somwhat he lipsed, for his wantonesse,
To make his English swete up-on his tonge;"

ALTHOUGH LISPING in "wantonesse" may have gone out of fashion, the effort of Chaucer's Friar "to make his English swete up-on his tonge" still lives. Some find this sweetness in imitating a few sounds of the British pronunciation of southern England; some in struggling to conquer the vowel sounds of an older New England; some in reproducing the intonations peculiar to our southern "quality." Our schools, however, seem less concerned with cultivating a charming speech than with trying to develop "correct pronunciation." And just as the rules of the common school grammars have been looked upon as the infallible guide to correct constructions so our purists in pronunciation have usually found measures of a similar character which furnished the objects of their idolatry.

The most common of these idols to be worshipped as the infallible guide to correct pronunciation is the pronouncing dictionary and those books of lesser dignity, the little handbooks of "correct speech."[1] Of course the attitude upon which this practice rests is simply another manifestation and survival of the eighteenth century views of language. The dictionaries, like the grammars, have fulfilled the function of an "academy" in setting up standards by which to judge good speech from bad. Thus whenever a question arises concerning any pronunciation the first impulse of most of us is to ask, "What does the dictionary say?" It is practically always *the* dictionary that is called for, as if there were but one; we never specify a particular one. And despite the date of publication, the pronunciation recorded in any dictionary, elementary or unabridged, or in any speech manual which happens to be at hand, is accepted as the *correct* one. Fortunately for our faith we seldom consult more than one book for the same word and thus raise no questions concerning the disagreements of the various "authorities."

To be convinced that such disagreements exist one needs only to consult the lists given in the unabridged editions of both Webster's *New International Dictionary* and the *Standard Dictionary*. In the latter the "Disputed Pronunciations" occupy pages 2763 to 2779 inclusive, a list of more than 2200 words. A similar list of something over 1600 words is given in the former dictionary, pages LIX to LXXVIII. Both lists contain only those words in respect to which the important dictionaries record and prefer essentially different pronunciations. An interesting as well as an enlightening exercise for one who has never tried it is to record first his own pronunciation of some words like those in the following list, and then to note and compare the pronunciations given in at least four different diction-

[1] Typical handbooks are Vizetelly's *A Desk-Book of 25,000 Words Frequently Mispronounced*, Pfyfe's *18,000 Words often Mispronounced*, and J. W. Abernethy's *Correct Pronunciation, a Manual of 2000 Common Words Frequently Mispronounced.*

aries:[2] *Asiatic, adult, Christian, glacial, nausea, suggest, codify, isthmus, gaseous, apron.*

Of course it would be a perfectly reasonable attitude to insist that any pronunciation appearing in any dictionary is to be approved; that where dictionaries differ the variant sounds are equally acceptable. Too frequently in practice, however, the pronunciation recorded in the particular book consulted is not only accepted as *a* correct one but as *the* correct one and all others condemned as wrong. Thus to use a dictionary as a final authority of correct pronunciation and to condemn all variations from the one or two renderings there recorded is entirely contrary to the views of the editors of our recent dictionaries,[3] if their statements as given in the prefaces fairly represent their attitude toward the marking of pronunciation.

The function of a pronouncing dictionary is to record as far as possible the pronunciations prevailing in the best present usage, rather than to attempt to dictate what that usage should be. In so far as a dictionary may be known and acknowledged as a faithful recorder and interpreter of such usage, so far and no farther may it be appealed to as an authority. . . .

In the case of diverse usages of extensive prevalence, the dictionary must recognize each of them, preferring that pronunciation which is used by the majority of the well-educated; . . .

Even when the actual usage to be adopted as a standard is determined upon, only approximation to exactness can be attained in its indication. The sounds which must be indicated by the same symbol are often subject to a considerable variation as spoken, not only by members of different communities, but also, frequently by members of the same community. . . .

There exist . . . especially in some of the vowel sounds, actual variations in pronunciation (all equally good, or allowable) that are so wide as to require special mention. Such, for example, are the sounds of *o* in *glory*, and the *a* in *vary*. The vowel sounds indicated in marking pronunciations are rarely invariable; what is marked in any case is the average or typical sound, around which the one actually spoken may vary according to conditions.[4]

[2] The four outstanding dictionaries of today seem to be *The New English Dictionary* (also frequently called the *Oxford English Dictionary*), *The Century Dictionary, Webster's New International Dictionary,* (1934) and *the Standard Dictionary.*

[3] The editors of the older dictionaries, those of the latter part of the eighteenth century and the early nineteenth century, did attempt to legislate on the matter of pronunciations. . . .

[4] *Webster's New International Dictionary* (1925), pp. XXXVIII.

Correctness in pronunciation, like correctness in diction, depends upon the consensus of usage among educated people. There are many words in the language regarding the correct pronunciation of which expert orthoepists and scholars as well as dictionaries do not agree. The correctness of English pronunciation should obviously be determined by the best and widest usage among the English speaking people.[5]

Still greater than the variation in the orthography, even the accepted orthography, of English words, is the variation in the pronunciation. . . . No attempt is made to record all the varieties of popular, or even of educated, utterance, or to report the determinations made by different recognized authorities. It has been necessary, rather, to make a selection of words to which alternative pronunciations should be accorded, and to give preference among these according to the circumstances of each particular case, in view of the general analogies and tendencies of English utterance.[6]

From the composite character of the English Vocabulary, the pronunciation, also, of many words is in a very unsettled state. This is the fact not merely with words from other modern languages, the pronunciation of which depends largely upon the linguistic knowledge and taste of the person who uses them, but also with derivatives from Latin or Greek, for which there exist two or more analogies. . . . The conflict of analogies, or the absence of any analogy, appears still more in purely scientific words, in which there may be said to be no general standard of pronunciation. The Editor was once present at a meeting of a learned society, where, in the course of discussion, he heard the word *gaseous* systematically pronounced in six different ways by as many eminent physicists.[7]

Two more considerations must be kept in mind in our attempt to judge the dictionaries as measures of correct pronunciation. It is to be noted, first, that although all these editors insist that correctness of pronunciation must rest fundamentally upon usage there has never been a comprehensive and scientific survey of English pronunciation and thus the records offered in any book are necessarily limited to the observations of the particular staff who worked on it. Our trust in the validity of the markings must depend solely upon our faith in the *opinions* of those individuals who edited the dictionary. More than that, all agree that usage in the matter of pronunciation is continually changing. As a record of usage, therefore, any dictionary, by the time the material has been collected and printed, and the books offered for sale, is already behind the times. In some respects,

[5] *The Standard Dictionary*, p. XII.
[6] *The Century Dictionary*, p. XIII.
[7] *The New English Dictionary*, p. XXIV.

at least, usage will have changed and the printed record be inaccurate.

Second, most of us need to be reminded that all our dictionaries (with the exception of the great *Oxford English Dictionary*) have been the product of private business enterprises. Quite frankly the purposes of these firms have been neither philanthropic nor scientific; they have invested capital in the making of books that would sell and return a profit. In line with good business policy they have sought the best editors and staff they could secure for the salaries they could afford to pay but have seldom attracted to the actual work of dictionary making the very best scholars in the field of English language.[8] The particular materials to be included in the dictionaries have been dictated primarily by the practical considerations of selling values. As a policy, no such dictionaries, even for the sake of scientific truth and language accuracy, could afford to oppose the prejudices and the common beliefs of the school public which buys the dictionaries. That public has demanded an authoritative standard of pronunciation and the dictionaries have in practice provided it[9] despite the careful statements of some editors to the contrary. Our blind faith in *the dictionary* as the authoritative measure of right and wrong in pronunciation has called forth from our scholars in the English language such statements as the following from the late Professor T. R. Lounsbury of Yale University:

> It seems never to have occurred to any of the compilers of dictionaries, and to but few of those who consult them, that the simple solution of the whole difficulty is that in the matter of pronunciation there is no standard of authority at all. Nor, as things now are, can there be. Pronunciation must and will vary widely among persons of equal intelligence and cultivation. A dictionary which sets out to establish on a solid base an authoritative standard is bound to take into account the practice of the whole body of educated men the world over who are entitled to consideration. How is that to be ascertained? The mere statement of the fact shows its physical impossibility. It is a task beyond the power of any one person or any number of persons to accomplish.
>
> Even this is not the worst. If everybody worth consulting could be consulted, we should still be left in precisely the same state of uncertainty in which we were before. . . . Still this belief in the existence of a standard

[8] This situation has improved considerably in the past few years. There are now a number of good dictionaries that have been prepared with the help of competent linguistic scientists. [eds.]

[9] G. & C. Merriam Company advertise *Webster's New International Dictionary* as "The 'Supreme Authority'."

authority is one that will die hard even with the educated class. With the semi-educated class it will never die at all.[10]

A second idol reverenced by many as a sound guide to correct pronunciation is the spelling. Mr. Vizetelly says, for example,

> Unfortunately, we have with us a large class of persons who speak without thinking how our words are spelled, and who, therefore, squeeze all the juice out of our speech by refusing to enunciate carefully all the niceties of sound that the words contain.[11]

It seems also to be a regard for the spelling which lies at the basis of such rules as the following:

> Pronounce clearly and distinctly the first syllables of words beginning with *be* or *de:*

de cide	*not*	di *or* duhcide
de note	*not*	di *or* dunote
de test	*not*	di *or* duhtest
be lieve	*not*	bi *or* buhlieve

> Pronounce carefully the final syllables in the following words:

fountain	*not*	fountun
mountain	*not*	mountun
certain	*not*	certun
Boston	*not*	Bostun
pupil	*not*	pupul
angel	*not*	angul
hovel	*not*	hovul[12]

From this point of view it is insisted that the *spelling* demands four syllables in the pronunciation of *usually* and three in *every;* that there must be no "p" in *warmth*, or in *something*, or in *comfort;* that *Arctic* has a *c* in the first syllable and must therefore be pronounced [arktɪk];[13] that *recognize* is spelled with a *g* and is therefore correctly pronounced [rɛkagnaɪz]; that in the words *hundred* and *children* the *r* precedes the *e* in the final syllable and therefore these words must be pronounced [həndrɛd] and [čɪldrɛn] not [həndərd] and [čɪldərn]; and finally that the vowels in the unstressed syllables of words, to be pronounced correctly, must be given the sounds of the letters with

[10] T. R. Lounsbury, *The Standard of Pronunciation in English*, pp. 213-216.

[11] F. H. Vizetelly, *A Desk-Book of 25,000 Words Frequently Mispronounced*, p. VIII.

[12] Annie E. Polk, *Better Speech*, p. 13.

[13] For a table of phonetic symbols, see p. 235. Note that Fries later uses [ər] for [ə˞]. [eds.]

which they are spelled and not reduced to the obscure and colorless [ə] sound.

This view underlies the arguments offered in many discussions of correct pronunciation although it is not often expressly stated as a general principle. In attempting to test its validity three considerations demand attention.

First, the editors of at least three of our most important dictionaries have, in the prefaces to those works, made vigorous statements condemning the approach to modern English pronunciation through the spelling.

> The pronunciation is the actual living form or forms of a word, that is, *the word itself*, of which the current spelling is only a symbolization —generally, indeed, only the traditionally-preserved symbolization of an earlier form, sometimes imperfect to begin with, still oftener corrupted in its passage to our time. . . .
>
> In modern English speech, vowels are regularly obscured in syllables that have neither primary nor secondary stress, especially in those that follow the main stress; they then approach, or fall into, the sound of the mid-mixed vowel or [ə].[14]
>
> One of the most peculiar characteristics of English pronunciation is the way in which it slights the vowels of most unaccented syllables, not merely lightening them in point of quantity and stress, but changing their quality of sound. To write (as systems of re-spelling for pronunciation, and even systems of phonetic spelling generally do) the vowels of unaccented syllables as if they were accented, is a distortion, and to pronounce them as so written would be a caricature of English speech.[15]
>
> The spoken form of language is always more changeable than the written form, and changes in pronunciation are only slowly reflected in the spelling. Moreover since the invention of printing, English spelling has tended to become more and more conventional and fixed, while changes in pronunciation have continued. One has only to call to mind such common words as *busy, bosom, colonel, women, bough, enough, tough, night,* to realize how unphonetic their spelling is with reference to their present pronunciation. Again the written forms of some words, as *mountain, fountain, evil, devil, often, soften, Christmas, chestnut, handsome, handkerchief,* more nearly phonetic, mislead many persons, who feel that they should speak as they write, into pronunciations that depart from the best usage by making *-tain* rime with *rain, -il* rime with *hill,* by sounding the *t* in *often, Christmas,* etc.[16]

[14] *The New English Dictionary*, Preface, p. XXIV.
[15] *The Century Dictionary*, Preface, p. XIV, XV.
[16] *Webster's New International Dictionary* (1925), p. XXXVIII.

Second, the general principle of "pronouncing all the letters of our words as they are now spelled" is not only incapable of any wide application because of the acknowledged unphonetic character of the spelling of many words but it is also incapable of consistent application even in any narrow group of words. Not even the strongest advocate of spelling as the guide to pronunciation would dare sound the following words as they are spelled: *deign, sovereign, foreign, doubt, debt, island, aisle, know, knight, knee, knave, mortgage, any, many, English, two, whole, fatigue, tongue, ghost, does, calm, limb, lamb, sepulchre, choir, answer, sword, write.* Nor can one pronounce in any single way the same groups of letters. What, for instance should be the single sound given to the combination *ing* in the following words: *singer, finger, ginger?* What sound for the *eo* spelling in *Leopold, leopard, pigeon* and *people?* If *hoof, roof, root,* because of the *oo* spelling, must be pronounced as [huf], [ruf], [rut], and never [hʊf], [rʊf], [rʊt], should we consistently demand the same pronunciation of the following words which historically had the same vowel sound and retain a similar spelling, *book, good, stood, hood, hook?* I did find one teacher, and that in a large city school system, who with the courage of strong conviction was bound to be consistent. She insisted that the word *laughter* since it was spelled like *daughter* and *slaughter* must be pronounced in similar fashion, thus [lɔtər], and was drilling her pupils to pronounce it that way.

Even in the matter of following in pronunciation the order of the letters as they stand in the spelling one can hardly be consistent. He may say [həndrɛd] and [čɪldrɛn]; he may even school himself to say [eprən] rather than [epərn] for the word *apron.* He will hardly, however, say [airən] for the word *iron* rather than [aiərn]. If he does he invents a pronunciation, one not recorded in any of our dictionaries nor heard in the usage of people.

As a third consideration respecting the validity of spelling as a guide to correct pronunciation one must view a few of the important facts in the history of English spelling.[17] "How came we to spell as we do, and how is it that the written symbol so frequently gives a

[17] The history of English spelling is treated at some length by W. W. Skeat in *Principles of English Etymology,* First Series, Chapter XVI (pp. 294-333), and is touched upon by A. J. Ellis in *Early English Pronunciation,* Chapter VI (pp. 565-632), and by Henry Sweet in *A History of English Sounds,* pp. 59-73.

totally false impression of the true sound of the spoken word?" Although the writing of French shows probably a greater "divergence between sound and symbol," "English shows the maximum of irregularity and arbitrariness."[18] During the Old English period (*i.e.*, before 1100 A. D.) and even during a large part of the Middle English period (1100-1500) the spelling of English was fairly phonetic and changed with the changing pronunciation. Consistency of spelling was not then a virtue. Chaucer, for instance, spells the word *high* in three different ways within a space of fifty lines, thus:

and hye on horse he sat	A-271[19]
and ful of hy sentence	A-301
and for his heigh renoun	A-316

Differences in spelling usually furnished some evidence of differences in sound. Even at this time, however, the spelling not only lagged behind changes in pronunciation, but it had been subjected to such treatment as further to spoil its phonetic accuracy. The practice of doubling vowel letters to indicate vowel length (hōf—hoof, hrōf—roof, bōk—book, cwēn—queen) was only partly carried out as was also that other practice of doubling the consonant after a short vowel (biter—bitter, soper—supper, somer—summer). Many long vowels still remained single in spelling and many short vowels were still followed by single consonants (meddle, medal; mettle, metal; copper, proper). The respelling of the language by Anglo-French scribes in the thirteenth and fourteenth centuries accounts for many changes from the particular letters in use during the Old English period. Thus, for example, *cw* was replaced by *qu*, þ and ð were replaced by *th*, and *c* was used at times to represent the sound [s].

The two most important facts in the development of English spelling for our view here, however, are matters of the fifteenth and sixteenth centuries. First, the introduction of printing and the increase of books worked to crystallize or conventionalize the spelling and prevent it from further adapting itself to the pronunciation. From the printers' point of view the ideal spelling is one that is absolutely uniform and unchangeable. It has been this influence that has led to the setting up of "correct" spelling and adherence to this *uniformity* as a skill to be cultivated.

[18] Encyclopædia Britannica, article *Phonetics*, 11th edition, Vol. 21, p. 459.
[19] This instance should probably not be included, for *hye* is here an adverb, not an adjective as it is in the other instances.

At the time that the influence of the printers was making for a hard and fast system of spelling, the so-called "etymological" idea was introduced. The sixteenth-century pedants, who were enthusiastic for the classics, attempted to find traces of Latin in English words. Some, indeed, insisted that all the English language came from Latin. In order then to render this connection between English and Latin words more evident to the eye they changed the spellings of many words. Of course this kind of etymologizing could be applied to but a part of the language. It was the learned words rather than the very common words which were thus treated to "etymological" spelling. Unfortunately the scholarship of these pedants was unequal even to the task of dealing with the learned words of the vocabulary, and they introduced many errors. Thus an *s* was inserted in the word *island* to show a connection with the Latin word *insula*, although *island* (spelled by Chaucer *iland*) is not in any way related to *insula* but is in fact a good old Anglo-Saxon word, *ig-land*, meaning *water-land*. Many of these errors still exist and account for some of the worst of our present spellings; witness, for instance, the *g* in *sovereign* and in *foreign*.

English spelling since the sixteenth century has been dominated by two principles. The phonetic principle has applied to popular words and the so-called "etymological" principle has applied to the more learned words. But neither principle has been carried out consistently even in its own province. More than that, pronunciation changes since the sixteenth century have been very great while spelling changes have been comparatively few. We have thus today a petrified system of spelling which very imperfectly represented the pronunciation of English during the time of Shakespeare but is now used to represent a twentieth century pronunciation. With such a situation, despite the fact that there is enough phonetic connection between the written symbols and the word sounds to enable us to guess approximately the pronunciation of many words we cannot ever be sure as to any particular word and we cannot by any means accept the view of Dr. Johnson "to consider those as the most elegant speakers who deviate least from the written words."[20]

In addition to dependence upon the spelling as the basis for determining the proper sounds of words and the reverence for the pronouncing dictionaries as the authority, there is a third idol very

[20] Samuel Johnson, Preface to *Dictionary*, 1755.

generally worshipped as a guide to *correct* pronunciation. It is the principle that borrowed words must continue their sounds from the language from which they come. From this point of view it is asserted that the only correct pronunciation for a borrowed French word is the sound which that word has in French; that the "analogies" of the Latin language should determine the pronunciation of Latin words in English. Thus in application of this view, it is demanded that *inquiry* should be pronounced [ɪ'nkwaɪ rɪ] never [ɪ'nkwɪrɪ]; that *acclimate* must be [æklaɪ'mɪt] never [æ'klɪmet]; that *arbutus* must be stressed on the first syllable and *abdomen* on the second. By similar reasoning it is insisted that *prestige* must be pronounced [prɛsti'ž] never [prɛst'i'ǰ], and *garage* always [gəra'ž] never [gəra'ǰ] and certainly not [gæ'rɪǰ].

As a matter of fact it is the borrowed words in our language which cause many of the problems of pronunciation. English has an immense number of these foreign words from many sources. Nearly half of our vocabulary is made up of words from the Latin language, if we include as Latin element both direct borrowings from Latin itself and also those words that have come through French. Some of these borrowed words remain learned words, restricted in their use to those people who are likely to have some familiarity with the language from which they come. These words cling to their foreign sounds and accent even after centuries of use. Thus *caprice*, a seventeenth-century borrowing, shows in usage no signs of shifting from its present pronunciation, [kəpri's]. It is not a word used by the ordinary man of the street. On the other hand, words which become popular and are used by many who are unfamiliar with the sounds of the foreign language tend to a pronunciation adjusted to English sounds and English stress. Thus the word *garage*, although of comparatively recent importation, is used by people of all stations in life for almost every family has one. The Englishing of the pronunciation of this word has come rather quickly. In many communities it has become [gæ'rɪǰ]; certainly [gəra'ǰ] is more general than [gəraž].

As a principle to guide pronunciation the attempt to continue the foreign sound of a borrowed word is impossible of consistent application.[21] Even those who are most careful to observe the foreign

[21] It is really impossible for most of us to jump suddenly into the speech pattern of a foreign language in the midst of an English sentence. Our rendering of the pronunciation of a foreign word is, therefore, only approximately cor-

sounds of the comparatively few words to which their attention happens to be directed would not, in accord with that principle, insist upon stressing the following words on the next to the last syllable, *audi'tor*, *ora'tor*, *sena'tor*, *victo'ry*. If this principle is sufficient ground for condemning the pronunciation [gæ'rɪǰ] as incorrect, then to pronounce *courage* and *carriage* as most of us do is equally incorrect. Even in the matter of foreign proper names the principle of preserving the foreign pronunciations cannot be maintained in the cases of names that become very generally used. The word *Paris* is a case in point, or the name *Beatrice*.

In passing, we need but call attention to the fact that most of those who cling to the belief that a word borrowed from another language is correctly pronounced only when it maintains the foreign sounds apply the principle only to words from those languages with which they happen to be familiar. Words from Arabic or Hebrew or the American Indian languages are Englished with no apologies. In the pronunciation of the many foreign words in our language, therefore, we cannot accept this principle as the standard of acceptable pronunciation.

If, then, we must repudiate all three of the measures of correct pronunciation so commonly used what can we offer as the standards of acceptable English speech? First of all, the actual sound of the word as it is heard in the present usage of English speakers, not the spelling, not the etymology, must be the basis of all the "correctness" there can be in pronunciation. The *practical* standard of pronunciation must thus be the speech of those we actually *hear*. With the development in means of communication, increasing travel and moving from place to place, and especially the rapidly spreading use of the radio, these personal contacts are likely to have a much wider range than formerly and, as a result, there ought to be an increasing number of people with speech characteristics of approximate similarity. Certainly those who carry on the affairs of English-speaking people are now more frequently and more widely heard by voice than could have been possible in preceding times. I should insist,

---

rect, rarely accurate. See, for instance, the comment of Jespersen in *How to Teach a Foreign Language* (p. 92).

"Let me remark in passing that I have always given my pupils French names [in classes in French] immediately in one of the first lessons; . . . the teacher has the advantage of being able to use their names in the middle of a French sentence without marring the run of the language."

then, that the pronunciations common in the usage of those in positions of influence and respect must furnish the starting point for determining what is acceptable English in respect to pronunciation.

When one examines this usage, even superficially, he discovers very soon that the same word is frequently pronounced differently *by the same person* when used in differing circumstances. We must conclude, then, that there is no *one* pronunciation of a word that is the true pronunciation for that word under all circumstances. The amount of stress given the word in a sentence and the character of the surrounding sounds must organically affect the pronunciation. The word *him*, for instance, stressed in such a sentence as "Give it to hím, not to Máry," has a very distinct initial [h]. But in the following sentence, with a heavy stress on the words *to* and *from*, "Give it tó him—don't take it fróm him," the initial aspirate disappears and the word becomes [ɪm]. Again, no one actually speaking *English* would give the same sounds to both the conjunction *that* and the demonstrative *that* in such a combination as "in order *that that* nation might endure." This difference between the sounds of words when pronounced alone or under stress and when sounded in an unemphasized part of a sentence the dictionaries generally recognize. Such recognition, however, is usually expressed only in the preface and most of us miss it.

> The difference between the pronunciation of a word when taken alone and as it occurs in a sentence should also be kept carefully in mind; thus *and* considered alone is *and*, but in such a combination as *bread and butter* it is usually weakened to *'nd*, or even to *'n; a* in the phrase *for a day* becomes ȧ (sof′ *ȧ*), etc.[22]

Again, even a superficial examination of the pronunciation of those speakers of English in positions of respect and influence reveals also the fact that there are many differences in these pronunciations from speaker to speaker. The lists of the so-called "disputed pronunciations" in our dictionaries (see above page 256) offer some evidence for this assertion. As in the case of grammar, the problems arise out of these differences of usage. It is because many people who rightfully claim our respect pronounce the word *suggest* [səǰɛst] and many others meriting equal respect insist on the pronunciation [səgǰɛst] that we raise the question as to which is the *correct* sound. When these differences amount to more than mere individual pecu-

[22] *Webster's New International Dictionary* (1925), p. XXXVIII.

liarities and become really significant divisions of usage, one can maintain the following point of view:

(1) Where this general spoken usage differs in respect to the sound of any word, no *one* pronunciation is the *sole* correct one. The several pronunciations in actual usage are thereby acceptable.[23]

(2) In such cases of divided usage, however, a reasonable choice may be made in accord with the following considerations:

(a) In the matter of borrowed words, for that pronunciation which is in harmony with English sounds and English accent.

(b) For that pronunciation which is in harmony with the tendencies of English speech in the matters of unstressed vowels, and organically phonetic assimilations of consonants.

Concerning the unstressed vowels the quotations from *The New English Dictionary* and *The Century Dictionary*, given above on page 261, indicate the practice in English.

Phonetic assimilation in the case of consonants is illustrated in part by the following quotation from *The Century Dictionary*.

On the side of consonant utterance, there is a very large class of cases where it can be made a question whether a pure *t* or *d* or *s* or *z* is pronouncd with an *i*- or *y*-sound after it before another vowel or whether the consonant is fused together with the *i* or *y* into the sounds *ch, j, sh, zh* respectively—for example, whether we say *natūre* or *nachur, gradūal* or *grajöal, sūre* or *shör, vizūal* or *vizhöal.* There are many such words in which accepted usage has fully ranged itself on the side of the fused pronunciation: for example, *vizhon*, not *vizion*, for vision; *azhur*, not *azūre* for azure; but with regard to the great majority usage is less decided, or else the one pronunciation is given in ordinary easy utterance and the other when speaking with deliberation or labored plainness, or else the fused pronunciation is used without the fact being acknowledged.[24]

Other examples of such assimilations are the following pronuncia-

[23] The very definite use of ambiguous symbols in the dictionaries would substantiate this view. In the Preface of the *New English Dictionary* (p. xxiv) we have the following, "The vowel in p*a*ss, comm*a*nd, variously identified by different speakers with *a* in m*a*n, and *a* in f*a*ther, is symbolized by the avowedly ambiguous *a̱*. Similarly, the doubtful length of the *o* in *o*ff, s*o*ft, l*o*st (by some made *short* as in g*o*t, by some long as in C*o*rfe, by others medial) is indicated by ǫ̀." In this connection I must again call attention to the fact that I am in these chapters discussing standards of *acceptable* English, not the problem of *beautiful* or *artistic* language

[24] *The Century Dictionary*, Preface, p. xiv.

tions: *chestnut* as [čɛsnət], *friends* as [frɛnz], *something* as [sʌmpθɪŋ], *length* as [lɛŋkθ], *ink* as [ɪŋk], *handkerchief* as [hæŋkərčɪf], *pumpkin* as [pʌŋkɪn].

(c) For that pronunciation which maintains a careful discrimination of those sounds that the English speech pattern uses to distinguish many meanings. Two quotations may aid to clarify this point although it is by no means simple.

The latitude of correctness is very far from being the same in different languages. Some sounds in each language move within narrow boundaries, while others have a much larger field assigned to them; each language is punctilious in some, but not in all points. Deviations which in one language would be considered trifling, in another would be intolerable perversions."[25]

The voiced or voiceless character of the consonants and the quality of the vowel sounds in stressed syllables are examples of such important points in the English speech pattern. Thus, for instance we distinguish many words simply by a differentiation of a single vowel sound: heat [hit], hit [hɪt], hate [het], hat [hæt], hut [hət], hot [hat], hoot [hut], height [haɪt]. Examples of differentiation by means of voicing only are the following: pin-bin, tin-din, cold-gold, fine-vine.

The second quotation touches my point from another angle:

I found that it was difficult or impossible to teach an Indian to make phonetic distinctions that did not correspond to 'points in the pattern of his language,' however these differences might strike our objective ear, but that subtle, barely audible, phonetic differences, if only they hit the 'points in the pattern,' were easily and voluntarily expressed in writing. In watching my Nootka interpreter write his language, I often had the curious feeling that he was transcribing an ideal flow of phonetic elements which he heard inadequately from a purely objective standpoint, as the intention of the actual rumble of speech.[26]

If the view of English pronunciation given in this chapter has any validity it must be evident that in dealing with matters of pronunciation, especially in attempting to determine what is acceptable English speech, it is well to cultivate the virtue of tolerance. There is comparatively little difficulty in settling upon some one pronunciaion for any word that must be acknowledged acceptable. Justly to render a

[25] Otto Jespersen, *Language*, p. 283.
[26] Edward Sapir, *Language*, p. 58 (footnote).

negative judgment, however, to condemn any pronunciation that one hears generally used, demands much greater caution as well as knowledge. The suggestions here given as considerations to guide one's choice in matters of divided usage are to be taken as standards of acceptable pronunciation only from the positive point of view. It must not be assumed that all other pronunciations are necessarily unacceptable.

SUGGESTED ASSIGNMENTS

1. The following passage is taken from the Preface to *A Critical Pronouncing Dictionary and Expositor of the English Language* by John Walker (1732-1807), a lexicographer whose work was highly regarded during the first half of the nineteenth century:

   > . . . If the analogies of the language had been better understood, it is scarcely conceivable, that so many words in polite usage would have a diversity of pronunciation which is at once so ridiculous and embarrassing: nay, perhaps it may be with confidence asserted, that if the analogies of the language were sufficiently known, and so near at hand as to be applicable on inspection to every word, that not only many words which are wavering between contrary usages would be settled in their true sound, but that many words, which are fixed by custom to an improper pronunciation, would by degrees grow regular and analogical; and those which are so already would be secured in their purity, by a knowledge of their regularity and analogy.

   Write a theme in which you discuss (1) the assumptions held by Walker, and (2) the fallacies involved in his solution to the "ridiculous and embarrassing" problem.

2. In each of the following pairs of sentences the "same" word is used, but the pronunciation is not the same. Read each sentence aloud in a natural, conversational tone and rhythm.

   a. Yes, they *are!*
   b. They *are* at the station.

   c. She is good to look *at.*
   d. Look *at* him go!

   e. You should do everything you *can.*
   f. I *can* see it in the distance.

   g. He gets better from *day* to *day.*
   h. Sun*day* is the best time.

   i. Who is it *for?*

j. Look *for* the answer in the book.

k. Look at *him*, not her.
l. I saw *him* at the station.

m. He is a *just* man.
n. *Just* a minute, I'm coming.

o. *There* he is.
p. *There* were three of them in the room.

How, specifically, does the underlined word in the second sentence of each pair differ in pronunciation from its counterpart in the first sentence? What causes the difference?

3. Pronounce each of the following expressions in a natural, conversational way:
   a. snow and ice
   b. cup and saucer
   c. bread and butter
   d. up and down
   e. jack and queen
   f. this and that, not this or that

   How many different pronunciations did you have for *and?* How many of these different pronunciations of *and* are listed in your dictionary? Who is right, you or the dictionary?
4. Examine one of the How-to-Improve-Your-Speech books written for the popular market and available in most drugstores and supermarkets. Write a theme on the discussion of pronunciation which you find in it. You might consider some of the following points: a. Is pronunciation discussed in terms of isolated words or of actual running speech? b. What attitude, if any, is expressed toward assimilation? c. Is any mention made of the desirability of adapting one's speech to various situations?
5. Force yourself to listen for fifteen minutes to a radio announcer or commentator who you think has speech mannerisms that cause you to react negatively to him or her. Prepare a talk in which you analyze the reasons for your reactions, citing specific evidence from the program. If you could tape-record the program, it would be helpful in illustrating your points.
6. In *College English*, October 1951, there is an article entitled "The Eye, the Ear, and the Misspelled Word." The main idea of the essay is that misspelling is often the result of mispronunciation. Read the essay, examine the evidence presented, and then write a theme in which you evaluate the author's position.
7. Write a theme in which you discuss tendencies leading toward greater uniformity of pronunciation in the United States.

FURTHER READINGS

1. Bronstein, Arthur J. *The Pronunciation of American English.* New York: Appleton-Century-Crofts, Inc., 1960. On standards of pronunciation, see pp. 3-18; on assimilation, pp. 207-215.
2. Hall, Robert A., Jr. *Linguistics and Your Language.* New York: Doubleday & Company, Inc. (Anchor Books), 1960. On the sound-system, see Chapter 6.
3. Kenyon, John Samuel. *American Pronunciation,* 10th ed. Ann Arbor, Michigan: George Wahr Publishing Company, 1961. On the sound-system, see especially pp. 33-73; on assimilation, pp. 76-80.
4. ——— "Cultural Levels and Functional Varieties of English," *College English,* Vol. 10 (October 1948), pp. 31-36.
5. Robertson, Stuart and Frederic G. Cassidy. *The Development of Modern English.* Englewood Cliffs, New Jersey: Prentice-Hall, Inc., 1954. On the sound-system, see pp. 52-76; on assimilation, pp. 79-80; on spelling and spelling reform, pp. 353-374 (there is a useful bibliography on p. 374); on pronunciation, Chapter 12.
6. Thomas, Charles Kenneth. *Phonetics of American English,* 2d ed. New York: The Ronald Press Company, 1958. On standards of pronunciation, see pp. 253-260.
7. Sapir, Edward. *Language.* New York: Harcourt, Brace & World, Inc., 1921. On the sound-system, see Chapter III.

6. Usage

BARGAIN BASEMENT ENGLISH

Wilson Follett

Our relationship to knowledge is paradoxical. We have, on the one hand, an insatiable desire for knowledge, a questing spirit that will not be denied. Yet when new knowledge is discovered it is not always welcomed. Indeed, at times it is strongly resisted and comes to be accepted only gradually and reluctantly. One of the hardest things to do is to accept new knowledge that runs counter to what we have been taught. It means giving up old knowledge, relinquishing what we have regarded as established fact. One would think that a "fact," of all things, would remain constant. Yet the history of knowledge is built, in part, on the shattered facts of the past. Astrology and alchemy long ago gave way to astronomy and chemistry. And even today Newtonian physics, long accepted and firmly established, has given way to the more modern theories of Einstein and his successors. So too in language. Until fairly recently, most people accepted unquestioningly principles and rules of usage and grammar laid down by eighteenth-century grammarians. Contemporary linguists, however, have not only challenged but have actually repudiated many of the eighteenth-century views. They assert that just as the "laws" of Newtonian physics can no longer be accepted as an adequate description of the natural universe, so too the

From *The Atlantic Monthly*, February 1960. Originally published as "Grammar Is Obsolete." Title changed by request of the author; reprinted by his permission.

"rules" of the eighteenth-century grammarians constitute an outmoded and inaccurate description of our language, both in usage and in grammar.

It should come as no surprise to learn that these new views have not been welcomed with open arms by all. Indeed, instead of embracing the new knowledge, adherents of the older tradition have taken up arms of a different sort to engage in intellectual combat. Nor have proponents of the new been unmilitant in advancing their cause. This running battle has been going on for more than thirty years. During this period the ground has shifted a number of times, positions have not always been clear, and misunderstanding, on both sides, has been ever present. Although it is clear that the forces of the new hold the field, the battle is not entirely over. A recent skirmish occurred in the pages of the Atlantic, *from which the next two readings were taken. In the first one, Wilson Follett, author and editor, deplores what he regards to be the consequences of modern linguistic scholarship.*

LINGUISTIC SCHOLARSHIP, once an encouragement to the most exacting definitions and standards of workmanship, has for some time been dedicating itself to the abolition of standards; and the new rhetoric evolved under its auspices is an organized assumption that language good enough for anybody is good enough for everybody. We have come into a time when the ideals preached and, sometimes, practiced by exalted authority can only take shape in uses of English that are at best tolerable and at worst revolting. Such official pressure as is now put on the young learner is no longer in the direction of forcing him to ask himself whether his way of saying something could have been made better at a bearable cost—as, in a language so rich and various as ours, it generally could have. Everything now taught him concentrates on the lowly question, Will it do at a pinch?

For the handiest possible conspectus of what the new ideal is, one can do no better than to glance at a recent comprehensive manual of rhetorical practice. *A Dictionary of Contemporary American Usage,* by Bergen Evans and Cornelia Evans, comes from authors of prestige and influence, one of them a university professor of English and conductor of a radio and television program devoted to questions of spoken and written usage, the other a writing consultant in the Department of Health, Education, and Welfare and a prize-winning novelist. The reason for turning to this 570-page, 600,000-word volume is not that its publisher proclaims it to be "up-to-date, complete, authoritative"—an assertion of three attributes inherently unattainable by any such work compiled by mortals—but rather that it is declared with strict accuracy to be "based on modern linguistic scholarship." It is essentially a popularization of findings about modern English arrived at and promulgated by contemporary philologists, semanticists, virtuosos of historical and descriptive (as opposed to prescriptive) grammar and morphophonetics, and learnedly implacable assailants of the discarded idea that to speak or write well means hard work, the taking of sometimes painful thought, the constant rejection of labor- and thought-saving alternatives, and the practice of canons that are mastered only by arduous self-cultivation and discipline.

The Evanses manage to convey, along with many shrewd discriminations and salutory warnings often very engagingly phrased, an overall impression that acceptable usages are arrived at by a process about as automatic as breathing; that to torment oneself with questions of better and not so good is to be a seeker after gratuitous trouble and, what is worse, a purist; and that the way to attain effective expression is to keep our ears open, bank on our natural and inescapable linguistic inheritance, and cultivate an English that will make us indistinguishable from the ostensibly educated surrounding majority. Let us see where anyone will come out if he accepts and applies the combination of what these authors recommend, what they defend or condone, and what they do themselves. He will come out speaking and writing an American English faithfully represented by the scattering that follows:

"Ask whoever you see." "He had as much or more trouble than I did." "He works faster than me"; "he is taller than me." "More unique." "Different than." "The reason is because. . . ." "I can't imagine it being him." "Let's you and I"; "let's you and me." "Bob as well as Frank were there." "Neither D. nor A. are at home"; "neither he nor I are timid"; "either of them are enough to drive a man to distraction"; "neither of them had their tickets"; "I do not think either of them are at home"; "each carried their own pack"; "each of the men were willing to contribute." "Every member brings their own lunch"; "either the boy or the girl left their book." "I cannot help but think." "Nobody was killed, were they?" "Less than three." "If one loses his temper." "We did not find a one." "The sheriff with all his men were at the door." "Not one of them were listening." "Some grammarians claim that this is not permissible." "He allowed that we were right." "Refer back to." "Back of" (behind). "Between each house"; "between every pause." "He blamed it on me." "I haven't but a minute to spare." "I don't doubt but that you are surprised." "Who did you see?" "Who are you looking for?" "Children whom we know are hungry." "Everyplace"; "anyplace"; "someplace"; "someway"; "noplace"; "I have looked everyplace." "It is not I who is angry." "These kind of men are dangerous." "You don't know Nellie like I do." "It is you who will be blamed for it, not them." "That's her at the door now." "A minimum of sufficiency." "We most always go shopping on Saturday." "Very amused." "Overly cautious." "Datas"; "phenomenas"; "much data"; "very little data"; "the data is now in." "I asked him what was he doing." "The rationale for his attack on the President." "As regards." "Somebody left their umbrella." "I will get one someway." "There will only be him left." "Subsequent to his release from the Air Force he got a job with a commercial air line." "A continuous use [of a word in a specified way] is vulgar." "He went no further than Philadelphia." "Neither of these reasons justify the use of the present tense." "He failed, due to carelessness."

This little anthology could be several times multiplied from the same source; thus much will do to imply a general pattern. Some of the specimens are patently better, or less bad, than others. Say of the whole, if you wish: "Some of it might be worse." There is no point in using a microscope on the gradations or on the merits of the arguments used to defend this locution or that. It is enough if we perceive—as we cannot very well escape doing—that collectively they define a stratum of diction that invites defense and seems to require it, one that it is now fashionable to defend with all the resources of specialized learning. No one could possibly contemplate any such handful and then declare its components above challenge and in no need of condoning; no one could associate them with an unremitting effort to discover and to utilize the best that our common language is capable of. A collection of the same size could hardly vary much from this one if it deliberately set out to specialize in the marginal, the dubious, the suspect. What it seems to represent is the pattern of habits deliberately adopted by the educated when they set out to show that they are no better than anyone else, if as good. It goes to show the lengths to which we can carry conformism and the terror of being noticeable in a society that is (as Bierce said of the republic long before H. L. Mencken was heard of) daft with democracy and sick with sin.

If anyone wanted to execute a piece of writing that would be from beginning to end the densest possible concentration of what the elder rhetoricians classified as solecisms, he could hardly do better than to attune his prose to the dicta laid down in *A Dictionary of Contemporary American Usage*. The book is an astute, artful, and tireless harvesting of whatever in American speech is barely tolerable to those who do not make a virtue of pushing either tolerance or intolerance to pathological extremes. And it is a translation into practical advice of what the most erudite philologists and lexicographers have for some time been telling us about the sources of health and vitality in our language. The great nuclear principle seems to be that we should speak and write not as well as we can learn how, but ignobly enough to escape notice.

Now, a resort to this kind of first aid may result in some tactical advantage to the purveyor of insurance or real estate, the chairman of a fund-raising campaign, the soapbox orator, the candidate for minor office. Even that advantage can be doubted: there seems to be a fairly powerful undertow of envious popular respect for the man who uses language with easy distinction, provided that he does it in quiet assurance with no air of showing off or of spitting on his hearers to see if they can swim, as the rude old Yankee folk saying has it. An instance is the standing that ex-Governor Adlai Stevenson seems to have with all classes of his fellow countrymen, whether they applaud his political opinions or not. But whatever the practical momentary advantages of slovenly diction, what is its long-range bearing on education, on the language itself, on its literature? Will, say, two or three consecutive generations of calculated effort to speak and write without excellence enhance the prospect of our producing an Irving, a Hawthorne, a Melville, a Henry James, a Howells, a Sarah Orne Jewett, a Willa Cather? Or will it tend to blight that prospect? Did the virtue of English prose, from Sir Thomas

Browne and the King James translators to Bernard Shaw, come out of the acceptance of language on the permissive or lowest-common-denominator basis—out of a preoccupation with what was tolerable, what could barely be endured in default of better?

Is it not one of the shames of modern scholarship that it has so little to say for what is really good, what is best, and so much to say for what is merely allowable or defensible? Scholarship is trying, of course, to discount the factor of taste as nonscientific: but is it scientific to discount it? Taste is the faculty of criticism, the faculty of intelligent choice; and to it belongs the last word about any given use of language. After all, the argument from usage carries only a permissive force, not a mandatory one. Even if it were possible to prove an overwhelming preponderance for "He failed, due to carelessness" and "You don't know Nellie like I do," the proof could mean only that one may use these expressions without being condemned. There would be nothing to say that anyone has to use them, and all of us would still have the freedom of "His failure was due to carelessness" or "Carelessness caused him to fail" and "You don't know Nellie as I do" or "the way I do," which will never raise any problems or any eyebrows.

Nobody is under compulsion to like a construction just because it exists or to use it if he does not like it. This is a principle that applies equally to present and to past usages. We have the whole range of linguistic resources at our disposal; and there is no virtue in flirting with ways of expression that we think dubious or inferior when there are alternative ways—as there always are—to which no exception can be taken. The formation of any style, even a bad one, is an affair of constant acceptances and rejections; and everyone has to lean on his own taste for acceptance of the better and rejection of the worse.

The discussion of usage was probably never shrouded in more fog than it is now. Those who want to fling wide the gates to all manner of laxity maintain firmly that change is the great inescapable law, that the only criterion is what people are doing with language *now*, and they can find no words severe enough for resistance to change, especially when resistance takes the form of quoting classic sources; but if they can unearth in Chaucer or Wycliffe or Donne or Hazlitt some parallel to whatever change is being resisted, they cite it as if it settled the matter forever. Whether the use cited was typical or exceptional in that author is a question not raised; it is enough that the passage exists. The Evanses give us a list of twenty authors, Shakespeare to Maugham—a list as easily extended back to Chaucer—who use *like* as a conjunction, but there is no attempt to show that any one of them regularly or even frequently used it so. A dictionary that illustrates a secondary meaning with a quotation may, for all we can tell, be using the only known occurrence of the word in that sense.

The radical, the innovator, the grammatical iconoclast and libertine is ready to beat down all opposition as tradition-bound and ridiculously conservative, but he is equally ready to demonstrate that whatever is objected to has been English for four or five hundred years. Both forms of argument are supposed to be unanswerably crushing. If some locution now current defies a past consensus, so much the worse for the past; but at the same time any locution ever written by a good writer is *ipso facto* attack-proof, and if a precedent can be adduced for anything, however shabby, the case is closed.

Actually not everything ever written by a good writer, or even by quite a number of good writers, is good, any more than everything ever written by a bad writer is bad. Every good writer has committed himself at one time or another to practices without which he would have been a better writer. It is our privilege to pick and choose, alike from the superior and the inferior, alike from the past and the present. For the winnowing of the past we have the guidance of perspective in addition to taste; for the present, taste alone has to suffice. For taste there is no substitute, nor is there any excuse for not using as much of it as we have. The unexpressed excuse that underlies most refusals to use it is the delusive feeling that every demolition of a barrier, old or new, is a freeing of the language from needless restraints and a further emancipation of its users.

What is overlooked is that language and its users grow by restraints, too. Especially in a time when looseness of many kinds is a dominant fashion, it may be salutary to cultivate a tightness and exactitude not customarily demanded. Linguistic resources are expanded not only by the seizing of new liberties as fast as they become available but also by the rejection of liberties that may be only license. A writer is not alone what he writes; he is likewise everything that he will not write because he finds it not good enough, and his power may be as much a function of his renunciations as of his self-indulgences. The libertarians will pity him as self-deprived and call his austerity a crotchet, but he and we are the gainers by his discriminations, and the language may be the loser by the indiscrimination of the loose constructionist.

In no domain is there a clearer illustration of the power of negative choice than in the domain of diction. Good writing has always been marked, and is marked today, by selection of words for their central and not their peripheral meanings. A word, particularly an abstract word, has a core of meaning from which it gradually spreads over associated meanings, perhaps in several directions, until it overlaps words that have likewise spread out from entirely different, possibly remote centers.

The liberalistic view now regnant ranks all such extensions as improvements of language, all as equally good. But the fine writer or speaker is habitually aiming at bull's-eyes, not at general target areas, and he does not care for the idea of shelling the woods with language. His dictionary gives *apparent* as one synonym of *evident*, and vice versa, but he still finds an important kind of integrity in applying *apparent* to the thing that seems to be so whether it is or not and in saving *evident* for that which both seems to be and is so. *Infer* once meant exactly what *imply* means now—it is generally, perhaps always, so used in the seventeenth-century plays of John Ford—but the two words have developed a clear differentiation whereby *imply* goes with the transmitting end and *infer* with the receiving end of the same process of deduction; smoke *implies* fire, but when you smell smoke you *infer* fire. It is a clear loss, not a gain, when we ignore the differentiation in such sentences as these from the best-selling murder story of the decade: "The defense is trying to infer that the prosecution is trying to conceal something." "And surely you do not mean to infer that it would be an unjust verdict if X. were acquitted on the ground of temporary insanity?" *Infer* is being so chronically abused by many who should know better that lexicography no longer quite sees what to do with it, but a decent writer sees, and he is well aware that the widespread confusion makes the English vocabulary not richer, but poorer. True, "language grows," as Greenough and Kittredge said in 1901, "by the felicitous misapplication of words"; but there is no profit to be had out of misapplication per se, without the felicity—a reservation that brings us straight back to the necessity of taste.

The obvious and growing indifference of many publishing houses to hundreds or thousands of such distinctions as those illustrated cannot be called one of the more gladdening signs of the times. No practicing editor of any great competence ever sees a book manuscript for which he could not do appreciable favors if he had a free hand and time, and ninety-nine of any hundred published books could have profited by good offices that they never received. But these phenomena, depressing as they are, seem not quite so shocking as the latter-day hospitality of the very learned to every popular usage that volunteers to make the language more fuzzy, inarticulated, and fumbling.

What steadily preoccupies everyone fit to be called a writer is the possibility of improving everything in his work that is improvable. In no other way can he contribute his much or his little to the effectiveness of language as an instrument of precision combined with power. The linguistic scholarship that impedes and discourages where it might help him is operating beneath its privilege, not to say beneath its obligation. Let those who choose define usage as what a swarm of folk say or write by reason of laziness, shiftlessness, or ignorance; the tenable definition is still what the judicious do as a result of all that they can muster of conscious discrimination. It is time we had a philosophy of usage grounded in the steadfast conviction that the best, whether or not we have it in us to attain it, is not too good to be aspired to.

The assignments for all the essays in this section have been placed on page 314.

GRAMMAR FOR TODAY

Bergen Evans

It would hardly do to call this essay a companion piece to Wilson Follett's "Bargain Basement English," since, figuratively at least, the two authors could not break bread comfortably together. Bergen Evans, Professor of English at Northwestern University, has made a name for himself as a writer and speaker on American English.

From *The Atlantic Monthly*, March 1960. Reprinted by permission of the author.

Though frequently criticized by upholders of the eighteenth-century tradition, Professor Evans has done much to bring before the public the views of our twentieth-century linguists. "Grammar for Today" was published as a reply to Mr. Follett's charges against modern linguistic scholarship. You will notice that the differences in attitude expressed in these two essays toward contemporary usage stem from fundamentally different beliefs about the nature of language.

In 1747 Samuel Johnson issued a plan for a new dictionary of the English language. It was supported by the most distinguished printers of the day and was dedicated to the model of all correctness, Philip Dormer Stanhope, Fourth Earl of Chesterfield. Such a book, it was felt, was urgently needed to "fix" the language, to arrest its "corruption" and "decay," a degenerative process which, then as now, was attributed to the influence of "the vulgar" and which, then as now, it was a mark of superiority and elegance to decry. And Mr. Johnson seemed the man to write it. He had an enormous knowledge of Latin, deep piety, and dogmatic convictions. He was also honest and intelligent, but the effect of these lesser qualifications was not to show until later.

Oblig'd by hunger and request of friends, Mr. Johnson was willing to assume the role of linguistic dictator. He was prepared to "fix" the pronunciation of the language, "preserve the purity" of its idiom, brand "impure" words with a "note of infamy," and secure the whole "from being overrun by . . . low terms."

There were, however, a few reservations. Mr. Johnson felt it necessary to warn the oversanguine that "Language is the work of man, a being from whom permanence and stability cannot be derived." English "was not formed from heaven . . . but was produced by necessity and enlarged by accident." It had, indeed, been merely "thrown together by negligence" and was in such a state of confusion that its very syntax could no longer "be taught by general rules, but [only] by special precedents."

In 1755 the *Dictionary* appeared. The noble patron had been given a great deal more immortality than he had bargained for by the vigor of the kick Johnson had applied to his backside as he booted him overboard. And the *Plan* had been replaced by the *Preface*, a sadder but very much wiser document.

Eight years of "sluggishly treading the track of the alphabet" had taught Johnson that the hopes of "fixing" the language and preserving its "purity" were but "the dreams of a poet doomed at last to wake a lexicographer." In "the boundless chaos of living speech," so copious and energetic in its disorder, he had found no guides except "experience and analogy." Irregularities were "inherent in the tongue" and could not be "dismissed or reformed" but must be permitted "to remain untouched." "Uniformity must be sacrificed to custom . . . in compliance with a numberless majority" and "general agreement." One of the pet projects of the age had been the establishment of an academy to regulate and improve style. "I hope," Johnson wrote in the *Preface*, that if "it should be established . . . the spirit of English liberty will hinder or destroy [it.]"

At the outset of the work he had flattered himself, he confessed, that he would reform abuses and put a stop to alterations. But he had soon discovered that "sounds are too volatile and subtle for legal restraints" and that "to enchain syllables and to lash the wind are equally undertakings of pride unwilling to measure its desires by its strength." For "the causes of change in language are as much superior to human resistance as the revolutions of the sky or the intumescence of the tide."

There had been an even more profound discovery: that grammarians and lexicographers "do not form, but register the language; do not teach men how they should think, but relate how they have hitherto expressed their thoughts." And with this statement Johnson ushered in the rational study of linguistics. He had entered on his task a medieval pedant. He emerged from it a modern scientist.

Of course his discoveries were not strikingly original. Horace had observed that use was the sole arbiter and norm of speech and Montaigne had said that he who would fight custom with grammar was a fool. Doubtless thousands of other people had at one time or another perceived and said the same thing. But Johnson introduced a new principle. Finding that he could not lay down rules, he gave actual examples to show meaning and form. He offered as authority illustrative quotations, and in so doing established that language is what usage makes it and that custom, in the long run, is the ultimate and only court of appeal in linguistic matters.

This principle, axiomatic today in grammar and lexicography, seems to exasperate a great many laymen who, apparently, find two hundred and five years too short a period in which to grasp a basic idea. They insist that there are absolute standards of correctness in speech and that these standards may be set forth in a few simple rules. To a man, they believe, of course, that they speak and write "correctly" and they are loud in their insistence that others imitate them.

It is useless to argue with such people because they are not, really, interested in language at all. They are interested solely in demonstrating their own superiority. Point out to them—as has been done hundreds of times—that forms which they regard as "corrupt," "incorrect," and "vulgar" have been used by Shakespeare, Milton, and the Bible and are used daily by 180 million Americans and accepted by the best linguists and lexicographers, and they will coolly say, "Well, if they differ from me, they're wrong."

But if usage is not the final determinant of speech, what is? Do the inhabitants of Italy, for example, speak corrupt Latin or good Italian? Is Spanish superior to French? Would the Breton fisherman speak better if he spoke Parisian French? Can one be more fluent in Outer Mongolian than in Inner Mongolian? One has only to ask such questions in relation to languages other than one's own, languages within which our particular snobberies and struggles for prestige have no stake, to see the absurdity of them.

The language that we do speak, if we are to accept the idea of "corruption" and "decay" in language, is a horribly decayed Anglo-Saxon, grotesquely corrupted by Norman French. Furthermore, since Standard English is a development of the London dialect of the fourteenth century, our speech, by true aristocratic standards, is woefully middle-class, commercial, and vulgar. And American speech is lower middle-class, reeking of counter and till. Where else on earth, for instance, would one find crime condemned because it didn't *pay!*

In more innocent days a great deal of time was spent in wondering what was the "original" language of mankind, the one spoken in Eden, the language of which all modern tongues were merely degenerate remnants. Hector Boethius tells us that James I of Scotland was so interested in this problem that he had two children reared with a deaf and dumb nurse on an island in order to see what language they would "naturally" speak. James thought it would be Hebrew, and in time, to his great satisfaction, it was reported that the children were speaking Hebrew!

Despite this experiment, however, few people today regard English as a corruption of Hebrew. But many seem to think it is a corruption of Latin and labor mightily to make it conform to this illusion. It is they and their confused followers who tell us that we can't say "I am mistaken" because translated into Latin this would mean "I am misunderstood," and we can't say "I have enjoyed myself" unless we are egotistical or worse.

It is largely to this group—most of whom couldn't read a line of Latin at sight if their lives depended on it—that we owe our widespread bewilderment concerning *who* and *whom.* In Latin the accusative or dative form would always be used, regardless of the word's position in the sentence, when the pronoun was the object of a verb or a preposition. But in English, for at least four hundred years, this simply hasn't been so. When the pronoun occurs at the beginning of a question, people who speak natural, fluent, literary English use the nominative, regardless. They say "Who did you give it to?" not "Whom did you give it to?" But the semiliterate, intimidated and bewildered, are mouthing such ghastly utterances as a recent headline in a Chicago newspaper: WHOM'S HE KIDDING?

Another group seems to think that in its pure state English was a Laputan tongue, with logic as its guiding principle. Early members of this sect insisted that *unloose* could only mean "to tie up," and present members have compelled the gasoline industry to label its trucks *Flammable* under the disastrous insistence, apparently, that the old *Inflammable* could only mean "not burnable."

It is to them, in league with the Latinists, that we owe the bogy of the double negative. In all Teutonic languages a doubling of the negative merely emphasizes the negation. But we have been told for a century now that two negatives make a positive, though if they do and it's merely a matter of logic, then three negatives should make a negative again. So that if "It doesn't make no difference" is wrong merely because it includes two negatives, then "It doesn't never make no difference" ought to be right again.

Both of these groups, in their theories at least, ignore our idiom. Yet idiom—those expressions which defy all logic but are the very essence of a tongue—plays a large part in English. We go to school and college, but we go to *the* university. We buy two dozen eggs but a couple *of* dozen. *Good and* can mean *very* ("I am good and mad!") and "a hot cup of coffee" means that the coffee, not the cup, is to be hot. It makes a world of difference to a condemned man whether his reprieve is *upheld* or *held up*.

There are thousands of such expressions in English. They are the "irregularities" which Johnson found "inherent in the tongue" and which his wisdom perceived could not and should not be removed. Indeed, it is in the recognition and use of these idioms that skillful use of English lies.

Many words in the form that is now mandatory were originally just mistakes, and many of these mistakes were forced into the language by eager ignoramuses determined to make it conform to some notion of their own. The *s* was put in *island*, for instance, in sheer pedantic ignorance. The second *r* doesn't belong in *trousers*, nor the *g* in *arraign*, nor the *t* in *deviltry*, nor the *n* in *passenger* and *messenger*. Nor, so far as English is concerned, does that first *c* in *arctic* which so many people twist their mouths so strenuously to pronounce.

And grammar is as "corrupted" as spelling or pronunciation. "You are" is as gross a solecism as "me am." It's recent, too; you won't find it in the Authorized Version of the Bible. *Lesser*, *nearer*, and *more* are grammatically on a par with *gooder*. *Crowed* is the equivalent of *knowed* or *growed*, and *caught* and *dug* (for *catched* and *digged*) are as "corrupt" as *squoze* for *squeezed* or *snoze* for *sneezed*.

Fortunately for our peace of mind most people are quite content to let English conform to English, and they are supported in their sanity by modern grammarians and linguists.

Scholars agree with Puttenham (1589) that a language is simply speech "fashioned to the common understanding and accepted by consent." They believe that the only "rules" that can be stated for a language are codified observations. They hold, that is, that language is the basis of grammar, not the other way round. They do not believe that any language can become "corrupted" by the linguistic habits of those who speak it. They do not believe that anyone who is a native speaker of a standard language will get into any linguistic trouble unless he is misled by snobbishness or timidity or vanity.

He may, of course, if his native language is English, speak a form of English that marks him as coming from a rural or an unread group. But if he doesn't mind being so marked, there's no reason why he should change. Johnson retained a Staffordshire burr in his speech all his life. And surely no one will deny that Robert Burns's rustic dialect was just as good as a form of speech as, and in his mouth infinitely better as a means of expression than, the "correct" English spoken by ten million of his southern contemporaries.

The trouble is that people are no longer willing to be rustic or provincial. They all want to speak like educated people, though they don't want to go to the trouble of becoming truly educated. They want to believe that a special form of socially acceptable and financially valuable speech can be mastered by following a few simple rules. And there is no lack of little books that offer to supply the rules and promise "correctness" if the rules are adhered to. But, of course, these offers are specious because you don't speak like an educated person unless you are an educated person, and the little books, if taken seriously, will not only leave the lack of education showing but will expose the pitiful yearning and the basic vulgarity as well, in such sentences as "Whom are you talking about?"

As a matter of fact, the educated man uses at least three languages. With his family and his close friends, on the ordinary, unimportant occasions of daily life, he speaks, much of the time, a monosyllabic sort of shorthand. On more important occasions and when dealing with strangers in his official or business relations, he has a more formal speech, more complete, less allusive, politely qualified, wisely reserved. In addition he has some acquaintance with the literary speech of his language. He understands this when he reads it, and often enjoys it, but he hesitates to use it. In times of emotional stress hot fragments of it may come out of him like lava, and in times of feigned emotion, as when giving a commencement address, cold, greasy gobbets of it will ooze forth.

The linguist differs from the amateur grammarian in recognizing all of these variations and gradations in the language. And he differs from the snob in doubting that the speech of any one small group among the language's more than 300 million daily users constitutes a model for all the rest to imitate.

The methods of the modern linguist can be illustrated by the question of the grammatical number of *none*. Is it singular or plural? Should one say "None of them is ready" or "None of them are ready"?

The prescriptive grammarians are emphatic that it should be singular. The Latinists point out that *nemo*, the Latin equivalent, is singular. The logicians triumphantly point out that *none* can't be more than one and hence can't be plural.

The linguist knows that he hears "None of them are ready" every day, from people of all social positions, geographical areas, and degrees of education. He also hears "None is." Furthermore, literature informs him that both forms were used in the past. From Malory (1450) to Milton (1650) he finds that *none* was treated as a singular three times for every once that it was treated as a plural. That is, up to three hundred years ago men usually said *None is*. From Milton to 1917, *none* was used as a plural seven times for every four times it was used as a singular. That is, in the past three hundred years men often said *None is*, but they said *None are* almost twice as often. Since 1917, however, there has been a noticeable increase in the use of the plural, so much so that today *None are* is the preferred form.

The descriptive grammarian, therefore, says that while *None is* may still be used, it is becoming increasingly peculiar. This, of course, will not be as useful to one who wants to be cultured in a hurry as a short, emphatic permission or prohibition. But it has the advantage of describing English as it is spoken and written here and now and not as it ought to be spoken in some Cloud-Cuckoo-Land.

The descriptive grammarian believes that a child should be taught English, but he would like to see the child taught the English actually used by his educated contemporaries, not some pedantic, theoretical English designed chiefly to mark the imagined superiority of the designer.

He believes that a child should be taught the parts of speech, for example. But the child should be told the truth—that these are functions of use, not some quality immutably inherent in this or that word. Anyone, for instance, who tells a child—or anyone else—that *like* is used in English only as a preposition has grossly misinformed him. And anyone who complains that its use as a conjunction is a corruption introduced by Winston cigarettes ought, in all fairness, to explain how Shakespeare, Keats, and the translators of the Authorized Version of the Bible came to be in the employ of the R. J. Reynolds Tobacco Company.

Whether formal grammar can be taught to advantage before the senior year of high school is doubtful; most studies—and many have been made—indicate that it can't. But when it is taught, it should be the grammar of today's English, not the obsolete grammar of yesterday's prescriptive grammarians. By that grammar, for instance, *please* in the sentence "Please reply" is the verb and *reply* its object. But by modern meaning *reply* is the verb, in the imperative, and *please* is merely a qualifying word meaning "no discourtesy intended," a mollifying or de-imperatival adverb, or whatever you will, but not the verb.

This is a long way from saying "Anything goes," which is the charge that, with all the idiot repetition of a needle stuck in a groove, the uninformed ceaselessly chant against modern grammarians. But to assert that usage is the sole determinant in grammar, pronunciation, and meaning is *not* to say that anything goes. Custom is illogical and unreasonable, but it is also tyrannical. The least deviation from its dictates is usually punished with severity. And because this is so, children should be taught what the current and local customs in English are. They should not be taught that we speak a bastard Latin or a vocalized logic. And they should certainly be disabused of the stultifying illusion that after God had given Moses the Commandments He called him back and pressed on him a copy of Woolley's *Handbook of English Grammar.*

The grammarian does not see it as his function to "raise the standards" set by Franklin, Lincoln, Melville, Mark Twain, and hundreds of millions of other Americans. He is content to record what they said and say.

Insofar as he serves as a teacher, it is his business to point out the limits of the permissible, to indicate the confines within which the writer may exercise his choice, to report that which custom and practice have made acceptable. It is certainly not the business of the grammarian to impose his personal taste as the only norm of good English, to set forth his prejudices as the ideal standard which everyone should copy. That would be fatal. No one person's standards are broad enough for that.

DIFFERENCES IN LANGUAGE PRACTICES

Charles Carpenter Fries

That there are sharply conflicting attitudes toward contemporary usage should be evident from your reading of the two preceding essays. That these attitudes derive from differing basic assumptions about the nature of language should be equally clear. In the following essay, Professor Fries explains more fully the cleavage that separates the two points of view. At the same time, he presents the rationale of the scientific point of view in the study of language, arrives at a sound definition of Standard American English, and discusses the obligation of the schools with respect to differences in language practices. The essay is the introductory chapter of his American English Grammar, *a revolutionary book in the teaching of English. Professor Fries has already been identified on p. 255.*

"ENGLISH" MAINTAINS its place as the most frequently *required subject* of our school and college curriculums because of the unanimous support given it both by the general public and by education authorities. This support rests upon the general belief that the mastery of *good English* is not only the most important asset of the ambitious but also an obligation of every good citizen. There is, however, in many quarters, a very hazy idea of the specific elements which make *good English.* A great deal of vigorous controversy ignores all the larger problems of effective communication and centers attention upon the criteria to be applied in judging the acceptability of particular words and language forms. All of this controversy is direct

From *American English Grammar* by Charles Carpenter Fries. Reprinted by permission of the author and the National Council of Teachers of English, copyright 1940. Published by Appleton-Century-Crofts, Inc.

evidence that there do exist many differences in the language practice of English speaking people; for no controversy could arise and no choice be offered unless differing language forms presented themselves in the actual practice of English speech. It is the purpose of this chapter to set forth the general character of these differences and to analyze their significance in relation to the obligations resting upon our schools. The chapter as a whole will therefore present the principles underlying this whole investigation and the point of view which has determined its material and method.

I

Underlying many of the controversies concerning words and language forms is a very common attitude which I shall call here the "conventional point of view." Frequently stated explicitly, sometimes only implied, it appears in most handbooks and manuals of correct English, in grammars and rhetorics, in educational tests and measures, and in many editorials of the press. This conventional point of view assumes not only that there is a correctness in English language as absolute as that in elementary mathematics but also that the measures of this correctness are very definite rules. The following quotations are typical:

> A college professor rises to defend 'ain't' and 'it is me' as good English. The reed upon which he leans is majority usage. . . . 'Ain't,' as a legitimate contraction of 'am not,' would not require defense or apology if it were not for widespread misuse. Unfortunately the same cannot be said of 'it is me.' This solecism could not be given the odor of good English by a plurality as great as Warren G. Harding rolled up in 1920. . . . A vast amount of wretched English is heard in this country. The remedy does not lie in the repeal of the rules of grammar; but rather in a stricter and more intelligent enforcement of those rules in our schools. . . . This protest against traditional usage and the rules of grammar is merely another manifestation of the unfortunate trend of the times to lawlessness in every direction. . . . Quite as important as keeping undesirables out of the vocabulary is the maintaining of respect for the rules of grammar, which govern the formation of words into phrases and sentences. . . . Students should be taught that correct speaking is evidence of culture; and that in order to speak correctly they must master the rules that govern the use of the language.[1]

[1] From an editorial in *The Detroit Free Press*, December 9, 1928.

Grammar consists of a series of rules and definitions. . . . Since . . . ninety-five per cent of all children and teachers come from homes or communities where incorrect English is used, nearly everyone has before him the long, hard task of overcoming habits set up early in life before he studied language and grammar in school. . . . Such people are exposed to the ridicule of those who notice the error, and the only way in which they can cure themselves is by eternal vigilance and the study of grammar.[2]

This is a test to see how well you know correct English usage and how well you can select the *rule or principle in accordance with which a usage is correct.* In the left hand column a list of sentences is given. In each sentence there are two forms in parentheses, one correct, and the other incorrect. In the right hand column a list of rules or principles is given, some one of which applies to each sentence. . . .

Sentences	*Principles*
( ) 1. (Whom) (Who) did you meet?	*a.* The indirect object is in the objective case.
( ) 2. He told John and (I) (me) an interesting story.	*b.* The subject of the verb is in the nominative case.
	c. The object of a verb is in the objective case.

. . . Read the first sentence in Section I; then mark out the incorrect form. Read the rules in Section I, until you find one that applies to this first sentence. Place the letter of this rule in the square preceding the first sentence.[3]

One purpose of this report is to describe and illustrate a method of constructing a grammar curriculum upon the basis of the errors of school children. . . . it is apparent that the first step is *to ascertain* the rules which are broken and to determine their relative importance.[4]

The point of view expressed in these quotations, assuming as it does that certain definite rules[5] are the necessary standards by which to measure language correctness, also repudiates *general usage* as a valid guide to acceptability, even the usage of the so-called "edu-

[2] W. W. Charters, *Teaching the Common Branches* (New York, The Macmillan Co., rev. ed., 1924), pp. 96, 98, 115.

[3] T. J. Kirby, *Grammar Test,* University of Iowa Standard Tests and Scales.

[4] "Minimal Essentials in Language and Grammar," in *Sixteenth Yearbook* of the National Society for the Study of Education (Bloomington, Ind., Public School Publishing Co., 1917), pp. 86, 87.

[5] For a statement of the development of this point of view see C. C. Fries, *Teaching of the English Language* (New York, Thomas Nelson and Sons, 1927), Ch. I, "The Rules of Grammar as the Measure of Language Errors."

cated." The following quotation represents dozens of similar statements:

> The truth is, however, that authority of general usage, or even of the usage of great writers, is not absolute in language. There is a misuse of words which can be justified by no authority, however great, and *by no usage however general.*[6]

From this, the "conventional point of view," the problem of the differences in our language practice is a very simple one. Only two kinds of forms or usages exist—correct forms and mistakes. In general, the mistakes are thought to be corrupt forms or illegitimate meanings derived by carelessness from the correct ones. In some cases a grudging acquiescence accepts some forms which are contrary to the rules when these forms are sanctioned by an overwhelming usage, but here the view remains that these forms, although established by usage, are still *incorrect* and must always be incorrect. To this point of view these incorrect forms sanctioned by usage are the "idioms" of the language. In all the matters of differing language practices, therefore, those who hold this point of view regard the obligation of the schools as perfectly clear and comparatively simple —the schools must root out the *mistakes* or *errors* and cultivate the language uses that are *correct according to the rules.*[7]

Opposed to this "conventional point of view" is that held by the outstanding scholars in English language during the last hundred years. I shall call it here "the scientific point of view." Typical expressions of it abound.

> In considering the use of grammar as a corrective of what are called 'ungrammatical' expressions, it must be borne in mind that the rules of grammar have no value except as statements of facts: whatever is in general use in a language is for that very reason grammatically correct.[8]
>
> The grammar of a language is not a list of rules imposed upon its speakers by scholastic authorities, but is a scientific record of the actual phenomena of that language, written and spoken. If any community habitu-

[6] R. G. White, *Words and Their Uses* (Boston, Houghton Mifflin Co., rev. ed., 1899), p. 14.

[7] "Some better reason than a custom arising from ignorance . . . is needed for changing the English language. It would seem to be still the part of the schools to teach the language *strictly according to rule,* and to place emphasis on such teaching, rather than to encourage questionable liberties of usage." From an editorial in *The Christian Science Monitor,* Boston, February 23 1923.

[8] Henry Sweet, *New English Grammar,* Vol. I (Oxford, Clarendon Press, 1891), p. 5.

ally uses certain forms of speech, these forms are part of the grammar of the speech of that community.[9]

It has been my endeavor in this work to represent English Grammar not as a set of stiff dogmatic precepts, according to which some things are correct and others absolutely wrong, but as something living and developing under continual fluctuations and undulations, something that is founded on the past and prepares the way for the future, something that is not always consistent or perfect, but progressing and perfectible—in one word, human.[10]

A Grammar book does not attempt to teach people how they ought to speak, but on the contrary, unless it is a very bad or a very old work, it merely states how, as a matter of fact, certain people do speak at the time at which it is written.[11]

In these typical expressions of "the scientific point of view" there is, first of all, a definitely stated opposition to the fundamental principle of the "conventional attitude." All of them insist that it is unsound to take the rules of grammar as the necessary norms of correct English and to set out to make all usage conform to those rules. In these expressions of the scientific view there is, also, a clear affirmation of the fundamental principle of the attitude that usage or practice is the basis of all the *correctness* there can be in language.[12] From this, the scientific point of view, the problem presented by the differences in our language is by no means a simple one. Instead of having to deal with a mass of diverse forms which can be easily separated into the two groups of *mistakes* and *correct language* according to perfectly definite measures, the language scholar finds himself confronted by a complex range of differing practices which must be sorted into an indefinite number of groups according to a set of somewhat indistinct criteria called "general usage."[13] Those who

[9] Grattan and Gurrey, *Our Living Language* (London, Thomas Nelson and Sons, 1925), p. 25.

[10] Otto Jespersen, *A Modern English Grammar* (Heidelberg, 1909), I, Preface.

[11] H. C. Wyld, *Elementary Lessons in English Grammar* (Oxford, Clarendon Press, 1925), p. 12.

[12] This statement must not be taken to imply that *mere correctness* is to be considered the ultimate ideal of language. The scientific point of view does not in any way conflict with the artistic view of *good English*. See the discussion of "The Scientific and the Artistic Points of View in Language," in C. C. Fries, *The Teaching of the English Language*, pp. 102-121.

[13] One should, perhaps, call attention at this point to the fact that the great *Oxford English Dictionary* is the outstanding document in this "scientific view of language." The principle underlying the production of the *Oxford Dictionary*, the very foundation of its method, was the insistence upon use or practice as the sole criterion of the legitimate meaning of words. Compare, for

hold this scientific point of view insist, therefore, that the first step in fulfilling the obligation of the schools in the matter of dealing with the English language is to record, realistically and as completely as possible, the facts of this usage.

This investigation and report assumes as its first principle this scientific point of view with its repudiation of the conventional attitude toward language errors. We shall, therefore, ignore the conventional classification of *mistakes* and *correct forms,* and attempt to outline the types of differences that appear in our American language practices.

II

All of us upon occasion note and use for the purpose of identification the many differences in the speech of those about us. By differences in pitch of voice, for instance, we can usually tell whether the person talking to us over the telephone is a man, or a woman, or a child. By certain characteristic differences of pronunciation and of grammar, the speech of "Amos and Andy" as it comes over the radio makes us visualize two uneducated negroes. Through the speech of "Clara, Lou, and Em," we see three women of little education who have had a very limited range of social contacts. In similar fashion we should with little difficulty recognize the speech of a Scot like Harry Lauder as differing from that of a native of Georgia or Alabama. If one could conjure up Shakspere or Spenser or Milton, he would find their English strange to his ears not only in pronunciation but in vocabulary and in grammar as well. The speech of Chaucer and of Wycliffe would sound even less like English. In other words, even if one ignores such details as separate the speech of every single person from that of any other, there are at least four large types of differences to be noted in our discussion here.

First, there are historical differences. Chaucer used, as we do, *they* as the nominative plural of the pronoun of the third person, but he did not use *their* as the genitive and *them* as the dative-accusative form. Instead, he used the forms *her* or *hir*, for the genitive plural, and *hem* for the dative-accusative or objective forms. In Chaucer's language it was still the practice to distinguish carefully between the

---

example, the treatment of the word *nice* (especially sense 15) in this dictionary with the usual statements concerning it as given in the conventional handbooks.

singular and plural forms of the past tense of many verbs. He would say *I rood* (rode) but we *ride (n)*, *he sang* but they *sunge (n)*. In the late sixteenth century it was no longer the practice to distinguish between the singular and plural in the past tense, and Shakspere therefore used *we rode* as well as *I rode*. For him, however, *learn* was often used with the meaning we give to *teach*, and *thou* was frequently used to address those of inferior rank or intimate friends. Thus the language forms of each age have differed in some respect from those of any other time. Constant change is the outstanding characteristic of a live language used by an intellectually active people. The historical changes do not come suddenly, nor do they affect all the users of a language equally. Thus at any time there will be found those who cling to the older methods and those who use the newer fashion. Many of the differences we note in the language of today find their explanation in this process of historical change. These older forms constitute a fairly large proportion of the materials usually called errors by those who maintain the conventional point of view. The so-called double negative, as in "They didn't take no oil with them," is thus a perpetuation of an old practice exceedingly common in the English language for centuries. It was formerly the normal way of stressing a negative. The form *foot*, in such expressions as "He is six foot tall," "The height of the bar is now six foot and two inches," is again the perpetuation of an old practice in the English language which the modern fashion has abandoned. It is an old genitive plural following the numeral. A few other examples out of dozens of such historical differences are *clomb*, usually spelled *clum*, as the past tense of the verb *climb*, instead of *climbed; wrought*[14] as the past tense of the verb *work*, instead of *worked; stang* as the past tense of the verb *sting*, instead of *stung*. Such differences belong not only in this group called "historical differences" but often also to some of the other three groups to be explained below. In fact, the four types of differences are not by any means mutually exclusive classifications but merely loose divisions with convenient labels.

Second, there are regional differences. In the south of England, in early Modern English, the inflectional ending of the verb in the third person singular present indicative was *-eth*, as in "God *loveth* a cheer-

[14] One should note that in the case of *wrought* the old form has not the flavor of "vulgar" English as have the other examples here given but suggests super-refinement.

ful giver." In the north of England this inflectional ending was *-es*, as "God *loves* a cheerful giver." Late Modern English has adopted the form that was used only in the northern region. In the language practice of the United States, *gotten* as a past participle form of *get* is fairly general; in England it seldom appears. *You all* as a plural of *you* is especially characteristic of southern United States. In some colleges one takes a course *under* a professor; in others it is *from* one or *with* one; in still others it is *to* one. Some of the differences we note in the language practices of those about us find their explanation in the fact that the fashions in one community or section of the country do not necessarily develop in others. Regional or geographical differences show themselves more clearly in matters of vocabulary. That part of an automobile that is called a *hood* in the United States is called a *bonnet* in England. That which they call the *hood* in England we call the *top. Lumber*, to most of us in the United States means *timber;* in England it still means *rubbish.* In some sections of the United States a *paper bag* is usually called a *sack*, in others a *poke.* Such regional differences become especially noticeable when a person from one section of the country moves into another bringing with him the peculiar fashions of the district from which he comes. In the new community these language differences challenge attention and give rise to questions of correctness and preference.

Third, there are literary and colloquial differences. The language practices of conversation differ in many subtle ways from those used in formal writing. Most apparent is the abundance of contractions in the language of conversation. Thoroughly unnatural would sound the speech of those who in conversation did not constantly use *I'm, you'll, isn't, don't, aren't, they'd better, we've*, instead of the fully expanded *I am, you will, is not, do not, are not, they had better, we have.* And in similar fashion the formal writing that habitually employed such contractions would seem equally unnatural because of the impression of very informal familiarity which they would create. Apparent, too, although less obvious are the differences between conversation and formal writing in the matter of sentence completeness. Conversation abounds in groups of words that do not form conventionally complete and logical sentences. Many verbs are omitted; clauses are uttered which are to be attached to the whole context of the conversation rather than to any particular word in a parsable sentence; single words stand for complete ideas. In formal writing the situation demands much more logical completeness of expression, and most of the sentences appear to satisfy the demands of a conventional grammatical analysis. Less apparent but not less real are the differences which arise out of the fact that many perfectly familiar expressions occur practically only in conversational situations and are found very seldom in literary English unless they appear in attempts to report conversation in writing. Occasions seldom arise in anything except conversational situations to use *Who* (or *whom*) *did you call?* or *It is me* (or *I*).

Many assume that the language practices of formal writing are the best or at least that they are of a higher level than those of colloquial or conversational English. When, therefore, they find an expression marked "colloquial" in a dictionary, as is the phrase "*to get on one's nerves*" in Webster's *New International Dictionary*, they frown upon its use. As a matter of fact, thus to label an expression "colloquial" is simply to say that it occurs in good conversation but not in formal writing.[15] Unless one can assume that formal writing is in itself more desirable than good conversation, the language practices peculiar to conversation cannot be rated in comparison with those of formal writing. Each set of language practices is best in its own special sphere of use; one will necessarily differ from the other.

Fourth, there are social or class differences. Despite the fact that America in its national life has struggled to express its belief in the essential equality of human beings and to free the paths of opportunity from arbitrary and artificial restraints, there still do exist some clear differences between the habits and practices of various social groups. It is, of course, practically impossible to mark the limits of any social class in this country. It is even extremely difficult to describe the special characteristics of any such class because of the

[15] The word *colloquial* as applied to English words and structures is frequently misunderstood, even by teachers of English. Some confuse it with *localism*, and think of the words and constructions marked "colloquial" as peculiarities of speaking which are characteristic of a particular locality. Others feel that some stigma attaches to the label "colloquial" and would strive to avoid as *incorrect* (or as of a *low level*) all words and phrases so marked. The word *colloquial*, however, as used to label words and phrases in a dictionary like Webster's *New International Dictionary* has no such meaning. It is used to mark those words and constructions whose range of use is primarily that of the polite conversation of cultivated people, of their familiar letters and informal speeches, as distinct from those words and constructions which are common also in formal writing. As a matter of fact, even the language of our better magazines and of public addresses has, during the last generation, moved away from the formal toward the informal.

comparative ease with which one passes from one social group to another, especially in youth, and the consequent mixture of group habits among those so moving. Our public schools, our churches, our community welfare work, our political life, all furnish rather frequent occasions for social class mixture. All that can be done in respect to such a description is to indicate certain facts which seem generally true for the *core* of any social group, realizing that these same facts may also be true separately of many who have connections with other groups. There are, for example, those who habitually wear formal dress clothes in the evening and those who never wear them. Many of the former frequent the opera and concerts of the best music; many of the latter find their entertainment solely in the movies. The families of the wealthy, especially those whose wealth has continued for several generations, ordinarily mix but little with the families of unskilled laborers; and the families of college professors even in a small city have usually very little social life in common with the families of policemen and firemen.

Just as the general social habits of such separated social groups naturally show marked differences, so their language practices inevitably vary. Pronunciations such as "*ketch*" for *catch* and "*git*" for *get;* and grammatical forms such as "He *seen* his mistake as soon as he *done* it" or "*You was*" are not the characteristic modes of speech of university professors, or of the clergymen who preach from the pulpits in our large city churches, or of the judges of the supreme court, or of the presidents of our most important banks, or even of those who habitually patronize the opera. Such language practices, therefore, if used in these particular social groups attract as much attention as a pair of overalls might at an evening gathering where custom demands formal dress clothes. In fact, part of the significance of the social differences in language habits can well be illustrated by a comparison with clothes. Fundamentally the clothes one wears fulfill the elementary practical functions of comfort by keeping one warm and of modesty by avoiding indecent exposure of one's person. These two practical purposes could just as well be accomplished by rather shapeless simple garments produced over a standard pattern for every one and worn upon all occasions. Such clothes could be made to fulfill their primary functions very efficiently with a minimum of cost. In such a situation, however, aside from the significance of differing degrees of cleanliness, the clothes would show us very little concerning the individuals who wore them. With our present habits of dress the clothes connote or suggest, in a broad general way, certain information concerning the wearers. Among other things they suggest the *circumstances in which we usually see them worn.* A dress suit suggests an evening party (or in some places a hotel waiter); overalls suggest a piece of dirty work or possibly a summer camp. In like manner language forms and constructions not only fulfill a primary function of communicating meaning; they also suggest the circumstances in which those particular forms and constructions are usually employed. If, then, one uses the pronunciations and grammatical forms given earlier in this paragraph, they may serve to communicate his meaning unmistakably, but they will also suggest that he habitually associates with those social groups for whom these language forms are the customary usage and not with those for whom they are not characteristic. We must, therefore, recognize the fact that there are separate social or class groups even in American communities and that these groups differ from one another in many social practices including their language habits.

As indicated earlier the four kinds of differences in language practice here outlined are by no means mutually exclusive. Many historical differences and some sectional differences have become also social differences. For our purpose here the social or class differences are of most concern; other types of differences will be treated only as they bear upon these social or class dialects.

III

In order to grasp the significance of these social differences in language practice for the obligation of the schools one must understand clearly what is meant by "standard" English, and that can perhaps best be accomplished by tracing the course by which a particular kind of English became "standard." As one examines the material written in England during the twelfth and thirteenth centuries—a period from one hundred to two hundred years after the Norman Conquest—he finds a situation in which three things are of especial note:

1. Most of the legal documents, the instruments which controlled the carrying on of the political and the business affairs of the English people, were not written in the English language but in French or in Latin. This fact was also true of much of the literature and books of learning familiar to the upper classes.

2. Although some books, especially historical records and religious and moral stories and tracts, were written in English, there was no single type of the English language common to all English writings. The greatest number used what is called the Southern dialect. This particular kind of English had been centered in Winchester, which was the chief city of King Alfred and his successors until the time of the Norman Conquest.

3. There was, therefore, no "standard" English in twelfth and thirteenth century England, for no single type of the English language furnished the medium by which the major affairs of English people were carried on. Instead, English people used for these purposes French, Latin, and at least four distinct varieties of English. The particular kind of English spoken in southern England came nearest to fulfilling the function of a "standard" English because more writings and more significant writings were produced in this type of English than in any other.

In the fourteenth and early fifteenth centuries, however, this situation changed. London had become the political and in some respects the social head of English life in a much more unified England. Many of the major affairs of the realm had to be handled in London. More and more the English language, the English of London, was used in the legal documents of politics and business. Solely because of the fact that more of the important affairs of English life were conducted in this London English rather than in Winchester English, London English became "standard" English. Naturally, then, the growing use of this particular type of English for the important affairs of English life gathered such momentum that even writers to whom other types of English were more natural felt constrained to learn and to use the fashionable London English. Gower, for example, a Kentishman, did not write his native kind of English but practically the same forms, constructions, and spellings as Chaucer, a Londoner born. Naturally, too, this London English gained a social prestige because of the fact that its use connoted or suggested relations with the center of affairs in English life, whereas the inability to use London English suggested that one did not have such social contacts. "Standard" English, therefore, is, historically, a local dialect, which was used to carry on the major affairs of English life and which gained thereby a social prestige.[16]

[16] "Standard" French, "Standard" Italian, "Standard" Dutch, etc., have similar histories.

Many changes occurred in this dialect of English and these changes especially affected the usage of the younger rather than of the older generations in the centers of fashionable social life. Thus the continued use of the older forms rather than the newer changes always suggested a lack of direct contacts with those who were active in the conduct of important matters. In this connotation lay the power of "standard" English to compel the ambitious to conform to its practices.

In America, however, we have had no one recognized center for our political, business, social, and intellectual affairs. More than that, the great distances between various parts of the United States made very difficult frequent actual social contacts in the earlier days. Our coast cities, Boston and New York, maintained direct relations with London long after the earlier settlers had moved west, but the middle western settlements had practically no relations with Boston and New York. This fact can probably explain the differences between our middle-western speech and that of nineteenth century Boston and New York. Because of the fact that New England so long dominated our intellectual life there has been a good deal of feeling in many parts of the United States that the language usages of New England connoted a connection with a higher culture than did the language of the Middle West. Hence the rather widespread attempt to imitate certain New England speech characteristics. On the whole, however, if we ignore the special differences that separate the speech of New England, the South, and the Middle West, we do have in the United States a set of language habits, broadly conceived, in which the major matters of the political, social, economic, educational, religious life of this country are carried on. To these language habits is attached a certain social prestige, for the use of them suggests that one has constant relations with those who are responsible for the important affairs of our communities. It is this set of language habits, derived originally from an older London English, but differentiated from it somewhat by its independent development in this country, which is the "standard" English of the United States. Enough has been said to enforce the point that it is "standard" not because it is any more correct or more beautiful or more capable than other varieties of English; it is "standard" solely because it is the particular type of English which is used in the conduct of the important affairs of our people. It is also the type of English used by the *socially acceptable* of most of our communities and insofar as that is true it has become a social or class dialect in the United States.

IV

With this analysis it is not difficult to understand the nature of the obligation assumed by our schools in respect to the teaching of the English language. Long have we in our national life adhered to the principle that no individual in his attempts to rise to the highest positions should be disqualified by artificial restraints. Our people have been devoted to education because education has furnished the most important tool of social advancement. Our public schools have therefore held to the ideal that every boy and girl should be so equipped that he shall not be handicapped in his struggle for social progress and recognition, and that he may rise to the highest positions. In the matter of the English language it is clear that any one who cannot use the language habits in which the major affairs of the country are conducted, the language habits of the socially acceptable of most of our communities, would have a serious handicap. The schools, therefore, have assumed the burden of training every boy and girl, no matter what his original social background and native speech, to use this "standard" English, this particular social or class dialect. To some pupils it is almost a foreign language; to others it is their accustomed speech. Many believe that the schools have thus assumed an impossible task. Certainly the widespread and almost unanimous condemnation of the results of their efforts convinces us that either the schools have not conceived their task adequately or they have chosen the wrong materials and methods to accomplish it. We shall find, I think, that seldom have school authorities understood the precise nature of the language task they have assumed and very frequently have directed their energies to teaching not "standard" English realistically described, but a "make-believe" correctness which contained some true forms of real "standard" English and many forms that had and have practically no currency outside the classroom.[17]

A few brief statements will serve both to summarize the preceding discussion and to bring into a single view the principles which underlie this investigation and report.

[17] See, for example, H. B. Allen's article "The Standard of Usage in Freshman Textbooks," in *English Journal* (college ed.), Vol. 24, 1935, pp. 564-571; and R. C. Pooley, *Grammar and Usage in Textbooks on English*, Bulletin 14, Bureau of Educational Research, University of Wisconsin, 1933.

1. All considerations of an *absolute* "correctness" in accord with the conventional rules of grammar or the dicta of handbooks must be set aside, because these rules or these dicta very frequently do not represent the actual practice of "standard" English but prescribe forms which have little currency outside the English classroom. We assume, therefore, that there can be no "correctness" apart from usage and that the *true* forms of "standard" English are those that are actually used in that particular dialect. Deviations from these usages are "incorrect" only when used in the dialect to which they do not belong. These deviations suggest not only the particular social dialect or set of language habits in which they usually occur, but also the general social and cultural characteristics most often accompanying the use of these forms.

2. It is the assumed obligation of the schools to attempt to develop in each child the knowledge of and the ability to use the "standard" English of the United States—that set of language habits in which the most important affairs of our country are carried on, the dialect of the socially acceptable in most of our communities.

3. The first step in fulfilling that obligation is the making of an accurate and realistic survey and description of the actual language practices in the various social or class dialects. Only after we have such information in hand can we know what social connotations are likely to attach to particular usages.

NOTES ON THE INFLECTED GENITIVE IN MODERN AMERICAN PROSE

Russell Thomas

Even today one can still find statements like the following in college textbooks: "Caution: Use an of phrase *instead of the possessive when writing of inanimate objects,"* or *"Do*

From *College English*, January 1953. Reprinted by permission of the author and the National Council of Teachers of English.

not attribute possession to an inanimate object; use an of-phrase." *Such prohibitory "rules" have been handed down for generations in our textbooks, and have been taught unquestioningly to generations of students by teachers who assumed that the "rules" were inviolable. Fortunately this type of teaching according to the "rule" is decreasing. Ever since the recognition of the principle that the ultimate authority of Standard American English is the actual usage of educated people, linguists have been observing and recording the facts of contemporary usage, writers have been incorporating them in their textbooks, and enlightened teachers have been teaching in accordance with these facts. The following essay by Russell Thomas, Professor of English at Northern Michigan College, is one of the many usage studies made in recent years.*

SEVERAL YEARS AGO Professor C. C. Fries showed that the inflected genitive in present-day American English is not confined to the "possessive" meaning.[1] And, after reading his article, I wondered about the status of the inflected genitive when the word inflected names something other than a human being, for, in those examples which Professor Fries lists (except for some which represent either a genitive of measure or the genitive with gerund), the word inflected denotes a human being. Furthermore, inasmuch as many grammarians have condemned the use of this genitive for inanimate objects, I decided to investigate the problem beyond the limits of my previous study[2] as well as those by Fries, Jespersen, Hall, Curme, and other historical grammarians. My results are based upon an examina-

[1] In "Some Notes on the Inflected Genitive in Present-Day English," *Language*, XIV (April-June, 1938), 121-33. His materials consisted of "some three thousand personal letters copied from those in the files of one of the government bureaus at Washington" and revealed that the inflected genitives of nouns were distributed as follows: "Possessive genitive (liberally interpreted)—40%; Subjective genitive 23%; Genitive of origin—6%; Objective genitive—17%; Descriptive genitive—10% and one example each of the Genitive with gerund and the Absolute Genitive."

[2] "Syntactic Processes Involved in the Development of the Adnominal Periphrastic Genitive in the English Language" (unpublished doctoral dissertation, University of Michigan, Ann Arbor, 1931).

tion of, roughly, 10,000-12,000 pages of material, the far greater portion of which dates from 1930 to 1952. It includes works of fiction, critical essays and books, scientific essays and books, book reviews, editorials, news stories, and informal essays.[3]

I have classified my materials (with the exception of one group) on the basis of the meaning of the inflected word, instead of on that which Fries used as indicated in note 1 above. Although my procedure is open to some criticism, I have decided to use it because I feel it clarifies further the whole problem of the construction.[4]

Most readers of this article will be interested at once, I suppose, in what I found concerning the inflected genitive with inanimate objects.[5] I have 47 examples, most of which date within the last ten years. Some of these are "the bed's head," "the building's roof," "a car's axle," "the clock's tick," "the hat's crown," "the big hall's location," "the arrow's shank," "the bomb's angle of contact," etc.

The next group consist of examples where the inflected genitive denotes, as stated in note 5, the general name for an individual publication, such as *book, novel, poem, play*, etc. I have 96 examples, ranging from 1926 to the present, but the greater portion date from within the last six years. This locution seems to be favored by college and university professors and by others who write book reviews for our leading periodicals. I examined certain issues of three periodicals (*Yale Review*, *Nation*, and *Harper's Magazine*) in the 1930's and early 1940's and found that there were fewer examples in these

[3] I excluded all poetry because exigencies of meter very often force the poet to use the inflected genitive. Some of the periodicals which I examined are the *Yale Review, PMLA, Atlantic Monthly, Nation, Harper's Magazine, Saturday Review of Literature, New England Quarterly, Sewanee Review, New Republic, Kenyon Review, et al.*

[4] One of the earliest studies of the problem was published in J. Lesslie Hall's *English Usage* (Chicago: Scott, Foresman & Co., 1917), pp. 202-7. His study of the "possessive case of inanimate objects" is based on "87 authorities and 700 passages" selected from literature dating from John Mandeville down to Stevenson and Chesterton and also includes American authors. However, outside of a few quotations, he makes no attempt to classify his material. For example, he lumps together such locutions as Matthew Arnold's "the creative power's exercise," Poe's "the world's view," Hawthorne's "tomorrow's dinner," Emersons "life's book," and Ruskin's "his table's head."

[5] I have placed in a separate group all inflected words which designate certain publications, such as *books, novels, poems, stories*, etc., because my data show that there has been a slight encroachment of the inflected genitive on the periphrastic (phrasal) genitive with these particular words within the last thirty years.

early issues than in those within the last six years, thus leading me to conclude that locutions of the type included in this group are beginning to encroach upon the phrasal genitive.[6] Examples are "the story's genesis," "the play's philosophy," "a poem's sources," "the book's true importance," "this book's intention," "the novel's rhythm," etc.

In the next group, consisting of 18 excerpts which range from 1940 to the present, the inflected genitive names some branch of knowledge, such as "modern poetry's desertion of the genteel tradition," "fiction's two possible worlds," "art's frontal attacks," "science's influence on society," "archeology's job," and "history's ugliest marauder."

The inflected genitive is used fairly frequently when the writer has in mind some geographic and/or political areas or units, such as "world," "country," "nation," "city," "town," and "region." I have 71 examples of this type, all but one of which date anywhere from 1950 to 1952, the one lone exception dating from 1915. The following is a sampling: "the world's life," "the world's economic organization," "the nation's chief waterways," "the region's lack," "the earth's interior," "the country's name," "the town's foreign flavor," "the city's beauty," "the city's working maelstrom," etc.[7]

Words which denote a certain period of time have shown genitival inflection for centuries. I have 63 examples of this type, varying stylistically from such expressions as "a day's work" to "the next year's baptisms," "the decade's post-mortem," "today's cold war," "a winter's program of reading," "at the year's turn," "November's voters," "the future's course," "today's and tomorrow's business," and "this summer's suspense novels."

The next group, for which I have 104 examples, has a kind of homogeneity in that it includes words which designate a group or body of people more or less closely united—most of them for some

[6] This locution is not, furthermore, an Americanism, for I picked up examples of it from recent British periodicals, such as the *Times* (London) *Literary Supplement* and *The Nineteenth Century* and from essays in criticism by such scholars as E. M. W. Tillyard and Lord David Cecil. This same comment applies also to some of the other groups of locutions discussed in this article.

[7] I have omitted all examples where the inflected genitive designates specific cities, towns, rivers, countries, etc., such as "Los Angeles's story," "Minnesota's placards," "America's future," "Japan's guilt." They occur so frequently that to include them would be as superfluous as shipping iron ore to Upper Michigan.

purpose. But these purposes are of a heterogeneous nature, as will be seen from the following examples: "the Church's corruption," "communism's aims," "Christianity's attackers," "democracy's probable course," "a government's conviction," "the majority's platform," "the right's President," "the court's action," "the party's elder statesmen," "the agency's outlook," "in labor's ranks," "the company's working capital," "the trust's profits," "the railroad's past exploitation," "the law school's failure," etc. I have also included in this group 17 examples of words which denote large blocks or divisions of people who are not united for any specific purpose. Examples: "society's oscillation," "the public's convenience," "the race's oldest and strongest institutions," "humanity's orations," "youth's problems," "childhood's comprehension," etc.

During my reading I collected a small number of examples for each of the words "war," "life," and "mind." For the word "war," I have 12 examples, dating from 1940 to 1952. Examples: "war's growing indecisiveness," "the war's outbreak," "the war's end," "war's cruelty." The data for the word "life" are interesting. I have nine examples from American usage and also one each from an Icelander (the novelist, Anne Crone), a Dane (the late Professor Jespersen), and an Englishman (the Honorable Winston Churchill). The Americans represented come from varied walks of life; a private in the United States Army (in a letter to the London *Times Literary Supplement*), a former dean of women of Brown University, a Methodist pastor, a professor of philosophy at Yale, a columnist, etc. Variety, thy name is human! Some examples are: "life's open air," "life's struggles," "life's security," and "life's purpose." I have but three examples of the word "mind," all from recent material. Examples: "with the mind's general development," "through the mind's last mode of beautiful sound," and "the mind's knowledge of its objects."

The next group consists of 20 examples of expressions which may be classed as "stock formulas," where the important word is the noun which the genitive modifies. These are examples of the influence of analogy. They range from 1915 to the present, but the majority are fairly recent. Some examples follow: "for war's sake," "for experience's sake," "for authority's sake," "for my soul's sake," "for pure virility's sake," "the water's edge," "the valley's edge," "the cliff's edge," "sheep's clothing," "a finger's breadth," "the lion's share," etc.

I found only 14 instances of genitive inflection with the names of animals. One of these dates from 1926, while the others are from the last three years. A few examples are: "the rat's brain," "the bird's leg," "a horse's skeleton," "the dog's collar."

The last group consists of 32 examples which I am unable to classify. Again, the greater portion dates from the last two decades. I list these in alphabetical order:

battle–in the battle's front
benefit–for the benefit's time
bill–the bill's introduction
body–the body's descent
cardboard–the cardboard's time
death–death's tomb
desert–the desert's nature
dollar–four hundred dollars' difference
fleet–our fleet's spectacular cruise
freedom–in freedom's name
garden–the garden's vitality
law–the law's existence
mile–a mile's distance
operation–the operation's end
personality–the personality's urge
polio–polio's behavior
program–the insurance program's failure
project–the project's editors
radio–radio's most human contributions
rain–the rain's midst
rainbow–the rainbow's arch
stock–the stock's descent
strike–the strike's end
sun–the sun's exterior
telegraph–the telegraph's report
television–television's future
thought–a thought's meaning
treaty–the treaty's ratification
valley–the valley's forests
water–the water's uses
wind–the wind's last dissolving sigh
word–a word's function

Table 1 summarizes the data gathered for this study.

TABLE I

Type or Group	No. of Examples
1. Inanimate objects	47
2. Publications	96
3. Branch of knowledge	18
4. Geographic and political areas	71
5. Periods of time	63
6. Groups of people	104
7. Three isolated words ("war," "life," "mind")	24
8. Stock formulas	20
9. Animals	14
10. Miscellaneous (unclassified) words	32
Total	489

In concluding this article, I should like to make a few comments as to the reasons for the use of these inflected genitives, several of which no doubt strike a harsh stylistic note. In the first place, all of them can be traced back to similar examples in the Old English period, when the inflected genitive was used 99.5 per cent of the time, as I demonstrated in my doctoral thesis. Another reason why some of the locutions are present today is that their use lends itself to the practice of piling up pre-noun modifiers, as, for example, in these two excerpts:

> Added to the American public's then moral attitude to such subjects. . . .
>
> There are in the Lockwood Library's Spender notebook, six. . . .

Then, too, I found an occasional example where euphony seemed to demand the inflected genitive. On the other hand, there were instances where the phrasal genitive could have been used just as effectively. Occasionally I found an excerpt, such as the one given below, where the writer used both types in successive sentences, thus:

> What are these things which endanger the position of our colleges? What are these things which jeopardize the college's position?

Of course, it is possible to use an uninflected adjective instead of either type of genitive, as was done by a minister recently, who said, "These are times when religion's flame burns low." And a few minutes later he spoke of "the flame of religion," and then of "the religious flame."

By and large, I do not see that much can be done about ostracizing these constructions. A large portion of my data is from writers who cannot exactly be classed as "skimmed milk." Such novelists as Faulkner, Hemingway, Evelyn Eaton, and Sherwood Anderson, such literary figures as Louis Untermeyer and Archibald MacLeish, such scholars and critics as David Daiches, Howard M. Jones, O. J. Campbell, John Mason Brown, and the *New York Times*—to mention a few sources for my materials—presumably know something about style. In fact, when I sent an inquiry to Professor Campbell about his use of the locution "the play's structure," I received—pronto—a red-hot reply in defense of it.

"THERE IS" AGAIN

Robert J. Geist

The basic word-order pattern of English statements is that of subject followed by verb. The "There is" construction is unusual in that the subject follows the verb. "There," in other words, functions only as a filler; hence it is called an expletive, a word that "fills out" the sentence pattern. Because of this unusual situation, most grammar texts make a special point of reminding the reader to be sure to follow the rule that the verb agrees with the subject in number and person. That actual usage does not always conform to the "rule" is shown by the following study by Robert J. Geist, Professor of English at Michigan State University, East Lansing, Michigan.

In a previous Forum article (Nov., 1952), "without any attempt to insure statistical accuracy" I indicated that, in published writing, after the "there is" formula a compound subject with a singular first

From *College English*, December 1954. Reprinted by permission of the author and the National Council of Teachers of English.

member frequently occurs with a singular verb, probably more frequently than with a plural verb. To gather some statistics about the construction, I read four recent issues of both the *Atlantic Monthly* and *Harper's Magazine* (Dec., 1952, Jan., Feb., Mar., 1953). To discover whether usage had changed in recent years, I also read the eight issues published just thirty years earlier. Approximately 1900 pages provide the following statistics:

	There is	*There are*
Harper's Dec. '52—Mar. '53	18	2
Atlantic Dec. '52—Mar. '53	29	2
Harper's Dec. '22—Mar. '23	36	1
Atlantic Dec. '22—Mar. '23	28	1

The six plural constructions follow:

There were softball and horseshoe pitching for the active boys and men; books, games, music, television, and radio for the less athletic.
Mary Heaton Vorse, *Harper's*, Feb., 1953, p. 88.

There have already been at least one [novel] about a military institute, one about a girls' school out West, and four or five about boys' schools and colleges in New England.
Gilbert Highet, *Harper's*, Feb., 1953, p. 103

. . . there were clothing and shoes for the Army assembled in Boston and no money anywhere for their transportation to the Hudson.
Richard E. Danielson, *Atlantic*, Dec., 1952, p. 76

There were misery, humiliation, nervous breakdowns, and broken homes all around.
Giorgio de Santillana, *Atlantic*, Mar., 1953, p. 58

And there are Lionel Dedwent and his wife, Mabel, being shown in by Annette, the stage maid.
Stephen Leacock, *Harper's*, Mar., 1923, p. 436

There are in it the captain, major, colonel, general, and field marshall, graded according to size.
Ruth Rose, *Atlantic*, Dec., 1922, p. 742.

Sentences using a singular verb illustrate such conceivably relevant factors as the following:

conjunction *and;* no comma

Yet if great books were wanted there was Sir Joshua Reynold's *Discourses* and *Delacroix's Journal.*
Jacques Barzun, *Atlantic,* Dec., 1952, p. 84

comma; no *and*

There is a priceless encounter with Baldwin, a game of croquet with Yeats.
Charles J. Rolo, *Atlantic,* Dec., 1952, p. 99

comma; *and*

. . . there was a general hatred of Asians, and a desire, so far as possible, to have no non-Europeans except Negroes.
Bertrand Russell, *Atlantic,* Dec., 1952, p. 37

series; commas

There is a small dressing room and closet, a dazzling lavatory and shower, and a kitchenette with china and utensils, a gas stove, and a refrigerator.
Charles W. Morton, *Atlantic,* Dec., 1952, p. 104

series; no commas

On one side there was a pump and an outhouse and the foundations of the burned barn.
Frances McFadden, *Harper's,* Jan., 1953, p. 41

intervening words

. . . there is a list of eight directors of the company, including Mr. Alfred Knopf, and a roster of nearly fifty advisers.
Gilbert Highet, *Harper's,* Jan., 1953, p. 96

common modifier

. . . there is too much blood and disease and dirt on the food we eat. . . .
Mary Heaton Vorse, *Harper's,* Feb., 1953, p. 93

inanimate things as subjects
See any of the above.

persons as subjects

. . . there is a tennis trainer in summer and an ice-skating champion in winter.
Joseph Wechsburg, *Atlantic,* Mar., 1953, p. 95

negative subjects

. . . there was no rustle of falling leaves, no high-pitched voices of Chinese, no dulled explosions. . . .
Robert Payne, *Harper's,* Feb., 1953, p. 82.

The statistics from the *Atlantic* and *Harper's* clearly indicate that the singular verb is far more frequent than the plural verb in this construction. In fact, they indicate a higher frequency in favor of the singular than my casual collecting, which has resulted in slightly over 200 *there is* forms against about 30 *there are* forms.

The comparison between 1953 and 1923 reveals no significant change in the last thirty years. . . .

SUGGESTED ASSIGNMENTS

1. Most good dictionaries identify by means of usage labels the level or variety of a particular word or of different senses of a word, e.g., *Colloq., Dial.* In order to discuss usage intelligently you should know what these usage labels mean. Look up the definitions of the following: *archaic, colloquial, dialect, localism, slang, obsolete.* Note especially the meaning of *colloquial;* many people confuse it with *localism* or identify it with *slang.*
2. Are high school and college freshman composition textbooks reliable guides to current usage? This question was investigated by Dr. Jean Malmstrom, who spent five years making a study of 57 items of American usage. Some of her findings have been published in an article entitled "Linguistic Atlas Findings versus Textbook Pronouncements on Current American Usage," *The English Journal*, April, 1959. Read the article and prepare an oral summary of it for your class.
3. Some textbooks still cite elaborate rules for the use of *shall* and *will.* Read Fries' discussion of this topic in his *American English Grammar*, p. 151ff., and make a report to the class on the origin of the rules and their validity.
4. Many composition textbooks and handbooks contain a section on items of usage, often entitled "Glossary of Usage" or "Glossary of Diction" (sometimes "Faulty Diction"), with comments about the acceptability or nonacceptability of these items as Standard American English and their appropriateness to various language situations. Compare the judgments of any three textbooks about each of the following: *aggravate, different from-different than, due to, enthuse, farther-further, like, who-whom* (interrogative). Then look up each of the items in three dictionaries, compare the dictionary statements with each other and with your original findings, and present your data to the class for discussion.
5. The whole of the English language can be partitioned into various groupings. In the readings of this section, we have seen it divided into two social dialects, standard and nonstandard English. Still another grouping consists of those words which are used in limited areas of

discourse, like the special vocabularies of skiers, carpenters, astronauts, skin divers, and so on. Such specialized groups of words are called shoptalk.

Make a list of shoptalk expressions in a particular area of life with which you are familiar, e.g., jazz, trout fishing, hi-fi, boxing, amateur radio work, dog raising, woodworking, painting, stamp collecting, theater, hot rods. Include only those expressions that you believe are not understood by the general public. Bring them to class, where a discussion of the lists will probably reveal how much of our own language many of us do not know.

6. Running through all varieties of English is a special vein called slang. Slang is a roguish kind of language. At its best it is piquant and picturesque, and holds for us the black-sheep attraction of forbidden pleasures. But when the novelty of a new slang expression wears thin, its sparkle dwindles away and it becomes dull as an old penny. Although slang cannot be defined with precision, most students of language will probably agree that the following statements can be made about it:
   a. It occurs more frequently in speech than in writing.
   b. It is found in both standard and nonstandard English.
   c. It seems to originate from a desire for novelty and freshness of expression.
   d. It tends to change more rapidly than the rest of the language.
   e. It consists largely of these kinds of words:
      (1) Old words with new meanings.
      (2) Newly invented words.
      (3) Standard words used in a figurative sense.
      (4) Words borrowed from shoptalk.
      (5) Clipped words.[1]

   Meet with a friend and see how many slang expressions you can jot down in fifteen minutes. Classify them according to the divisions under *e*. How would you classify those that you have left over?
7. The youth of each generation seems to have its special slang terms to express such meanings as these: an attractive girl, a handsome young man, an objectionable person, a girl of questionable virtue, a girl of impregnable virtue, a dance, a party, drunk, very good, very bad. What are your slang terms, if any, for these meanings? Interview a person of middle age whom you suspect of having had a lively youth and write a theme comparing his or her slang with yours.
8. Write a theme on one of these subjects:
   a. Slang, Sparkling and Stale

[1] A clipped word is a word that has been reduced to one of its parts. Examples: *lab, exam, plane, phone, flu, still, co-ed, prom.* [eds.]

b. Slang That Has Endured
c. Some Slang of the 19th Century
d. Slang of the Sports Page
e. The Slang My Father Used

9. Write a paragraph describing a person or relating an event in nonstandard English. Then write a second paragraph doing the same in standard English. In class, when students' paragraphs are compared, be prepared to comment on such matters as liveliness, breadth of vocabulary, complexity of sentence structure, and grammatical forms.
10. Imagine that you are interested in getting a job at a summer camp as a counselor. Write a close friend about it, explaining why you think you are qualified for the job. Then write a letter of application to the camp director setting forth your qualifications. Try to write naturally in each case, adapting your language to the recipient.

FURTHER READINGS

1. Allen, Harold B., ed. *Readings in Applied English Linguistics*. New York: Appleton-Century-Crofts, Inc., 1958. See especially the section "Linguistics and Usage," pp. 193-294.
2. Baugh, Albert C. *A History of the English Language*, 2d ed. New York: Appleton-Century-Crofts, Inc., 1957. For discussion of the eighteenth-century grammarians and their attitude towards the language, see Chapter 9.
3. Evans, Bergen and Cornelia Evans. *A Dictionary of Contemporary American Usage*. New York: Random House, Inc., 1957.
4. Fries, Charles C. *The Teaching of English*. Ann Arbor, Michigan: George Wahr Publishing Co., 1949. See especially Chapter I, "The Rules of Grammar as the Measure of Language Errors;" Chapter II, "Standards of Acceptable English: Grammar;" Chapter III, "Standards of Acceptable English: Vocabulary."
5. Hall, Robert A., Jr., *Linguistics and Your Language*. New York: Doubleday & Company, Inc., 1960. See Chapter 1, "Which Should I Say?" and Chapter 2, "Right vs. Wrong."
6. Jesperson, Otto. *Mankind, Nation and Individual*. London: George Allen & Unwin, Ltd., 1946.
7. Laird, Charlton. *The Miracle of Language*. Cleveland: The World Publishing Company, 1953. See Chapter 6, "The King's English in a Democratic World."
8. Perrin, Porter G. *Writer's Guide and Index to English*, 3d ed. Chicago: Scott, Foresman and Company, 1959. On varieties of English, see Chapter 1.
9. Robertson, Stuart and Frederic G. Cassidy. *The Development of*

Modern English. Englewood Cliffs, New Jersey: Prentice-Hall, Inc., 1954. See pp. 291-325.
Several periodicals frequently publish articles on usage, especially *American Speech, College English,* and *The English Journal.* The latter two have a section devoted to usage: "Current English Forum" in *College English* and "Current English" in *The English Journal.*

7. Linguistic Geography

SOME WORDS STOP AT MARIETTA, OHIO

Gledhill Cameron

Linguistic geography, also called dialect geography, is the systematic study of language differences within a specified area, usually a country or a part of a country. The differences are those of pronunciation, vocabulary, and grammar. To get accurate information, trained linguists hold long interviews with native informants, who have been carefully selected so as to offer a representative sampling of the speech of the area.

When all the information has been collected and edited, it is made public by a series of maps (See pages 331, 352, 353) or by books and articles. As a result, we get a detailed account of both regional and social dialects.[1] *One caution*

[1] The 416 informants for the *Linguistic Atlas of New England* were classified into these types:

"Type I: Little formal education, little reading and restricted social contacts.
Type II: Better formal education (usually high school) and/or wider reading and social contacts.
Type III: Superior education (usually college), cultured background, wide reading and/or extensive social contacts.
Type A: Aged, and/or regarded by the field worker as old-fashioned.
Type B: Middle-aged or younger, and/or regarded by the field worker as more modern."

From Hans Kurath, *Handbook of the Linguistic Geography of New England* (Washington, D. C.: American Council of Learned Societies, 1939), p. 44.

With this information we can generalize on the social class using any given *must be urged here. As you study the data in the readings of this section, you must remember that this information pertains to the SPOKEN language, and may or may not be true of the written language.*

The first reading below, by Gledhill Cameron, is an entertaining but sound report on the field work of the linguistic geographer.

WHAT LANGUAGE do you speak? Would you call it "plain American"? If so, you may be surprised to learn that despite the vast influence of radio, TV, the movies, magazines, books and national advertising, many of the words and expressions you use every day might not even be understood by people elsewhere in the United States—who also speak "plain American."

If you're a housewife, do you make bacon and eggs in a frying pan—or, as many other American women do, in a *spider*, *creeper*, or *drip-drop?* When you clean house, do you *straighten up* or *tidy up*, *rid up* or *redd up* (as women do in some parts of New England, Ohio and Indiana); *make ménage* (as in New Orleans), or *muck out* (as in some Colorado mining communities)?

If Junior sneaks away from school, do your neighbors say he *skips*, *bags* or *lays out of* school, or that he *plays hooky* or *hooks Jack?* When he reports on how he spent his time, does he tell you he climbed trees, or that he *clim*, *clum*, *clome*, *cloom*, *clam* or *clammed* them? If he ate too many green apples, does he get sick *to*, *at*, *in*, *with* or *about* his stomach?

To chart the differences in vocabulary, grammar and pronunciation from one American community to another, a small band of language experts—professors and graduate students representing a number of universities—has been traveling around the country for the last 20 years, asking people what words they use for all sorts of simple, everyday objects and actions. They have compiled long lists of variants for everything from the words for the clavicles of a chicken (*wishbone*, *witch bone*, *pull bone*, *pully bone*, *lucky bone*, *merry-*

---

pronunciation, word, or grammatical form. In other words, we can decide which forms are standard English and which are nonstandard English, also called "substandard English" and "vulgate." [eds.]

thought) to our expressions for the woman who's going to have a baby (she might be *in health*, *in the family way*, *in preggety*, *on the road to Boston*, *fragrant* or *footbroke*—the last a local Southern expression derived from an African word).

Sometimes the linguistic geographers use tape or disc recordings, but most of their minutely detailed data are collected in thousands of bulky notebooks, in a special phonetic script which can reproduce about 400 differences in vowel sounds alone. Using this script, the interviewers write down the casual conversations of men and women all over America exactly as they talk on their own front porches (*stoops*, *piazzas*, *galleries*).

The linguistic fieldworker must be part historian and part sociologist; he must also have in him the spirit of the bloodhound and more than a trace of the gossip. He will go wherever he can find an informant willing to give the six to 20 hours it takes to answer his questions, which cover from 500 to 800 items of everyday speech. The language experts have carried their notebooks into saloons, cotton fields, race tracks, mines, hospitals, schools, courthouses, shops and factories. One linguist obtained a fruitful interview while riding around in a patrol car with the chief of police of a small Southern town, then got another by sitting for hours on a sidewalk curb, chatting with his subject.

A second researcher spent one whole day quizzing a hard-working barber; another day talking to a railroad-crossing watchman who kept a nervous lookout for the road detective (visitors, inquiring professors included, were contrary to regulations); another day perched on a tractor interviewing a farmer; and another in a hospital, where the subject was recovering from an unexpected operation which had interrupted their first interview.

The information so exhaustively collected is going into a colossal work titled *Linguistic Atlas of the United States and Canada* (Canada is included to cover colloquial expressions which ignore the international boundary). When the atlas is finished, an estimated 10 years from now, it will contain thousands of maps showing local and regional speech differences and the geographical boundaries, called isoglosses, that limit the areas in which the words and expressions are used. The work is being done under the direction of the University of Michigan's Dr. Hans Kurath—an internationally known linguist who has been a leader of the atlas project since its origin in 1929.

AT WORK ON MANY LINGUISTIC ATLASES

The atlas actually will consist of a series of regional sets, the first of which, *Linguistic Atlas of New England*, already has been published. Its six volumes (price for the set: $185) were brought out by Brown University and the American Council of Learned Societies from 1939 to 1943, at a cost of about $250,000. Additional atlases are in various stages of completion, two at the University of Michigan, and others at the Universities of Minnesota, Colorado, New Mexico and California, the University of Washington at Seattle and Louisiana State University. Preliminary studies have been made for still another at the University of Texas.

Three kinds of map are used by the researchers to plot variations. First there's the lexical map, which shows the different words Americans use to indicate the same object or action. For example, "something extra" is *lagniappe* in New Orleans, something *to boot* in Kentucky, a *brawtus* in Charleston, South Carolina, a *pillon* in New Mexico—all good American words.

The linguists use a second, phonetic map to show differences in the pronunciation of the same words. The classic example is provided by the old lady in North Carolina who said about her crop of tomatoes, "Oh, we'll eat what we *kin*, and what we *cain't* we'll *can*."

The morphological map, the third type, indicates differences in grammar. Widespread education is rapidly wiping out grammatical variations, the linguists have found. One Georgia man summed up the changes that are occurring: "I used to say, 'I drink water' and 'I have drinked,' " he proudly told an atlas fieldworker. "Now I say, 'I drink,' 'I drank' and 'I have drank.' "

Most of the regional departures from the common language of Americans (technically, we all speak what linguists call American English) involve the homey aspects of life: family relationships, kitchens and cookery, farm work, daily chores, children's play and other activities which are relatively immune from outside influences. Some of these localisms are confined to very small geographic areas, says Dr. Kurath. If you say *hook Jack*, meaning to be absent from school without leave, you are most probably from Cape Cod. If you call cows by hollering *chay!*, you're from Williamsburg County, South Carolina. If you're an old-timer from eastern Long Island, you might call a barnyard or cowpen a *pightle* (it rhymes with "title").

New England, which had many isolated settlements in colonial times, still carries the traces of that isolation in its current colloquialisms. A deep-dish apple pie is *apple Jonathan* in Rhode Island, *apple grunt* around Plymouth and on Cape Cod, in Massachusetts, and *apple slump* in the Narragansett-Bay region. A garbage pail is an *orts pail* in Essex County, Massachusetts, and (as far as the researchers can tell) nowhere else. A spring onion is a *rareripe* only in certain sections of eastern New England.

According to some people in the great valley of Pennsylvania, a horse doesn't whinny, it *laughs,* and a setting hen may be known in the same region as a *clook.*

Judging from research to date, it's only in Indiana that a child coasting down a hill on a sled or wagon goes *bellity-bump;* and only around New London that he goes *belly-kuhchunk!* In the upper Midwest he may go downhill *boy fashion* and in Louisiana he'll go *scooting* or *head fo'most.* In other parts of the country he may go *belly flop, gut, bunt, bump, bumpus, button, bust, booster, wop, whack, womp, slide, slam, kuhchug* or *grinder.*

A QUAINT TALE OF COURTSHIP

The rural areas retain some of the most colorful speech localisms. In some sparsely settled parts of Maine, for example, you might still hear of a *gorming* (stupid) man who gets *all of a biver* (excited) about a *ding-clicker* (a pretty young woman) and invites her to a *hog-wrestle* (a dance). But he wouldn't propose until he was sure she wasn't *pizen neat* (too neat) or a *drozzel tail* (slovenly person).

It's also in the more remote sections that linguistic geographers report the greatest resistance to interviews. One of the most successful of the atlas fieldworkers is Dr. Raven Ioor McDavid, Jr., of Western Reserve University, Cleveland,[2] a South Carolinian who has conducted chatty sessions with 470 housewives, farmers, lumbermen, miners, businessmen, politicians, Civil War veterans, literary ladies and stenographers all over the country. Dr. McDavid recalls an occasion in Georgia where he couldn't get *anyone* to talk to him. He finally discovered that the small town he was visiting had recently been described by a metropolitan newspaper as a "typical hick town." The citizens were now so sensitive that almost no one was willing to talk to any stranger, whatever his apparent purpose. (The

[2] Now at the University of Chicago. [eds.]

local grocer eventually consented to see McDavid—after insisting that the interview be conducted in the back of his store, at night.)

In his home state of South Carolina, McDavid—who customarily carries 15 or 16 colored pencils, mechanical pencils and fountain pens in his pocket for marking symbols—was accused of being an FBI agent by a man who shut the door on him.

Dr. Harold B. Allen of the University of Minnesota, who has conducted almost 200 interviews for the Atlas of the Upper Midwest, says he was accused of being a Communist spy once, by a hardware merchant in Bemidji, Minnesota. ("Who else," said the hardwareman reasonably, "would ask all those questions?")

The late Dr. Guy S. Lowman, Jr., who did most of the field interviews for the New England, Middle and South Atlantic regions, once came out of a house in West Virginia to find the air let out of his automobile tires. (He had been mistaken for a revenuer.) Another time he was chased out of a house by the irate son of a genteel Southern lady, who felt that the linguist had put an indelicate question to his mother: "Madam, what do you call the male kind of cow?" (Cityfolk may not realize it, but the word "bull" is never used in mixed company in some parts of the country. Among the more polite substitutes linguistic geographers have recorded are the *masculine*, rhyming with "vine" and heard only on Nantucket Island, Massachusetts, and in West Virginia, the *surley*, in eastern New Mexico and some parts of Texas, and, more generally, the *old man*, the *roarer*, the *mister*, the *master*, *male critter*, *toro*, *gentleman cow*, *preacher cow*, *beast*, *brute*, *jock*, *major*, *top cow*, *tuppin' ox*, *ranger* and the *he*.)

But fieldworkers get only too hospitable a welcome in most places. That is one of the joys, as well as one of the burdens, of a linguistic geographer's life. In the good cause of recording our American speech, they have eaten veritable mountains of home-made cakes, pies, cookies, breads and biscuits of varying degrees of specific gravity, as well as countless doughnuts (*crullers*, *olicooks*, *fat-cakes*, *fried cakes*, *riz doughnuts*, *fossnocks*).

McDavid recalls with satisfaction the day he shared a lunch of mule ears or meat pastys (it rhymes with "nasty") with miners in northern Michigan, and heard a classic argument as to whether the pastys, which provide the miners with a substantial midday meal, keep better carried in the shirt or in the boot.

But a home-cooked meal in Georgia in "lay-by time," when the cotton is opening up and before it's ready to pick, is best remembered as the occasion for what McDavid, who prides himself on "blending in with the foliage," describes as his greatest tribute.

"The lunch was a mess of something pretty greasy and full of red pepper," he says, "but I fell to. I noticed my informant's elderly sister, who had cooked the meal, watching me with great satisfaction. Then she said: 'I could have gone and kilt a chicken, Mr. McDavid. But I figured *you* didn't want to be treated like no preacher.' "

The fieldworkers admit that it is surprising that people are willing to be interviewed and to talk long, readily and freely. Except in the most general way, they aren't told exactly what the interview is about; if they knew, they might become self-conscious—and it's the unguarded response of natural, everyday conversation that the linguist hopes to capture.

Armed with lists of the kinds of words he wants the subject to use, the researcher conducts the interview in as close an approximation to casual conversation as he can. He must also be keenly alert to pronunciation and grammar. McDavid usually starts out with what he calls shotgun questions: "What do you call this room that we're in?" "What are those utensils on the stove?" "What do you call other rooms in the house?" The fieldworker never asks a subject to repeat, and answers are never directly suggested.

"For example," explains Dr. Allen, "I'll say to the person, 'I suppose you fry your eggs in a . . .' then he'll take it from there and fill in 'skillet' or 'frying pan' or whichever word comes most naturally. Often he'll look surprised that I don't know. Each person requires a different approach. We ask about familiar things—expressions of time, weather, farm crops, and utensils, vehicles, animals, food, the family and its relations, the human body, social life and institutions, religion and so on.

"I usually start out by explaining we're making a study of the changing names for things. That pleases the old folks, who have thought all along that kids nowadays are pretty dumb not to know the difference between a 'hame' and a 'chokestrap' (parts of a harness)."

A community is selected for interviews only after a careful study of its history, population shifts and the influence of foreign groups who may have settled there. McDavid wouldn't be surprised, for example, to hear a native of Hudson, New York, say he *ran afoul of* something, instead of *ran across* or *ran onto*. The seafaring expression comes naturally in Hudson because it was settled by whalers from Nantucket, Massachusetts.

Around Marietta, Ohio, he'd be prepared to hear people use such New England terms as *pail* instead of bucket, *chipmunk* instead of ground squirrel, and *boss!* instead of *sook* when they call a cow—although the second expressions are the more common elsewhere in Ohio. A New England commercial company once sent an entire community to Marietta early in its settlement days, so that linguists today call Marietta and its environs a Yankee "speech island."

The linguistic geographer tries to talk to two distinct types of people in each community studied. The first type is an older person with family roots deep in the community, someone with limited education, and with few outside social contacts which might tend to blur or even erase certain localisms from his speech. The second type is younger, usually middle-aged, with more education and broader social contacts or travel experience. In some communities, a third type of informant—representing the "cultivated" speech of the community—is also interviewed. By sampling the speech of these three groups, the linguist can determine which local expressions are used by everyone in the community, which tend to disappear, and, if so, what replaces them as the community grows more educated or "cultured." An interesting discovery: one town's speech vulgarity may be a perfectly acceptable regionalism in another community, even among the "cultivated" inhabitants.

Linguists believe that recording the living language of America for the first time should lead to a more realistic approach to the teaching of English in schools and colleges. For, they ask, isn't it a waste of time for English teachers to try to stop New Englanders from saying "hadn't ought to" when linguistic studies show that this grammatically "wrong" expression is used by nearly everyone in New England, educated or not? Or to try to remove "ain't" from the speech of Southerners, when it is generally accepted in the colloquial speech of cultivated persons in the South?

Thus far, a major fact established by atlas investigations is that although there's a popular idea of Northern and Southern speech, divided by the Mason and Dixon's line in the Eastern part of the country, there are, in fact, three distinct speech areas in the East. The third is a clear Midland dialect area between North and South, corresponding to the Pennsylvania settlement area of early days. The North-Midland speech boundary runs in a westerly direction from below Sandy Hook in New Jersey through northern Pennsylvania; the line separating Midland from South runs in a southwesterly direction from Dover, Delaware, through Baltimore and along the Blue Ridge in Virginia. And in the Eastern states from Maine to South Carolina, linguistic geographers can plot 18 dialect divisions largely created by the original colonial settlements and the subsequent routes of migration.

This Eastern coastal area, oldest in point of settlement, still retains the nation's greatest diversity of speech from one community to another. But then, as the dialect divisions flow westward on the map—the way our population did—they begin to unravel, and strands of the three begin to overlap.

"Man takes his speech ways with him wherever he goes," Dr. Kurath explains. "The three main types of English were carried westward and blended into new regional varieties; new words were coined, old words came to be used in new senses, and words were borrowed from the Indian languages, from the German and Scandinavian languages spoken in the Midwest, and from the Spanish of the Southwest. But the main stock of English vocabulary in this country is nevertheless clearly derived from the earlier settlements on the Atlantic slope."

While the trend today is away from regional words and expressions, linguistic geographers don't anticipate complete uniformity in the speech of democratic America—where the way we talk, as well as the way we live, is based on the belief that men can be different, and still be equal.

"While some vocabulary and grammatical differences may disappear," says Dr. McDavid, "the differences in word pronunciation are likely to persist. I don't think anyone can impose a single set of patterns on Americans—for speech or for anything else."

The assignments for all the essays in this section have been placed on page 357.

REGIONAL AND SOCIAL VARIATIONS

Albert H. Marckwardt

In this selection Albert H. Marckwardt, Professor of English at the University of Michigan, discusses the origins of American regional dialects, explains the making of a linguistic atlas, and presents information on class or social dialects. Professor Marckwardt is director of the Linguistic Atlas of the North-Central States *project, which includes the territory of Wisconsin, Michigan, Illinois, Kentucky, Ohio, Indiana, and part of Ontario. The materials for this area are now at the University of Michigan, and preliminary editing has been begun.*

THE ENGLISH LANGUAGE is spoken natively in America by no less than 145 million persons over an area of some three million square miles. Various parts of the United States differ considerably from each other with respect to climate, topography, plant and animal life, economic conditions, and social structure. Sociologists and historians recognize at least six regional cultures within the continental borders of the country. The assumption that differences in culture and environmental background bring about differences in language will[1] justify the inference that the language is likely not to be uniform throughout the country. The American novelist John Steinbeck in his *Grapes of Wrath* offers convincing evidence of the plausibility of this assumption:

"I knowed you wasn't Oklahomy folks. You talk queer kinda—That ain't no blame, you understan'."

[1] Text slightly but not materially altered by permission of the author. [eds.]

"Everbody says words different," said Ivy. "Arkansas folks says 'em different, and Oklahomy folks says 'em different. And we seen a lady from Massachusetts, an' she said 'em differentest of all. Couldn' hardly make out what she was sayin'."

Early travelers to America and native commentators on the language agree on the existence of regional differences at an early period in our national history. Mrs. Anne Royal called attention to various Southernisms in the works which she wrote during the second quarter of the nineteenth century, and as early as 1829, Dr. Robley Dunglison had identified many of the Americanisms, in the glossary he compiled, with particular portions of the country. Charles Dickens recognized regional differences in the English he encountered in his first tour of the United States, and William Howard Russell, reporting on Abraham Lincoln't first state banquet, at which he was a guest, mentions his astonishment at finding "a diversity of accent almost as great as if a number of foreigners had been speaking English."

A number of other observers, however, were sufficiently impressed by the uniformity of the language throughout the country to make this a matter of comment. De Tocqueville, in a rather extended treatment of the language of the young republic, flatly declared, "There is no patois in the New World," and John Pickering, along with Noah Webster easily the most distinguished of our early philologists, also remarked on the great uniformity of dialect through the United States, "in consequence," as he said, "of the frequent removals of people from one part of our country to another."

There is truth in both types of comment. People in various parts of the United States do not all speak alike, but there is greater uniformity here than in England or in the countries of Western Europe, and this makes the collection of a trustworthy body of information upon the regional variations in American English a somewhat difficult and delicate matter.

The gathering of authentic data on the dialects of many of the countries of Western Europe began in the latter decades of the nineteenth century. The *Atlas linguistique de la France* followed closely upon the heels of the *Sprachatlas des deutschen Reichs*, and the activities of the English Dialect Society were initiated about the same time. In 1889 a group of American scholars organized the American Dialect Society, hoping that the activities of this organization might result in a body of material from which either a dialect dictionary or a series of linguistic maps, or both, might be compiled. The society remained relatively small, however, and although some valuable information appeared in its journal *Dialect Notes*, a systematic survey of the regional varieties of American English has not yet resulted from its activities.

The past quarter of a century, however, has seen the development of such a survey. Beginning in 1928, a group of researchers under the direction of Professor Hans Kurath, now of the University of Michigan, undertook the compilation of a *Linguistic Atlas of New England* as the first unit of a projected *Linguistic Atlas of the United States and Canada*. The New England atlas, comprising a collection of some 600 maps, each showing the distribution of a single language feature throughout the area, was published over the period from 1939 to 1943. Since that time, field work for comparable atlases of the Middle Atlantic and of the South Atlantic states has been completed, and the materials are awaiting editing and publication. Field records for atlases of the North Central states and the Upper Middle West are virtually complete, and significant beginnings have been made in the Rocky Mountain and the Pacific Coast areas. Surveys in Louisiana, in Texas, and in Ontario are also under way. It is perhaps not too optimistic to predict that within the next twenty-five years all of the United States and Canada as well will have been covered in at least an initial survey.

For a number of reasons it is not easy to collect a body of valid and reliable information on American dialects. The wide spread of education, the virtual extinction of illiteracy, the extreme mobility of the population—both geographically and from one social class to another—and the tremendous development of a number of media of mass communication have all contributed to the recession of local speech forms. Moreover, the cultural insecurity of a large portion of the American people has caused them to feel apologetic about their language. Consequently, they seldom display the same degree of pride or affection that many an English or a European speaker has for his particular patois. Since all dialect research is essentially a sampling process, this means that the investigator must take particular pains to secure representative and comparable samples from the areas which are studied. Happily, the very care which this demands has had the result of developing the methodology of linguistic geography in this country to a very high level.

In general, the material for a linguistic atlas is based upon the natural responses of a number of carefully selected individuals representing certain carefully chosen communities, which in themselves reflect the principal strains of settlement and facets of cultural development in the area as a whole. Since the spread of education generally results in the disappearance of local or regional speech forms, and since the extension of schooling to virtually all of the population has been an achievement of the past seventy-five years, it became necessary for the American investigator to differentiate between the oldest generation, for whom schooling beyond the elementary level is not usual, and a middle-aged group who is likely to have had some experience with secondary schools. In addition, it is highly desirable to include some representatives of the standard or cultivated speech in each region, that their language may serve as a basis of comparison with the folk speech. Accordingly, in the American atlases, from each community represented, the field worker will choose at least two, and sometimes three representatives, in contrast to the usual practice of European researchers, who may safely content themselves with one. Moreover, it is equally necessary to make certain that the persons chosen in any community have not been subject to alien linguistic influences; consequently, only those who have lived there all of their lives, and preferably those who represent families who have long been identified with the area in question, are interviewed, although as one moves westward into the more recently settled areas this is not always possible.

Since complete materials are available only for the eastern seaboard and for the area north of the Ohio River as far west as the Mississippi, tentative conclusions relative to the regional variations in American English can be presented only for the eastern half of the country. The principal dialect areas presented in Kurath's *Word Geography of the Eastern United States* are indicated on the accompanying map.

The three major dialect boundaries, it will be noted, cut the country into lateral strips and are labeled by Professor Kurath *Northern*, *Midland*, and *Southern* respectively. The line which separates the Northern and Midland areas begins in New Jersey a little below Sandy Hook, proceeds northwest to the east branch of the Susquehanna near Scranton, Pennsylvania, then goes westward through Pennsylvania just below the northern tier of counties. In Ohio the boundary dips below the Western Reserve, then turns northwest again, passing above Fort Wayne, Indiana. When it approaches South Bend it dips slightly to the southwest and cuts through Illinois, reaching the Mississippi at a point slightly above Quincy. The other principal boundary, that separating the Southern and Midland areas, begins at a point somewhat below Dover in Delaware, sweeps through Baltimore in something of an arc, turns sharply southwest north of

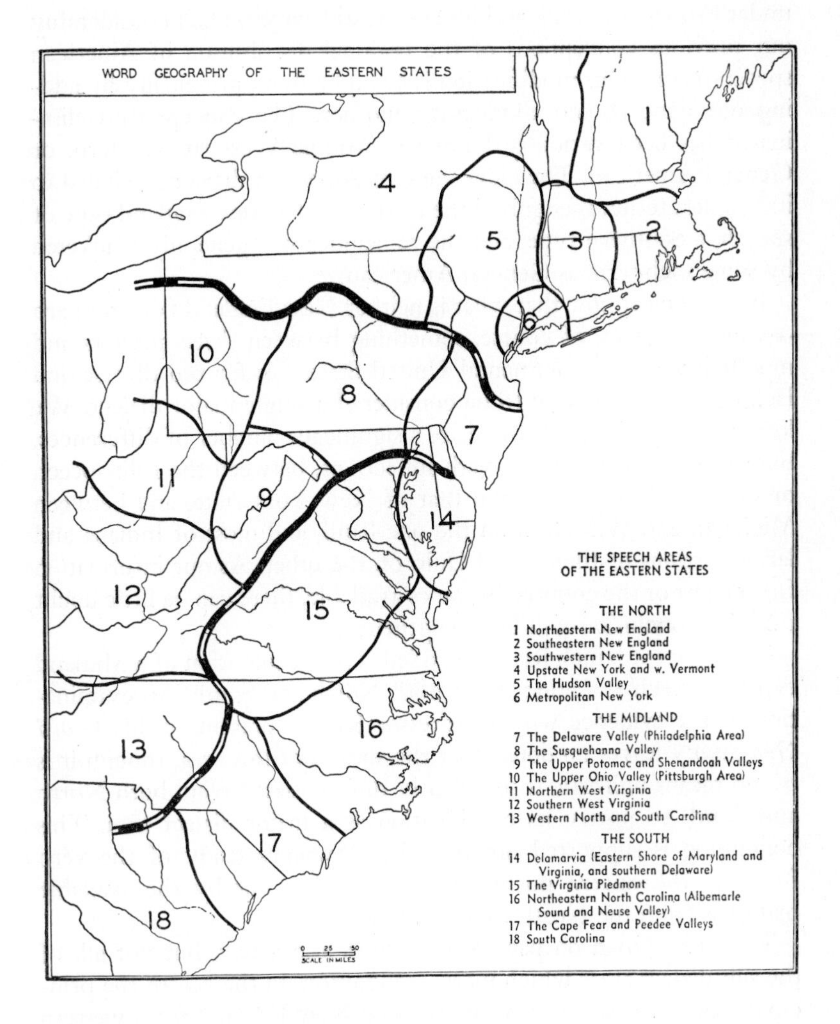

From *A Word Geography of the Eastern United States* by Hans Kurath. Reprinted by permission of the publisher, The University of Michigan Press, copyright 1949.

the Potomac, follows the crest of the Blue Ridge in Virginia, and south of the James River swerves out into the North Carolina Piedmont. As we approach the lower part of South Carolina and Georgia the boundary is as yet unknown.

Even these necessarily incomplete results of the survey carried on under Professor Kurath and his associates have modified considerably our previous conceptions of the regional distribution of American speech forms. This modification is brought about principally by adding one concept and eliminating another. The concept thus eliminated has been variously known as Middle Western, Western, or General American. The older view of American dialects, reduced to its simplest terms, recognized the existence of a New England type of speech, a Southern type, and the remainder was generally blanketed by some such term as General American.

It seems clear now that what is neither New England nor Southern —which includes, of course, something between three-quarters and nine-tenths of the continental United States—is far too diverse and lacking in homogeneity to be considered a single major dialect. We know, for example, that there are a significant number of differences, both in vocabulary and in verb inflections, between the folk speech of most of Pennsylvania and that of New York state, and between Michigan and Wisconsin on the one hand, and most of Indiana and large portions of Illinois and Ohio on the other. As our information for the rest of the country becomes available, there can be little doubt that this conclusion will be strengthened.

The concept which has been added is the recognition of a Midland type of speech as distinct from both North and South. An examination of the evidence which Professor Kurath presents in his *Word Geography* leaves no doubt that the speech of this area, though it is by no means uniform, is sufficiently differentiated from both North and South to justify its classification as a major dialect area. This conclusion is supported not only by Atwood's study of the verb forms in the eastern portion of the country but by the available materials from the North Central States.

The map shown on page 331 includes also a few, but not all, of the sub-dialect areas which merit recognition. In the North the principal area is that which separates coastal New England from western New England, New York state, and the territory to the west. In general, this boundary follows the line of the Green Mountains, the Berkshire Hills, and the Connecticut River. The Metropolitan New

York area consists of a board circle with the city itself at the center; the Hudson Valley area encompasses the original Dutch settlements in New York and northern New Jersey, spreading into northeastern Pennsylvania. The Midland area is divided into northern and southern sub-areas, the line of demarcation being just a little south of the Old National Road in Ohio, Indiana, and Illinois. Within the Southern dialect region, the Virginia Piedmont and the Delmarva peninsula constitute distinct sub-areas.

Thus far it is the lexical materials gathered in connection with the various atlas projects which have been analyzed most extensively, and as the title of Professor Kurath's work indicates, his plotting of the major dialect areas is based upon vocabulary evidence. For example, characteristic Northern expressions that are current throughout the area include *pail*, *swill*, *whiffletree* or *whippletree*, *comforter* or *comfortable* for a thick quilt, *brook*, *co-boss* or *come-boss* as a cow call, *johnnycake*, *salt pork*, and *darning needle* for a dragonfly. In the Midland area we find *blinds* for roller shades, *skillet*, *spouting* or *spouts* for eaves, a *piece* for food taken between meals, *snake feeder* for a dragonfly, *sook* as the call to calves, *armload* for an armful of wood; and one *hulls* beans when he takes off the shells. A quarter *till* the hour is a typical Midland expression, as is the elliptical *to want off*, or *out*, or *in*. The South has *lightwood* as the term for kindling, a *turn* of wood for an armful; stringbeans are generally *snap beans*; *hasslet* is the term for the edible inner organs of a pig, *chittlins* for the small intestine; and in this area cows are said to *low* at feeding time.

The sub-dialect areas also have their characteristic forms. In coastal New England, for instance, *pigsty* is the normal term for pigpen, *bonny clapper* for curdled sour milk, *buttonwood* for a sycamore, and *pandowdy* for a cobbler type of dessert. Eastern Virginia has *cuppin* for a cowpen, *corn house* for a crib. *Lumber room* survives as the term for a storeroom. A grasshopper is known as a *hopper grass*, and *batter bread* is used for a soft cornbread containing egg.

As far as the sectors of the American lexicon which reflect regional differences are concerned, the matter is trenchantly summarized in Kurath's *Word Geography*, where the author points out first of all that the vocabularies of the arts and sciences, of industries, commercial enterprises, social and political institutions, and even many of the crafts, are national in scope because the activities they reflect are organized on a national basis. He then goes on to say:

Enterprises and activities that are regionally restricted have, on the other hand, a considerable body of regional vocabulary which, to be sure, may be known in other parts of the country, even if it is not in active use. The cotton planter of the South, the tobacco grower, the dairy farmer, the wheat grower, the miner, the lumberman, and the rancher of the West have many words and expressions that are strictly regional and sometimes local in their currency.

Regional and local expressions are most common in the vocabulary of the intimate everyday life of the home and the farm—not only among the simple folk and the middle class but also among the cultured . . . Food, clothing, shelter, health, the day's work, play, mating, social gatherings, the land, the farm buildings, implements, the farm stocks and crops, the weather, the fauna and flora—these are the intimate concern of the common folk in the countryside, and for these things expressions are handed down in the family and the neighborhood that schooling and reading and a familiarity with regional or national usage do not blot out.

It is not only in the vocabulary that one finds regional differences in American speech. There are pronunciation features as well. Throughout the Northern area, for example, the distinction between [o] and [ɔ] in such word pairs as *hoarse* and *horse, mourning* and *morning* is generally maintained; [s] regularly occurs in *grease* (verb) and *greasy*, and *root* is pronounced by many with the vowel of *wood*.[2] Within the Northern area such sub-dialects as coastal New England and Metropolitan New York also show many characteristic forms; the treatment of the vowel of *bird* is only one of these, and words of the *calf, pass, path, dance* group constitute another. In the Midland area speakers fail to distinguish between *hoarse* and *horse*. Rounding is characteristic of the vowels of *hog, frog, log, wasp* and *wash*, and in the last of these words an *r* often intrudes in the speech of the not too highly educated. The vowels of *due* and *new* will resemble that of *food* rather than *feud*. In the South, *r* is 'lost' except before vowels, as it is in eastern New England and New York City but not in the Northern area generally. Words like *Tuesday, due*, and *new* have a y-like glide preceding the vowel, and final [z] in *Mrs.* is the normal form.

Among the older, relatively uneducated group and even to some extent among the middle-aged informants who have had some secondary schooling there are also regional differences in inflectional

[2] See page 235 for the sounds represented by the phonetic symbols in brackets here. [eds.]

forms and syntax. For example, *hadn't ought* for "oughtn't," *see* as a past tense form, *clim* for "climbed" among the oldest sector of the population, *wan't* for "wasn't," *be* in such expressions as *How be you?*, and the choice of the preposition *to* in *sick to his stomach* are all characteristic of the Northern area. *Clum* for "climbed," *seen* for "saw," *all the further* and *I'll wait on you* are to be found in the Midlands, whereas *belongs to be, heern* for "heard," *seed* as the past tense of "to see," *holp* for "helped," *might could* and *mought have* are characteristic of the South.

All of this raises the question as to how the regional forms of American English developed in our three and one-half centuries of linguistic history. The first factor which must be taken into account is settlement history. Where did our earliest settlers come from, and what dialects did they speak? . . . at the time of the earliest settlements, English local and regional dialects were in a stronger position than they are today in that they constituted the natural speech of a greater portion of the English-speaking population and were in customary use farther up the social scale.

Moreover, it is quite unlikely that any single local settlement, even at the outset, ever consisted entirely of speakers of the same dialect. Of ten families of settlers gathered in any one place, two might well have spoken London English, three or four others one of the southern or southeastern county dialects. There would be in addition a couple of families speaking northern English and another two or three employing a western dialect. In the course of their being in constant contact with each other, compromises for the everyday terms in which their dialects differed would normally have developed, and one could reasonably expect to find a southern English term for a water receptacle, a northern word for earthworm, and a western designation for sour milk. Matters of pronunciation would eventually, perhaps after a slightly longer time, be compromised in much the same manner. Moreover, the resultant compromises for various localities would be different. In the first place, no two localities would have had exactly the same proportions of speakers of the various English dialects, and even if they had, the two localities would not have arrived at precisely the same set of compromises. Thus, early in our history we developed, at various points on the Atlantic seaboard, a number of local cultures, each with distinctive social characteristics of its own—including a dialect which was basically a unique blend of British types of speech, supplemented in its vocabulary by borrowings from the Indians and from Dutch and German neighbors.[3]

With the beginning of the nineteenth century, three changes occurred which were to have a profound effect upon the language situation in America. First, the industrial revolution resulted in the growth of a number of industrial centers, uprooting a considerable proportion of the farm population and concentrating it in the cities. The development of the railroad and other mechanical means of travel increased greatly the mobility of the average person. The large-scale migrations westward also resulted in some resettlement and shifting, even among those who did not set out on the long trek. All of this resulted in a general abandonment of narrowly local speech forms in favor of fewer, more or less general, regional types. Some local speech forms have remained even to the present day. These are usually known as relics, particularly when they are distributed in isolated spots over an area rather than in concentration. *Open stone peach*, for example, is a relic for freestone peach, occurring in Maryland. *Smurring up*, "getting foggy," survives as a relic in eastern Maine and more rarely on Cape Cod and Martha's Vineyard.

Even prior to the shifts in population and changes in the culture pattern, certain colonial cities such as Boston, Philadelphia, and Charleston had acquired prestige by developing as centers of trade and foci of immigration. They became socially and culturally outstanding, as well as economically powerful, thus dominating the areas surrounding them. As a consequence, local expressions and pronunciations peculiar to the countryside came to be replaced by new forms of speech emanating from these centers. A fairly recent instance of this is to be found in the New England term *tonic* for soda water, practically co-extensive with the area served by Boston wholesalers. Professor Kurath considers the influence of these centers as second only to the influence of the original settlement in shaping the regional types of speech on the Atlantic seaboard and in determining their geographic boundaries.

Nor was the general process of dialect formation by any means completed with the settlement of the Atlantic seaboard. As the land to the west came to be taken up in successive stages (for example, western New York, Michigan, Wisconsin in the North; southern

[3] See selection by Thomas Pyles on page 93. [eds.]

Ohio, Indiana, and southern Illinois in the Midland area) the same mixtures of speech forms among the settlers were present at first, and the same linguistic compromises had to be worked out. The same processes occurred in the interior South, in Texas, and later on in the Far West. Consequently, the complete linguistic history, particularly with respect to regional forms, of the United States will not be known until all of the facts concerning the present regional distribution of speech forms have been collected, and until these facts have been collated with the settlement history of the various areas and the speech types employed by the settlers at the time they moved in. In its entirety this would necessitate a greater knowledge of the local dialects of seventeenth-century England than we have at present.

Moreover, such environmental factors as topography, climate, and plant and animal life also play their parts in influencing the dialect of an area, just as they did in the general transplanting of the English language to America. The complexity and size of the network of fresh-water streams will affect the distribution and meaning of such terms as *brook*, *creek*, *branch*, and *river*. In parts of Ohio and Pennsylvania, for example, the term *creek* is applied to a much larger body of water than in Michigan. It is even more obvious that in those parts of the country where snow is a rarity or does not fall at all, there will be no necessity for a battery of terms to indicate coasting face down on a sled. It is not surprising that those areas of the country where cows can be milked outside, for at least part of the year, will develop a specific term for the place where this is done: witness *milk gap* or *milking gap* current in the Appalachians south of the James River. The wealth of terms for various types of fences throughout the country is again dependent, in part at least, on the material which is available for building them, be it stones, stumps, or wooden rails.

Different types of institutions and practices which developed in various parts of the country also had their effect upon regional vocabulary. Those settlements which did not follow the practice of setting aside a parcel of land for common grazing purposes had little use for such terms as *green* or *common*. The meaning of *town* will vary according to the place and importance of township and county respectively in the organization of local government. The same principle applies equally well to foods of various kinds, which reflect not only materials which are readily available but folk practices as well. The German custom of preparing raised doughnuts as Lenten fare survives in the Pennsylvania term *fossnocks*, shortened from *Fastnachtskuchen.*

Finally, a new invention or development introduced into several parts of the country at the same time will acquire different names in various places. The baby carriage, for example, seems to have been a development of the 1830's and '40's, and this is the term which developed in New England. Within the Philadelphia trade area, however, the article became known as a *baby coach*, whereas *baby buggy* was adopted west of the Alleghenies and *baby cab* in other regions throughout the country. Nor have we necessarily seen an end to this process. Within the last two decades the building of large, double-lane, limited-access automobile highways has been undertaken in various parts of the country, yet the terminology for them differs considerably. In eastern New York, Connecticut, and Rhode Island these are *parkways*, but *turnpikes* in Pennsylvania, New Jersey, New Hampshire, Maine, Massachusetts, Ohio, and Indiana. In New York *thruway* is used, and they are *expressways* in Michigan and *freeways* in California. These would seem to be regionalisms in the making.

It is of interest also to look at the dialect situation from the point of view of various words which are employed in various parts of the country for the same concept. One of the most interesting and instructive distributions is to be found in connection with the terms used for *earthworm*. This word is used by cultivated speakers in the metropolitan centers. *Angleworm* is the regional term in the North, *fishworm* in the Midland area, and *fishing worm* in the coastal South. *Fish bait* and *bait worm* occupy smaller areas within the extensive *fishworm* region, but are also distributed over a wide territory.

In addition, there is a large number of local terms, many of which are used principally by the older and less-educated inhabitants. The Merrimack Valley, in New Hampshire, and Essex County, Massachusetts, have *mud worm*. *Eace worm* is used in Rhode Island. *Angle dog* appears in upper Connecticut, and *ground worm* on the Eastern Shore of Virginia. *Red worm* is used in the mountains of North Carolina, and an area around Toledo, Ohio, uses *dew worm*. Scattered instances of *rainworm* appear on Buzzards Bay in Massachusetts, throughout the Pennsylvania German area, and in German settlements in North Carolina, Maine, and Wisconsin. We have, thus, a wealth of older local terms, three distinct regional words, and the cultivated *earthworm* appearing in addition as a folk word in South Carolina and along the North Carolina and Virginia coast. Where and how did the various terms originate, and what can be determined about their subsequent history?

Earthworm itself is not an old word; it appears to have been compounded only shortly before the earliest English migrations to America. The earliest *Oxford English Dictionary* citation of the word in its present form is 1591; it appears also as *yearth worm* some thirty years earlier. The various regional terms all seem to have been coined in America; the dictionaries either record no British citations or fail to include the words at all.

The local terms have a varied and interesting history. *Mud worm* seems to occur in standard British English from the beginning of the nineteenth century on. *Eace worm*, as a combined form, goes back at least to Middle English; the first element was a term for "bait" as early as Aelfric; it is used today in a number of southern counties in England from Kent to Gloucester. *Angle dog* is used currently in Devonshire. *Ground worm*, though coined in England, was transferred to North Carolina and Maryland in the eighteenth century. *Red worm* appears first in England in 1450 and continues through to the mid-nineteenth century, though chiefly in books on fishing, as does *dew worm*, which goes back even farther, to the late Old English period. *Rainworm*, though it appears in Aelfric as *renwyrm*, may be a reformation, even in British English, on the pattern of *Regenwurm* in German, for there is a gap of seven centuries in the citations in the *Oxford English Dictionary* and there is reason to believe that its revival in 1731 was influenced by the German form. Moreover, with but one exception, it has been cited for the United States only in areas settled by Germans.

Thus we have in the standard cultivated term one of relatively recent British formation. Apparently the regional terms were compounded in America, whereas the local terms represent survivals either of dialect usage or anglers' jargon and one loan translation.[4] It is worth noting that the common Old English term, *angle twicce*, surviving as *angle twitch* in Cornwall and Devon, seems not to have found its way to America, and there are, furthermore, such other English formations as *tag worm*, *marsh worm*, and *garden worm* which have not been recorded in America.

[4] A loan translation is a composite form made up of a literal translation of the component parts from the foreign tongue into the new tongue. Examples: English *skyscraper* becomes French *gratte-ciel;* French *ça va sans dire* becomes English *that goes without saying.* [eds.]

At times, too, changes in meaning seem to have entered into the dialect situation, as is illustrated by the development of the regional terms *skillet* and *spider*, the former current in the Midland and the Virginia Piedmont, the latter in the North and in the Southern tidewater area. *Frying pan* is the urban term and is slowly supplanting the others. *Spider* was originally applied to the cast-iron pan with short legs, from which the name was presumably derived, but it was ultimately transferred to the flat-bottomed pan as well. This would seem also to explain the local term *creeper*, used in Marblehead, Massachusetts. *Skillet*, a term of doubtful etymology, first appears in English in 1403, when it was applied to a long-handled brass or copper vessel used for boiling liquids or stewing meat. It is still so used in dialects throughout England. The shift in meaning to a frying pan took place only in America, but an advertisement of 1790, offering for sale "bakepans, spiders, skillets," would suggest that even as late as this a distinction between the two was recognized. The examples above have been offered only as a suggestion of the various language processes which have played a part in the distribution and meaning of some of our dialect terms. It is quite obvious that no definitive conclusions about these matters can be reached until the actual facts of dialect distribution are better known than they are at present.

Thus far our concern has been only with regional dialects or speech differences, although we have recognized these as occurring particularly on certain social levels. This raises the question of the extent to which social dialects occur in American English. Is there a so-called vulgate which has reasonably uniform characteristics throughout the country, and if so, what is it?

For the most part, the language of the uncultivated will be recognized in terms of its inflectional characteristics, or at any rate it is this aspect of the language for which the most authentic information is available. Before these matters are taken up in detail, therefore, one or two points about the operation of inflections should be clearly understood.

First, we must recognize that our inflectional endings are in reality a series of patterns which are applied quite automatically whenever a situation demanding their use occurs. Even in highly inflected languages, such as Modern Finnish or Ciceronian Latin, the speaker does or did not find it necessary to recite a paradigm to determine the proper case ending. Second, throughout the history of the language, there are two forces constantly at work upon the inflectional system:

sound change, which often introduces irregularities or disturbances in the system, and analogy,[5] which tends to simplify or to straighten these out by extending the scope of the already existing pattern. As we look at some of the features of present-day substandard English, we shall see how these forces operate.

Possibly the one inflectional form most characteristic of the nouns in substandard American English is the unchanged plural after numbers: *six mile down the road*, *five foot tall*, and similarly applied to *month*, *year*, and *gallon*. Actually this is the preservation of an old partitive genitive plural after numbers,[6] which resisted the analogical extension of the *-s* inflection to cases other than the nominative and accusative. The lesson to be learned from this is that the substandard language frequently preserves linguistically older forms than Standard English, a fact not too surprising when it is recalled that substandard English depends entirely on oral transmission from one generation to another.

Certain of the pronoun inflections, however, demonstrate precisely the contrary tendency: the development of innovations or new forms and patterns in substandard English. This is true, for example, of the possessive pronoun in its so-called absolute form,[7] which in the standard language represents a strange and inconsistent mixture of patterns indeed. *Mine* and the archaic *thine* are formed from the adjectival form by adding *-n*. *Hers*, *ours*, *yours*, and *theirs*, on the other hand, add *-s* to the adjectival form, probably on the pattern of the noun genitive. *His* and *its* are indistinguishable so far as their secondary and absolute forms are concerned. In contrast, the substandard *mine*, *yourn*, *hisn*, *hern*, *ourn*, *theirn* present a perfectly regular pattern formed by an analogical extension of *mine* and *thine* to the third person singular and to the plural forms. At one time or another, several of these forms appeared in Standard English, but they seem never to have caught on and were, as we have seen, replaced in part by the *-s* forms. But the substandard language carried out the innovation completely and consistently except for *its*, which is virtually never used in the absolute form anyway.

A further point worth mentioning is that although speakers of the

[5] See selection by Eugene Nida on page 86. [eds.]

[6] E.g., the Old English genitive plural *siex fōta* (six of feet) before an adjective developed into the modern English *six foot*. [eds.]

[7] The form used when the possessive pronoun does not precede a noun: *mine, thine, his, hers, its, ours, yours, theirs*. [eds.]

substandard language are rarely trained in school grammar, their language observes its own laws—not those of Standard English—in a thoroughly rigorous manner. *Hisn*, for example, is the absolute, not the secondary or adjectival form, and the two are never confused. Most speakers of the substandard language might be expected to say *the book is hisn*; no speaker of substandard English would ever say *hisn book*.

The reflexive pronouns give us another instance of a more regular operation of analogy on the substandard level than on the standard. In Standard English, *myself*, *yourself*, *ourselves*, and *yourselves* are combinations of the genitive pronoun plus the singular or plural of the *-self* form; *himself* and *themselves* employ the object form of the pronoun, whereas *herself* and *itself* could be either. Substandard English, in substituting *hisself* and *theirself* in the third person and adhering to the singular of *self* in *ourself* and *yourself* (plural), is not only more consistent but more economical in that the latter combinations signal the plural only once and avoid the tautology of the plural *-selves*. The only ambiguity is in the second person, but the second personal pronoun has lost its distinctions between singular and plural anyway, except for the Southern form *you all*.

One curious feature of the substandard pronoun is the substitution of the object for the subjective form in such sentences as *Us girls went home*, *John and her was married*, *Me and him was late*. This seems to occur principally when the subject is compound or when one or more words intervene between the pronominal subject and verb, as in *us girls*. Postverbally the reverse type of substitution (subject for object form) is often found, as in *She gave it to mother and I*, *She took all of we children*. Since these locutions are found considerably higher up the social and educational scale than those previously mentioned, it is possible, at least, that they are the result of overcorrection.

Space does not permit an exhaustive treatment of all the inflectional forms of substandard English, but a few that are typical deserve brief mention. *Them* as a demonstrative adjective (*them books*) probably harks back to the days when the English article and the demonstrative *that* (dative *ðǣm*) were one and the same form. The multiple negative[8] was also a regular and accepted feature of older English, as was the so-called flat adverb[9] without the *-ly* derivative

[8] E.g., Shakespeare's "I will not budge for no man's pleasure, I." [eds.]
[9] E.g., Go *slow;* come *quick*. [eds.]

suffix. However, since the standard and substandard languages are undoubtedly farthest apart with respect to verb forms, some features of the verbs of the vulgate, as they were once called by the late Robert Menner, should be described.

First of all, with respect to the present tense, there is some tendency to dispose of the distinctive inflection for the third person singular, either by eliminating it in such forms as *he want, she write,* etc., or by extending the peculiar form of the third person to the first and second—*I has some good friends, You is in lots of trouble.*

It is in the preterit[10] and past participle forms, chiefly of those verbs which are somewhat irregular in Standard English, that the widest deviations occur. Again one may recognize here the two opposing tendencies: the retention of older forms and the simplification of irregularities through analogical processes.

The older forms retained in the substandard language owe their origin chiefly to the fact that the so-called strong verb[11] in earlier stages of the language had four principal parts, a past tense singular as well as a past tense plural, in addition to the infinitive and present participle. Thus *writ* as a past tense of *write* represents an older preterit plural form, as do *begun* and *swum.*

On the other hand, the overwhelming tendency in English verb development throughout the last seven or eight centuries has been toward an aggrandizement of the regular or weak inflection[12] at the expense of the older minor conjugations. This is in effect a tendency toward a two-part verb, the infinitive or present stem opposed to an identical past tense and past participle. In general, this has been brought about through analogical processes. Deviant substandard forms are usually the result of analogies which have not operated in Standard English and which take one of two directions: either the extension of the weak past inflections to such irregular verbs as *know* and *see* (*knowed, seed*) or the amalgamation of the strong preterit or past participle with the complementary form (*I taken, he done* as preterits; *have gave, have wrote, has went* as past participial forms).

In one sense, therefore, the differences between the grammatical

[10] The preterit means the simple past tense, e.g., He *swam* across. [eds.]

[11] A "strong verb" is one that forms its past tense by an internal vowel change, e.g., *drink, drank; write, wrote; steal, stole.* (This is an oversimplified statement of a complex situation.) [eds.]

[12] A "weak verb" is one that forms its past tense by the addition of a *-t, -d,* or *-ed,* e.g., *dreamt, told, started.* For the phonetic aspect of these endings, see page 238, assignment 7. [eds.]

systems of standard and substandard English represent a difference in the direction and rapidity of inflectional changes. Unquestionably the easy transition from one social class to another in the United State has resulted in a very hazy line of demarcation between what is acceptable and what is considered illiterate. According to the most rigorous schoolbook standard, some of the language employed in American legislative councils and in business life would not pass muster. The awareness of this, combined with an unrealistic treatment of language in our schools, has resulted at times in a defiance of these questionable standards. More often it has given people a guilt complex about the language they use. James West, in his community study entitled *Plainville, U.S.A.* makes a pertinent comment upon this very point:

> "Inferior" English has been selected as a primary and almost universal trait for apology because the school teacher, the press, and the radio have all cooperated to arouse self-consciousness concerning dialect forms, phrases, and phonetics. All but the "most backwoodsy" speakers frequently ridicule and parody the stratum or strata of speech beneath or older than their own, and at the same time feel uncertain about their own usages.

Consequently, few Americans, even among the well-educated, are confident and assured of the essential aptness and correctness of their speech. It will take at least a half-century of a more enlightened attitude toward language in the public schools to bring about any perceptible change in this state of affairs. In the meantime, what is sadly needed is an entertaining, yet scientific, treatment of vulgate speech to demonstrate how interesting a phenomenon it really is.

ON ACCEPTING PARTICIPIAL *DRANK*

Harold B. Allen

The use of drank *as a past participle, as in "He has* drank *his morning coffee," is generally condemned by textbooks as nonstandard English. Harold B. Allen, Professor of English at the University of Minnesota, here brings together evidence from the collected data from three linguistic atlases to show that* drank *is a standard English past participle in spoken English of the East and Midwest. Professor Allen is director of the* Linguistic Atlas of the Upper Midwest *project, covering the Dakotas, Minnesota, Iowa, and Nebraska.*

As ADDITIONAL FIELDWORK is completed for the regional atlases associated in *The Linguistic Atlas of the United States*, additional evidence accumulates about numerous grammatical forms long adjudged controversial. A case in point is provided by the new data for the past participle *drank*.

The verb *drink* has come down to us from that interesting third class of Old English strong verbs with two stem vowels in the past tense forms: one (*a*) peculiar to the past and found in the first and third persons singular; the other (*u*) used in the second person singular and in the plural but also identical with the stem vowel of the past participle.[1] In this class the subtle power of analogy,[2] operating with increasing strength in Middle English as inflectional changes

From *College English*, February 1957. Reprinted by permission of the author and the National Council of Teachers of English.

[1] The Old English conjugation of the past tense of *drincan*, to drink, is as follows: *ic dranc, þu drunce, he dranc, we druncon, ge druncon, hie druncon.* The Old English past participle is *druncen.* [eds.]

[2] For analogy, see the selection from Eugene Nida, page 86. [eds.]

lost their phonetic distinctiveness, also inevitably favored the more frequently occurring *u* in the process of simplifying the verb patterns.

By the eighteenth century this process had gone so far that the *u* vowel was comfortable and exclusively established in the preterit[3] of the following third class strong verbs: *bind*, *cling*, *fight*, *fling*, *grind*, *slink*, *spin*, *sting*, *string*, *swing*, *win*, *wind*, and *wring*.[4] In the other surviving members of this class the process was now to be retarded, though not blocked, by the prestigious pronouncement of Dr. Johnson in the Grammar prefaced to his *Dictionary* in 1755. Reflecting the philosophy of the ancient Greek Analogists, Johnson believed that every grammatical function should have its own overt grammatical form, and accordingly declared: "He shall seldom err who remembers, that when a verb has a participle distinct from its preterite, as *write*, *wrote*, *written*, that distinct participle is more proper and elegant, as *The book is written*, is better than *The book is wrote*, though *wrote* may be used in poetry."

Although even the prestige of Johnson's *Dictionary* and the authoritative copying of his dictum in scores of school grammars were unable to stop the trend toward the simple *u* in the preterit, a great many cultivated speakers were undoubtedly influenced by the bald injunction that nothing but *a* can be the proper preterit vowel. As a result, for the past one hundred and fifty years there actually has been divided usage among cultivated speakers.

We may look at *shrink* as typical of the larger group of those strong verbs which in moving toward a single form for past and participle have popularly used the vowel common to both. Although the textbooks list the contrast between *shrank* as preterit and *shrunk* as participle, actually the findings of the fieldwork for *The Linguistic Atlas of the Upper Midwest* indicate that 86.5% of all informants responding to this item use *shrunk* as the preterit. Nor do the findings reveal the existence of a small educated minority clinging to a favored *shrank*, for the relative frequency of *u* is nearly the same in all three groups: 89% of the uneducated, 89% of the high school graduates, and 86% of the college graduates.

[3] Preterit means the simple past tense, as *rode*, *clung*, *spun*, *swung*, *drank*. [eds.]

[4] Because the original Old English *u* underwent phonetic change through the influence of certain neighboring sounds, some of the past tense forms now in use, such as *fought* and *ground*, do not immediately betray their historical membership in the class.

Some regional variation, hardly enough to be significant, may be suggested by the slightly lower frequency in Midland than in Northern speech areas: Minnesota, 96%; North Dakota, 92%; Iowa, 86%; South Dakota, 81% and Nebraska, 72%. But within the divided usage the general dominance of *shrunk* is certain, despite the contrary statements of the textbooks.

The inaccuracy of the textbooks with respect to the past of *shrink* and of other verbs exhibiting the tendency toward the *u* vowel in the preterit is matched by their inaccuracy with respect to the one verb which stands out in exception to the trend. The verb *drink* is the only verb in this group that in moving toward simplicity has tended not only to retain the original *a* vowel in the preterit, but also to entrench it in the past participle. Indeed, Professor Walter S. Avis has recently suggested that "we cannot refuse to accept the participle *drank* as Standard American English, at least in the regions where the evidence argues for its acceptance."[5]

It is true that even without Avis's evidence some grammarians have not been as dogmatic as the textbook writers in their attitude toward participial *drank*. Even Goold Brown, back in the mid-nineteenth century, said in his many-editioned and voluminous *Grammar of English Grammars* that "*drank* seems to be a word of greater delicacy, and perhaps it is sufficiently authorized." Among recent linguistic grammarians, Curme in his *Parts of Speech and Accidence* (1935) said of *drank* as a participle, "sometimes used in older English in the literary language. It survives in popular speech." And Jespersen, in the sixth volume of his *Modern English Grammar* (1942), wrote, ". . . a participle *drank* has been in frequent use for centuries, possibly to avoid misunderstanding with *drunk* 'intoxicated.' It is now getting rare, but instances occur in all the best-known authors from Bunyan down to our time." He cited Scott, Shelley, Keats, Trollope, and Kingsley, and referred to Mencken as listing *drank* as a participle.

Nor are current dictionaries more accurate in describing contemporary usage. The Merriam-Webster *NID* (2nd ed.) offers *drunk*. Similarly with the Thorndike-Barnhart dictionaries, although the Barnhart-edited *ACD*, less pressed for space, takes room to admit cagily, "sometimes *drank*." The *WNW* does give *drank* as participle but labels it "archaic."

[5] Walter S. Avis, *American Speech*, XXVIII (May 1953), 106-111.

Yet such recognition as that by Curme and the *ACD* is nothing like Avis's bold statement based upon Atlas evidence. This evidence is that even in New England, "the citadel of the prestige dialect," 38% of the cultivated informants regularly use *drank* as the participle and an additional 11.9% use it along with *drunk*, while in New York 27.7% of such speakers use it, in West Virginia 83.3%, and in Pennsylvania 43.7%. For the North Central states (except Kentucky, where fieldwork is still in process) revised figures later than Avis's are now provided by Virginia McDavid (Mrs. Raven I. McDavid, Jr.) in her recent unpublished Minnesota dissertation. In the North Central area, 54% of the interrogated high school graduates and 33% of the college graduates use the participle *drank*.

To all this evidence there now can be added a whole new set of data from the recently completed field records of *The Linguistic Atlas of the Upper Midwest.*[6] In this large five-state area Avis's conclusion finds even stronger corroboration. Here 80.5% of the interviewed high school graduates use *drank* as the past participle, and nearly half (47%) of the cultivated speakers. There is no significant regional variation within the Upper Midwest, almost the same relative frequencies being found in Minnesota, Iowa, the Dakotas, and Nebraska. Certainly it would appear that in this area, as well as in New England and the North Central states, *drank* is an accepted standard form of the past participle.

Explanation of the exceptional development with *drink* usually coincides with that offered by Jespersen, namely, that there is an aversion to the historical *drunk* because of the link with intoxication. On the supposition that women might feel greater hesitation on this score than men would, a further breakdown of the Upper Midwest figures was made. The complete picture, including the data for uneducated speakers, is of some interest. Of the 9.7% of uneducated informants who use *drunk* as the participle not one is a woman. Of the male high school graduates 12% use *drunk*; of the female high school graduates, 28.3%. Of the male college graduates 60% use *drunk;* of the female college graduates, 40%. Certainly there is aversion by women to the use of *drunk*, but chiefly among the uneducated. Among cultivated speakers the distinction by sex is hardly significant. But since linguistic taboos of this type seem to be stronger among uneducated people, it may well be that the association with

[6] For significance of such records in the field of usage see H. B. Allen, *English Journal*, XLV (April 1956), 188-194.

intoxication is the ultimate cause for the preference for participial *drank*.

Whatever the cause of the large-scale rejection of *drunk*, however, the general acceptance of competing *drank* by from one-third to one-half of the cultivated speakers in New England, the North Central states, the Midland area, and the Upper Midwest supports the conclusion that we have here a condition of divided usage, with no sound basis for present objection to either *drank* or *drunk* as the single exclusive form in standard spoken English.

LINGUISTIC ATLAS FINDINGS

Work on the regional linguistic atlases for different parts of the United States is in various states of progress. For New England all of the data have been gathered, and the atlas is in print. For three regions—the Middle and South Atlantic States, the North Central States, and the Upper Mid-West—the collecting of data has been completed. These collections are a rich mine of primary source material about contemporary American English, and researchers are making use of them for books and articles. To date, three books have been published, from two of which the excerpts below have been chosen. Hans Kurath's A Word Geography of the Eastern United States *describes the distribution of vocabulary items and sets forth the dialect and subdialect areas of the Eastern States. Professor Kurath was the editor of the* Linguistic Atlas of New England *and is now editor of the* Middle English Dictionary *at the University of Michigan. The second book is E. Bagby*

The first three items—*creek, bull, you-all*—are from *A Word Geography of the United States* by Hans Kurath. Reprinted by permission of the publisher, the University of Michigan Press, copyright 1949. The following four items—*dive, lie, he doesn't, ought not*—are from *A Survey of Verb Forms in the Eastern United States* by E. Bagby Atwood. Reprinted by permission of the publisher, the University of Michigan Press, copyright, 1953.

Atwood's A Survey of Verb Forms in the Eastern United States. *Here Professor Atwood confines his attention to variant verb forms. To get his information, he examined the* Linguistic Atlas *field records of more than 1400 informants, about 400 from New England and about 500 each from the Middle Atlantic States and the South Atlantic States. Mr. Atwood is Professor of English at the University of Texas, which in recent years has become an important linguistics center.*

CREEK

Creek is the most common word for a small fresh-water stream in the Eastern States. It is current everywhere except in the greater part of New England, where *brook* or *river* are the usual terms.

Outside New England, Long Island, and Metropolitan New York *brook* is rare as a common noun, but it appears in the proper names of many streams in the New England settlement area as far west as Erie, Pennsylvania.

The Midland term for a smaller stream is *run*, but in Pennsylvania and the northern half of West Virginia *creek* is now the common noun. However, *run* occurs in the names of many streams in this area. As a common noun, *run* is now characteristic of an area extending from Delaware Bay to the James River (except Lower Delamarvia) and westward to the Shenandoah and the upper reaches of the Potomac in West Virginia. It is also fairly common along the Neuse in North Carolina.

In the South and in the South Midland as far north as the Kanawha Valley *branch* is the usual designation of the tributary of a *creek* or a *river*. *Branch* is also current on Delaware Bay beside *run*.

The Dutch word *kill* for a small watercourse survives only in the names of certain creeks or rivers in the Dutch settlement area, such as the *Batten Kill* in Vermont, the *Catskill Creek* in New York, and the *Schuylkill River* in Pennsylvania.

BULL

The plain term *bull* is current everywhere, and in the North Midland and New York State other expressions are rare. In New England, the South, and the South Midland, however, the plain term is not used by older folk of one sex in the presence of the other. Even many of the younger generation prefer the veiled expressions of the Victorian era.

New England expressions for the bull are: *sire*, *animal* or *male animal*, *critter*, *toro* (New Hampshire and Vermont), *seed ox* (rare), *gentleman cow*, *gentleman ox* (found also on Chesapeake Bay), and *masculine* (riming with *fine*, on Nantucket).

Southernisms are equally varied: *male* and *male cow* in Virginia, adjoining parts of North Carolina, and on Delamarvia (occasionally also in New England); *beast*, *stock beast*, *male beast* in the coastal section of the Carolinas; *stock brute*, *male brute* in westernmost North Carolina; *steer* from southern Maryland to Albemarle Sound; *ox* in the Virginia Tidewater, central West Virginia, and sporadically elsewhere; *gentleman cow* on Chesapeake Bay (also in New England); and *masculine* (riming with *fine*) in southern West Virginia (also on Nantucket). West Virginia further contributes *Durham*, *jock*, and *major*.

Some of these expressions are now rare or are used only jestingly, but in the Southern area such expressions as the *male*, the *beast*, and the *brute* are common, and if one used the plain word *bull* to a lady, one might be in trouble.

YOU-ALL

The form *you* is used as a plural in all parts of the Eastern States. By the side of *you*, the greater part of the Midland and all of the South have the specific, emphatic, or "generous" plural forms *you'ns*, *you-all*, and *mongst-ye*. All these forms have a possessive case: *you'ns's*, *you-all's*, *mongst-ye's*. See p. 352.

You-all is current throughout the South and the South Midland (in all of West Virginia, except the northwestern section around Wheeling and Parkersburg).

You'ns is the Midland form and occurs in the folk speech of Pennsylvania west of the Susquehanna, in large parts of West Virginia, and in the westernmost parts of Virginia and North Carolina.

The form *mongst-ye* is common in the folk speech of the central part of Delamarvia, and rare instances are found from the mouth of Chesapeake Bay to Albemarle Sound.

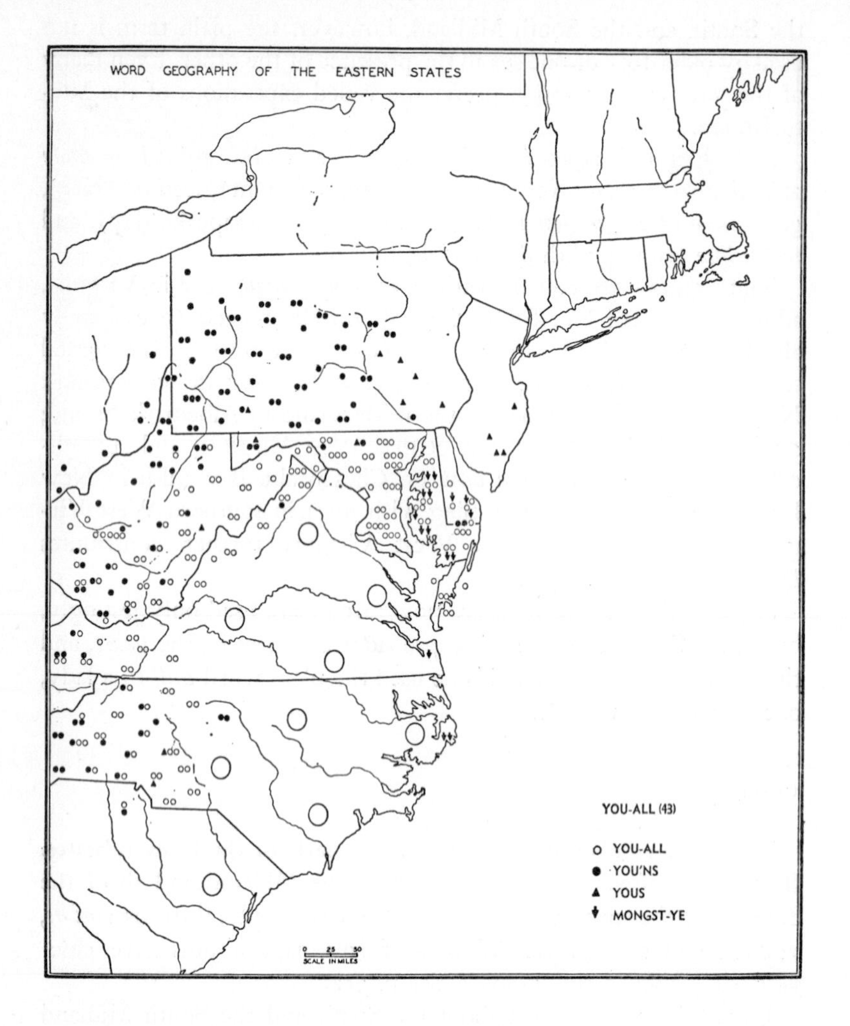

From *A Word Geography of the Eastern United States* by Hans Kurath. Reprinted by permission of the publisher, The University of Michigan Press, copyright 1949.

DIVE

The preterite is recorded in the context "He (dived) in."

The geographical distribution of the forms is indicated on p. 353.

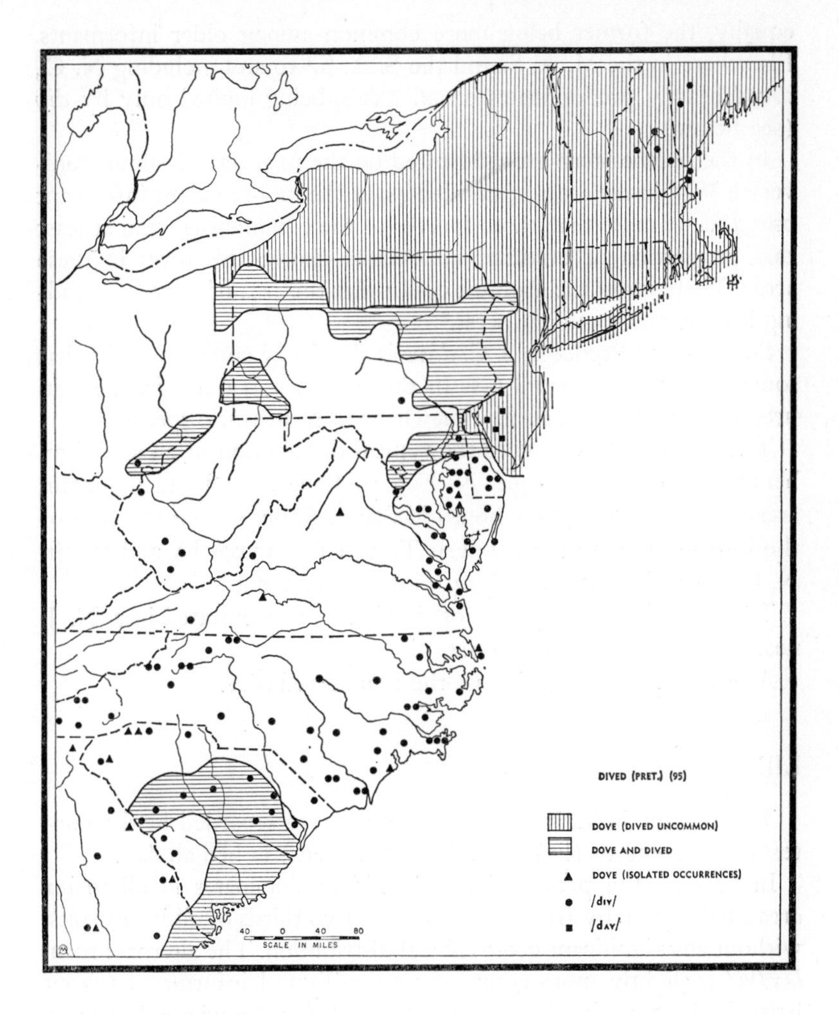

From *A Survey of Verb Forms in the Eastern United States* by E. Bagby Atwood. Reprinted by permission of the publisher, The University of Michigan Press, copyright 1953.

Dived/daivd/ is uncommon throughout N. Eng., N. Y., n. Pa., and e. N. J.; in this whole territory it is used by less than one out of 15 of the informants, without distinction as to type (about one eighth of the cultured informants in N. Eng. use it). In a belt in n. c. and e. Pa. and along the upper Ohio, *dived* and *dove*/dov/ occur about equally, the former being more common among older informants. Elsewhere in the M. A. S. and the S. A. S.[1] to and including N. C., *dived* heavily predominates on all levels, being limited only by *div* (see below).

In the northeastern area indicated on the map *dove* is almost universal. Within the areas of divided usage the more modern informant uses *dove* in more than three fourths of the communities, and at least that proportion of cultured informants choose this form in these areas. There is not the slightest doubt that the area of *dove* is extending itself to the south and west.[2]

South of the Peedee in S. C. *dove* is also fairly common, and it has some currency in coastal Ga. In these areas it is quite frequent in urban and cultured speech, somewhat less so in rustic speech.

The form *div*/dɪv/ shows the typical distribution of an archaism, being most common in n.e. N. Eng. and the coastal and mountain areas of the South and the South Midland. About six out of seven of the informants who use it fall in Type I (or Types IA and IIA in N. Eng.), and three N. C. Negro informants use it.

There are five occurrences of *duv*/dʌv/, concentrated in s. N. J. near the mouth of the Delaware.

A few Negro informants use the uninflected *dive*.

LIE

The present infinitive and the preterite are recorded in the contexts "I'm going to (lie) down" and "He (lay) in bed all day."

In general, the present form *lie*/lai/ predominates in all major areas, being used by from three fifths to two thirds of all informants, without any significant geographical distribution. The alternate form *lay*/le/ is slightly more common among Type I informants (about half of whom use it) than among Type II. On the whole, however, *lay* seems characteristic of certain communities, rather than of certain more old-fashioned informants within those communities. Only

[1] The Middle Atlantic States (M.A.S.) include New York, New Jersey, Pennsylvania, eastern Ohio, and West Virginia. The South Atlantic States (S.A.S.) include Delaware, Maryland, Virginia, North Carolina, South Carolina, and approximately the eastern half of Georgia. [eds.]

[2] Another characteristic of an advancing form is its appearance in the more populous centers ahead of the main line of advance (in this instance, the Pittsburgh, Baltimore, and Washington areas). Professor Robert Hall has applied the metaphor "parachuting" to this phenomenon.

a scattering of cultured informants give the present form *lay*, and then usually alongside *lie*.

The preterite forms can best be surveyed in terms of their corresponding present forms. The combination *lie : lay* is of very limited occurrence. In n. N. Eng. and in e. N. Eng. (except for a few points in R. I. and e. Conn.) this combination is quite rare outside of cultured speech, and only about half the cultured informants in these areas use it. In s.w. N. Eng. *lie : lay* is universal in cultured usage and occurs among a fair number of noncultured informants as well.

In the entire M. A. S. *lie : lay* is uncommon among noncultured informants (being used by less than one twelfth of the group), and is confined to about one third of the cultured group.

In the S. A. S. *lie : lay* is rare in Del., Md., and the Piedmont area of Va., but becomes much more common (and might even be called the dominant popular usage) on the Eastern Shore of Va. and throughout most of N. C. and part of S. C. A little less than half the cultured informants in the S. A. S. use the *lie : lay* combination.

A much more common practice is the combination of the present *lie* with the *laid*/led/ ("going to lie down" : "laid in bed"). Of those who use the present *lie*, a considerable majority (two thirds in N. Eng., four fifths in the M. A. S.) combine it with the preterite *laid*. Only in N. C. and on the Eastern Shore of Va. is this combination somewhat uncommon. In e. N. Eng. about half the cultured informants give *lie : laid;* in the M. A. S. and the S. A. S. something more than half do so.

Some eight informants in N. Eng. and five in other areas use the combination *lie : lied*/laid/. This feature shows no concentration and may represent a groping for a "correct" form rather than habitual usage.

Of those who use the present *lay*, a heavy majority in most areas form the preterite as *laid*. An exception may be found in N. C., where a considerable number use the leveled present and preterite *lay : lay*. This leveling also occurs in a very scattered way in N. Eng. and parts of Pa.

Nearly all Negro informants use the forms *lay : laid;* one (S. C.), however, uses the leveled forms *lie : lie*.

In summary, we may say that as a present form *lie* is predominant in all areas, and that as the preterite of both *lie* and *lay*, *laid* is very heavily predominant everywhere except in the areas of the S. A. S. mentioned above where *lay* predominates as preterite.

HE DOESN'T

The third person singular of the negative form is recorded in the context "He (doesn't) care."

In contrast to the positive form (*does*), the negative form lacks the inflectional -*s*/z/ among a large majority of informants in all areas.

In N. Eng. *he don't*/dont/ is used by about two fifths of the cultured informants (mostly in the older group) and by more than five sixths of the other types. It is most common in Type IA (nearly nine tenths use it) and decreases in frequency in proportion to the youth and better education of the informants, occurring among only 6/17 of Type IIIB.

In the M. A. S. *he don't* is all but unanimous in Types I and II, there being but 15 or 20 occurrences of *doesn't* in these groups. Of the cultured informants, nearly three fourths use *he don't* (in a few instances alongside *doesn't*). Cultured informants who use only *doesn't* are mostly to be found in or near New York City or Philadelphia.

In the S. A. S., also, *don't* is universal in Types I and II. About half of the cultured informants use *don't*, occasionally alongside *doesn't*.

OUGHT NOT

The negative form of *ought* is recorded in the context "He (oughtn't) to."

In the southern two thirds of Pa. and nearly everywhere to the southward oughtn't/ɔtənt/ is in universal use in all types. In the South Midland and throughout N. C. phonetic, and probably phonemic, /r/ very generally appears in this form: /ɔrtənt/.

In N. Eng., N. Y., n. Pa., and most of N. J. the usual form is *hadn't ought*. . . . Throughout most of this area nearly all the noncultured informants use this form; however, in s. N. Eng. only about half the informants use it, often alongside *oughtn't* or *ought not*. One third of the cultured informants in N. Eng. (nearly all of those who were interviewed in the northeast) use *hadn't ought*. There are only three instances of *didn't ought* in N. Eng.

In a small area of s. Ohio extending northeast from Marietta, and in part of n. e. N. C. *hadn't ought* is also current, though not universal.

SUGGESTED ASSIGNMENTS

1. Here are fifteen groups of words in which dialect differences in pronunciation exist: 1. *barn, dark, far, far away;* 2. *curl, first, bird;* 3. *orange, foreign;* 4. *greasy, Miss, Mrs.;* 5. *dog, frog, lot, pot;* 6. *ask, aunt, calf, afternoon;* 7. *ice, mine, time;* 8. *Tuesday, new, tune, duty;* 9. *Mary, merry, marry;* 10. *morning, mourning, horse, hoarse;* 11. *wash, water;* 12. *caller, collar;* 13. *house, out, town, down;* 14. *poor, sure;* 15. *on, from* (in stressed positions, as "Is it *on?*" and "Where are you *from?*") Select five groups and put the words into simple, natural sentences. Then find a student from a part of the country different from yours and ask him to read them. Make a note of the pronunciations that differ from yours and be prepared to contribute these to a class discussion of dialect differences.
2. One can often ascertain the vocabulary items of a dialect by direct questions such as these:
   a. What do you call the yellow part of an egg? (*yolk* or *yelk*)
   b. When does *evening* begin? (After midday in the South)
   c. What time does my watch show? (The setting is fifteen minutes before the hour to elicit "a quarter *to, till,* or *of* . . ."

   Write five questions designed to elicit vocabulary items from the following groups. Most of these words are taken from Hans Kurath's *A Word Geography of the Eastern United States.*
   a. *bag, poke, sack*
   b. sick (*at, to, till, on*) the stomach
   c. *porch, piazza, stoop*
   d. *creek, brook, run, branch, kill*
   e. *frying pan, spider, skillet*
   f. *you, you-all* (plurals)
   g. *doughnut, raised doughnut, cruller, fried cake, nut cake, fat cake, olicook, cookie.* (Use an informant east of the Alleghenies for these, and distinguish between the raised and the unraised, sweetened variety.)
   h. *pancake, griddle cake, fritter, hot-cake, flannel cake, batter-cake, flapjack*
   i. *earthworm, night crawler, fish worm, angle worm, mud worm, angle dog, ground worm, red-worm, rain worm*
   j. *pop, soda, tonic, soda pop, soda water*

   Choose a speaker from a region other than yours and ask him your questions. Note his responses for class discussion. Although Kurath's material is taken from the eastern seaboard and New England, you can use a speaker from elsewhere because many of these terms have spread.

3. Assume that you are a linguistic field-worker planning an interview with an informant. You want to find out which grammatical forms he uses in sentence situations like those listed below. If you ask him point-blank, he may report the one he thinks to be "correct" instead of what he normally uses. Devise the means whereby you can get him to use the forms in parentheses below, or whatever he naturally uses instead of them, and then go ahead with an interview.
   a. He (*dived* *dove*) from the high board.
   b. She (*had drank* *had drunk*) all her medicine.
   c. You (*hadn't ought* *ought not*) to drive so fast.
   d. Yesterday he (*lay* *laid*) in bed all day.
   e. My shirt (*shrank* *shrunk*) in the laundry.
   f. It (*don't* *doesn't*) matter.
   g. He (*waked up* *woke up*) early.
   h. She lives (*on* *in*) Broad Street.
   i. This is (*all the further* *as far as* *all the farther*) I go.
   j. Who (*rang* *rung*) the bell?
4. We have seen that, within the boundaries of our country, there are dialects and subdialects. But we can go further. Any small, closely knit group, such as a family or a group of close friends, is likely to have language peculiarities of its own. It may even be truly said that the speech of every person is unique. This individual speech of a single person we call an *ideolect*. Observe carefully for a week the speech of a person of whom you see a good deal every day. Make a list of the specific ways in which his speech differs from yours–in his pronunciation of words, in his choice of grammatical forms, and in his choice of words and word-combinations. Bring this list to class for discussion.
5. To convey some meanings there is no nationally used word. Instead, there are only various regional words. What, for example, does one call the strip of ground between the sidewalk and the street. Ask as many students as you know from different parts of the country and list the words they use.
6. When you have completed the readings, exercises, and class discussions on linguistic geography, write a theme on "Dialect Differences I Have Observed."

FURTHER READINGS

1. *American Speech, a Quarterly of Linguistic Usage*. New York: Columbia University Press. This periodical contains many articles on dialect terms, as well as a current bibliography of matters of linguistic interest.

2. Bloomfield, Leonard. *Language.* New York: Holt, Rinehart and Winston, Inc., 1933. See chapter on dialect geography, pp. 321-345.
3. Francis, W. Nelson. *The Structure of American English.* New York: The Ronald Press Company, 1958. For a short, up-to-date (1958) description of linguistic geography and its accomplishment to date, see pp. 485-499. Emphasis is on American work.
4. Hall, Robert A., Jr. *Linguistics and Your Language.* New York: Doubleday & Co., 1960. See pp. 135-156.
5. Hockett, Charles F. *A Course in Modern Linguistics.* New York: The Macmillan Company, 1958. See pp. 471-484.
6. Potter, Simeon. *Modern Linguistics.* London: Andre Deutsch, 1957. See pp. 123-140. Emphasis is on European and British scene.
7. Randolph, Vance and George P. Wilson. *Down in the Holler.* Norman, Oklahoma: University of Oklahoma Press, 1953. See pages 37-49, "Backwoods Grammar," for a discussion of the speech of the Ozarks.

8. Structural Grammar

REVOLUTION IN GRAMMAR

W. Nelson Francis

For two centuries we have been using in English a grammar based on Latin, constructed by British grammarians of the eighteenth century. This grammar is entrenched in our dictionaries and is widely taught in the schools. It is serviceable in certain ways; for example, it gives us a technical vocabulary with which to discuss problem of writing and speaking, and it enables us to analyze English sentences in a rough-and-ready way. But with the advance of linguistic science in recent decades, the new grammarians find this Latinized grammar too crude an instrument for the thorough linguistic analyses they wish to make. Beginning with new premises, they have been forging new grammars that are highly refined and that enable us to see with greater clarity the marvelously complex structure of our language. W. Nelson Francis discusses these two types of grammars, the Latinized and the scientific, in the important article below. Professor Francis, of Brown University, is the author of The Structure of American English, *a college textbook that offers an excellent insight into the new point of view toward grammar.*

I

A LONG OVERDUE revolution is at present taking place in the study of English grammar—a revolution as sweeping in its consequences as the Darwinian revolution in biology. It is the result of the application

From *Quarterly Journal of Speech,* October 1954. Reprinted by permission of the Speech Association of America.

to English of methods of descriptive analysis originally developed for use with languages of primitive people. To anyone at all interested in language, it is challenging; to those concerned with the teaching of English (including parents), it presents the necessity of radically revising both the substance and the methods of their teaching.

A curious paradox exists in regard to grammar. On the one hand it is felt to be the dullest and driest of academic subjects, fit only for those in whose veins the red blood of life has long since turned to ink. On the other, it is a subject upon which people who would scorn to be professional grammarians hold very dogmatic opinions, which they will defend with considerable emotion. Much of this prejudice stems from the usual sources of prejudice—ignorance and confusion. Even highly educated people seldom have a clear idea of what grammarians do, and there is an unfortunate confusion about the meaning of the term "grammar" itself.

Hence it would be well to begin with definitions. What do people mean when they use the word "grammar"? Actually the word is used to refer to three different things, and much of the emotional thinking about matters grammatical arises from confusion among these different meanings.

The first thing we mean by "grammar" is "the set of formal patterns in which the words of a language are arranged in order to convey larger meanings." It is not necessary that we be able to discuss these patterns self-consciously in order to be able to use them. In fact, all speakers of a language above the age of five or six know how to use its complex forms of organization with considerable skill; in this sense of the word—call it "Grammar 1"—they are thoroughly familiar with its grammar.

The second meaning of "grammar"—call it "Grammar 2"—is "the branch of linguistic science which is concerned with the description, analysis, and formulization of formal language patterns." Just as gravity was in full operation before Newton's apple fell, so grammar in the first sense was in full operation before anyone formulated the first rule that began the history of grammar as a study.

The third sense in which people use the word "grammar" is "linguistic etiquette." This we may call "Grammar 3." The word in this sense is often coupled with a derogatory adjective: we say that the expression "he ain't here" is "bad grammar." What we mean is that such an expression is bad linguistic manners in certain circles. From the point of view of "Grammar 1" it is faultless; it conforms just as completely to the structural patterns of English as does "he isn't here." The trouble with it is like the trouble with Prince Hal in Shakespeare's play—it is "bad," not in itself, but in the company it keeps.

As has already been suggested, much confusion arises from mixing these meanings. One hears a good deal of criticism of teachers of English couched in such terms as "they don't teach grammar any more." Criticism of this sort is based on the wholly unproved assumption that teaching Grammar 2 will increase the student's proficiency in Grammar 1 or improve his manners in Grammar 3. Actually, the form of Grammar 2 which is usually taught is a very inaccurate and misleading analysis of the facts of Grammar 1; and it therefore is of highly questionable value in improving a person's ability to handle the structural patterns of his language. It is hardly reasonable to expect that teaching a person some inaccurate grammatical analysis will either improve the effectiveness of his assertions or teach him what expressions are acceptable to use in a given social context.

These, then, are the three meanings of "grammar": Grammar 1, a form of behavior; Grammar 2, a field of study, a science; and Grammar 3, a branch of etiquette.

II

Grammarians have arrived at some basic principles of their science, three of which are fundamental to this discussion. The first is that a language constitutes a set of behavior patterns common to the members of a given community. It is a part of what the anthropologists call the culture of the community. Actually it has complex and intimate relationships with other phases of culture such as myth and ritual. But for purposes of study it may be dealt with as a separate set of phenomena that can be objectively described and analyzed like any other universe of facts. Specifically, its phenomena can be observed, recorded, classified, and compared; and general laws of their behavior can be made by the same inductive process that is used to produce the "laws" of physics, chemistry, and the other sciences.

A second important principle of linguistic science is that each language or dialect has its own unique system of behavior patterns. Parts of this system may show similarities to parts of the systems of other languages, particularly if those languages are genetically related. But different languages solve the problems of expression and communication in different ways, just as the problems of movement through water are solved in different ways by lobsters, fish, seals, and penguins. A couple of corollaries of this principle are important. The first is that there is no such thing as "universal grammar," or at least if there is, it is so general and abstract as to be of little use. The second corollary is that the grammar of each language must be made up on the basis of a study of that particular language—a study that is free from preconceived notions of what a language should contain and how it should operate. The marine biologist does not criticize the octopus for using jet-propulsion to get him through the water instead of the methods of a self-respecting fish. Neither does the linguistic scientist express alarm or distress when he finds a language that seems to get along quite well without any words that correspond to what in English we call verbs.

A third principle on which linguistic science is based is that the analysis and description of a given language must conform to the requirements laid down for any satisfactory scientific theory. These are (1) simplicity, (2) consistency, (3) completeness, and (4) usefulness for predicting the behavior of phenomena not brought under immediate observation when the theory was formed. Linguistic scientists who have recently turned their attention to English have found that, judged by these criteria, the traditional grammar of English is unsatisfactory. It falls down badly on the first two requirements, being unduly complex and glaringly inconsistent within itself. It can be made to work, just as the Ptolemaic earth-centered astronomy can be, but at the cost of great elaboration and complication. The new grammar, like the Copernican sun-centered astronomy, solves the same problems with greater elegance, which is the scientist's word for the simplicity, compactness, and tidiness that characterize a satisfactory theory.

III

A brief look at the history of the traditional grammar of English will make apparent the reasons for its inadequacy. The study of English grammar is actually an outgrowth of the linguistic interest of the Renaissance. It was during the later Middle Ages and early Renaissance that the various vernacular languages of Europe came into their own. They began to be used for many kinds of writing which had previously always been done in Latin. As the vernaculars, in the hands of great writers like Dante and Chaucer, came of age as members of the linguistic family, a concomitant interest in their grammars arose. The earliest important English grammar was written by Shakespeare's contemporary, Ben Jonson.

It is important to observe that not only Ben Jonson himself but also those who followed him in the study of English grammar were men deeply learned in Latin and sometimes in Greek. For all their interest in English, they were conditioned from earliest school days to conceive of the classical languages as superior to the vernaculars. We still sometimes call the elementary school the "grammar school"; historically the term means the school where Latin grammar was taught. By the time the Renaissance or eighteenth-century scholar took his university degree, he was accustomed to use Latin as the normal means of communication with his fellow scholars. Dr. Samuel Johnson, for instance, who had only three years at the university and did not take a degree, wrote poetry in both Latin and Greek. Hence it was natural for these men to take Latin grammar as the norm, and to analyze English in terms of Latin. The grammarians of the seventeenth and eighteenth centuries who formulated the traditional grammar of English looked for the devices and distinctions of Latin grammar in English, and where they did not actually find them they imagined or created them. Of course, since English is a member of the Indo-European family of languages, to which Latin and Greek also belong, it did have many grammatical elements in common with them. But many of these had been obscured or wholly lost as a result of the extensive changes that had taken place in English—changes that the early grammarians inevitably conceived of as degeneration. They felt that it was their function to resist further change, if not to repair the damage already done. So preoccupied were they with the grammar of Latin as the ideal that they overlooked in large part the exceedingly complex and delicate system that English had substituted for the Indo-European grammar it had abandoned. Instead they stretched unhappy English on the Procrustean bed of Latin. It is no wonder that we commonly hear people say, "I didn't really understand grammar until I began to study Latin." This is eloquent testimony to the fact that the grammar "rules" of our present-day textbooks are largely an inheritance from the Latin-based grammar of the eighteenth century.

Meanwhile the extension of linguistic study beyond the Indo-European and Semitic families began to reveal that there are many different ways in which linguistic phenomena are organized—in other words, many different kinds of grammar. The tone-languages of the Orient and of North America, and the complex agglutinative languages of Africa, among others, forced grammarians to abandon the idea of a universal or ideal grammar and to direct their attention more closely to the individual systems employed by the multifarious languages of mankind. With the growth and refinement of the scientific method and its application to the field of anthropology, language came under more rigorous scientific scrutiny. As with anthropology in general, linguistic science at first concerned itself with the primitive. Finally, again following the lead of anthropology, linguistics began to apply its techniques to the old familiar tongues, among them English. Accelerated by the practical need during World War II of teaching languages, including English, to large numbers in a short time, research into the nature of English grammar has moved rapidly in the last fifteen years. The definitive grammar of English is yet to be written, but the results so far achieved are spectacular. It is now as unrealistic to teach "traditional" grammar of English as it is to teach "traditional" (i.e. pre-Darwinian) biology or "traditional" (i.e. four-element) chemistry. Yet nearly all certified teachers of English on all levels are doing so. Here is a cultural lag of major proportions.

IV

Before we can proceed to a sketch of what the new grammar of English looks like, we must take account of a few more of the premises of linguistic science. They must be understood and accepted by anyone who wishes to understand the new grammar.

First, the spoken language is primary, at least for the original study of a language. In many of the primitive languages,[1] of course, where writing is unknown, the spoken language is the *only* form. This is in many ways an advantage to the linguist, because the written language may use conventions that obscure its basic structure. The reason for the primary importance of the spoken language is that language originates as speech, and most of the changes and innovations that

[1] "Primitive languages" here is really an abbreviated statement for "languages used by peoples of relatively primitive culture"; it is not to be taken as implying anything simple or rudimentary about the languages themselves. Many languages included under the term, such as native languages of Africa and Mexico, exhibit grammatical complexities unknown to more "civilized" languages.

occur in the history of a given language begin in the spoken tongue.

Secondly, we must take account of the concept of dialect. I suppose most laymen would define a dialect as "a corrupt form of a language spoken in a given region by people who don't know any better." This introduces moral judgments which are repulsive to the linguistic scholar. Let us approach the definition of a dialect from the more objective end, through the notion of a speech community. A speech community is merely a group of people who are in pretty constant intercommunication. There are various types of speech communities: local ones, like "the people who live in Tidewater Virginia"; class ones, like "the white-collar class"; occupational ones, like "doctors, nurses, and other people who work in hospitals"; social ones, like "clubwomen." In a sense, each of these has its own dialect. Each family may be said to have its own dialect; in fact, in so far as each of us has his own vocabulary and particular quirks of speech, each individual has his own dialect. Also, of course, in so far as he is a member of many speech communities, each individual is more or less master of many dialects and shifts easily and almost unconsciously from one to another as he shifts from one social environment to another.

In the light of this concept of dialects, a language can be defined as a group of dialects which have enough of their sound-system, vocabulary and grammar (Grammar 1, that is) in common to permit their speakers to be mutually intelligible in the ordinary affairs of life. It usually happens that one of the many dialects that make up a language comes to have more prestige than the others; in modern times it has usually been the dialect of the middle-class residents of the capital, like Parisian French and London English, which is so distinguished. This comes to be thought of as the standard dialect; in fact, its speakers become snobbish and succeed in establishing the belief that it is not a dialect at all, but the only proper form of the language. This causes the speakers of other dialects to become self-conscious and ashamed of their speech, or else aggressive and jingoistic about it—either of which is an acknowledgment of their feelings of inferiority. Thus one of the duties of the educational system comes to be that of teaching the standard dialect to all so as to relieve them of feelings of inferiority, and thus relieve society of linguistic neurotics. This is where Grammar 3, linguistic etiquette, comes into the picture.

A third premise arising from the two just discussed is that the difference between the way educated people talk and the way they write is a dialectal difference. The spread between these two dialects may be very narrow, as in present-day America, or very wide, as in Norway, where people often speak local Norwegian dialects but write in the Dano-Norwegian *Riksmaal.* The extreme is the use by writers of an entirely different language, or at least an ancient and no longer spoken form of the language—like Sanskrit in northern India or Latin in western Europe during the Middle Ages. A corollary of this premise is that anyone setting out to write a grammar must know and make clear whether he is dealing with the spoken or the written dialect. Virtually all current English grammars deal with the written language only; evidence for this is that their rules for the plurals of nouns, for instance, are really spelling rules, which say nothing about pronunciation.

This is not the place to go into any sort of detail about the methods of analysis the linguistic scientist uses. Suffice it to say that he begins by breaking up the flow of speech into minimum sound-units, or phones, which he then groups into families called phonemes, the minimum significant sound-units.[2] Most languages have from twenty to sixty of these. American English has forty-one: nine vowels, twenty-four consonants, four degrees of stress, and four levels of pitch. These phonemes group themselves into minimum meaningful units, called morphemes. These fall into two groups: free morphemes, those that can enter freely into many combinations with other free morphemes to make phrases and sentences; and bound morphemes, which are always found tied in a close and often indissoluble relationship with other bound or free morphemes. An example of a free morpheme is "dog"; an example of a bound morpheme is "un-" or "ex-." The linguist usually avoids talking about "words" because the term is very inexact. Is "instead of," for instance, to be considered one, two, or three words? This is purely a matter of opinion; but it is a matter of fact that it is made up of three morphemes.

[2] E.g., /l/ is a phoneme because it is significant, that is, because it can be used to signify differences in meaning. It is the /l/, for instance, that distinguishes *light* from such words as *night, might, sight, tight, right, bite, height.* But there is more than one *l* sound: the last sound in *well* differs from the *l* in *light* in that it is preceded by an *uh* sound. However, the difference between these two *l*'s does not distinguish meaning; if you pronounce *well* with the *l* of *light,* it is still the same word, though it will sound a little foreign. Thus these two *l*'s are not two different phonemes but simply two members of the family known as the /l/ phoneme. [eds.]

In any case, our analysis has now brought the linguist to the point where he has some notion of the word-stock (he would call it the "lexicon") of his language. He must then go into the question of how the morphemes are grouped into meaningful utterances, which is the field of grammar proper. At this point in the analysis of English, as of many other languages, it becomes apparent that there are three bases upon which classification and analysis may be built: form, function, and meaning. For illustration let us take the word "boys" in the utterance "the boys are here." From the point of view of form, "boys" is a noun with the plural ending "s" (pronounced like "z"), preceded by the noun-determiner "the," and tied by concord to the verb "are," which it precedes. From the point of view of function, "boys" is the subject of the verb "are" and of the sentence. From the point of view of meaning, "boys" points out or names more than one of the male young of the human species, about whom an assertion is being made.

Of these three bases of classification, the one most amenable to objective description and analysis of a rigorously scientific sort is form. In fact, many conclusions about form can be drawn by a person unable to understand or speak the language. Next comes function. But except as it is revealed by form, function is dependent on knowing the meaning. In a telegraphic sentence like "ship sails today"[3] no one can say whether "ship" is the subject of "sails" or an imperative verb with "sails" as its object until he knows what the sentence means. Most shaky of all bases for grammatical analysis is meaning. Attempts have been made to reduce the phenomena of meaning to objective description, but so far they have not succeeded very well. Meaning is such a subjective quality that it is usually omitted entirely from scientific description. The botanist can describe the forms of plants and the functions of their various parts, but he refuses to concern himself with their meaning. It is left to the poet to find symbolic meaning in roses, violets, and lilies.

At this point it is interesting to note that the traditional grammar of English bases some of its key concepts and definitions on this very subjective and shaky foundation of meaning. A recent English grammar defines a sentence as "a group of words which expresses a complete thought through the use of a verb, called its predicate, and a subject, consisting of a noun or pronoun about which the verb has

[3] This example is taken from C. C. Fries, *The Structure of English* (New York, 1952), p. 62. This important book will be discussed below.

something to say."[4] But what is a complete thought? Actually we do not identify sentences this way at all. If someone says, "I don't know what to do," dropping his voice at the end, and pauses, the hearer will know that it is quite safe for him to make a comment without running the risk of interrupting an unfinished sentence. But if the speaker says the same words and maintains a level pitch at the end, the polite listener will wait for him to finish his sentence. The words are the same, the meaning is the same; the only difference is a slight one in the pitch of the final syllable—a purely formal distinction, which signals that the first utterance is complete, a sentence, while the second is incomplete. In writing we would translate these signals into punctuation: a period or exclamation point at the end of the first, a comma or dash at the end of the second. It is the form of the utterance, not the completeness of the thought, that tells us whether it is a whole sentence or only part of one.

Another favorite definition of the traditional grammar, also based on meaning, is that of "noun" as "the name of a person, place, or thing"; or, as the grammar just quoted has it, "the name of anybody or anything, with or without life, and with or without substance or form."[5] Yet we identify nouns, not by asking if they name something, but by their positions in expressions and by the formal marks they carry. In the sentence, "The slithy toves did gyre and gimble in the wabe," any speaker of English knows that "toves" and "wabe" are nouns, though he cannot tell what they name, if indeed they name anything. How does he know? Actually because they have certain formal marks, like their position in relation to "the" as well as the whole arrangement of the sentence. We know from our practical knowledge of English grammar (Grammar 1), which we have had since before we went to school, that if we were to put meaningful words into this sentence, we would have to put nouns in place of "toves" and "wabe," giving something like "The slithy snakes did gyre and gimble in the wood." The pattern of the sentence simply will not allow us to say "The slithy arounds did gyre and gimble in the wooden."

One trouble with the traditional grammar, then, is that it relies heavily on the most subjective element in language, meaning. Another is that it shifts the ground of its classification and produces the elementary logical error of cross-division. A zoologist who divided

[4] Ralph B. Allen, *English Grammar* (New York, 1950), p. 187.
[5] *Ibid.*, p. 1.

animals into invertebrates, mammals, and beasts of burden would not get very far before running into trouble. Yet the traditional grammar is guilty of the same error when it defines three parts of speech on the basis of meaning (noun, verb, and interjection), four more on the basis of function (adjective, adverb, pronoun, conjunction), and one partly on function and partly on form (preposition). The result is that in such an expression as "a dog's life" there can be endless futile argument about whether "dog's" is a noun or an adjective. It is, of course, a noun from the point of view of form and an adjective from the point of view of function, and hence falls into both classes, just as a horse is both a mammal and a beast of burden. No wonder students are bewildered in their attempts to master the traditional grammar. Their natural clearness of mind tells them that it is a crazy patchwork violating the elementary principles of logical thought.

V

If the traditional grammar is so bad, what does the new grammar offer in its place?

It offers a description, analysis, and set of definitions and formulas —rules, if you will—based firmly and consistently on the easiest, or at least the most objective, aspect of language, form. Experts can quibble over whether "dog's" in "a dog's life" is a noun or an adjective, but anyone can see that it is spelled with " 's" and hear that it ends with a "z" sound; likewise anyone can tell that it comes in the middle between "a" and "life." Furthermore he can tell that something important has happened if the expression is changed to "the dog's alive," "the live dogs," or "the dogs lived," even if he doesn't know what the words mean and has never heard of such functions as modifier, subject, or attributive genitive. He cannot, of course, get very far into his analysis without either a knowledge of the language or access to someone with such knowledge. He will also need a minimum technical vocabulary describing grammatical functions. Just so the anatomist is better off for knowing physiology. But the grammarian, like the anatomist, must beware of allowing his preconceived notions to lead him into the error of interpreting before he describes —an error which often results in his finding only what he is looking for.

When the grammarian looks at English objectively, he finds that it conveys its meanings by two broad devices: the denotations and connotations of words separately considered, which the linguist calls "lexical meaning," and the significance of word-forms, word-groups, and arrangements apart from the lexical meanings of the words, which the linguist calls "structural meaning." The first of these is the domain of the lexicographer and the semanticist, and hence is not our present concern. The second, the structural meaning, is the business of the structural linguist, or grammarian. The importance of this second kind of meaning must be emphasized because it is often overlooked. The man in the street tends to think of the meaning of a sentence as being the aggregate of the dictionary meanings of the words that make it up; hence the widespread fallacy of literal translation—the feeling that if you take a French sentence and a French-English dictionary and write down the English equivalent of each French word you will come out with an intelligible English sentence. How ludicrous the results can be, anyone knows who is familiar with Mark Twain's retranslation from the French of his jumping frog story. One sentence reads, "Eh bien! I no saw not that that frog has nothing of better than each frog." Upon which Mark's comment is, "if that isn't grammar gone to seed, then I count myself no judge."[6]

The second point brought out by a formal analysis of English is that it uses four principal devices of form to signal structural meanings:

1. Word order—the sequence in which words and word-groups are arranged.
2. Function-words—words devoid of lexical meaning which indicate relationships among the meaningful words with which they appear.
3. Inflections—alterations in the forms of words themselves to signal changes in meaning and relationship.
4. Formal contrasts—contrasts in the forms of words signaling greater differences in function and meaning. These could also be considered inflections, but it is more convenient for both the lexicographer and the grammarian to consider them separately.

Usually several of these are present in any utterance, but they can be separately illustrated by means of contrasting expressions involv-

[6] Mark Twain, "The Jumping Frog; the Original Story in English; the Retranslation Clawed Back from the French, into a Civilized Language Once More, by Patient and Unremunerated Toil," *1601 . . . and Sketches Old and New* (n.p., 1933), p. 50.

ing minimum variation—the kind of controlled experiment used in the scientific laboratory.

To illustrate the structural meaning of word order, let us compare the two sentences "man bites dog" and "dog bites man."—The words are identical in lexical meaning and in form; the only difference is in sequence. It is interesting to note that Latin expresses the difference between these two by changes in the form of the words, without necessarily altering the order: "homo canem mordet" or "hominem canis mordet." Latin grammar is worse than useless in understanding this point of English grammar.

Next, compare the sentences "the dog is the friend of man" and "any dog is a friend of that man." Here the words having lexical meaning are "dog," "is," "friend," and "man," which appear in the same form and the same order in both sentences. The formal differences between them are in the substitution of "any" and "a" for "the," and in the insertion of "that." These little words are function-words; they make quite a difference in the meanings of the two sentences, though it is virtually impossible to say what they mean in isolation.

Third, compare the sentences "the dog loves the man" and "the dogs loved the men." Here the words are the same, in the same order, with the same function-words in the same positions. But the forms of the three words having lexical meanings have been changed: "dog" to "dogs," "loves" to "loved," and "man" to "men." These changes are inflections. English has very few of them as compared with Greek, Latin, Russian, or even German. But it still uses them; about one word in four in an ordinary English sentence is inflected.

Fourth, consider the difference between "the dog's friend arrived" and "the dog's friendly arrival." Here the difference lies in the change of "friend" to "friendly," a formal alteration signaling a change of function from subject to modifier, and the change of "arrived" to "arrival," signaling a change of function from predicate to head-word in a noun-modifier group. These changes are of the same formal nature as inflections, but because they produce words of different lexical meaning, classifiable as different parts of speech, it is better to call them formal contrasts than inflections. In other words, it is logically quite defensible to consider "love," "loving," and "loved" as the same word in differing aspects and to consider "friend," "friendly," "friendliness," "friendship," and "befriend" as different words related by formal and semantic similarities. But this is only a matter of convenience of analysis, which permits a more accurate description of English structure. In another language we might find that this kind of distinction is unnecessary but that some other distinction, unnecessary in English, is required. The categories of grammatical description are not sacrosanct; they are as much a part of man's organization of his observations as they are of the nature of things.

If we are considering the spoken variety of English, we must add a fifth device for indicating structural meaning—the various musical and rhythmic patterns which the linguist classifies under juncture, stress, and intonation. Consider the following pair of sentences:

Alfred, the alligator is sick.
Alfred the alligator is sick.

These are identical in the four respects discussed above—word order, function-words, inflections, and word-form. Yet they have markedly different meanings, as would be revealed by the intonation if they were spoken aloud. These differences in intonation are to a certain extent indicated in the written language by punctuation—that is, in fact, the primary function of punctuation.

VI

The examples so far given were chosen to illustrate in isolation the various kinds of structural devices in English grammar. Much more commonly the structural meaning of a given sentence is indicated by a combination of two or more of these devices: a sort of margin of safety which permits some of the devices to be missed or done away with without obscuring the structural meaning of the sentence, as indeed anyone knows who has ever written a telegram or a newspaper headline. On the other hand, sentences which do not have enough of these formal devices are inevitably ambiguous. Take the example already given, Fries's "ship sails today." This is ambiguous because there is nothing to indicate which of the first two words is performing a noun function and which a verb function. If we mark the noun by putting the noun-determining function-word "the" in front of it, the ambiguity disappears; we have either "the ship sails today" or "ship the sails today." The ambiguity could just as well be resolved by using other devices: consider "ship sailed today," "ship to sail today," "ship sail today," "shipping sails today," "shipment of sails today," and so on. It is simply a question of having enough formal devices in the sentence to indicate its structural meaning clearly.

How powerful the structural meanings of English are is illustrated by so-called "nonsense." In English, nonsense as a literary form often consists of utterances that have a clear structural meaning but use words that either have no lexical meanings, or whose lexical meanings are inconsistent one with another. This will become apparent if we subject a rather famous bit of English nonsense to formal grammatical analysis:

> All mimsy were the borogoves
> And the mome raths outgrabe.

This passage consists of ten words, five of them words that should have lexical meaning but don't, one standard verb, and four function-words. In so far as it is possible to indicate its abstract structure, it would be this:

> All . . . .y were the . . . . .s
> And the . . . . . .s . . . . . .

Although this is a relatively simple formal organization, it signals some rather complicated meanings. The first thing we observe is that the first line presents a conflict: word order seems to signal one thing, and inflections and function-words something else. Specifically, "mimsy" is in the position normally occupied by the subject, but we know that it is not the subject and that "borogoves" is. We know this because there is an inflectional tie between the form "were" and the "s" ending of "borogoves," because there is the noun-determiner "the" before it, and because the alternative candidate for subject "mimsy," lacks both of these. It is true that "mimsy" does have the function-word "all" before it, which may indicate a noun; but when it does, the noun is either plural (in which case "mimsy" would most likely end in "s"), or else the noun is what grammarians call a mass-word (like "sugar," coal," "snow"), in which case the verb would have to be "was," not "were." All these formal considerations are sufficient to counteract the effect of word order and show that the sentence is of the type that may be represented thus:

> All gloomy were the Democrats.

Actually there is one other possibility. If "mimsy" belongs to the small group of nouns which don't use "s" to make the plural, and if "borogoves" has been so implied (but not specifically mentioned) in the context as to justify its appearing with the determiner "the," the sentence would then belong to the following type:

> (In the campaign for funds) all alumni were the canvassers.
> (In the drought last summer) all cattle were the sufferers.

But the odds are so much against this that most of us would be prepared to fight for our belief that "borogoves" are things that can be named, and that at the time referred to they were in a complete state of "mimsyness."

Moving on to the second line, "and the mome raths outgrabe," the first thing we note is that the "And" signals another parallel assertion to follow. We are thus prepared to recognize from the noun-determiner "the," the plural inflection "s," and the particular positions of "mome" and "outgrabe," as well as the continuing influence of the "were" of the preceding line, that we are dealing with a sentence of this pattern:

> And the lone rats agreed.

The influence of the "were" is particularly important here; it guides us in selecting among several interpretations of the sentence. Specifically, it requires us to identify "outgrabe" as a verb in the past tense, and thus a "strong" or "irregular" verb, since it lacks the characteristic past-tense ending "d" or "ed." We do this in spite of the fact that there is another strong candidate for the position of verb: that is, "raths," which bears a regular verb inflection and could be tied with "mome" as its subject in the normal noun-verb relationship. In such a case we should have to recognize "outgrabe" as either an adverb of the kind not marked by the form-contrast "ly," an adjective, or the past participle of a strong verb. The sentence would then belong to one of the following types:

> And the moon shines above.
> And the man stays aloof.
> And the fool seems outdone.

But we reject all of these—probably they don't even occur to us—because they all have verbs in the present tense, whereas the "were" of the first line combines with the "And" at the beginning of the second to set the whole in the past.

We might recognize one further possibility for the structural meaning of this second line, particularly in the verse context, since we are used to certain patterns in verse that do not often appear in speech of prose. The "were" of the first line could be understood as doing double duty, its ghost or echo appearing between "raths" and "outgrabe." Then we would have something like this:

> All gloomy were the Democrats
> And the home folks outraged.

But again the odds are pretty heavy against this. I for one am so sure that "outgrabe" is the past tense of a strong verb that I can give its present. In my dialect, at least, it is "outgribe."

The reader may not realize it, but in the last four paragraphs I have been discussing grammar from a purely formal point of view. I have not once called a word a noun because it names something (that is, I have not once resorted to meaning), nor have I called any word an adjective because it modifies a noun (that is, resorted to function). Instead I have been working in the opposite direction, from form toward function and meaning. I have used only criteria which are objectively observable, and I have assumed only a working knowledge of certain structural patterns and devices known to all speakers of English over the age of six. I did use some technical terms like "noun," "verb," and "tense," but only to save time; I could have got along without them.

If one clears his mind of the inconsistencies of the traditional grammar (not so easy a process as it might be), he can proceed with a similarly rigorous formal analysis of a sufficient number of representative utterances in English and come out with a descriptive grammar. This is just what Professor Fries did in gathering and studying the material for the analysis he presents in the remarkable book to which I have already referred, *The Structure of English.* What he actually did was to put a tape recorder into action and record about fifty hours of telephone conversation among the good citizens of Ann Arbor, Michigan. When this material was transcribed, it constituted about a quarter of a million words of perfectly natural speech by educated middle-class Americans. The details of his conclusions cannot be presented here, but they are sufficiently different from the usual grammar to be revolutionary. For instance, he recognizes only four parts of speech among the words with lexical meaning, roughly corresponding to what the traditional grammar calls substantives, verbs, adjectives and adverbs, though to avoid preconceived notions from the traditional grammar Fries calls them Class 1, Class 2, Class 3, and Class 4 words. To these he adds a relatively small group of function-words, 154 in his materials, which he divides into fifteen groups. These must be memorized by anyone learning the language; they are not subject to the same kind of general rules that govern the four parts of speech. Undoubtedly his conclusions will be developed and modified by himself and by other linguistic scholars, but for the present his book remains the most complete treatment extant of English grammar from the point of view of linguistic science.

VII

Two vital questions are raised by this revolution in grammar. The first is, "What is the value of this new system?" In the minds of many who ask it, the implication of this question is, "We have been getting along all these years with traditional grammar, so it can't be so very bad. Why should we go through the painful process of unlearning and relearning grammar just because linguistic scientists have concocted some new theories?"

The first answer to this question is the bravest and most honest. It is that the superseding of vague and sloppy thinking by clear and precise thinking is an exciting experience in and for itself. To acquire insight into the workings of a language, and to recognize the infinitely delicate system of relationship, balance, and interplay that constitutes its grammar, is to become closely acquainted with one of man's most miraculous creations, not unworthy to be set beside the equally beautiful organization of the physical universe. And to find that its most complex effects are produced by the multi-layered organization of relatively simple materials is to bring our thinking about language into accord with modern thought in other fields, which is more and more coming to emphasize the importance of organization—the fact that an organized whole is truly greater than the sum of all its parts.

There are other answers, more practical if less philosophically valid. It is too early to tell, but it seems probable that a realistic, scientific grammar should vastly facilitate the teaching of English, especially as a foreign language. Already results are showing here; it has been found that if intonation contours and other structural patterns are taught quite early, the student has a confidence that allows him to attempt to speak the language much sooner than he otherwise would.

The new grammar can also be of use in improving the native speaker's proficiency in handling the structural devices of his own language. In other words, Grammar 2, if it is accurate and consistent, *can* be of use in improving skill in Grammar 1. An illustration is that famous bugaboo, the dangling participle. Consider a specific instance of it, which once appeared on a college freshman's theme, to the mingled delight and despair of the instructor:

Having eaten our lunch, the steamboat departed.

What is the trouble with this sentence? Clearly there must be something wrong with it, because it makes people laugh, although it was not the intent of the writer to make them laugh. In other words, it produces a completely wrong response, resulting in total breakdown of communication. It is, in fact, "bad grammar" in a much more serious way than are mere dialectal divergences like "he ain't here" or "he never seen none," which produce social reactions but communicate effectively. In the light of the new grammar, the trouble with our dangling participle is that the form, instead of leading to the meaning, is in conflict with it. Into the position which, in this pattern, is reserved for the word naming the eater of the lunch, the writer has inserted the word "steamboat." The resulting tug-of-war between form and meaning is only momentary; meaning quickly wins out, simply because our common sense tells us that steamboats don't eat lunches. But if the pull of the lexical meaning is not given a good deal of help from common sense, the form will conquer the meaning, or the two will remain in ambiguous equilibrium—as, for instance, in "Having eaten our lunch, the passengers boarded the steamboat." Writers will find it easier to avoid such troubles if they know about the forms of English and are taught to use the form to convey the meaning, instead of setting up tensions between form and meaning. This, of course, is what English teachers are already trying to do. The new grammar should be a better weapon in their arsenal than the traditional grammar since it is based on a clear understanding of the realities.

The second and more difficult question is, "How can the change from one grammar to the other be effected?" Here we face obstacles of a formidable nature. When we remember the controversies attending on revolutionary changes in biology and astronomy, we realize what a tenacious hold the race can maintain on anything it has once learned, and the resistance it can offer to new ideas. And remember that neither astronomy nor biology was taught in elementary schools. They were, in fact, rather specialized subjects in advanced education. How then change grammar, which is taught to everybody, from the fifth grade up through college? The vested interest represented by thousands upon thousands of English and Speech teachers who have learned the traditional grammar and taught it for many years is a conservative force comparable to those which keep us still using the chaotic system of English spelling and the unwieldy measuring system of inches and feet, pounds and ounces, quarts, bushels, and acres. Moreover, this army is constantly receiving new recruits. It is possible in my state to become certified to teach English in high school if one has had eighteen credit hours of college English—let us say two semesters of freshman composition (almost all of which is taught by people unfamiliar with the new grammar), two semesters of a survey course in English literature, one semester of Shakespeare, and one semester of the contemporary novel. And since hard-pressed school administrators feel that anyone who can speak English can in a pinch teach it, the result is that many people are called upon to teach grammar whose knowledge of the subject is totally inadequate.

There is, in other words, a battle ahead of the new grammar. It will have to fight not only the apathy of the general public but the ignorance and inertia of those who count themselves competent in the field of grammar. The battle is already on, in fact. Those who try to get the concepts of the new grammar introduced into the curriculum are tagged as "liberal" grammarians—the implication being, I suppose, that one has a free choice between "liberal" and "conservative" grammar, and that the liberals are a bit dangerous, perhaps even a touch subversive. They are accused of undermining standards, of holding that "any way of saying something is just as good as any other," of not teaching the fundamentals of good English. I trust that the readers of this article will see how unfounded these charges are. But the smear campaign is on. So far as I know, neither religion nor patriotism has yet been brought into it. When they are, Professor Fries will have to say to Socrates, Galileo, Darwin, Freud, and the other members of the honorable fraternity of the misunderstood, "Move over, gentlemen, and make room for me."

The assignments for all the essays in this section have been placed on page 414.

SENTENCE ANALYSIS AND PARTS OF SPEECH

Charles Carpenter Fries

In 1952 a highly important contribution to American grammar appeared. It was C. C. Fries's The Structure of English. *In this analytical work Fries used as his basic data some fifty hours of conversations, recorded mechanically, of about three hundred speakers of Standard English. With these data Fries produced an original descriptive study of such grammatical matters as kinds of sentences, parts of speech, and functions of sentence elements. Though the book was a center of linguistic controversy, its findings have been incorporated into a number of textbooks of grammar. In the following two selections from this book, Professor Fries explains his major basic assumption—that structural signals are matters of form—and discusses parts of speech in the light of this assumption.*

IN THE ANALYSIS OF SENTENCES to be carried out here, just as in our establishing of a practically useful definition of the sentence and in our classifying of the various kinds of sentences, the procedure differs markedly from that usually employed in the schools. Perhaps it will help clarify our discussion to bring into sharp contrast the characteristic features of the conventional approach to the analysis of sentences and those of the approach to be used here.

In the usual approach to the grammatical analysis of sentences one must know the total meaning of the utterance before beginning any analysis. The process of analysis consists almost wholly of giving technical names to portions of this total meaning. For example, given the sentence *the man gave the boy the money*, the conventional grammatical analysis would consist in attaching the name "subject" to the word *man*, the name "predicate" to the word *gave*, the name "indirect object" to the word *boy*, the name "direct object" to the word *money*, and the name "declarative sentence" to the whole utterance. If pressed for the basis upon which these names are given to these words, one would, in accord with the traditional method, say that the word *man* is called "subject" because it "designates the person about whom an assertion is made"; that the word *gave* is called "predicate" because it is "the word that asserts something about the subject"; that the word *boy* is called "indirect object" because it "indicates the person to or for whom the action is done"; and that the word *money* is called "direct object" because it "indicates the thing that receives the action of the verb."[1] The sentence is called a "declarative sentence" because it "makes a statement." The whole procedure begins with the total meaning of the sentence and consists solely in ascribing the technical terms "subject," "predicate," "indirect object," "direct object," and "declarative sentence" to certain parts of that meaning. "Knowing grammar" has thus meant primarily the ability to apply and react to a technical terminology consisting of approximately seventy items.[2] It is this kind of "grammatical knowledge" that is assumed in the usual discussions of the value of "grammar" for an effective practical command of English, or for English composition, or for mastery of foreign language. It is this kind of grammatical analysis, this starting with the total meaning, *and the using of this meaning as the basis for the analysis*—an analysis that makes no advance beyond the ascribing of certain technical terms to parts of the meaning already known—it is this kind of grammatical analysis that modern linguistic science discards as belonging to a prescientific era.

What, then, have we, in contrast, to substitute for this type of grammatical analysis? Let us begin again with the sentence given above, *the man gave the boy the money*. First of all, we need to

[1] These definitions appear in nearly all the school textbooks that contain any "grammar."

[2] See *Report of the Joint Committee on Grammatical Terminology*, reprinted 1918, adopted by the Modern Language Association of America, the National Education Association, and the American Philological Association. See also the thirty items in C. D. Thorpe, *Preparation for College English* (Ann Arbor, 1945), p. 13. Also *English Grammar for Language Students*, by Frank X. Braun (Ann Arbor, 1947).

distinguish sharply at least two kinds of meaning in the total meaning of this utterance. There are, for example, the meanings of the separate words as the dictionary would record them—the lexical meanings. The dictionary would tell us something of the kinds of creatures referred to by the words *man* and *boy;* it would tell us the sort of thing the word *money* represents; and it would tell us the kind of action indicated by the word *gave*. Beyond these meanings the dictionary does not go. And yet we get from this sentence a whole range of meanings not expressed in the lexical records of the words themselves. We are told, for example, that the "man" performed the action, not the "boy"; we are told that only one man and only one boy are involved; we are told that the action has already taken place, it is not something in process, not something planned for the future; the information is given to us as a statement of fact, not something that is questioned, nor something that is requested. Such meanings constitute what we shall call the *structural meanings* of the sentence.[3] The total linguistic meaning of any utterance consists of the lexical meanings of the separate words plus such structural meanings. No utterance is intelligible without both lexical meanings and structural meanings. How, then, are these structural meanings conveyed in English from the speaker to a hearer? Structural meanings are not just vague matters of the context, so called; they are fundamental and necessary meanings in every utterance and are signalled by specific and definite devices. It is the devices that signal structural meanings which constitute the grammar of a language. *The grammar of a language consists of the devices that signal structural meanings.*

The contrast between the older traditional procedure of grammatical analysis and the approach used here lies in the fact that the conventional analysis starts from the undifferentiated total meaning of an utterance and raises the question, "What names apply to various parts of this meaning?" whereas our analysis[4] starts from a description of the formal devices that are present and the patterns that make them significant *and arrives at the structural meanings as a result of the analysis.* From a practical point of view we are concerned, too, with the utterances in which clear grammatical signals are not pres-

[3] The borderline between lexical meanings and structural meanings in a language like English that uses "function" words is not always sharp and clear. . . . More important, perhaps, is the fact that meanings which in one language are signalled by patterns of form and arrangement, in another language may depend upon the choice of vocabulary items.

[4] The word *analysis* here does not mean our procedure for the investigator.

ent, and thus *when* and *why* the structural meanings of any utterance become ambiguous.

Does a child of four who has learned to talk English as his native language know the grammar of that language? The answer to this question will depend upon the particular meaning one attaches to the word *know*. If *know* means the ability to make generalizing statements about the devices that signal structural meanings in English, then certainly he does not know the grammar of his language; nor, for that matter, do most adult speakers of English. But how will he react if he hears directed to him such an utterance as *is your mother home?* Will he recognize it as a question and reply with an answer? In other words, has he learned to respond to the particular devices by which English signals the fact that a particular utterance is a question? Or, again, when he hears, in the story that is being read to him, that *the hunters killed the wolf*, will he know that it was the hunters that survived and not the wolf? In so far as he has learned to respond to the signals of such structural meanings as these, he "knows" the grammar of his language. One cannot speak or understand a language without "knowing" its grammar—not consciously, of course, but in the sense of making the proper responses to the devices that signal structural meanings and also of producing the proper signals of his own structural meanings.

One of the earliest steps in learning to talk is this learning to use automatically the patterns of form and arrangement that constitute the devices to signal structural meaning. So thoroughly have they become unconscious habits in very early childhood that the ordinary adult speaker of English finds it extremely difficult not only to describe what he does in these matters but even to realize that there is anything there to be described.[5] One of the basic assumptions of our approach here to the grammatical analysis of sentences is that all the structural signals in English are strictly formal matters that can be described in physical terms of forms, correlations of these forms, and arrangements of order. An example of part of what this basic assumption covers is furnished by a comparison of an Old English sentence with a parallel word-for-word arrangement of the Modern English lexical equivalents.

[5] Several months ago even a college professor confronted with the demand to explain how he knew that the utterance *is the teacher here* is a question, could offer no better answer than, "Because it asks for information."

O. E.	Glædne	giefend	lufað	God
Mdn. E.	Cheerful	giver	loves	God

But the Modern English word for word equivalents of the Old English words do not represent the meaning of the Old English sentence. The lexical meanings are the same but the structural meanings differ. In the Old English sentence the *–ne* on the end of the word *glædne* signals the fact that the *glædne giefend* (the cheerful giver) is the object of God's love. The inflectional ending of the word, not the word order within the sentence, constitutes the structural signal in the Old English sentence. To render this structural meaning in Modern English the positions of the words must be changed to *God loves cheerful giver.* In the sentences

O. E.	Glædne	giefend	lufað	God
Mdn. E.	God	loves	cheerful	giver

the structural meanings are the same, but the formal devices that signal these similar meanings differ.

The following comparison will furnish another example.

O. E.	In	ænium	oþerum	mynstres	þingum
Mdn. E.	In	any	other	monastery's	things

As these expressions stand, the structural meaning of the Modern English rendering does not represent the structural meaning of the Old English phrase. In the Modern English expression the word-order arrangement signals the fact that *any* and *other* go with the word *monastery*. In the Old English sentence, however, the *–um* endings on the words *ænium* (*any*) and *oþerum* (*other*) signal the fact that these belong to *þingum* (*things*) which has the same *-um* ending. The Modern English equivalent of the structural meaning of the Old English expression cannot be rendered with the words in the same order as they stand in Old English. To represent the Old English meaning the Modern English words would have to be *in any other things of the monastery*, with *any* and *other* preceding the word *things*, and the word-group *of the monastery* following it. In the Old English example, the endings or the forms of the words are the determining signals indicating the word to which *any* and *other* are to be attached; in the Modern English rendering, the word-order arrangement is the important feature of the structural signal. In each, however, there is a definite formal device to signal this particular structural meaning. The lexical meanings of the words themselves give no clue concerning such a meaning. Some type of formal grammatical device, the endings or forms of the words, the order of the words, or both, must signal the direction of modification. We have thus assumed that the signals of all structural meanings in English are similarly formal matters that can be described in terms of forms, correlations of these forms, and arrangements of order.

Another of the basic assumptions of our approach here to the grammatical analysis of sentences is that the formal signals of structural meanings operate in a system—that is, that the items of form and arrangement have signalling significance only as they are parts of patterns in a structural whole. An illustration may help to explain the significance of this second assumption.

A man stands sixty feet away from a flat object lying on the ground. He throws a ball of a certain size so that it passes directly over the flat object at a height of three feet, and two inches inside the right edge. This act is of practically no significance in itself, but if this throwing occurs within the structural frame of a baseball game, by virtue of the patterns of that game, it gets a special significance—it is a "strike." Again, the man may throw the ball so that it passes over the flat object (the "plate") at a height of only two and a half feet, but three inches inside the left edge. In spite of all the specific differences, because of the patterns of the game, this also has the same significance; it too is a "strike." Again, the thrown ball may pass directly over the center of the plate but at a height of four and a half feet. According to the pattern this may or may not be a "strike." It will depend upon a different kind of contrast, upon whether the "batter" is a tall or a short man. The height of the ball over the plate must be above the knees but not above the shoulders of the batter. Or again, the ball may not pass over the plate at all, but six inches outside the right edge. This, according to the pattern, may be a "ball"; but, by a still different significant contrast, that is, if the batter attempts to hit the ball with his bat and misses, it can also be a "strike." Or again, the batter may strike at the ball and hit it so that it drops to the ground outside the playing "diamond." This is, of course, a "foul"; but if the batter has not already had two "strikes" against him, it is also a "strike." In spite of the very great specific differences from all the others, this "strike" is structurally the "same" as the others. Every one of these throwings by the "pitcher" differs from all the others, and yet, as far as the patterns of the game are concerned, they are the "same." They are all significant as "strikes." The number of specifically different throwings that can fit into the pattern of the "strike" is almost infinite, as is the number of differing actions that can fit into the pattern of an "out." But the number of the patterns themselves in the structural whole of the game of baseball is very limited. The game itself is a system of contrastive patterns that give significance to an infinite variety of specific actions.[6] In similar fashion, a language as a whole consists of a system of contrastive patterns that give significance to an infinite variety of specific acts of speech. It is only these patterns that can give significance to the features of form and arrangement that operate as the devices of structural meaning. It is our task, therefore, not only to describe the items of form and arrangement which constitute the devices that signal structural meanings, but also, and especially, to set forth the contrastive patterns of the system through which these items acquire signaling significance.

What then are the basic items of the patterns of grammatical structure in present-day English?

Sometimes, at street intersections, signs which alternately show the single words *Go* and *Stop* control the traffic. When the word *Go* appears, the traffic facing that sign moves forward. When the word *Stop* appears, that traffic ceases its forward movement. We recognize these single-word utterances as "commands" or "requests." To other single-word utterances such as *Waiter, Mother, Boy* we respond differently; we recognize these as "calls." Would an utterance of the single word *Skip* be a "call" like *Waiter, Mother, Boy*, or a "command" like *Go, Stop, Walk?*[7] It could be either; as it stands, with no other clues to the situation in which it is uttered, it is ambiguous. As the nickname for a boy, it would be a call. If no such boy is present, it would be a command. The linguistic difference between single-word utterances such as *Waiter, Mother, Boy, Dad, John* on the one hand and those of *Go, Stop, Walk, Run, Smile* on the other is a matter of the "form-class," the "part of speech," to

[6] Animals other than man can be taught to throw a ball, to catch it, to hit it, and to perform various other specific acts that occur in the game of baseball; but, so far as I can discover, they cannot be taught to "play the game" of baseball—they cannot grasp the system of contrastive patterns that give significance to the specific acts of one who is "playing the game."

[7] The lines indicate a drop from a voice pitch above normal to the low pitch below normal. This is discussed in the following reading by Paul Roberts. [eds.]

which the words belong. The ambiguity of single-word utterances like *Skip* (or *Hope* or *Rush*) without further clues arises from the uncertainty concerning the form-class or part of speech to which this word, in this particular utterance, belongs. Some type of structural ambiguity always results in English whenever the form-classes of the words are not clearly marked.

The utterance *ship sails today* (which might appear in a telegram) is ambiguous as it stands because of the absence of clear part-of-speech markers. If a clear part-of-speech marker, *the*, is put before the first word as in "*The* ship sails today" there is no ambiguity; we have a statement. If, however, the same marker is put before the second word as in "Ship *the* sails today" there is also no ambiguity, but the utterance is different; we then have a request. Other clear part-of-speech markers would also resolve the ambiguity, as with the addition of such a marker as the ending *-ed*.

> Shipp*ed* sail today
> Ship sail*ed* today

Newspaper headlines very frequently are structurally ambiguous because of the lack of definite part-of-speech or form-class markers. Some typical examples out of many are the following:

1. "Vandenberg Reports Open Forum."

The ambiguity of this heading could be cleared by the use of such markers as *the* or *an*, as:

> Vandenberg Reports Open *the* Forum
> Vandenberg Reports *an* Open Forum

2. "Unfavorable Surveyor Reports Delayed Michigan Settlement."

The ambiguity of this heading would be cleared by the use of such markers as *have* or *a:*

> Unfavorable Surveyor Reports *Have* Delayed Michigan Settlement
> Unfavorable Surveyor Reports *a* Delayed Michigan Settlement

3. "Briton to Be Tried for Missing Jewish Youth's Murder." Such a marker as *a* would clear the ambiguity here:

> Briton to Be Tried for *a* Missing Jewish Youth's Murder
> Briton to Be Tried for Missing *a* Jewish Youth's Murder

4. "Marshall Calls on Congress to Help Prostrate Europe." Here again the markers *a* or *-ed* would clear the ambiguity:

Marshall Calls on Congress to Help Prostrat*ed* Europe
Marshall Calls on Congress to Help *a* Prostrate Europe

Or the marker *to* would make unmistakable the other meaning.

Marshall Calls on Congress to Help *to* Prostrate Europe

As we examine the utterances of English, we shall find that unless certain large form-classes or parts of speech have their characteristic markers the structural meanings of the utterance will be ambiguous.

We have assumed in our approach here that the signals of all structural meanings are formal matters that can be described in terms of form and arrangement. We have assumed, too, that these items operate in a system, that they have signalling significance only as they are parts of patterns in a structural whole. In our attempt to describe the contrastive patterns of the system through which the structural meanings of English are signalled we find that the basic items to be distinguished are certain large form-classes of the words, the lexical units. *An English sentence then is not a group of words as words but rather a structure made up of form-classes or parts of speech.* In order to know the structural meanings signalled by the formal arrangements of our sentences *one need not know the lexical meanings of the words but he must know*[8] *the form-classes to which the words belong.* Our description of the patterns of devices to signal structural meanings will, therefore, be in terms of the selection of these large form-classes or parts of speech and the formal arrangements in which they occur.

PARTS OF SPEECH

A number of examples given in the preceding pages were used to demonstrate the fact that, in English, some type of structural ambiguity results whenever an utterance consists of certain important form-classes or parts of speech without clear markers. The markers that distinguish these important parts of speech in English are therefore of primary importance in our description of the patterns of the devices that signal structural meanings—a description which will be made in terms of the selection of these parts of speech and the formal arrangements in which they occur. What parts of speech, then, can we—or, rather, must we—recognize in English for a basic description

[8] "Know" in the sense of "respond to."

of our utterances, and what are the special markers of these parts of speech?

All the conventional school grammars deal extensively with the "parts of speech," usually given as eight in number, and explained in definitions that have become traditional. It has often been assumed that these eight parts of speech—noun, pronoun, adjective, verb, adverb, preposition, conjunction, interjection—are basic classifications that can be applied to the "words" of all languages[9] and that the traditional definitions furnish an adequate set of criteria by which to make the classifications.

As a matter of fact our common school grammars of English have not always used eight parts of speech. Some have named ten, making the "article" and the "participle" separate classes.[10] Some have included the "adjective" under the name "noun" and have given as subclasses of "nouns" the "noun substantive" and the "noun adjective."[11] Others have insisted that "interjections" are not "parts of speech" but "sentence words." Some of the early Greek grammarians recognized only three parts of speech, *ὄνομα* (names), *ῥῆμα* (sayings), and *συνδέσμοι* (joinings or linkings). The Latin grammarian, Varro, distinguished four parts of speech: (1) words with cases (nouns), (2) words with tenses (verbs), (3) words with both cases and tenses (participles), (4) words with neither cases nor tenses (particles). The current conventional classification of words into the particular eight parts of speech now common seems to have begun with Joseph Priestley and to have been generally accepted in the grammars since 1850.[12] We cannot assume without question that the eight parts of

[9] "The distinctions between the various parts of speech . . . are distinctions in thought, not merely in words." John Stuart Mill, *Rectorial Address at St. Andrews*, 1867.

[10] See Goold Brown, *The Grammar of English Grammars* (10th ed., New York, 1868), pp. 220-23.

[11] "How mony partyse of speche ben þer? Viii. Wych viii? Nowne, pronowne, verbe, aduerbe, partycypull', coniunccion, preposicion, and interieccion. . . . How mony maner of nownys ben' there? Ii. Wyche ii? Nowne substantyfe & nowne adiectyfe." From Douce Ms. 103 (fifteenth century). Text printed in *PMLA*, 50 (1935), 1012-32.

"Nouns are distinguished into two sorts, called noun substantives and noun adjectives." William Ward, *A Practical Grammar of the English Language* (London, 1765), p. 324.

[12] "I shall adopt the usual distribution of words into eight classes. . . . All the innovations I have made hath been to throw out the *Participle*, and substitute the *Adjective*, as more evidently a part of speech." Joseph Priestley, *Rudiments of English Grammar* (London, 1769; 1st ed., 1761), p. 3.

speech thus inherited from the past will be the most satisfactory or the essential classification of the form-classes of present-day English, but will instead examine anew the functioning units in our collection of utterances, with a view to establishing the minimum number of different groups needed for a basic description of the signals of the most important structural meanings.

Unfortunately we cannot use as the starting point of our examination the traditional definitions of the parts of speech. What is a "noun," for example? The usual definition is that "a noun is the name of a person, place, or thing." But *blue* is the "name" of a color, as is *yellow* or *red*, and yet, in the expressions *a blue tie*, *a yellow rose*, *a red dress* we do not call *blue* and *yellow* and *red* "nouns." We do call *red* a noun in the sentence *this red is the shade I want. Run* is the "name" of an action, as is *jump* or *arrive. Up* is the "name" of a direction, as is *down* or *across.* In spite of the fact that these words are all "names" and thus fit the definition given for a noun they are not called nouns in such expressions as "We *ran* home," "They were looking *up* into the sky," "The acid made the fiber *red*." The definition as it stands—that "A noun is a name"—does not furnish all the criteria necessary to exclude from this group many words which our grammars in actual practice classify in other parts of speech.

In the expressions *a blue tie*, *a yellow rose*, *a red dress*, the words *blue*, *yellow*, and *red*, in spite of the fact that according to their meanings they are "names" of colors, are called "adjectives," because the adjective is defined as "A word that modifies a noun or a pronoun." A large part of the difficulty here lies in the fact that the two definitions—the definition of the noun and the definition of the adjective—are not parallel. The one for the noun, that "a noun is a name," attempts to classify these words according to their *lexical meanings;* the one for the adjective, that "an adjective is a word that modifies a noun or a pronoun," attempts to classify the words according to their *function in a particular sentence*. The basis of definition slides from meaning to function. For the purposes of adequate classification, the definitions of the various classes must consider the same kind of criteria.

Even with the usual definition of an adjective the criteria are not always consistently applied. Many grammars will not classify *boy's* as an adjective in *the boy's hat*, nor *his* as an adjective in *his hat*, in spite of the fact that both these words, *boy's* and *his*, "modify" the word *hat*, and thus fit the definition. *Boy's* is usually called "noun in the possessive case," and *his*, a "possessive pronoun" or a "pronoun in the possessive case." Here again, criteria that are not included in the definition—in this case certain formal characteristics—are used in practice to exclude from the classification items that fit the definition.

The common definition for a pronoun presents even more difficulty. "A pronoun is a word used instead of a noun." But just what kind of substitution is to be called "pronoun" in the following examples? In the sentence *John and James brought their letters of recommendation* there should be no question that *John* and *James*, as the names for two persons, are nouns. In the following series of words "substituted for these two nouns" just which are to be called pronouns and why?

John and James
The two boys
The undersigned
A few
The two
Two
A couple
Several
Some
Both
These
They

} brought their letters of recommendation

A slightly different kind of series, substituted for the noun *Wednesday* in the sentence *Wednesday is the time to see him*, presents the same problem. Which of the following substitutes are "pronouns"?

Wednesday
Tomorrow
Today
Next week
Later
Now
When
This
That
It

} is the time to see him

Obviously even in the usual procedure of classifying words into "parts of speech"—noun, adjective, pronoun—the criteria indicated in the definitions, that "names" are nouns, the "modifiers of nouns" are adjectives, and that "substitutes for nouns" are pronouns, do not include all that is actually used, and these definitions, therefore, cannot provide the basis for our approach here. We cannot use "lexical" meaning as the basis for the definition of some classes, "function in the sentence" for others, and "formal characteristics" for still others. We must find, as the basis for our grouping into parts of speech, a set of criteria that can be consistently applied.

Two problems then confront us:

1. We have concluded above that the structural signals of English consist of arrangements, not of words as words, but of words as parts of speech. We should be able, then, to express our descriptions of the patterns that signal structural meanings in terms of formulas with the various parts of speech as the units. Our first problem, then, is to discover just how many different kinds of these functioning units the formulas for English require, and precisely what they are.

2. We have insisted that unless these functioning units, these parts of speech, are clearly marked, are identifiable in an utterance, some type of structural ambiguity will result. The ambiguity of the following utterances, for example, arises because of the uncertainty of the kind of functioning unit of each of the italic words:

> *Ship sails* today
> *Time flies*
> The dogs looked *longer* than the cat
> Avoid infection by *killing* germs

The conventional definitions do not provide the necessary criteria. Our second problem is to discover just what the criteria are that the users of the language actually employ to identify the necessary various form-class units when they give and receive the signals of structural meaning.

You will remember Alice's experience with the poem of the Jabberwocky:[13]

> Twas brillig, and the slithy toves
> Did gyre and gimble in the wabe;

[13] For the suggestion of this type of use of nonsense words I am indebted to Prof. Aileen Traver Kitchin. I had used algebraic symbols for words but not with the success she has attained with "Jabberwocky" material.

All mimsy were the borogoves,
And the mome raths outgrabe. . . .

"Somehow [she said], it seems to fill my head with ideas —only I don't exactly know what they are!"

What are the "ideas" she gets and how are they stimulated? All the words that one expects to have clearly definable meaning content are nonsense, but any speaker of English will recognize at once the frames in which these words appear.

Twas ——, and the ——y ——s
Did —— and —— in the ——;
All ——y were the ——s,
And the —— ——s ——.

The "ideas" which the verse stimulates are without doubt the structural meanings for which the framework contains the signals. Most of these nonsense words have clearly marked functions in frames that constitute familiar structural patterns. These "ideas" seem vague to the ordinary speaker because in the practical use of language he is accustomed to dealing only with total meanings to which lexical content contributes the elements of which he is conscious.

For the Jabberwocky verse certain familiar words of the frame in which the nonsense appeared furnished important clues to the structures; but such clues are often unnecessary. One need not know the lexical meaning of any word in the following:

1. Woggles ugged diggles
2. Uggs woggled diggs
3. Woggs diggled uggles

If we assume that these utterances are using the structural signals of English, then at once we know a great deal about these sequences. We would know that *woggles* and *uggs* and *woggs* are "thing" words of some kind; that in each case there is more than one of these "things," and that they at some time in the past performed certain "actions"; and that these actions were directed toward other "things," *diggles, diggs,* and *uggles.*

As speakers of English, given the three utterances above, we should not hesitate to make such new utterances as the following:

4. A woggle ugged a diggle
5. An ugg woggles diggs
6. A diggled woggle ugged a woggled diggle

We would know that *woggles* and *uggs* and *woggs* are "thing" words, in sentences 1, 2, 3, because they are treated as English treats "thing" words—by the "positions" they occupy in the utterances and forms they have, in contrast with other positions and forms. We would know that *ugged* and *woggled* and *diggled* are "action" words in these same sentences because they are treated as English treats "action" words—by the "positions" they occupy and the forms they have, in contrast with the positions and forms of the other "words."

We would make the new utterances 4, 5, 6 with confidence because in these we simply proceed to continue to treat the various units of the utterances in accord with the formal devices which constitute the grammar of English. For all of this it has not been necessary to know the meaning of a single word. As native speakers of English we have learned to use certain formal clues by which we identify the various kinds of units in our structures. The process is wholly unconscious unless some failure attracts attention;—just as unconscious as our responses to sight clues with the muscular adjustments of balancing when we walk. . . .

INTONATION

Paul Roberts

In the preceding selection, C. C. Fries defined grammar in this way: "The grammar of a language consists of the devices that signal structural meanings." By structural meanings he meant all the meaning that remains in a sentence after the dictionary meanings have been subtracted. Now, since some of these structural meanings are signaled by three voice features—stress, pitch, and juncture—these features must be considered a part of grammar. A few examples may be appropriate. In the sentence "I think that man is honest" the word that *is either a conjunction or a demonstrative, depending on the stress you give it. Next, consider* who *in this example: "The boss is going to get a new secretary." "Who?" The answer you will get to "Who?" depends on whether you pronounce it with a rising or a falling pitch. The third voice feature, juncture, refers to the divisions we sense in the flow of speech. For instance, it is one of the four kinds of juncture that enables us to distinguish between such pairs as "see Mabel" and "seem able," "cease taking" and "ceased aching." In the selection following, Paul Roberts explains in a simple way these three grammatical features. Professor Roberts is the author of three textbooks of grammar that are notable for their lucidity and good sense.*

BESIDES THE thirty-three vowels and consonants, English has a series of phonemes of an entirely different kind—or rather of three different kinds. These are the features called **stress, pitch,** and **juncture.** Taken together, stress, pitch, and juncture make up what we call **intonation.** Every time we utter a sentence, we use some kind of intonation, and the meaning of our sentences changes according to the intonation we use.

The whole story of English intonation is a very complicated matter, and we won't try to explain all the details here. But it is easy to see some of the contrasts of intonation and to realize that we react accurately to them whenever we hear English.

STRESS

Probably the simplest feature of intonation to understand is stress. **Stress** is simply the loudness or softness with which we utter the different syllables in the speech stream. We make use of stress all the time in forming our sentence patterns. For instance, if we use the word *subject* as a noun, we pronounce the *sub* louder than the *ject:*

What's the súbject?

But if we use it as a verb, we pronounce the *ject* part louder:

We'll subjéct him to an examination.

We have the same contrast in *íncrease* and *incréase*, *prótest* and *protést*, *réfuse* and *refúse*, and many other pairs.

But that's by no means all there is to stress in English. Each speaker of English makes use of four different stresses—four degrees of loudness—when he speaks his sentences. The names and symbols for them are these:

Primary, the loudest degree /ˊ/
Secondary, the next to loudest /ˆ/
Tertiary, the third from loudest /ˋ/
Weak, the softest /˘/

Here's a sentence that has all of them:

Thĕ Whíte Hoùse ĭs ă whîte hóuse.

If you'll pronounce the sentence naturally, you'll see that you don't say "White House" quite as you say "white house." The difference is mainly in the stress.

Stress usually distinguishes adjectives modifying nouns from nouns modifying nouns. You may remember our ambiguous sentence "He's a sweet salesman," where you can't tell whether the salesman is sweet or sells candy. But this is ambiguous in writing only. In speech, *sweet* will have secondary stress if it's an adjective but primary stress if it's a noun.

Hê's ă swêet sálesmăn. (The salesman is sweet.)
Hê's ă swéet sàlesmăn. (He sells candy.)

Stress is so important that if the speaker gets the stresses mixed up the result is likely to be nonsense. You might not be surprised to get a "wrítĭng dèsk" for Christmas. But you would probably be very much surprised if you got a "wrîtĭng désk."

PITCH

The second feature of intonation is pitch. **Pitch** is caused by the vibration of the sounds as they come from our mouths. If they vibrate fast—say 800 times a second—we get what we call **high pitch.**

If they vibrate slowly—say 200 times a second—we get **low pitch.**

We are all familiar with pitch, because we know, for example, that women's voices are generally higher than men's and that adults' voices are lower than children's. What most people don't realize, however, is that each of us—whether his voice is generally high or generally low—makes use of four contrasting pitch points or pitch phonemes. We give these numbers, not names. The highest pitch phoneme is /4/; the next to highest is /3/; the next to lowest is /2/; the lowest is /1/.

We can also indicate them by drawing lines above and below the letters. A line just over the letters means pitch /3/; a line well above the letters means pitch /4/; a line just under the letters means pitch /2/; and a line well below the letters means pitch /1/.

For instance, suppose we want to mark the pitch on the sentence "What are you doing?" This could be said in several ways, but the most common way would be to begin on pitch /2/, to stay on that until the stressed syllable is reached, to rise to /3/ on the stressed syllable, and then to fall to /1/. Like this:

What are you | do | ing?

We use pitch for many purposes in our sentences. It is closely bound up with the structural patterns of our sentences. But we also use it to express such meanings as surprise, indignation, insistence, panic, boredom, and many others. For example, one could put a note of panic into the question "What are you doing?" by rising to the fourth pitch instead of the third:

What are you | do | ing?

Or if one is just sort of exasperated with the other person and what he's doing, he might say:

What | are | you | do | ing?

Often we make jokes by deliberately using the wrong pitch. Here's one:

What did you put in the | sa | lad? Alice?

In place of:

What did you put in the | sa | lad, Alice?

JUNCTURE

The third part of intonation is juncture. **Juncture** is a way of breaking or stopping the speech flow. English intonation seems to go in fours, and there are four junctures just as there are four stresses and four pitches; the first one, however, is quite different from the other three. Junctures are named after the symbols used to indicate them.

The first juncture is called **plus juncture** because it is marked with a plus sign: /+/.

The second juncture is called **single bar juncture.** It is marked with one upright line or bar: /|/.

The third juncture is called **double bar juncture.** It is marked with two upright lines: /||/.

The last juncture is called **double cross juncture.** It is marked with two crossing lines: /#/.

Plus juncture is a special kind of break between phonemes. It is the difference between *I scream* and *ice cream.* In *I scream* we have plus juncture before the /s/ phoneme: /ay+skriym/. In *ice cream* the plus juncture comes after the /s/ phoneme: /ays+kriym/. The reason that the two sounds are different is that in *I scream* we have the kind of /s/ that comes at the beginning of a word and the kind of /k/ that comes after /s/; but in *ice cream* we have the kind of /s/ that comes at the end of a word and the kind of /k/ that comes at the beginning. This is what plus juncture does; it breaks up the phonemic flow and makes words, although the phonemic words are not always identical with the ones we commonly write.

The other junctures come at the end of groups of words. These junctures are closely tied up with stress and pitch. If a sentence has only one primary (loudest) stress, then we won't have any junctures inside the sentence. But if we have two primary stresses, then we will have a single bar or double bar juncture between them.

For instance, we can say the sentence "The man on your right is her brother" with just one primary stress; then there is no juncture inside the sentence:

The man on your right is her bróther.

Or we can say it with two primary stresses; then there will be a single bar juncture after the first primary stress:

The man on your ríght | is her bróther.

If there are three primary stresses, there will be two single bar junctures:

The mán | on your right | is her bróther.

This would be a very slow and emphatic way of saying the sentence.

The difference between single bar, double bar, and double cross juncture is a matter of what happens to the pitch. If the pitch stays the same, we have single bar; if it goes up a little (but not to the next pitch level) we have double bar; if it goes down a little, we have double cross.

The sentence "The man digging in the garden is Mr. Jones" might have one or two single bar junctures, depending on the number of primary stresses; or it might have none at all:

The mán | digging in the gárden | is Mr. Jónes.

The man digging in the gárden | is Mr. Jónes.

The man digging in the garden is Mr. Jónes.

But the sentence "Mr. Jones, digging in his garden, found a worm" would be pronounced quite differently. There would be three primary stresses with double bar junctures separating them:

Mr. Jónes || digging in his gárden || found a wórm.

That is, the pitch would rise slightly after *Jones* and after *garden*. The pitch would be something like this:

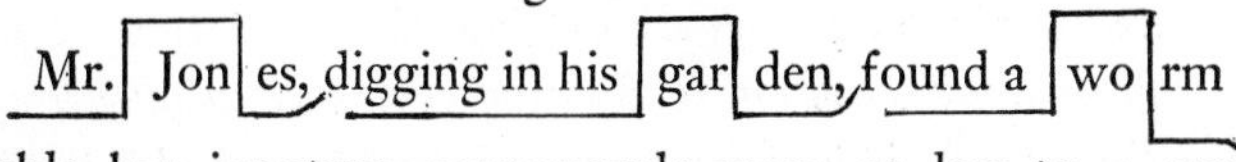

Mr. Jon es, digging in his gar den, found a wo rm

Double bar juncture corresponds more or less to a comma in writing.

Double cross juncture is a slight drop in pitch. Notice in the last example that a slight drop is shown at the very end, after *worm*. This is a double cross juncture, in its usual place at the end of a sentence:

Mr. Jones || digging in his garden || found a worm #

By and large, double cross junctures in speech correspond to semicolons and periods in writing.

Here are a few more examples showing primary stresses and the different junctures. There would be other ways of saying some of these of course:

Where are you góing #

Where aré | you góing #

Running into the hóuse || Agnes told us the néws #

We invited Ál || who had a cár #

Ál || who had a cár || offered to take ús #

Al had a cár # therefore we had to invíte him #

Al had a cár # he wóuldn't || howéver || let us úse it #

People who own cars are pretty lúcky #

People who own cárs | are pretty lúcky #

FORMS IN PIDGIN ENGLISH

Robert A. Hall, Jr.

Melanesian Pidgin is one of the four main varieties of Pidgin English in the world. Pidgin English is a hybrid of English and a native language. Its vocabulary is small and is composed largely of English words. It has a simple grammatical system of its own which is an outgrowth of English. It is always a second language and is used for communication between those who have no native language in common (often white men and natives). If it should become the mother tongue of a group, it is then classified as a creolised language. Melanesian Pidgin is spoken in the islands north of Australia—New Guinea, the Bismarcks, and the Solomons. In the selection below you are given a sample of how a linguistic scientist goes about constructing a descriptive statement of the gram-

mar of a foreign tongue. Robert A. Hall, Jr., is Professor of Linguistics at Cornell University. You will find his short Melanesian Pidgin Phrase-Book and Vocabulary *a fascinating little volume to dip into. His more extended account is* Melanesian Pidgin English: Grammar, Texts, and Vocabulary.

IN THE traditional grammar they teach us in school, we learn about nouns, adjectives, verbs and so forth. Usually, we are told that a noun is "the name of a person, place or thing," that an adjective names "a quality or accidence," and that a verb refers to "an action or state of being"—in other words, these grammatical terms are defined in a pseudo-philosophical manner. I say "pseudo," because actually these traditional definitions won't hold water. *Reflection*, for instance, is a noun, but it refers to motions of molecules in air or water, and is the name, not of any person, place or thing, but of a type of action; the same can be said of *electricity* and a host of other nouns. Similarly, *die* is certainly a verb, but it refers, not to action or state of being, but to cessation of all action and being! As a result of these meaningless definitions and other ineptitudes in the way we are taught formal grammar, most normal people find it valueless and forget it as soon as they can once they get out of school.

Yet if we are going to talk about language intelligently, we do have to have some framework in which to analyse and classify its phenomena. Modern linguistic analysis approaches the matter from a new angle—that of finding what the actual function and use of words is, what combinations they occur in, and what classes words fall into according to their formal characteristics. Meaning, as a basis on which to analyse language, is not wholly denied relevance, but it certainly must take second place to form. Every language that has as yet been analysed has been found to have at least two classes into which its forms are organised; but these classes do not by any means necessarily correspond to our English "nouns" and "verbs," and the criteria by which we establish them are often quite different from those of our traditional grammar. This is true even for English as contrasted with Latin. In Latin, a noun is any word which has different forms according to number and case, and belongs to not more than two genders, whereas an adjective belongs to all three genders.

English, however, has no grammatical gender at all[1] and, in nouns, no case; in English, a noun is any form in front of which we can place the article *the*, such as *the book, the reflection, the electricity*. We may often use traditional terms like "noun" and "verb" in linguistic analysis; but they have no absolute meaning, and must be carefully re-defined each time we use them for a different language.

One of the first tasks confronting us, when dealing with a new language, is therefore to find out which forms occur with which, and what classes we can set up on this basis. Here, we intentionally use the term *form*, rather than *word*, because often we shall be dealing with morphemes that are smaller than single words, for instance prefixes and suffixes like the *-s* of *hats* or the *-ing* of *working*.[2] This is where the distinction . . . between *free* and *bound* forms is essential, since we often find that certain bound forms occur only with certain other forms, and this is an invaluable guide to their classification.[3] In English, for example, the bound form *-ing* occurs only suffixed to one class of forms, those like *eat, organise, do;* this is one of the means by which we identify the class customarily called "verb."

Looking at Pidgin—any kind of Pidgin—in this way, we immediately find that it does not consist (as many people mistakenly think) of words thrown together any old way, nor yet wholly of independent words with no grammatical inflection at all. Melanesian Pidgin has three bound forms which function as suffixes in grammatical inflection, and one which is prefixed to predicates; with the aid of these bound forms, we can arrive at a satisfactory classification of the other forms of Pidgin. The three suffixes are *-fela*, with the meaning

[1] Even English pronouns have no gender; they have sex-reference, which is something quite different. Cf. R. A. Hall, Jr., "Sex-Reference and Grammatical Gender in English," American Speech, 26.170-2 (1951).

[2] A morpheme is the smallest linquistic unit that has meaning. It is either a word or a part of a word. For example, *talk* is composed of one morpheme; *mailman*, of two. We can add morphemes to *talk*, such as *-er* (person who acts), *-ing* (action is in progress), *-ed* (action happened in the past). [eds.]

[3] Professor Hall explains *free form* and *bound form* as follows: "In most languages, some morphemes may occur independently, and others normally do not. So, for instance, the forms *talk, read,* and *hear* can be used with or without added elements in English; but the elements we add to them, *-s* in the present third singular, *-(e) d* (and other changes) on the past, or *-ing,* cannot occur alone. If a form can be used independently, we call it a *free-form;* if it has to be used in conjunction with some other form, it is called a *bound form.*"

Thus, for example, *bigger* contains two morphemes, the free form *big* and the bound form *-er,* which means "more." *Cookstoves* contains three morphemes, two free forms and one bound form, *-s,* meaning "more than one." [eds.]

of "more than one;" another suffix *-fela*, with no separate meaning (which establishes it as a different suffix from the preceding); and *-im*, meaning "a direct object is involved." Here are some examples of the use of these three suffixes:—

GROUP A

mi go "I go"	*mifela go* "we go"
mi kaikai "I eat"	*mifela kaikai* "we eat"
em i-faitim mi "he hits me"	*em i-faitim mifela* "he hits us"
yu lukim mi "you see me"	*yu lukim mifela* "you see us"
haus bilong mi "house of me, my house"	*haus bilong mifela* "house of us, our house"
papa bilong mi "my father"	*papa bilong mifela* "our father"
long mi "to me"	*long mifela* "to us"
wantaim mi "with me"	*wantaim mifela* "with us"
yu go "you (singular) go"	*yufela go* "you (plural) go"
yu kaikai "you (sg.) eat"	*yufela kaikai* "you (pl.) eat"
em i-faitim yu "he hits you (sg.)"	*em i-faitim yufela* "he hits you (pl.)"
mi lukim yu "I see you (sg.)"	*mi lukim yufela* "I see you (pl.)"
haus bilong yu "your (sg.) house"	*haus bilong yufela* "your (pl.) house"
papa bilong yu "your (sg.) father"	*papa bilong yufela* "your (pl.) father"
long yu "to you (sg.)"	*long yufela* "to you (pl.)"
wantaim yu "with you (sg.)"	*wantaim yufela* "with you (pl.)"

GROUP B

gudfela man "(a) good man"
bigfela meri "(a) big woman"
blakfela man "(a) dark-coloured man"
smolfela haus "(a) little house"
nufela ankisip "(a) new handkerchief"
wanfela man "one man, a man"
tufela man "two men"
trifela man "three men"
forfela man "four men"
faivfela man "five men"
sikisfela man "six men"

sevenfela man "seven men"
disfela man "this man, these men"
samfela man "some man, some men"
plentifela man
plenti man "many men"
but:
liklik haus "(a) little house"
longlong man "(a) crazy man"
rabish man "(a) man without wealth or standing in the community"
olgeder man "all (the) men"

GROUP C

mi rid "I read"	*mi ridim buk* "I read a book"	*mi ridim* "I read it"
mi luk "I look"	*mi lukim man* "I see a man"	*mi lukim* "I see him"
yu fait "you fight"	*yu faitim birua* "you hit the enemy"	*yu faitim* "you hit him"
em i-singaut "she calls"	*em i-singautim meri* "she calls the woman"	*em i-singautim* "she calls her"
mashin i-bagarap "the machine is wrecked"	*em i-bagarimapim mashin* "he wrecked the machine"	*em i-bagarimapim* "he wrecked it"
abus i-kuk "the food cooks, is cooked"	*fair i-kukim abus* "the fire cooks, burns the meat"	*fair i-kukim* "the fire cooks, burns it"
ol i-kros "they are angry"	*ol i-krosim disfela boi* "they are angry at this native"	*ol i-krosim* "they are angry at him"
	but:	
i-gat wanfela man "there is a man, il y a un homme"	*mi gat tufela han* "I have two hands"	*mi gat* "I have it"

Look first at the examples given in Group A. Here we find the suffix *-fela*, with the meaning "plural," added to two morphemes: *mi* "I, me" and *yu* "you (singular)," thus making the plurals *mifela* "we, us" and *yufela* "you (plural)." These four forms are close enough in form and meaning to the customary definition of "pronoun" so that we can apply this label to them. In addition, we find two other forms: *em* "he, him; she, her; it" and *ol* "they; them," which do not follow the same formal pattern as *mi, mifela* and *yu, yufela,* but which do parallel them in meaning and function—that is, they can be used the same way in sentences, occurring as subjects, direct objects, and after such forms as *bilong* "of," *long* "to, at" and *wantaim* "with." In addition to these six pronominal forms, Melanesian Pidgin also has a special form, *yumi* "we = you and I, you and me." This form is often called "inclusive," because it includes the hearer, as opposed to *mifela* "we = the other person(s) and me, but excluding the hearer." Melanesian languages have exactly the same kind of distinction between inclusive and exclusive in their pronoun systems, and Pidgin *yumi* represents a direct carry-over from Melanesian patterns of thought.

We have now established one class of Pidgin forms, the pronouns; Group B gives us the means of distinguishing another class. We notice that *-fela,* without any separate meaning, is suffixed to a number of one-syllable elements like *gud* "good," *big* "large," *blak* "dark-coloured," *smol* "little" (and many others which we have not given here). It also occurs after *wan* "one," *tu* "two," and so on, including (in this group) *sikis* "six" and *seven* "seven," and after *dis-* "this," *sam-* "some," *nader-* "another," and (optionally) *plenti* "many." These forms to which our second suffix *-fela* can be added may safely be labelled "adjectives," with the special subdivisions of "numerals" for *wanfela, tufela, trifela,* etc., and "demonstratives" and "indefinites" for *disfela, samfela, naderfela* and *plenti(fela).* As with the pronouns *em* and *ol,* we likewise find in Group B a number of forms such as *liklik* "little," *longlong* "crazy," *rabish* "without standing," which behave like the others in the same group, except in that they never take *-fela;* note, also, that they are all of more than one syllable. We can class these latter forms as adjectives, too, on the basis of their behaviour in combination with other words.

Our definition of adjectives for Melanesian Pidgin, therefore, is: a class of forms which (a) when monosyllabic or numeral or demonstrative-indefinite, take the meaningless suffix *-fela,* and can stand before such words as *haus, man, meri;* (b) when of more than one syllable (not numeral or demonstrative-indefinite) do not take *-fela,* but in other respects behave like those of type (a) just mentioned.

Notice, by the way, that the old traditional pseudo-philosophical definition of adjectives as words "denoting a quality or accidence" has vanished; it is both less accurate and less helpful than the definition of the adjective we have just given in terms of its linguistic form and function in the language we are dealing with, in this case Melanesian Pidgin.

In Group C, we have a number of forms which can occur both with and without a suffixed element *-im*. The feature of meaning common to all the occurrences of *-im* can be summed up as "presence of a direct object in the situation," whether there is a further element in the sentence telling what that direct object is (as in the middle column) or not (as in the right-hand column). We can borrow two terms from Hungarian grammar, and call the forms without *-im* "subjective," and those with *-im* "objective." There is a close parallel between Hungarian and Melanesian Pidgin in this matter of subjective and objective conjugations:

	"I read"	"I read the book"	"I read it"
Mel. Pidgin	*mi rid*	*mi ridim buk*	*mi ridim*
Hungarian	*olvasok*	*olvasom a konyvet*	*olvasom*

One especial peculiarity of the suffix *-im* is that, when it occurs with a word already provided with an adverbial suffix like *-ap* "up," it is repeated both after the word itself and after the adverbial suffix; for example, on the word *haisap* "lift, hoist up," we form the objective *haisimapim.*

The presence of the objective suffix *-im* enables us to set up a third Pidgin form-class, which we can of course label "verbs." There is one exception, however, to the general rule that verbs take the suffix *-im;* at the bottom of Group C is given the one verb that never, in normal usage, takes this suffix, namely *gat* "to have." (To say *mi gatim* is a crass Europeanism, which no normal Melanesian speaker of Pidgin would ever use at the present time.) The very fact that Pidgin shows little peculiarities like this, is further proof that Pidgin is a true language; no linguistic structure is wholly watertight in its organisation, and Pidgin conforms to this rule. . . .

Though Pidgin verbs do not show tense in their inflectional variation, it is still possible to indicate the time of the action, if need be, by using adverbs like *bifor* "previously" for the past, *finis* "already" for action over and done with ("perfect"), or *baimbai* "soon" for the future: *mi go bifor* "I went previously"; *mi kaikai finis* "I have eaten, I've finished eating"; *baimbi mi kaikai* "I shall eat later." The auxiliary *bin* to indicate past time (as in *mi bin kaikai* "I ate") is a recent importation from Australian Pidgin, introduced first in the Rabaul area and spreading out from there.[4]

With the exception of these three classes—pronouns, adjectives, and verbs—the other forms of Pidgin are all invariable. Nevertheless, we can distinguish several different classes among them, by observing the combinations in which they occur with the classes we have already established. There is one type of word, like *man* "man," *haus* "house" and *boi* "native," and many others, which occurs after adjectives, and as the subject and object of verbs: *gudfela man* "(a) good man"; *disfela boi i-stap long haus kuk* "this native was in the kitchen;" *mi kisim stik* "I take the stick." These we will label "nouns." Another group of forms occurs only before others, normally nouns, pronouns or verbs: *bilong tebal* "of the table," *bilong mi* "for me; of me, my mine"; *long ples* "in, to, or at the village," *long em* "to him, her or it"; *wantaim yu* "with you." "Preposition" is the obvious name for this class of forms. A still further type of word comes after verbs and adjectives, modifying them, for instance *tumas* "greatly, very," *tru* "indeed," *nogud* "badly, with undesirable results": *plenti tumas* "very many"; *namberwan tru* "indeed excellent"; *em i-faitim mi nogud* "he beat me badly, gave me a bad beating." "Adverbs" is clearly the label for these. Such words as *godam!* "darn it! drat it!," which occur only alone in independent utterances, we can call "interjections." Are there any conjunctions in Pidgin?—only *spos* "if" and *na* "and, or" in normal use; *an(d)* "and," *or* "or" and *bekos* "because" are recent importations from English, still not really acclimatised in Pidgin. Occasionally, in somewhat Europeanised use, certain nouns are used as conjunctions: e.g., *taim Herodes i-king bilong Yuda* "(at the) time = when Herod was king of Judaea."

In its earlier stages, Pidgin had no definite or indefinite articles—another ground for recrimination from purists, who forgot that such eminently worthy and respectable languages as Latin, Russian and Chinese don't have articles either. Thus, *kanaka i-stap long ples* might mean "a native, natives, or the natives, is, are, were or will be in a village, the village, villages or the villages." No harm was done, since the context normally gave whatever indications might be needed as to number or definiteness of the noun, or tense of the verb. In more recent days, however, *ol* has come to be used very widely as a kind

[4] This paragraph is inserted from later in chapter. [eds.]

of plural article; *ol kanaka* "the natives," etc. So far as I have observed, though, *ol* is normally used to refer to several or more, not to two or three; therefore, when one finds in a local mimeographed newspaper an expression like *ol Territory—Papua na New Guinea* "the Territories of Papua and New Guinea," it seems strange and one is inclined to suspect a Europeanism. In some regions, too, especially the Sepik valley, *em* is used as a singular article: *em luluwai i-tok* "the luluwai (village government headman) spoke." For an indefinite article, *wanfela* "one" is sometimes used: *wanfela boi* "one native, a native," but this, too, is still a bit of a Europeanism. The situation with regard to the articles is clearly one of transition at present, and (chiefly under pressure from speakers of English, who feel unhappy without articles) Pidgin seems to be developing a set of articles, much as the Romance languages developed theirs out of Latin *ille* "that person" and *ipse* "he himself" for the definite article, and *unus* "one" for the indefinite.

When we work through the grammatical structure of Melanesian Pidgin, we do indeed come out with a set of form-classes or "parts of speech" which we can label "nouns," "verbs" and so forth, and which do correspond fairly well in their basic function to what we call by the same names in English and other Indo-European languages. But the linguistic elements which identify the "parts of speech" in Melanesian Pidgin are quite different from those of English or any other language. . . .

This basic correspondence of the form-classes of Pidgin with those of English and the Indo-European languages is one of the reasons why, from the point of view of linguistic history, we cannot go along with those who say "Pidgin English is simply a native language (Chinese, Melanesian, West African, as the case may be) spoken with English words." No: the surface characteristics of the various Pidgins are indeed non-English, and differ from one Pidgin to the next; but all varieties of Pidgin English have an underlying identity of structure with English, and their basic pattern shows that they are outgrowths of English, no matter how much they may have changed and have been brusquely restructured nearer the surface. This observation, incidentally, forces itself on the observer even against his will; three times I have begun work on a pidgin or creolised language (Melanesian Pidgin, Taki-Taki and Haitian Creole) with the determination to find in it a non-Indo-European structure, and each time the language itself has compelled recognition of its basically English and Indo-European pattern.

From what we have said, no one should be surprised by now that Pidgin does not have many of our familiar categories of grammatical inflection—number, case, gender, tense. However, in the American phrase, so what? Those particular categories are far from universal or essential, no matter how fundamental our own language habits may make us think they are. Most of the languages of the world get along very well without any distinction between singular and plural—not only "primitive" languages of American Indian and African tribes, but "civilised" languages like Chinese and Japanese. English itself has only a remnant of case, and only in its pronominal system. Gender?—English hasn't any, only sex-reference in the pronouns *he, she, it;* even this is far from necessary, as we see in Finno-Ugric languages such as Hungarian, where *o* means "he" and "she" and "it," like Melaneisian Pidgin *em* or Chinese Pidgin *hi.* The same may be said for tenses; many, perhaps even most, languages emphasise other features of verbal meaning and let tense go either partly or wholly. In Russian and the Slavic languages, for instance, the time of the action is much less important than the question of whether it is finished or still going on—a distinction known as "aspect." Latin, likewise, had a difference of aspect that pervaded its verbal system fully as much as the category of tense; compare *dico* "I am saying, the action of saying on my part is still going on," the imperfective, versus *dixi* "I have said, the action of saying on my part is over and done with," the perfective.

A QUICK LOOK AT ENGLISH

Waldo B. Sweet

In the selection entitled "Sentence Analysis and Parts of Speech" on pages 380-394, C. C. Fries asserts that the classification of English words into eight parts of speech is based on a logical fallacy, namely that the classification is not the same for all. To this asser natural rejoinder is, "Well, then, how should we set up these word classes that we call parts of speech?" A cogent answer is offered by Waldo B. Sweet in the meaty and highly condensed essay below. This was written for university students as a grammatical preface to a beginning course in Latin utilizing a structural approach. Mr. Sweet is Associate Professor of Latin at the University of Michigan.

ODDLY ENOUGH, in the past languages were taught on the assumption that they were fundamentally alike. It was believed that there was a universal grammar which applied to all languages, although it was often noted that language X was deficient in a certain respect or that language Y seemed to have an extra item or two in its inventory.

Now one important thing that languages do share in common is that they contain meaning. It is possible to take this meaning, analyze it, and give names to the divisions that result. You *can* make a classification of persons, places, and things, and if you wish to call these nouns, that is your privilege. The only trouble with it is that it isn't very consistent and it doesn't seem to describe the facts of language as well as the newer approach.

What is a noun in English? Does it have the marker *-tli*, like Nahuatl? What is an English verb? Does it end in *-t*, like Latin verbs?

In English, just as in every other language, there are formal markers for such distinctions. If no such markers can be found, then the language lacks this particular feature. Much of the difficulty which students have had with English grammar has arisen from the fact that they were asked to identify things which exist in Latin but are not present in English, since the "universal grammar" to which we referred above was based on Latin. Here then is a description of English, condensed into a single lesson.

PARTS OF SPEECH

In English we distinguish five major parts of speech: nouns, verbs, adjectives, adverbs, and a class with many subdivisions called function words. Sometimes morphology[1] clearly indicates the part of speech to which a word belongs, as in *breadth*, *broaden*, *broad*, and *broadly*. In many cases, however, it is necessary to see the morphology and *distribution*[2] of an English word before we can determine the form class. *Gardens* is a noun in *The gardens are beautiful this spring* but a verb in *He gardens with great pleasure*. The distribution tells us whether it is noun or verb.

A *noun* in English has the following characteristics:

1. Morphologically[3] it has a distinction between singular and plural (*man/men*) and between the common form and the possessive (*man/man's* and *men/men's*). In most nouns, if we disregard the apostrophe (which corresponds to nothing in the spoken language), the contrast is the same in both instances (*boy/boys*).
2. Distributionally it fits into the frame *The______is good* or ______*is good*.

There is a small but important subclass of nouns called *pronouns*. In addition to the contrast which nouns have between singular and plural and common case and possessive case, pronouns have a further contrast between subjective and objective case: *I/me*, *she/her*, etc. Although in general they have the same distribution as nouns they do not take the noun-markers *the* or *a*.

A *verb* in English has the following characteristics:

1. Morphologically it has a distinction between singular and plural of the present tense in the third person (*write/writes*) and between present and past (*write/wrote*).
2. Distributionally it fits into one or more of the following frames:
   a. *The man______s the house.*
   b. *The man______s there.*
   c. *The man______s wise.*

Verbs that fit into the first frame (*see*, *build*, etc.) are *transitive;* those that fit into the second (*sit*, *swim*, etc.) are *intransitive;* those that fit into the third (*look*, *is*, *seem*, etc.) are *connecting*. Some verbs fit into more than one frame (*run*, *sink*, etc.).

An *adjective* in English has the following characteristics:

[1] The form. [eds.]
[2] The positions in which a form occurs. [eds.]
[3] In form. [eds.]

1. Morphologically it has a distinction between the positive form, the comparative form, and the superlative form (*big, bigger, biggest*).
2. Distributionally it fits into both of these frames:
   a. *The______man arrived.*
   b. *The man is______.*

An *adverb* in English has the following characteristics:

1. Morphologically it has the morpheme *-ly*.
2. Distributionally it fits into the frame *The man fell______.*

Words which do not qualify morphologically but have the same distribution as one of these four parts of speech are called by names which have the suffix *-al* or *-ial*, as *adjectival, adverbial.*[4] The word *slow* in *Drive slow* (leaving aside the question of whether it is correct) is an adverbial; it does not have the morpheme marker *-ly*, but it fits into the frame *The man fell slow. Slowly*, in *Drive slowly*, is an adverb: it is morphologically marked by the *-ly* and fits into the frame *The man fell slowly*.

The real complexity of English grammar lies in the residue of words, called *function words:*

the, a, every, no (noun markers)
may, can, must, should (auxiliaries)
not (negator)
very, more, pretty, rather (qualifiers)
and, or, not, but, rather than (connectives)
for, by, in, from, of (prepositions)
when, why, where, how (interrogators)
because, after, when, although (subordinators)
well, oh, now, why (responders)

The criteria for establishing these classes is distribution. In *The dog is barking* we could substitute the other noun markers (*A dog, every dog, no dog*) but not the qualifiers or any other group.

[4] The other two are *verbal* (for verb) and *nominal* (for noun). These apply to grammatical units which can occupy the same positions as verbs and nouns respectively. For example, in the sentence "The poor are always with us," the word *poor* is morphologically an adjective because one can add to the form the ending *-er*, a characteristic of adjectives, but one cannot add the plural ending *-s*, a characteristic of nouns. Distributionally, however, it is a nominal because it is in a position normally occupied by nouns, e.g., "The *girl* is my sister," "The *girls* are my sisters." [eds.]

Bear in mind that every language has its own criteria for setting up such classes, whether by form or distribution or by both.

SYNTAX

Syntax (the formal signals that indicate meaning) is shown in English primarily by *word order* and *function words*, only secondarily by morphological change. Subject and object, for example, are indicated by word order:

The *man* sees the bear. (*man* is subject)
The bear sees the *man*. (*man* is object)

Latin does not signal subject and object in this way.

When pronouns replace nouns in the subject or object position, they generally take the subjective or objective forms:

He sees the bear.
The bear sees *him*.

It should be noted that word order is the primary signal, and the change in the pronoun is secondary. If you were to hear *John saw Mary and I downtown today*, the word order would tell you that *I* was object of the sentence in spite of the subjective case.

The situation is different in Latin, where, although there is a favorite order (subject, object, verb), about half the time we find one of the other five permutations (object, verb, subject; verb, subject, object, etc.) without any change in syntactical meaning.

In English there are a few variations of subject, verb, object:

"Stop!" cried the cop: object, verb, subject.
Came the dawn: verb, subject.
Did he see the bear? auxiliary, subject, verb, object.

Modification of nouns is shown in English by word order:

The *big* man sees the bear.
The man sees the *big* bear.

Modification is not signalled in Latin in this way.

In English most adjectives and adjectivals precede the noun they modify. A few petrified phrases, most long phrases, and all prepositional phrases follow:

God Almighty, house beautiful, courts-martial
The man, shaking all over, saw a bear.
The man who was here yesterday saw a bear.
The man with a gun saw a bear.

Verbs in English are modified by adverbs, adverbials, prepositional phrases, and certain function words. There is some freedom in the position of some of them:

We go to the lake in the summer.
We go in the summer to the lake.
In the summer we go to the lake.

Notice that although there is the same general meaning conveyed, there is a different emphasis. This shift in emphasis is meaning on a quite different level from the contrast between *The man saw the bear* and *The bear saw the man.*

The importance of word order in English may be seen in the pair *an awful pretty hat/a pretty awful hat.* Word order tells us that *awful* is a qualifier in the first and an adjective in the second. Notice too that the order of adjectives in series is fixed. In *all those fat little old American tourists over there* we cannot change the order of any of the modifiers. Such facts as these, traditionally ignored in grammars, are part of the machinery of the English language. To teach a foreigner English it is necessary to set up special drills that will teach him to respond *automatically* to these signals.

Nouns may modify nouns in English; the signal is the placing of a noun immediately before the noun it modifies. Notice the difference in the following pairs:

chair arm/arm chair
race horse/horse race
station bus/bus station
leather shoe/shoe leather

The following questions will test your comprehension of this chapter. Forget the old criteria of meaning and try to apply the new ones of form and distribution. For example, the word *home* in *d* of the first set is not a noun but an adverbial; in *e*, however, it is a noun.

1. Identify the parts of speech of the italicized words:
   a. John has an *inclination* to be lazy.
   b. The girl has a *pretty* dress.
   c. The dog was *pretty* ugly.
   d. The man ran *home.*

e. The woman ran her *home* well.
f. The catcher hit a *home* run.
g. The batter knocked the runner *home.*
h. The player hits *well.*
i. The driller hit a *well.*

2. If you saw on the menu the item "chicken lobster" what would you get if you ordered it, chicken or lobster? What is the signal?

3. Some English grammars have stated that in English we signal questions by raising the voice at the end. Observation shows, however, that whereas the voice is raised at the end of some questions, it must be lowered at the end of others, and it may be either raised or lowered at the end of still others. Test this by reading aloud the following sentences:

   "Where do you work?" "I work in New Jersey."
   "Where?" "In New Jersey, I said; didn't you hear me?"

   "Where do you work?" "I work in New Jersey."
   "Where?" "In Passaic." "Where?" "On Main Street."
   "Where?" "1905 Main."

4. How do we signal commands in English?

SUGGESTED ASSIGNMENTS

1. Review what C. C. Fries has to say about lexical and structural meanings. Then point out all the structural meanings in the following sentences and tell whether they are signaled by form or by word order.
   a. The swaggles faculated my gluddest neap.
   b. Her fillydoop, a swalish threet, was spooving his rambent dirm.
   c. That subful slig tiligates my spoom loubously.
2. Write three sentences like the foregoing to show as many structural meanings as you can. Note that you can use nonsense words only for those parts of speech that are traditionally called nouns, verbs, adjectives, and adverbs. Nearly all other kinds of words convey mostly structural meaning, though the line between lexical and structural meanings is sometimes hard to draw.
3. Fries points out that if a sentence contains words whose form-class (part of speech) classification is unclear, the sentence will contain a structural ambiguity, that is, it will have two possible meanings. In

the following newspaper headlines, point out the structural ambiguities caused by form-class uncertainty:

a. SUSPECT SHOT AFTER HOLDUP

b. EUROPE CROOKS
BECKONING FINGER
AT LOCAL RESIDENTS

c. OPEN HOUSE
FOR NEW SCHOOL

d. RULE BOOK NOT OBSCENE

4. In writing, the structural signals of stress, pitch, and juncture are absent. Thus there is always the possibility that the reader, by "hearing" these signals in a way different from that intended by the writer, may misinterpret. Read the following items aloud so as to bring out more than one meaning:
   a. Patent medicines are sold by frightening people.
   b. The soldiers were issued twenty four hour passes.
   c. Ground hog supper.
   d. Mammoth tooth found in creek near Vinton.
   e. A needy veteran's widow.
   f. Hot chestnut vendor.
   g. I am an outdoor lover.
   h. Modern language teaching.
   i. A clever boy's story.
5. Read these sentences aloud with a double-cross juncture just before the second clause:
   a. It was light enough to play *although the sun was already down.*
   b. Jack invited Helen to the prom, *which was what she had expected.*

   Many college freshmen write such clauses as complete sentences, preceded by a period and beginning with a capital letter. Explain why they do so.
6. Why do most people find talking so easy and writing so difficult? Write a theme on this question, choosing your own title.
7. Here is an exercise in descriptive grammar on which to try your wings. Collect about fifty sentences containing *some, something, any, anything.* You can get them from your reading, from spoken discourse, and by asking friends to devise a few for you. Then, using your collected data, write an accurate descriptive statement about how the four words are used that will show a foreigner how to use them as Americans do. Next, test your statement by trying to find exceptions. If you find exceptions, modify the statement to include them. See if your statement will help the Dutch high school students who uttered the following sentences:
   a. I want to ask you any questions about America.

b. Did you ever hear something about Leonardo da Vinci?
c. I want to tell you anything about the South Seas.
d. It is not the use to eat or drink something after that.
e. I want to tell you anything about dancing.
f. I do not have some paper today.
g. Any students think that Greek is easy.
h. I did not have some money left.

8. As a native speaker of English you have a working knowledge of English grammar; that is, you can construct sentences using the same forms and patterns as other Americans, with the result that you are understood and your language sounds natural. But you are perhaps not conscious of all the complexities of the intricate system that you use so easily. Here is a pertinent exercise. Study the sentences below, all of which were spoken by foreign students. Each group represents one kind of abnormality that makes it non-English. Choose one group and write an explanation of what is wrong in such a way that the speaker will be able to avoid the same kind of mistake in the future. It will not be very helpful merely to show the normal way to express the sentence. You will have to find a principle or general pattern that can be followed.

a. (1) We have very often clouds.
(2) I like very much sport.
(3) You learn quickly English.
(4) We could take each morning a bath.
(5) He has been for three weeks minister.

b. (1) . . . another big house where is a tennis court.
(2) Before the window is an ivy where lived many birds.

c. (1) I will be tomorrow there.
(2) We go at nine o'clock to bed.
(3) I went at ten o'clock to the office.

d. (1) What you like with your pancakes?
(2) Why you never come to our class?
(3) To which factory you wrote?
(4) How you like my speech?

e. (1) I have born in The Hague.
(2) Where did you born?
(3) Where have you born?
(4) Where are you born?

f. (1) He made the mistake to show his picture.
(2) We had no hope to see our cat back.

9. For the ambitious student here are some harder sentences to explain to the foreign student:

a. Yesterday I must go shopping.

b. It is not pleasant too.
c. The eggs were been packed in a box.
d. The game is during forty-five minutes.
e. It is much comfortable.

10. There has been a long-standing controversy as to whether the study of grammar improves one's ability to use his native language. Using your own experience as material, write a theme on "What Grammar Did to/for Me."

FURTHER READINGS

1. Hall, Robert A., Jr. *Linguistics and Your Language.* New York: Doubleday & Company, Inc., 1960, pp. 97-120.
2. Potter, Simeon. *Modern Linguistics.* London: Andre Deutsch, 1957, pp. 104-122.
3. Roberts, Paul. *Understanding Grammar.* New York: Harper & Brothers, 1954, pp. 1-24.
4. Sapir, Edward. *Language.* New York: Harcourt, Brace & World, Inc., 1921, pp. 59-126.
5. Smith, Henry Lee, Jr. *Linguistic Science and the Teaching of English.* Cambridge, Massachusetts: Harvard University Press, 1956.

9. Clear Thinking

ARE ALL GENERALIZATIONS FALSE?

Lionel Ruby

Occasionally one hears a person praised as a "smooth talker" or as having "the gift of gab." More often than not such expressions are disparaging, for they suggest mere verbalization, clever manipulation of words. We have spent a good deal of time in these readings trying to understand language as a structural system of meaningful signals. We must not forget that this marvelous system is after all symbolic, that it is, in Sapir's words, a "method of communicating ideas, emotions, and desires." We have an obligation to use verbal symbols, our language, responsibly—to speak and write with clarity and precision. And this involves clear thinking. In the readings that follow we shall be concerned with matters of clear thinking and with some of the traps that lie in wait for the unwary.

We constantly make inferences and judgments based on past knowledge and experience and on our observations of the world around us. We constantly make assumptions that what was true in one particular instance is true in another. In other words, we constantly generalize. Moreover, we act on the basis of these generalizations as if *they were in fact true. Sometimes we are right, and sometimes we are wrong. Which generalizations are reliable guides?*

From *The Art of Making Sense*, by Lionel Ruby. Copyright 1954 by Lionel Ruby. Published by J. B. Lippincott Company.

Can we ever be sure? Are all generalizations false? These are some of the questions Lionel Ruby deals with in the next selection. Professor Ruby is Chairman of the Philosophy Department at Roosevelt University in Chicago.

WE BEGIN with a generalization: human beings are great generalizers. Every race has its proverbs, and proverbs are generalizations. "It never rains but it pours." "Faint heart never won fair lady." "Familiarity breeds contempt." Sometimes, of course, these proverbs are incompatible with each other, as in "Absence makes the heart grow fonder," and "Out of sight, out of mind."[1]

Listen attentively to those around you, and note the generalizations that float into every conversation: Europeans are lazy and shiftless. European girls make good wives. American girls are selfish. Politicians are crooks. Gentlemen prefer blondes. On a somewhat more "intellectual" level, we find: Liberals never think a matter through. Intellectuals always show a lack of practical judgment. Americans are idealists. Americans are materialists. All American men suffer from "momism." Economics is bunk. Modern art is trash. Psychiatrists never bring up their own children properly. In the middle ages everyone was religious. And so on. After more of the same we may be tempted to agree with Justice Holmes that "the chief end of man is to frame general propositions, and no general proposition is worth a damn."

Our awareness of the inadequacy of "sweeping generalizations" may lead us to say that all generalizations are false. But this is truly a sweeping generalization! And worse: if it is true, then the witticism that "all generalizations are false, *including this one*" would appear to be justified. But this will not do either, for this generalization asserts that it itself is false, from which it follows that it is not the case that all generalizations are false. Or perhaps we should say that "all generalizations are half-truths—including this one"? But this is not much better. The fact of the matter is that some generalizations are true, others are false, and still others are uncertain or doubtful. The deadliness of this platitude may be forgiven because of its truth.

By a "generalization" is meant a general law or principle which is inferred from particular facts. As a sample of the way in which we

[1] Once translated by a foreign student as "invisible idiot."

arrive at such generalizations consider the following: Some years ago I visited France, and ate at a number of Parsian restaurants that had been recommended to me. The food was excellent in each. Then one day I was unable to get to any of my customary eating places. I ate in a small restaurant in an outlying district of Paris. The food was excellent. I then tried other restaurants, always with the same results. I ate in large restaurants, small restaurants, on ships and trains, and in railway station restaurants. I generalized: All French restaurants serve excellent meals.

A generalization is a statement that *goes beyond* what is actually observed, to a rule or law covering both the observed cases and those that have not as yet been observed. This going-beyond is called the "inductive leap." An inductive leap is a "leap in the dark," for the *generalization may not be true*, even though the *observations* on which it is based *are* true. Thus, somewhere in France there may be a poor French restaurant—happily I am ignorant of its location—but if so, then I should not say that *all* are good.

A generalization involves an "inductive leap." The word *induction*, from Latin roots meaning "to lead in," means that we examine particular cases (French restaurants), and "lead in" to a generalization. Induction is the method we use when we learn lessons from our experience: we generalize from particular cases. *Deduction*, on the other hand, refers to the process of "drawing out" the logical consequences of what we already know (or assume) to be true. By induction we learn that French cooking is delectable. If a friend tells us that he had tasteless meals while in Europe, then by deduction we know that he did not eat in French restaurants. Both induction and deduction are essential characteristics of rational thinking.

A generalization is a statement of the form: "All A's are B's." "All" means exactly what it says: *all* without exception. A single exception overthrows a generalization of this kind. Before we proceed further we must first dispose of a popular confusion concerning the expression: "The exception proves the rule." This is a sensible statement when properly interpreted, but it is sometimes understood in a manner that makes it nonsense. If I say that "all A's are B's," a single exception will make my statement false. Now, suppose that someone says: "The fact that there is a poor French restaurant proves that *all* are good because *it* is an exception, and the exception proves the rule!" Does a wicked woman prove that all women are saints? The sensible interpretation of the expression, "The exception proves the rule" is this: When we *say* that a certain case *is* an "exception," we imply that there is a rule which is generally true. When a mother tells her daughter, "Have a good time at the prom, and, for tonight, you have my permission to stay out until 3 A.M.," she implies that this is an exception to the rule which requires earlier reporting. A statement that *creates* an exception implies a rule for all non-exceptional cases; but a generalization that is stated as a rule without exceptions (all A's are B's) would be overthrown by a single exception.

All too often "general propositions are not worth a damn," as Holmes remarked. This is because we generalize too hastily on the basis of insufficient evidence. The fallacy called the "hasty generalization" simply refers to the fact that we jump too quickly to conclusions concerning "all." For example, we see a woman driving carelessly, and generalize: "All women are poor drivers." We see a car weaving in and out of traffic, and note that it has a California license: "Wouldn't you know," we say. "A California driver. That's the way they all drive out there." Anita Loos' gay heroine thought that gentlemen preferred blondes because she was a blonde and men were attracted to her.

We learn that Napoleon got along on five hours of sleep. From this we may conclude that "five hours of sleep is all that anybody really needs." Our assumption is that what Napoleon could do, anybody can do, until we learn that we are not Napoleons. (If we don't learn this eventually, we aren't permitted to circulate freely.) The next example is undoubtedly the worst example of generalizing ever committed: A man declared that all Indians walk single file. When challenged for his evidence, he replied, "How do I know that? I once saw an Indian walk that way."

Hasty generalizing is perhaps the most important of popular vices in thinking. It is interesting to speculate on some of the reasons for this kind of bad thinking. One important factor is prejudice. If we are already prejudiced against unions, or businessmen, or lawyers, or doctors, or Jews, or Negroes, then one or two instances of bad conduct by members of these groups will give us the unshakeable conviction that "they're all like that." It is very difficult for a prejudiced person to say, "Some are, and some aren't." A prejudice is a judgment formed *before* examining the evidence.

A psychological reason for asserting "wild" generalizations is exhibitionism: The exhibitionist desires to attract attention to himself. No one pays much attention to such undramatic statements as

"Some women are fickle," or that some are liars, or "Some politicians are no better than they ought to be." But when one says that "all women are liars" this immediately attracts notice. Goethe once said that it is easy to appear brilliant if one respects nothing, not even the truth.

Let us avoid careless and hasty generalizing. The proverb warns us that one swallow does not make a summer. Unfortunately, we usually forget proverbs on the occasions when we ought to remember them. We ought to emulate "the Reverend" in Faulkner's novel, *The Hamlet*. He was discussing the efficacy of a rural remedy. "Do you know it will work, Reverend?" his friend asked. "I know it worked once," the Reverend answered. "Oh, then you have knowed it to fail?" "I never knowed it to be tried but once." The fault of bad generalizing, however, need not make us take refuge in the opposite error: the refusal to generalize. This error is illustrated in the anecdote concerning the student who wrote an essay on labor relations, in which he argued for equal pay for women. Women, he wrote, work hard, they need the money, they are the foundation of the family, and, most important, they are the mothers of most of the human race! There is another old anecdote about the cautious man whose friend pointed to a flock of sheep with the remark, "Those sheep seem to have been sheared recently." "Yes," said the cautious man, "at least on this side."

Generalizations are dangerous, but we must generalize. To quote Justice Holmes once more: he said that he welcomed "anything that will discourage men from believing general propositions." But, he added, he welcomed that "only less than he welcomed anything that would encourage men to make such propositions"! For generalizations are indispensable guides. One of the values of knowledge lies in its predictive power—its power to predict the future. Such knowledge is stated in generalizations. It is of little help to me to know that water froze at 32° F. yesterday unless this information serves as a warning to put anti-freeze in my car radiator before winter comes. History, in the "pure" sense of this term, merely tells us what has happened in the past, but science furnishes us with general laws, and general laws tell us what *always* happens under certain specified conditions.

Science is interested in the general, rather than in the particular or individual. When Newton saw an apple fall from a tree in his orchard—even if this story is a fable, and therefore false in a literal sense, it is true in its insight—he was not interested in the size and shape of the apple. Its fall suggested an abstract law to him, the law of gravity. He framed this law in general terms: Every particle of matter attracts every other particle of matter with a force directly proportional to the product of their masses and inversely proportional to the square of their distances. Chemists seek general laws concerning the behavior of matter. The physician wants to know the general characteristics of the disease called myxedema, so that when he has a case he will recognize it and know exactly how to treat it. The finding of general laws, then, is the aim of all science—including history insofar as it is a science.

The problem of the scientist is one of achieving sound generalizations. The scientist is careful not to make assertions which outrun his evidence, and he refuses to outtalk his information. He generalizes, but recognizes that no generalization can be more than probable, for we can never be certain that *all* the evidence is in, nor can the future be guaranteed absolutely—not even future eclipses of the sun and moon. But the scientist knows that certain laws have a very high degree of probability.

Let us look at the logic involved in forming sound generalizations. The number of cases investigated in the course of formulating a scientific law is a factor in establishing the truth of the law, but it is by no means the most important one. Obviously, if we observed one hundred swans, all of which are white, our generalization that "all swans are white" does not have the same probability it would have if we observed one thousand swans. But no matter how great the number of specimens involved in this type of observation, no more than a high degree of probability is ever established. Countless numbers of white swans were observed throughout the ages (without any exceptions) and then in the nineteenth century black swans were observed in Australia.

The weakness of the method of "induction by simple enumeration of cases" is amusingly illustrated by Bertrand Russell's parable in his *A History of Western Philosophy:*

> There was once upon a time a census officer who had to record the names of all householders in a certain Welsh village. The first that he questioned was called William Williams; so were the second, third, fourth. . . . At last he said to himself: "This is tedious; evidently they are all called William Williams. I shall put them down so and take a holiday." But he was wrong; there was just one whose name was John Jones.

Scientific generalizations based on other types of evidence than simple enumeration often acquire a much higher degree of probability after only a few observations. When a chemist finds that pure sulphur melts at 125° C., in an experiment in which every factor is accurately analyzed and controlled, the law concerning the melting point of sulphur achieves as great a degree of certainty as is humanly attainable. Accurate control of every element of one case, then, is more important in establishing probabilities than is *mere enumeration* of many cases.

A single carefully controlled experiment, such as the sulphur experiment, can give us a much higher degree of probability than the mere observation of thousands of swans. The reason is that we also know that no chemical element thus far observed has a variable melting point under conditions of constant pressure. The chemical law is thus consistent with and is borne out by the rest of chemical knowledge, whereas the "law" holding that all swans are white was based on an "accidental" factor. Or consider the generalization concerning the mortality of mankind. This law is based not merely on the fact that countless numbers of human beings have died in the past, but also on the fact that all living beings must, by reason of physiological limitations, die; and that all matter wears out in time. So the harmony of a particular generalization with the rest of our knowledge is also a factor in giving it a high degree of probability.

So much for the logical analysis of generalizations. Thus far, we have been concerned with "uniform" generalizations, which take the form: "All A's are B's." A generalization, we have seen, is a statement that says something about "all" of a group, the evidence consisting of observations of items in which we always find a single characteristic. The observed cases are taken as a *sample* of the whole group or population with which we are concerned. We observe a number of swans, and take these as a sample of all swans, past, present, and future. We find that all are white, and make the inductive leap: Swans are always white, everywhere.

We shall now examine "statistical" statements. Statistical statements give us information not about characteristics possessed by *all* of a group or population, but by a definite proportion (or most) of the group or population, as when we say, "Most A's are B's," or "Sixty-five per cent of all A's are B's." The first thing to note here is that statistical statements may in fact be *generalizations*, and thus involve the notions of "all." This point involves very important (and common) misunderstandings.

In order to make this point clear, let us re-interpret our "uniform" generalizations. We say: "The sample is so-and-so (all observed swans are uniformly white)—*therefore*, the whole population of swans is uniformly white." Now, we do the same sort of thing in statistical generalizations. We say: "In the sample of red-heads we examined, fifty-three per cent were hot-tempered—therefore, fifty-three per cent of *all* redheads are hot-tempered." (Or: fifty-three per cent of the whole population of red-heads is hot-tempered.) Logically, both examples, uniform and statistical, are of the same type, for in each we make the inductive leap from the sample to the whole population. The only difference between them is that in the one case we assert a *uniform* character in the whole population; in the other we assert that a characteristic holds in a certain *proportion* in the whole population.

This fundamental point will help us to evaluate the degree of probability of a statistical generalization. We saw earlier that uniform generalizations can never be absolutely certain—though for practical purposes we often consider them so, especially in the physical sciences. The probability of a generalization depends especially on the *quality* and also on the *quantity* of the cases that constitute the sample. The same holds for statistical generalizations, which may have a high probability, depending on the character of the evidence. Though the inductive leap is involved in all generalizations, in some cases the leap is justified. Let us examine the criteria of justification for the leap.

Before we proceed we shall discuss an important distinction: that between the sample and the inference we draw from it. It is one thing to describe a sample accurately; quite another to draw an accurate inference. If I say, "I have observed ten swans [the sample] and all were white," we may assume that the sample is accurately described. But if I now go on to generalize (that is, draw the inference) concerning *all* swans, my inference may not be a good one. A generalization always involves a "leap in the dark," sometimes justified and sometimes not. Similarly, if I say, "I have talked to ten friends concerning their income, and six [sixty per cent] told me that they earned more than $10,000 a year," the description of the sample may be accepted as true. But suppose I now go on to make the following inference: "Therefore, sixty per cent of all Americans earn more than $10,000 a year." This would be a hasty generalization indeed.

We distinguish, then, between the sample and the inference. A statistical statement concerning the sample is purely descriptive. The book *They Went to College* is a statistical study as of 1947, of 9,064 college graduates. Averages are given. Fifty-three per cent were in business, sixteen per cent were doctors, lawyers or dentists, sixteen per cent were teachers. The doctors earned the most: over half making more than $7,500 a year. Teachers and preachers earned the least: median income $3,584. Now, these averages involve no inferences. They simply describe the actual facts *in the sample*. We draw an inference, on the other hand, when we assume that the whole population of six million college graduates will show the same kinds of averages as the sample. In our discussion, henceforth, we shall be concerned only with the logical problems involved in statistical inferences.

Suppose that a public opinion poll was recently taken. The polling organization tells us that fifty-eight per cent of the American people approve of the record of the present administration in Washington. How do they know this? Let us examine the evidence on which this finding is based. Obviously not everyone was consulted. A sample was taken. There were three thousand interviews. Since there are seventy-five million adults in the United States, each individual in this sample is taken as representative of twenty-five thousand adults. Further, in the sample, one thousand persons said that they had "no opinion." Eleven hundred and sixty said that they "approved," and eight hundred and forty said they did not. Thus fifty-eight per cent of those with opinions approved, and this means, we are told, that forty-three and one-half million Americans approve. The pollsters assume that the undecided individuals will probably divide in the same proportion as the others when they make up their minds.

Now, we are not raising any questions concerning the truth of the report made of the sample. But is the inductive leap from the sample to the generalization concerning seventy-five million people justified? It may be. It all depends upon the reliability of the sample. What makes a sample reliable? It must be *fair*, *unbiased*, and *representative* of the whole. But what determines whether it has these characteristics? This is the crucial question.

The size of the sample is obviously important. A sample of one hundred would not be so reliable as one of one thousand, and one thousand would not be so reliable as one of a million. But numbers in themselves are not the most important factor in establishing the reliability of generalizations or inferences.

The unimportance of large numbers as such is best illustrated by the ill-fated *Literary Digest* presidential election poll in 1936. The magazine sent pre-election ballots to ten million persons, and received over two million responses. The responses showed Landon running ahead of Roosevelt. In the election in November, however, Roosevelt got about twenty-eight million votes; Landon around eighteen million.

The reason for this colossal failure was the unrepresentative character of the sample. The *Digest* took names "at random" from telephone directories and lists of registered owners of automobiles. These were relatively well-to-do folk. The lower income groups, however, were completely, or almost completely, unrepresented.

An ideal sample is one taken "at random" from the entire population, and not from a selected portion of the population being studied. The Gallup, Roper, and Crossley polls have proved more successful —barring a spectacular failure in 1948—than the *Literary Digest* poll. Let us see how the Gallup poll operates. A sample of three thousand individuals is taken, but with great care to make the sample representative. The population is classified into sub-groups by geographic regions, by rural or urban residence, economic status, age, education, and declared politics. In 1948, for example, Gallup estimated that twenty-eight per cent of the American people live in the Middle Atlantic states, ten per cent on the West Coast; that thirty-four per cent live in cities of over 100,000 population; that twenty-three per cent are of an "average" economic station; that forty-three per cent are between the ages of thirty and forty-nine; that forty-two per cent have gone to high school; and that thirty-eight per cent call themselves Democrats, thirty-six per cent Republicans, and twenty-six per cent independents or members of smaller parties. The three thousand interviews in the sample are distributed so that each geographic area, each economic group, etc., will be represented in its appropriate numerical strength.

Individuals are then chosen "at random," rather than by selection, from within each sub-group, and the resulting sample is highly representative of the whole population. The Gallup poll enjoys a successful record, on the whole, except for 1948. In other words, the method works, and one must respect its findings. But no poll can ever eliminate the possibility of error, or guarantee accuracy except within a margin of error of several percentage points. And in a presidential election forecast the pollster is either completely right or completely wrong in predicting who will win. Odds of 10 to 1 against a candidate of one of the major parties are probably not justified even if all the polls are unanimous as to the final results. These were the odds against Harry Truman in 1948!

An election prediction can be judged by the election results, and a long series of successful predictions gives us confidence in the methods of the pollsters. This check cannot be made on polls which tabulate public opinion on issues of the day, for the whole population is never counted. Similarly for polls which rate television shows, for the whole audience is not counted. Such polls, of course, also generalize on the basis of samples. To illustrate the logical problems in assessing the reliability of a statistical study of the "public opinion poll" type we shall comment on *Sexual Behavior in the Human Female*, by Alfred C. Kinsey and his staff.

Kinsey's study tabulates and classifies data concerning 5,940 white American females, ages two to ninety. He does not claim that his averages necessarily apply to all human females, despite the title of his book, nor even to all American women, of whom there are approximately seventy millions. It is inevitable, however, that such inferences will be drawn, and our question is: Are such inferences justified? This depends entirely on the representativeness of Kinsey's sample.

Critics of Kinsey's report have emphasized the unrepresentativeness of his sample. His subjects are not distributed proportionately in geographic areas: most are from Illinois, Florida, and California. They are more highly educated than a representative cross-section of the population: seventy-five per cent of his subjects went to college, as compared with a national average of thirteen per cent. Three per cent of his women did not go beyond grade school as compared with the national average of thirty-seven per cent. A larger than average proportion are from middle and upper economic groups. Very few of the women were Roman Catholics or orthodox Jews.

Critics have also argued that the very nature of the study involves a kind of bias, for many women will refuse to discuss matters of such "delicate privacy" with interviewers, so that his volunteers must be unrepresentative of women in general. And there is also the problem of credibility. Critics have said that people who like to talk about such things tend to understate or overstate, and even to fabricate a little.

Kinsey, of course, recognizes the limitations and incompleteness of his sample, and, as noted, does not claim that it is representative of the whole population. But it will be interpreted in this way, and if Kinsey wished to avoid such interpretations, he should have called his study "Sexual Behavior of 5,940 Women." Inferences would probably be drawn, however, even if he had so titled his study.

The elements of distortion in Kinsey's sample detract from its reliability as a basis for generalizing. On the other hand, as a review of the book in *Life* put it, though the statistics are not perfect they are at any rate "the only statistics in town." His study is by no means worthless as an index of sexual behavior. We must not use an "all or nothing" approach here. The reliability of his sample with respect to university women as a single group, for example, is certainly much higher than that for the female population as a whole. But we cannot conclude that the whole female population resembles the sample since the sample is not a representative one.

Generalizations in statistics, then, are judged by the same logical criteria we use in judging any generalizations. Fallacies, however, are more common in statistical than they are in uniform generalizations. For it is easier to check on the reliability of a uniform generalization: one exception overthrows the general rule or "law." In statistics, however, since nothing is said about any specific individual, an "exception" is a meaningless term. An exceptional individual does not disprove an "average." But there is, as we have already noted, a method for checking the reliability of a statistical generalization concerning a population, and that is to count the whole "voting" population. But even a test of this kind is not conclusive, for many of the voters do not vote on election day, because of laziness, overconfidence, or some other reason.

Errors of inference in statistics are frequently overlooked because of the mathematical language in which statistics are presented. The spell which numbers weave often prevents us from seeing errors in arguments—errors which would be obvious were they not clothed in mathematical garb. And many dishonest reasoners take advantage of this fact and present highly selected data for purposes of propaganda rather than information. Misuses of the science of statistics have resulted in such jibes as, "Figures don't lie, but liars figure," and "There are three kinds of lies: ordinary lies, damnable lies, and statistics." But these cynical remarks should not be taken as criticisms of statistics. The fault never lies with the figures, or with the science, but with their careless use. It is simply not the case that "you can prove anything with figures" (or statistics), just as it is never the case that "you can prove anything by logic." To the uninitiated, it just *seems* that you can.

SUGGESTED ASSIGNMENTS

1. Study the following sample assignment: Stand near a soda fountain for exactly one hour during a rush period. Make a count of the male and female customers who order (1) coffee, cokes or other cola drinks, (2) sundaes, ice cream sodas, malted milks, milk shakes, pie, cake, and cookies, (3) sandwiches. From your assembled data, make any generalizations that seem justifiable. You might come up with generalizations like these:
   a. Women (or men) eat more fattening food than men (or women).
   b. At soda fountains, men prefer sandwiches while women prefer sweets.
   c. Men drink more stimulants than women do.
   d. At such and such a soda fountain between the hours of....and...., more men than women order sandwiches.
   e. Women get more hungry than men between the hours of .... and.....

   Bring to class any generalizations that seem valid to you, together with one or two that you think questionable, for class discussion.

   Now, try to devise a simple statistical study like the one above and write up your data, making one or more sound generalizations, if possible.
2. An AP feature story begins by pointing out that the four sons of a famous popular singer have given their father trouble. Then the story continues by telling of the children of other celebrities: "His brother Bob's son, Chris, 15, was once arrested when police said he tried to steal a car.

   "Edward G. Robinson, Jr., has been in the news repeatedly with drunk arrests.

   "John Barrymore, Jr., made the papers recently with a felony hit and run, drunk driving charge. His half-sister, Diana, wrote a teary book about her long battle with alcoholism.

   "Charles Chaplin, Jr., has a police record for drunkenness.

   "Barbara Ann Burns, daughter of the late comedian Bob Burns, was sentenced to 90 days for drug addiction.

"Chris Crawford, adopted son of Joan Crawford, was arrested on a delinquency charge . . . after a shooting spree with an air rifle. And then there was Cheryl Crane, daughter of Lana Turner, who killed her mother's lover—but was later absolved of blame."

On the basis of this evidence, what generalization could you safely make about the character of the children of movie actors and actresses?

3. The following case is based on fact, but the details are hypothetical. A university professor recently found some spelling tests that had been given to high school sutdents 25 years ago in the area of Indiana and Illinois, and he found the scores made by these students. He gave the same tests to 100 students each in 10 high schools in the same states. Then he compared the results. He found that the students he tested did appreciably better than those students who had taken the same tests 25 years ago. And from these cases he drew this conclusion, or generalization: "Our high schools today are teaching students to spell better than did the schools of 25 years ago." Write a paragraph discussing the soundness of his generalization.
4. The following events are both true:
   a. A news story carried by *Time* magazine for April 21, 1947 reported that a well-behaved high school sophomore, Stuart Allen, murdered a church sexton in cold blood by striking him over the head with a hammer as hard as he could. When arrested, he confessed readily and made it clear that he had never disliked the sexton. "He was a nice fellow," Stuart said. But he had to admit that he didn't feel a bit sorry. With an apologetic chuckle he confided, "I have no remorse at all." Stuart's father was the rector of the Christ Episcopal Church. Stuart had been adopted when he was three months old.
   b. Another news story given out by the Associated Press two days later reported that a 23-year-old youth had shot two policemen to death in a street corner battle. This youth was the son of a Northwestern University professor. He also had been adopted. From these cases what generalizations would you make about the following:
      (1) The character of adopted children
      (2) The kind of upbringing that professional men give their children.
      (3) The effect of heredity upon character
5. Specify two situations in which a single case is satisfactory for a generalization (e.g., the temperature of the water in a bath tub).
6. Comment on the following generalization: "Poets are crazy. Look at Blake and Cowper and Smart—they were all wacky and I can prove it."
7. Many of our folk proverbs are generalizations which are said to represent the accumulated wisdom of the people through many genera-

tions. How can we account for the presence of contradictory proverbs like these:

a. Two heads are better than one.
   Too many cooks spoil the broth.
b. He who hesitates is lost.
   Look before you leap.

8. A university professor who examined the letters of hundreds of college graduates found 45 "if" clauses containing either a *was* or a *were*. Of these clauses, 12 contained the construction type "If I were" and 33 contained an "If I was." From this evidence, what generalization could he safely make about the use of *was* or *were* in an "if" clause among college graduates?
9. Write a theme on "The Values and Hazards of Generalizing."

EVALUATION OF EVIDENCE

W. W. Little, W. H. Wilson, and W. E. Moore

Much of what is studied in college is presented in the form of theories, propositions, and conclusions. All of these involve not only facts but also inferences—somebody's interpretation of the facts. For example, inferences are involved in the study of sociology and that of economics, as well as in the study of history and of law. Whenever we read material of this kind, we engage, consciously or unconsciously, in a continuous process of acceptance, rejection, or suspended judgment. When the evidence is convincing, we accept what we read; when the evidence is unconvincing, we reject it; when no evidence is presented, or when we have no basis for evaluating the evidence, we mark the place with a mental question mark and withhold judgment. The interesting question in this process is how do we know when evi-

dence is convincing? Not all evidence is of the same sort, nor is it all equally reliable. If you were to make an assertion that seemed to you to be true, and were asked to give evidence to support your statement, you might reply that you arrived at your belief on the basis of personal observation, or the observation of others, or that you had it on good authority. In some instances, your conclusion might involve all three. These three different sorts of evidence and the problems involved in evaluating each kind are discussed in the next essay by Messrs. Little, Wilson, and Moore, all professors of logic at the University of Florida.

PERSONAL OBSERVATION

THE RAW MATERIAL of inference, we have noted, is *fact*, which we defined as "a thing which has been demonstrated to be true by direct observation, without inference or interpretation." When the witness testifies in court that he saw the defendant leaving the scene of the crime carrying a smoking revolver, he is *claiming* to be stating a fact, for the thing he says happened could have been verified by direct observation without benefit of inference or interpretation. Even so, the jury must decide whether to accept his statement as fact or to take it with reservations. For the witness could be lying or mistaken about what he saw. The jury must, in effect, judge the reliability of the testimony as evidence. Henceforth, to keep our meaning clear, let us label any statement which claims to be a description of what happened and to be free of inference or interpretation an *allegation of fact;* let us reserve the single word *fact* for statements which we have tested and found to be reliable. For example, let us label the testimony of our witness an allegation of fact until we have ample reason to believe that what he claimed happened actually did happen. In judging the reliability of allegations of fact we shall rely mainly on the correspondence theory, for what we want to know is whether or not the allegation coincides with reality. The criterion we shall apply, then, is observation through our sensory equipment.

If you have been in the habit of assuming that your personal observations are always reliable, the time has come to disillusion yourself. Observation is not so simple and accurate as we might like to think, for it involves a mental process called *perception*. Perception is interpretation of physical sensations. I see and hear an object coming down the road; I *perceive* that it is an automobile. The visual and auditory sensations are merely clues which I interpret to be coming from an automobile.

One need reflect only a moment to realize that we make innumerable errors of perception. We interpret the sparkle of dew in the grass for the dime we are looking for, we are frightened in the night when we interpret garments hanging on a chair to be a burglar, we interpret the backfire of an automobile to be a gunshot. In recent years deer hunting has become a dangerous sport because eager hunters sometimes interpret a movement in the underbrush to be a deer and fire away. They perceive the movement to be a deer without waiting for sufficient clues to make an accurate interpretation.

The degree of reliability of personal observations will depend on a number of factors, six of which are discussed here.[1]

1. The first of these factors is the *physical equipment* of the observer. Sensory acuity varies greatly among individuals. What one individual sees sharply at one hundred feet another will see only as a blur. What one individual hears distinctly another will not hear at all. Even the sharpest eye can be fooled by an optical illusion.[2] In scientific procedure, where accurate measurement is essential, elaborate instruments and techniques for measurement have been designed to reduce reliance on the senses as much as possible. The laboratory technician who estimated temperature and weight by feel, or length by sight, would not last long in his job.

2. The second factor is the *physical conditions* surrounding the observation. When one is sitting in the grandstand well to one side of home plate, his physical situation is not as favorable for calling balls and strikes as is that of the umpire. The coach at a football game is not in a good position to observe some aspects of the action on the field, and for that reason stations an observer in the press box high above the field. The further away you are from the scene of an accident the less reliable your perceptions of it will be. One should

[1] For a more complete discussion of observation, see Harold L. Larrabee, *Reliable Knowledge* (Boston: Houghton Mifflin, 1945), pp. 127-164.

[2] A number of these illusions appear on p. 146 of Larrabee, *op. cit.*

not expect his perceptions to be entirely reliable when the light is poor or when other conditions make accurate perception difficult.

3. Some types of observation require a high degree of *skill.* The observer stationed in the press box by the coach will be useless unless he is a skilled observer of football. The average spectator at the game would be quite unable to determine such matters as whether the linemen are charging properly or whether the blockers are carrying out their assignments.

4. The accuracy of observations is affected adversely by *prejudice.* What we see in a situation is determined to a considerable measure by what we are looking for. In a fight between two students, the fraternity brother of one of the participants may *see* that the other student provoked the fight and landed all the underhanded blows. The boxing coach, on the other hand, may *see* only the skill or the lack of it displayed by the two antagonists. A little experimentation will quickly show that observation is selective. We rarely perceive all the elements in a situation. Instead, we tend to perceive those elements in which we are interested or those which call themselves to our attention. All of us, walking into a dormitory room, would probably perceive a blazing wastebasket, but once the fire is extinguished the occupant of the room and a housing official would probably not perceive the same elements in the situation. We tend to perceive the things in which we are most interested.

5. Our accuracy as observers is affected adversely by *emotion.* To a person who is afraid, the snake looks bigger than it is; the rowboat in rough, open water seems smaller than it is; an approaching car seems to be moving faster than it is; and an innocent gesture by an antagonist becomes the motion of reaching for a gun. Under emotional stress a person is more susceptible to suggestion. If the emotional stress is strong enough, a person may become subject to hallucinations and delusions.

6. When we must depend upon *memory* to recall our observations, they are hardly ever exact. The more time that elapses between the observation itself and the moment we try to recall it, the more opportunity there is for our imaginations to help us re-create the situation to conform to what we wanted to happen. We seldom remember that which we feel no need to remember. Witness how quickly we forgot the telephone number we do not expect to use

again. If we are later called upon to recall something we did not expect to have to remember, we may unconsciously call upon our imaginations to supply the forgotten perceptions.

The careful thinker would do well to learn his own limitations as an observer and to be suspicious of his own observations whenever the situation demands skill or sensory acuity close to his limits, whenever prejudice or emotion are present, and whenever he must depend upon memory to recall what happened. Certainty is rarely obtainable in observation, and few observations should be accepted as facts unless they have been confirmed by more than one observer.

REPORTED OBSERVATIONS

When the evidence consists of observations made by persons other than ourselves, all the considerations affecting personal observations apply. In determining the reliability of the observation we should ask ourselves how good the observer's sensory equipment is, how favorable the physical conditions were for making such an observation, whether the observer had sufficient skill for making such an observation, what the observer's bias is, whether emotion was present in the observer, and how much the observer had to depend upon memory. And there is an additional question we should ask: is the observer telling the truth as he knows it?

Some of the problems of evaluating this type of evidence can be seen in a trial at law, where the testimony of witnesses may constitute most or even all of the evidence.[3] Over the years our courts have evolved an elaborate code to protect themselves against testimony which is false or undesirable from a judicial point of view. The code governs such matters as what kind of testimony may be admitted in evidence, who may give the testimony and under what circumstances and at what stage in the proceedings, and how the testimony of a witness may be attacked or questioned. One of the principal functions of the judge is to act as umpire in enforcing these rules of evidence. Should he make a questionable decision on whether a given bit of evidence may be admitted for consideration, the decision may be made the basis of an appeal for a new trial. So elaborate have these

[3] The student interested in a non-technical description of legal proof should read *You Be the Judge*, by Ernest Mortenson (New York: Longmans, Green and Co., 1940), pp. 343-399.

rules become and so encrusted with qualifications and exceptions that ten heavy volumes are required to cover them.

Any lengthy examination of the code of evidence would be out of place in this text, but a brief discussion of a few points will serve to illustrate some of the ways in which the flaws in reported observations may be revealed in everyday life as well as in the courtroom. A considerable part of the code of evidence is designed to determine the relevancy of evidence. The problem is a difficult one. If attorneys were permitted to introduce all evidence that might possibly be relevant, the trial might drag on interminably and result in intolerable expense to the state and to the litigants. On the other hand, no evidence that is vital to the case should ever be excluded. Ruling on this point has furrowed the brow of many a judge.

Even a superficial study of the rules of evidence will show that the courts have been concerned with the same problems of evaluation which were discussed under the first topic of this chapter. When one side has presented a witness, the rules permit the other side to show, if possible, either through cross-examination or through the introduction of other witnesses, that the witness did not have the physical equipment to observe accurately what he claimed to have observed, or that the physical conditions were not such as to make such observations accurate, or that he lacked the skill to make such an observation, or that he was motivated by prejudice or emotion, or that his memory was faulty. There are rules, of course, complete with exceptions, to govern how this may be done. For example, a person may not be disqualified as a witness because of any mental defect unless this defect renders his testimony substantially untrustworthy on the specific point at issue.

Any attempt to discredit the testimony of a witness by an attack on his character may, of course, involve the fallacy of argumentum ad hominem. The judge must decide whether a given attack is relevant, and the jury must decide the value of any such evidence after it has been admitted. As might be expected, many entries in the code cover this point. For example, the prosecution is not permitted to introduce testimony attacking the character of the defendant except in rebuttal where the defense has offered testimony to show the good character of the defendant. This seemingly innocent little rule may pose a critical question for the defense. If the defense introduces any testimony at all to show the good character of the defendant, the prosecution may, by rebuttal, introduce testimony devastating to the character of the defendant.

As a general rule, the courts will not admit hearsay evidence, that is, testimony based on what the witness has heard others say, because experience has shown this kind of evidence to be generally unreliable. The person making the statement may have been mistaken in the first place, and he is not available for cross-examination. In the second place, the witness may be lying, and his observations as to what the other person said are subject to the usual errors of perception and understanding of language.

The principal weapon used in court against the unreliable witness, and particularly against the witness who is lying, is cross-examination. Any inconsistency in testimony, even on a minor point, which the cross-examiner can bring out helps to discredit the remainder of the testimony. Only a very clever witness is able to fabricate testimony without being caught by a skillful cross-examiner. The use of cross-examination is illustrated by a famous story about Abraham Lincoln's first defense at a murder trial. The prosecution's case rested mainly on testimony of a witness who swore that he saw the defendant fire the fatal shot and run away. In cross-examining this witness, Lincoln led him into testifying to a number of details: that he was standing twenty feet or more from the defendant at the time of the shooting, that the shooting occurred in heavy timber, that he could see how the pistol was pointed, that the shooting occurred at night and the nearest lights were candles three quarters of a mile away, that he saw the shooting by moonlight. Then Lincoln dramatically produced an almanac, offered it in evidence, and read from it that the moon did not rise until several hours after the shooting. Under the strain of the excitement, the witness broke down and confessed that he had fired the fatal shot himself.[4]

EVIDENCE FROM AUTHORITY

Frequently in everyday life we must depend on the opinions of authorities and use their opinions instead of factual evidence. When we go to a physician for diagnosis of an ailment, we must depend on his analysis and interpretation of facts in the form of symptoms. We

[4] For an account of this and other cases in which cross-examination played a vital part, see Francis L. Wellman, *The Art of Cross-Examination* (New York: The Macmillan Company, 1911).

must either accept his opinion or keep trying new doctors until we find one whose opinion we are willing to accept. Courts of law are coming to depend increasingly on expert witnesses as crime detection becomes more and more scientific. Physicians, psychiatrists, ballistics experts, fingerprint experts, and handwriting experts are frequently called to give testimony. Without the assistance of these experts, the average layman sitting on the jury would be helpless in trying to determine whether the defendant is insane, or whether the bullet that caused the death of the decedent came from the gun belonging to the defendant, or whether the ransom note was written by the defendant, or whether the prints left at the scene of the crime are those of the defendant or of his brother-in-law.

As citizens we cannot ourselves go to Washington to conduct a personal investigation of the affairs of our government; we must depend on reports and commentaries in the newspapers and on the radio. In more complicated affairs we must frequently rely on interpretations by commentators. Elmer Davis, a well-known radio commentator, has pointed out that newspapers, in their effort to be objective, do not tell the whole truth.[5] When one political personage falsely accuses another of being a Communist, the newspaper, trying to be objective, reports merely that so-and-so says so-and-so is a Communist. It does not point out to its readers that the speaker has no great reputation for veracity and has no way of knowing whether the accused person is or is not a Communist. Yet, without this background information, the newspaper reader has little chance to evaluate the statement correctly. This is one explanation, Mr. Davis thinks, for the increasing popularity of newspaper columnists and radio commentators. They supply the interpretation for which the public feels a need.

We are especially dependent on authorities in the field of value judgments. If I paint a picture which I think is good and you think is terrible, we can argue at length, and I can point out why I think it is good and you can point out why you think it is not. If the argument progresses far enough we may consult an expert, and if his opinion is contrary to mine, I can go hunt another expert. In matters of taste and value in any of the arts, about the best sources of evidence we have are the experts who have devoted much of their lives to a study of the subject. In ethical judgments our authorities

[5] For an interesting discussion of this problem see Mr. Davis' article in the *Atlantic*, August, 1952.

are the philosophers. In religion the authorities we commonly turn to are the ministers of our own denomination.

How can we evaluate these authorities on whom we are forced to depend in making some of our most important decisions? There is no certain way, but there are certain earmarks which reliable authorities usually have and which unreliable ones frequently do not have.

In the first place, reliable authorities safeguard the accuracy of their conclusions by practicing the same techniques described in this book, together with some additional ones peculiar to their fields. They do not make snap judgments about important matters; they do carefully consider all the available evidence before making a decision. They do not search only for evidence to support the conclusions they wish to reach or have already reached; they do search for evidence contrary to the conclusions they would like to reach, and they weigh this evidence fully. They rarely commit such fallacies as undistributed middle.[6]

In the second place, reliable authorities do not resort to propaganda devices in presenting their findings. They do not merely present their opinions and depend on prestige, and perhaps confident manner, to gain acceptance for them; they do present the reasons for their conclusions, and they frequently express doubt about their conclusions, especially if the matter is difficult or complex. They do not present one-sided arguments; they do present both sides of the question fairly.

When an important issue is at stake, we need concern ourselves not only with the general reliability of the authority but with his reliability concerning the specific issue at stake. The student will be well advised to cultivate the habit of asking himself three questions about an authority before accepting his opinion.

1. *How much does he know about the specific question at issue?* We are likely to assume that, because a man has achieved renown as an authority in one field, he must be a person of superior intelligence and therefore a competent authority in other fields as well. But we may be mistaken, for the world's greatest authority on ballistics may

[6] A common logical fallacy which may be illustrated by this syllogism:

Communists favor disarmament without international inspection.
Joe Blavatsky favors disarmament without international inspection.

Therefore

Joe Blavatsky is a Communist. [eds.]

be the world's poorest authority on politics. Granted that he had to be a person of superior intellect to become a great authority in any field, he probably had to concentrate his effort on ballistics, to the neglect of other matters. When we consult an authority, it is his competence in the field in question that matters. While there is no completely reliable rule for determining competence, there are a number of clues which will be helpful. In the learned professions membership in learned societies may be a clue. It is not necessarily true that a surgeon who is a Fellow in the American College of Surgeons is a better surgeon than one who is not, but the fact that he has been recognized by such an organization makes it probable that he is. Another clue is the degrees held and the institutions granting them. Possession of a Ph.D. degree from a reputable institution is not an absolute guarantee of competence in the field of the degree, but it is strong evidence in that direction. But remember that a Ph.D. in zymology does not qualify its holder as an authority in English literature. Your librarian can usually assist you in looking up clues to an authority's competence.

2. *What is his personal interest in the matter in question?* Courts of law long ago recognized that the testimony of a witness is less reliable if he has a pecuniary or emotional interest in the matter on which he is testifying. If personal interest may make factual testimony unreliable, it may have an even more adverse effect on the reliability of opinions, and authorities are not exempt from this influence. In important matters it is well to try to ascertain what the authority's own peculiar interest is, if any, and discount his opinion accordingly. Civilian and military authorities may differ, for example, on how much money is needed for national defense. One should not infer that either of these authorities deliberately gives a false opinion in order to promote his own interests. Rather, the point is that as human beings they tend to see what they want to see. When the salesman tells you that the car he sells is the best in its field, he is not necessarily lying; he may be merely blinded by his enthusiasm, and he could be right. We should be careful not to overlook emotional interests, which may frequently be more powerful than pecuniary ones. For example, an authority who gains renown for an opinion or a conclusion tends to develop an emotional attachment for it which will not allow him to give it up easily.

3. *What do other authorities say about the matter?* When the issue

is important, one should never depend on a single authority. No matter how reliable he seems, he may still be mistaken. This question is particularly applicable to radio commentators. By hearing several of them, preferably from different networks, discuss the same issue, one may not only come nearer to the whole truth but also gain some evidence as to which is the most reliable—provided, of course, he listens critically and does not merely search for the commentator whose views most nearly coincide with his own.

SUGGESTED ASSIGNMENTS

1. In the present context, an observation is a statement of what one observes with his senses. An inference is a conclusion that one draws from his observations. Clip a large picture from a magazine. (Try to get one that is clear and has sharp contrasts so that it will be easy to see if your instructor projects it on the screen for discussion.) Write a series of observations about the picture, making sure to exclude all inferences. The class discussion will reveal whether you have been able to separate observations from inferences.
2. Clip a picture that is filled with detail. Ask two friends whom you know well, a man and a woman, to write a list of observations about the picture. Study the two lists to see whether they illustrate the old dictum: "We see things not as they are, but as we are."
3. Write a short, simple narrative or description of a situation, a place, or a person. Use only factual details and exclude inferences. Then show it to two friends and ask each to make as many inferences as he can from your observations. What do the two lists suggest about the reliability of hearsay?
4. Clip an advertisement that quotes a so-called authority to sell its product. Write a paragraph in which you apply the tests of authority given in the selection above and reach a conclusion about the validity of the testimonial.
5. Human knowledge is so vast today that one must rely on authority in many situations of daily life. And countless specialists are available for our consultation. Who, for example, would you consult if you
   Had an aching tooth?
   Were sued for an auto accident?
   Needed a stout pair of walking shoes?
   Wanted facts on Eisenhower's or Stevenson's life for a biographical sketch?
   Wanted to know the best material for a drip-dry summer dress?
   Wanted help in choosing your major, or your career?
   Were planning a bicycle tour of Europe next summer?

Had to organize a collection of material into a coherent speech?
Wanted to find a good picnic spot for your club?
Wanted to know the name and habits of a strange bird you have seen?
Wanted to learn to understand the paintings of abstract expressionism?

6. Find for yourself a theme subject relating to authority, compose a thesis sentence, and write a short theme developing your thesis. You might use a thesis sentence like one of these:
   a. An important part of college education is learning about reliable sources of information.
   b. Modern man is often victimized by his ignorance.
   c. It is difficult to choose a doctor in a strange community.
   d. A blind trust in the opinion of an obliging friend once taught me a valuable lesson.
   e. Long ago I learned not to ask everyone's advice.

POST HOC RIDES AGAIN

Darrell Huff

One of the most engaging characters in American fiction is Huckleberry Finn. Huck, you will remember, is generally pragmatic in his approach to things; he is particularly good at sizing up a situation, coming to his own conclusions, and then acting in accordance with the facts as he sees them. That he is also superstitious, putting his faith in charms and omens, does not make him an inconsistent character, as the following anecdote makes clear. Huck is speaking: "... I've always reckoned that looking at the new moon over your left shoulder is one of the carelessest and foolishest things a body can do. Old Hank Bunker done it once, and bragged about it; and in less than two years he got drunk and fell off of the shot-tower, and spread himself out so that he was just a kind of a

layer, as you may say; and they slid him edgeways between two barn doors for a coffin, and buried him so, so they say, but I didn't see it. Pap told me. But anyway it all come of looking at the moon that way, like a fool."
This miniature tall-tale illustrates in a humorous fashion the fallacy of post hoc, ergo propter hoc *(after this, therefore because of this), the topic of the next essay. Darrell Huff is primarily concerned with the occurrence of this fallacy in statistics. He writes in a style that is refreshingly breezy, but he is nonetheless serious. His warning is clear: Look for the facts behind the figures.*

Somebody once went to a good deal of trouble to find out if cigarette smokers make lower college grades than nonsmokers. It turned out that they did. This pleased a good many people and they have been making much of it ever since. The road to good grades, it would appear, lies in giving up smoking; and, to carry the conclusion one reasonable step further, smoking makes dull minds.

This particular study was, I believe, properly done: sample big enough and honestly and carefully chosen, correlation having a high significance, and so on.

The fallacy is an ancient one which, however, has a powerful tendency to crop up in statistical material, where it is disguised by a welter of impressive figures. It is the one that says that if B follows A, then A has caused B. An unwarranted assumption is being made that since smoking and low grades go together, smoking causes low grades. Couldn't it just as well be the other way around? Perhaps low marks drive students not to drink but to tobacco. When it comes right down to it, this conclusion is about as likely as the other and just as well supported by the evidence. But it is not nearly so satisfactory to propagandists.

It seems a good deal more probable, however, that neither of these things has produced the other, but both are a product of some third factor. Can it be that the sociable sort of fellow who takes his books less than seriously is also likely to smoke more? Or is there a clue in the fact that somebody once established a correlation between extroversion and low grades—a closer relationship apparently than the one between grades and intelligence? Maybe extroverts smoke more than introverts. The point is that when there are many reasonable explanations you are hardly entitled to pick one that suits your taste and insist on it. But many people do.

To avoid falling for the *post hoc* fallacy and thus wind up believing many things that are not so, you need to put any statement of relationship through a sharp inspection. The correlation, that convincingly precise figure that seems to prove that something is because of something, can actually be any of several types.

One is the correlation produced by chance. You may be able to get together a set of figures to prove some unlikely thing in this way, but if you try again, your next set may not prove it at all. As with the manufacturer of the tooth paste that appeared to reduce decay, you simply throw away the results you don't want and publish widely those you do. Given a small sample, you are likely to find some substantial correlation between any pair of characteristics or events that you can think of.

A common kind of co-variation is one in which the relationship is real but it is not possible to be sure which of the variables is the cause and which the effect. In some of these instances cause and effect may change places from time to time or indeed both may be cause and effect at the same time. A correlation between income and ownership of stocks might be of that kind. The more money you make, the more stock you buy, and the more stock you buy, the more income you get; it is not accurate to say simply that one has produced the other.

Perhaps the trickiest of them all is the very common instance in which neither of the variables has any effect at all on the other, yet there is a real correlation. A good deal of dirty work has been done with this one. The poor grades among cigarette smokers is in this category, as are all too many medical statistics that are quoted without the qualification that although the relationship has been shown to be real, the cause-and-effect nature of it is only a matter of speculation. As an instance of the nonsense or spurious correlation that is a real statistical fact, someone has gleefully pointed to this: There is a close relationship between the salaries of Presbyterian ministers in Massachusetts and the price of rum in Havana.

Which is the cause and which the effect? In other words, are the ministers benefiting from the rum trade or supporting it? All right. That's so farfetched that it is ridiculous at a glance. But watch out for other applications of *post hoc* logic that differ from this one only in being more subtle. In the case of the ministers and the rum it is easy to see that both figures are growing because of the influence of a third factor: the historic and world-wide rise in the price level of practically everything.

And take the figures that show the suicide rate to be at its maximum in June. Do suicides produce June brides—or do June weddings precipitate suicides of the jilted? A somewhat more convincing (though equally unproved) explanation is that the fellow who licks his depression all through the winter with the thought that things will look rosier in the spring gives up when June comes and he still feels terrible.

Another thing to watch out for is a conclusion in which a correlation has been inferred to continue beyond the data with which it has been demonstrated. It is easy to show that the more it rains in an area, the taller the corn grows or even the greater the crop. Rain, it seems, is a blessing. But a season of very heavy rainfall may damage or even ruin the crop. The positive correlation holds up to a point and then quickly becomes a negative one. Above so-many inches, the more it rains the less corn you get.

We're going to pay a little attention to the evidence on the money value of education in a minute. But for now let's assume it has been proved that high-school graduates make more money than those who drop out, that each year of undergraduate work in college adds some more income. Watch out for the general conclusion that the more you go to school the more money you'll make. Note that this has not been shown to be true for the years beyond an undergraduate degree, and it may very well not apply to them either. People with Ph.D.'s quite often become college teachers and so do not become members of the highest income groups.

A correlation of course shows a tendency which is not often the ideal relationship described as one-to-one. Tall boys weigh more than short boys on the average, so this is a positive correlation. But you can easily find a six-footer who weighs less than some five-footers, so the correlation is less than 1. A negative correlation is simply a statement that as one variable increases the other tends to decrease. In physics this becomes an inverse ratio: The further you get from a light bulb the less light there is on your book; as distance increases light intensity decreases. These physical relationships often have the kindness to produce perfect correlations, but figures from business or sociology or medicine seldom work out so neatly. Even if education generally increases incomes it may easily turn out to be the financial ruination of Joe over there. Keep in mind that a correlation may be real and based on real cause and effect—and still be almost worthless in determining action in any single case.

Reams of pages of figures have been collected to show the value in dollars of a college education, and stacks of pamphlets have been published to bring these figures—and conclusions more or less based on them—to the attention of potential students. I am not quarreling with the intention. I am in favor of education myself, particularly if it includes a course in elementary statistics. Now these figures have pretty conclusively demonstrated that people who have gone to college make more money than people who have not. The exceptions are numerous, of course, but the tendency is strong and clear.

The only thing wrong is that along with the figures and facts goes a totally unwarranted conclusion. This is the *post hoc* fallacy at its best. It says that these figures show that if *you* (your son, your daughter) attend college you will probably earn more money than if you decide to spend the next four years in some other manner. This unwarranted conclusion has for its basis the equally unwarranted assumption that since college-trained folks make more money, they make it because they went to college. Actually we don't know but that these are the people who would have made more money even if they had not gone to college. There are a couple of things that indicate rather strongly that this is so. Colleges get a disproportionate number of two groups of kids: the bright and the rich. The bright might show good earning power without college knowledge. And as for the rich ones . . . well, money breeds money in several obvious ways. Few sons of rich men are found in low-income brackets whether they go to college or not.

The following passage is taken from an article in question-and-answer form that appeared in *This Week* magazine, a Sunday supplement of enormous circulation. Maybe you will find it amusing, as I do, that the same writer once produced a piece called "Popular Notions: True or False?"

Q: What effect does going to college have on your chances of remaining unmarried?

A: If you're a woman, it skyrockets your chances of becoming an old maid. But if you're a man, it has the opposite effect–it minimizes your chances of staying a bachelor.

Cornell Universtiy made a study of 1,500 typical middle-aged college graduates. Of the men, 93 per cent were married (compared to 83 per cent for the general population).

But of the middle-aged women graduates only 65 per cent were married. Spinsters were relatively three times as numerous among college graduates as among women of the general population.

When Susie Brown, age seventeen, reads this she learns that if she goes to college she will be less likely to get a man than if she doesn't. That is what the article says, and there are statistics from a reputable source to go with it. They go with it, but they don't back it up; and note also that while the statistics are Cornell's the conclusions are not, although a hasty reader may come away with the idea that they are.

Here again a real correlation has been used to bolster up an unproved cause-and-effect relationship. Perhaps it all works the other way around and those women would have remained unmarried even if they had not gone to college. Possibly even more would have failed to marry. If these possibilities are no better than the one the writer insists upon, they are perhaps just as valid conclusions: that is, guesses.

Indeed there is one piece of evidence suggesting that a propensity for old-maidhood may lead to going to college. Dr. Kinsey seems to have found some correlation between sexuality and education, with traits perhaps being fixed at pre-college age. That makes it all the more questionable to say that going to college gets in the way of marrying.

Note to Susie Brown: It ain't necessarily so.

A medical article once pointed with great alarm to an increase in cancer among milk drinkers. Cancer, it seems, was becoming increasingly frequent in New England, Minnesota, Wisconsin, and Switzerland, where a lot of milk is produced and consumed, while remaining rare in Ceylon, where milk is scarce. For further evidence it was pointed out that cancer was less frequent in some Southern states where less milk was consumed. Also, it was pointed out, milk-drinking English women get some kinds of cancer eighteen times as frequently as Japanese women who seldom drink milk.

A little digging might uncover quite a number of ways to account for these figures, but one factor is enough by itself to show them up. Cancer is predominantly a disease that strikes in middle life or after. Switzerland and the states mentioned first are alike in having populations with relatively long spans of life. English women at the time the study was made were living an average of twelve years longer than Japanese women.

Professor Helen M. Walker has worked out an amusing illustration of the folly in assuming there must be cause and effect whenever two things vary together. In investigating the relationship between age and some physical characteristics of women, begin by measuring the angle of the feet in walking. You will find that the angle tends to be greater among older women. You might first consider whether this indicates that women grow older because they toe out, and you can see immediately that this is ridiculous. So it appears that age increases the angle between the feet, and most women must come to toe out more as they grow older.

Any such conclusion is probably false and certainly unwarranted. You could only reach it legitimately by studying the same women—or possibly equivalent groups—over a period of time. That would eliminate the factor responsible here. Which is that the older women grew up at a time when a young lady was taught to toe out in walking, while the members of the younger group were learning posture in a day when that was discouraged.

When you find somebody—usually an interested party—making a fuss about a correlation, look first of all to see if it is not one of this type, produced by the stream of events, the trend of the times. In our time it is easy to show a positive correlation between any pair of things like these: number of students in college, number of inmates in mental institutions, consumption of cigarettes, incidence of heart disease, use of X-ray machines, production of false teeth, salaries of California school teachers, profits of Nevada gambling halls. To call some one of these the cause of some other is manifestly silly. But it is done every day.

Permitting statistical treatment and the hypnotic presence of numbers and decimal points to befog causal relationships is little better than superstition. And it is often more seriously misleading. It is rather like the conviction among the people of the New Hebrides that body lice produce good health. Observation over the centuries had taught them that people in good health usually had lice and sick people very often did not. The observation itself was accurate and sound, as observations made informally over the years surprisingly often are. Not so much can be said for the conclusion to which these primitive people came from their evidence: Lice make a man healthy. Everybody should have them.

As we have already noted, scantier evidence than this—treated in the statistical mill until common sense could no longer penetrate to it—has made many a medical fortune and many a medical article in magazines, including professional ones. More sophisticated observers finally got things straightened out in the New Hebrides. As it turned out, almost everybody in those circles had lice most of the time. It was, you might say, the normal condition of man. When, however, anyone took a fever (quite possibly carried to him by those same lice) and his body became too hot for comfortable habitation, the lice left. There you have cause and effect altogether confusingly distorted, reversed, and intermingled.

SUGGESTED ASSIGNMENTS

1. Write a paragraph discussion of cause in relation to one of the following:
   a. From an advertisement: "Deanie Cates, Miss Florida, in the 19— Miss Universe Contest, was once a blimpish, unhappy teen-ager. Then she went to the Stauffer System. Stauffer remolded her figure and Deanie went on to become a beauty queen. Come in and learn what we can do for you."
   b. Several years ago in Florida a spry Confederate Veteran of 104 gave an interview to the press. He spoke cheerfully of his good health and attributed his long span of years to "living right, drinking plenty of good homemade moonshine liquor, and staying away from doctors."
   c. A former Commissioner of the Office of Education in Washington said in a newspaper interview that Americans are "among the most fortunate people in the world and this position is due in a substantial part to our schools."
   d. It has been shown by careful statistical studies that students who have cars get lower grades than those who don't.
   e. Students who major in mathematics generally rank high scholastically. Therefore, it is evident that the study of math sharpens the mind.
   f. In 1953, after the testing of several atomic bombs in Nevada, there were many tornadoes in the United States. Many people agitated against further testing on the grounds that it was the cause of dangerous tornadoes.
2. a. In one year figures showed that juvenile delinquency rose strikingly and that images of violence on TV increased markedly. What does this correlation show?

b. In one year the salaries of Iowa school teachers were raised generally, and, at the same time, the sale of whiskey in the state liquor stores rose. What does this show?

3. Publishers who advertise books purporting to increase the reader's vocabulary often use an argument like this one: "Out of a test group of 100 young men whose vocabularies were scientifically measured, all who passed in the upper 10 per cent had attained executive positions 5 years later—but not a single young man of the lower 25 per cent had become an executive!" The moral is obvious: buy our vocabulary-builder and become an executive. Write a brief analysis of this argument.

4. The official report of the Department of Public Safety of Iowa contains these facts about motor vehicle traffic deaths in 1955:

Occurred	on straight road	409
"	on other roads	102
"	on dry road	428
"	on icy road	35
"	between four and five a.m.	3
"	" five and six p.m.	44

Therefore, for safest driving one should drive on an icy, curved highway between four and five in the morning. Criticize this conclusion.

BLACK OR WHITE

Stuart Chase

Some situations in life offer only two possibilities. For example, the door is either locked or unlocked; you are either an American citizen or not; you sprained your ankle either before or after you signed the accident policy. Such either-or situations are called two-valued. Most situations, however, offer more possibilities, e.g., the grading system at a university, the scale of colors in the spectrum, the degree of a student's intelligence, the prizes at an art show. These are known as multi-valued situations.

It is when we impose a two-valued outlook upon a multi-valued situation that our thinking goes awry, as Stuart Chase shows in the following selection. Mr. Chase is the author of two popular books on language, The Tyranny of Words *and* The Power of Words.

THE MODERATOR of a famous radio debate program used to hold up a ball and ask the studio audience what color it was. When they answered "white," he would turn the ball around and ask again. "Black," they would say. Then he would point the moral; every question has two sides and we should listen to both. But, as Mr. Leo Cherne objects in a discussion of radio debates, the big issues today are no longer merely black or white, if indeed they ever were.[1] They have many sides, not just two sides, and we must allow for shades of gray.

Classical logicians, like debaters, tend to take the absolute position, impatient of in-between relationships. They like things open or shut, true or false, good or bad, right or wrong. This may give them the mental satisfaction of a tidy paper solution, but it does not help them understand their world. Whenever we force a problem which contains shades of gray into an unyielding pattern of black and white, we distort the solution and hamper our own understanding.

John and Mary are being divorced. Their friends line up in two hostile camps. One group declares that it is all *his* fault, the other that it is *her* fault. Quite possibly the fault lies with neither. Forces beyond the control of John and Mary may be causing them to separate. Their education or habits or religion may be sharply antagonistic. They may even possess incompatible blood types which prevent them from having children. For most broken marriages there is a process involved, a spiral of many causes. It is unreasonable to insist on a rigid one-cause-and-effect interpretation, with somebody exclusively to blame.

"Women are bad drivers!" says Mr. Roe, contemplating another bill for a crumpled fender. "You're wrong," cries his friend Doe, "women are good drivers, better than men!" And off they go, hammer and tongs. What are the facts? Records of accidents indicate that in some respects women drivers do better than men, in other

[1] *New York Times* Magazine, March 2, 1952.

respects worse, and two-valued reasoning over-simplifies the question. Women disorganize more fenders and bumpers, but have fewer crashes involving personal injury. Supporting evidence is found in lower insurance rates for women in some states.

MANY SITUATIONS ARE TWO-VALUED

In the early spring of 1955 I heard a man say: "It's either the Yankees or the Red Sox in the American League"—thereby shrinking an eight-valued question into two, before a ball had been pitched. But when in late September the pennants were clinched in both major leagues, a real two-valued choice appeared: Either the New York Yankees or the Brooklyn Dodgers would win the World Series. Plenty of pertinent discussion was in order, and the opportunity, as I remember it, was not neglected.

Many factual situations are legitimately two-valued. The electric current is either on or off, as every householder knows. When the trigger is pulled, the gun goes off or it doesn't. The car won't run or it will—though sometimes in fits and starts. The lady who said she was "only a little bit pregnant" had no case. Our task is to determine which situations are really two-valued, and which are multi-valued.

DEEP IN THE LANGUAGE

A major reason for black-or-white thinking is the structure of the English language, indeed, linguists say, of all the Indo-European languages, including Sanskrit, Greek, and Latin, as well as modern European tongues. Children speaking these languages are brought up to think in *opposites*—little vs. big, long vs. short, clean vs. dirty, hero vs. villain, love vs. hate, good vs. bad, life vs. death. It takes a real effort to break out of this linguistic conditioning.

Other languages do not have this hard and fast dichotomy, so that for their speakers the multi-valued approach is easier. A Chinese, for instance, says: "The long and the short are mutually related"; "the hard and the easy are mutually complementary"; "the front and the rear mutually accompany each other."[2] It is possible that the Marxists are going to have a lot of trouble forcing the two-valued notion of a choice between Capitalism or Communism on the Chinese

[2] Chang Tung-sun in *ETC.*, Spring, 1952.

rank and file. Russians accept it readily, as Russian is an Indo-European language.

Not only our language but our habits make Americans think this way. Living under pressure we feel that we must decide things fast. "Make up your mind, Mac!" We skip lightly to inferences and value judgments in order to come to the point of action—where indeed the situation may be a yes-or-no choice, often an irrevocable one, as in pulling a trigger. For many Americans it seems easier to act than to think, and when we do think, we like to make it fast. Our comic books and TV dramas feed our appetite for rapid action.

John Steinbeck, writing in the *Reporter*, described how his young son, Catbird, learned to tell the Good Guys from the Bad Guys in TV horse opera. It's simple, said Catbird, the Good Guy wears a white hat and the Bad Guy a black hat. The Good Guy is clean-shaven, the Bad Guy has dark stubble on his chin. Sometimes, said Catbird, there is an In-Between Guy in a gray hat, but he doesn't last. If he starts bad he ends good, and if he starts good he ends bad. The *Reporter* proceeds to editorialize: "Catbird's simple formula is attractive, but before long he will surely discover that it's not so simple to divide the world's cast of characters into Good Guys and Bad Guys, that black-and-white judgments need tempering, and that even the grays are deceptive."

But Washington, according to James Reston, keeps right on dividing the Good Guys from the Bad.[3] "Congress," he says, "is now dividing for and against John Foster Dulles, Secretary of State, and the main question, about the President's foreign policy decisions in the Korean, Formosan and Indo-China crises, is getting lost." The big issues were buried in a wrangle as to whether Mr. Dulles was right or wrong in his "brink of war" interview in *Life* magazine.

The case of Marriner Eccles, sometime Chairman of the Federal Reserve Board, is also instructive. During the depression of the 1930's he was known as a "spender," a disciple of Lord Keynes. With full employment and creeping inflation after the war, Eccles called for rigorous economy in government. Many financial experts could not believe their ears, for how could a "spender" preach economy? Once a spender, they reasoned, always a spender. But sound fiscal policy must be flexible, and the Keynes theory supports Mr. Eccles: spend in the downswings, save and pay off the debt in the upswings.

[3] *New York Times*, January 24, 1956.

SCIENCE IS MULTI-VALUED

Scientists, who take no conclusions for granted, come up from time to time with borderline cases that destroy a familiar, sharp division. When Frederick Wöhler synthesized urea in his laboratory in 1828, chemists at first refused to credit it. They had been taught to believe that "organic" and "inorganic" substances were forever different. But Wöhler broke out of the Aristotelian strait jacket, boldly took inorganic materials, and made them behave like the organic compound urea. This in effect turned a two-valued situation into a many-valued one and opened new vistas to science. The chemists, in the face of a laboratory demonstration which they themselves could repeat, gradually recovered from their shock, to the great advantage of the progress of chemistry.

Living things are still verbally classified as either "animal" or "vegetable," but this hard-and-fast distinction no longer holds for biologists. Here is Euglena, which digests food like an animal, and employs photosynthesis like a plant. Here are the Ascidians, usually classed as animals, but they produce cellulose, a unique function of plants.

For centuries medical men made a sharp distinction between mind and body. Today most of them accept the idea of psychosomatic medicine, where mind and body are treated as parts of one organism, the total man. It is now admitted that too much worry (psychic) about his balance sheet can give a big executive stomach ulcers (somatic); while too many strawberry sundaes (somatic) may cause Jackie to flunk his history exam (psychic). The mental healing of certain cases of physical illness is an established fact, but the attempt to cure *every* lesion by this means gives us yet another unfortunate example of two-valued thinking.

In 1953, Dr. Elizabeth Forbes-Sempill, forty years old, daughter of the late Lord Sempill, went into a private hospital for an operation, presently to emerge as Dr. Ewan Forbes-Sempill. She was no longer "female" but "male," and in line for the family title and estates. Dr. Elizabeth is only one case in many where modern surgery has reversed the supposedly irreversible fact of one's sex.

Fluorine is now the subject of a bitter two-valued debate. It is of course a *poison* in any considerable dose. But one part to a million in drinking water protects children's teeth against decay, and no deleterious effects have been detected. Certain towns in the West for years have been safely drinking local water containing up to thirty parts in a million. Many citizens apparently are reasoning, however, "fluorine is either a poison or it is not. If it is, we don't want any part of it in our drinking water." They are blocking adoption, and their children, one fears, are going to pay a heavy price for this exercise in bad logic.

You are either dead or alive—but are you? Here is Harry A. Jones, sixty-six, of Long Beach, California.[4] He was found by his wife slumped over his desk, and the doctor she summoned could find "no pulse, no heart beat nor any sign of breath." He was pronounced dead, and a hearse was called to take him to the mortuary. On the road, the blankets covering him began to move, causing the driver of the hearse a very bad moment. Mr. Jones happily "came back to life, and the astonished doctors at Long Beach Veterans Hospital said he was making a remarkable recovery."

ZONING AGAIN

Our town held a zoning hearing to discuss whether a man should be permitted to open a toy shop in an area zoned for residences. Arguments flew back and forth, each a little more general and a little more heated than the last, until an all-out battle began to rage between those who held that "little business" was good for rural towns, and those who were positive it was bad—a strictly black-or-white battle. The questions of what particular kind of business, the possible hardship to the applicant, the force of the zoning code already adopted—all were forgotten in the mighty hassle. The debate, stimulating as it was to the contestants, became meaningless so far as the problem in hand was concerned. Members of the Board who hoped to benefit by the hearing were only further confused.

Later, however, when the Board met in executive session, it had to make a two-valued decision—whether to allow the toy shop or deny it.[5] Many variables had to be considered for which the public hearing contributed almost nothing.

Local communities constantly run into similar discussions, discussions that are meaningless until they are pulled down to earth. You have heard plenty of them:

[4] AP dispatch, September 11, 1954.
[5] The Board denied.

Private schools vs. public schools.
City living vs. country living.
Chemical fertilizers vs. good old barn manure. (This one can get very bitter indeed, with manure usually way ahead on a decibel count.)
Science vs. religion.
Freedom vs. regimentation.

The last argument has been around for a long time. One side in the debate says we must have complete freedom or submit to slavery. But a philosopher saw the fallacy when he observed: "Your freedom to swing your arms ends where my nose begins." Freedom is always relative: freedom to do what? Using the two-valued approach in a situation that has many values is like stepping into a shower bath without a mixer, a stream which runs either scalding hot or freezing cold.

John Doe and Richard Roe are arguing about the respective places of Truman and Eisenhower in history. "Truman contained Russia with the Marshall Plan, to his eternal credit!" says Doe. "Eisenhower stopped the Korean War, to his eternal credit!" says Roe. . . . And so on, with steadily rising voices. To the listener, it soon appears that the argument is so two-valued for each contestant that their minds can never meet. There is a simple way to test this—provided the listener can get the floor. He asks John Doe: "Did Truman ever do anything wrong?" "No!" exclaims Doe. The listener turns to Roe. "Did Truman ever do anything right?" Another "No!" is clear proof that the situation is beyond human aid.

ARYANS AND NON-ARYANS

Hitler, like all fanatics and demagogues, preferred to operate in terms of black or white. He divided humanity into Aryans (good) and non-Aryans (bad). Then he proceeded to examine a great variety of things on the same basis. Is this piece of music Aryan or non-Aryan? If the latter, put the composer in a concentration camp! Is this painting Aryan? Does this book, this piece of architecture, this mathematics, physics, religion, system of calisthenics, cookery, conform to Aryanism? The Japanese, as valuable allies to Germany, posed a nice logical problem. Obviously they were "good," but also by no stretch of the imagination could they be classed as members of the Aryan race. The tough problem was solved by giving them the special designation of "non-non-Aryans." Ultimately it covered quite a group of allies.

The Russian Communists have had similar difficulties with their music, theater, ballet, novels, poetry, painting, women's clothes, science, and practically everything else. Conclaves of scientists have solemnly met in Moscow to decide what was "Marxian physics" and what was not. The Lysenko controversy about the principles of genetics was a strictly two-valued row.

In Moscow, everything the regime considers good is labeled "Communistic," everything bad is "capitalistic"; very little is in-between. Such thinking is characteristic of totalitarian regimes, which to stay in power must make sharp, police-court distinctions between friends and enemies. A man who says "a plague on both your houses" goes to Siberia. Reinhold Neibuhr sums it up:[6]

> Lenin did not, of course, originate the fanaticism that was inherent in the whole Marxist dogma, with its too simple distinctions between exploited and exploiter, its too-simple conception of the close structure of society, its too-simple derivation of all social evil from the institution of property, and its consequent division of the whole world into friends and enemies "of the people." Stalin boasted considerable flexibility . . . but it never dissolved the fanaticism. Thus, we could be allies of the Russians during the war, but it was not long before . . . the world was sharply divided once more into the hosts of good and evil.

REVERSE TWIST

Stalin and Hitler had no monopoly on totalitarian logic. It is incipient in every community where a leader strives for absolute power. Eternal vigilance is the price of political freedom. After World War II, when Americans relaxed this vigilance, certain demagogues managed to capture the headlines with arguments that not only divided the world into black and white nations (very few were white), but divided all U.S. citizens into either Communist sympathizers or "patriots." McCarthy's followers insisted that anyone who criticized the Senator was a Communist, or at best a fellow traveler.[7] Such reasoning turns an honest difference of opinion into a criminal charge, and can fill the land with fear and conflict.

[6] *New Leader*, October 3, 1955.

[7] This is also a circular argument. "Mr. X is a Communist." "How do you know?" "Because he disagrees with me." "Why does he disagree with you?" "Because I am against Communism."

After Bishop Sheil of Chicago criticized McCarthy in 1954, letters bristling with black-or-white choices began to appear in the papers, reading like this:[8]

Destroy all Communists in America—it's either them or us!

I am aware that some highly respected personalities have joined in the attack on McCarthy, but in my book, regardless of their big names, anyone who seeks to discredit McCarthy is sympathetic to the Reds.

Say! Whose side are you on anyway?

The attack on McCarthy is the front line of a continuing attack on the U.S. Congress which will end only in the destruction of the Communists or of the Congress.

A curious by-product appeared as demagogic voices grew more shrill. For a time it seemed that loyal citizens who dared not attempt a direct challenge were increasingly forced to take the *opposite* of every position assumed by Moscow. If Moscow advocates disarmament, we must oppose it; if Moscow is for peace, we must be for war; if Moscow demands economic aid to backward countries, we must be against it. In effect, such citizens were bound fast to the foreign policy of the Kremlin, leaving American policy no room in which to maneuver! Republicans and Democrats suffer from a similar obsession. When one party introduces a good bill in Congress, members of the other party feel bound to oppose it.

WE OR THEY

This brings us to the number one question threatening our planet—how to avoid World War III. For the present the belligerents are observing a thermonuclear truce, but the stockpiles are growing day by day in East and West. To avoid ultimate explosion, negotiation on various levels must be attempted—everything from joint weather stations to disarmament proposals. But how can negotiation be seriously considered, much less experimented with, if the East stubbornly insists that it cannot live in the same world with "capitalism," and the West stubbornly insists that it cannot live in the same world with "Communism"? C. L. Sulzberger, after a long interview with Molotov, reported that "Moscow continues to view the two systems as incompatible, as implacably hostile. There is no third or middle way."[9]

[8] Actual quotations from these letters. The last one is also a thin-entering-wedge case.

[9] *New York Times*, January 14, 1956.

HOMEWORK

A lot of us, however, lock ourselves up whenever such issues are before the house. Here is the front page of the *New York Times* for March 18, 1956. There are at least three headline stories which can be, and are, reduced to black-or-white reasoning. I will give the exact headline, and then my comments.

"TRUMAN ASSAILS GOP ASSERTION REDS ARE LOSING"

Reds are *either* gaining (Truman), *or* losing (Dulles). A terrific battle is in progress over Dulles' statement that the U.S. is in a stronger position, vis-à-vis Russia, in early 1956 than it was in early 1955. The arguers talk as if they were viewing a prize fight, and discussing who is ahead on points. Actually, of course, the Soviets are gaining in some places—as in the Middle East, and losing in other places—as in Germany, with the creation of the new German Army. Where the balance lies, nobody really knows, and it would take a large university staff to find out.

"ELLENDER WARNS SOUTH ON FORCE"

The Senator's warning is wise, but his logic takes the form: *either* peaceful and strong protest, *or* back to the days of reconstruction and the carpetbaggers. It is not so simple, Senator. The South of 1956 is not the South of 1866. Her economy is vastly different, with industrial penetration everywhere; relations with the North are very different; and above all the Negro population is now almost a hundred years away from slavery. Violence by Southerners may bring catastrophe, but it will not be that of reconstruction days.

"FRENCH AGAIN ADD TO ALGERIAN FORCE"

Algeria must *either* be free, *or* be enslaved by France—such seems to be the logic of the Algerian nationalists. Again too simple; it does not allow for more than a million Frenchmen living in Algeria, and for other profound complications.

Any front page on almost any day can give us similar homework in finding shades of gray.

SUGGESTED ASSIGNMENTS

1. In addition to the either-or situation with two possibilities, there are also these:

(2) (Third possibility between) Did we win or lose last night?
(3) (Neither possibility) Is Smith a Baptist or a Methodist?
(4) (Infinite possibilities between extremes) Is it very cold this morning?
(5) (Limited possibilities between extremes) What was his rank in the army?
(6) (Both possibilities) Is the blueprint for your house a good one or a poor one?

Which of these six situations is represented in the following questions?

a. Did you hit or miss the squirrel?
b. Is it above or below freezing?
c. Is it right or wrong that trees shed their leaves in the fall?
d. Are you going to vote Republican or Democratic?
e. Is she at home or out?
f. What grade did you get in trig?
g. Did you pass in trig?
h. At the time of the accident were you drunk or sober?
i. What color is this paint?
j. Is that diamond counterfeit or genuine?
k. Was the person you saw at the place of the murder a young man or an old man?
l. Was the window open or shut when you arrived?
m. Is Henderson a skilled or an unskilled worker?

2. The ardent sponsorship of a cause is likely to give one a two-valued outlook. The person who belongs to the WCTU, Society for PCA, the Anti-Vivisectionists, a political party, a vigorously sectarian church, the Communist Party, and countless others may have a hard time retaining a multi-valued outlook. Lovers, too, soldiers, pacifists, and the like, may be in the same predicament. Write a theme pointing out the pros and cons of a two-valued orientation in a specific case.
3. The very nature of our language does not permit us to handle easily an infinite-valued situation, as in judging the intelligence of a student. How do we handle such situations?
4. The law sometimes requires us to make a two-valued judgment in a multi-valued situation, e.g., Was the accused sane or insane, drunk or sober, guilty or innocent? What other cases of the same kind can you think of? Choose one and write a paragraph showing how society has chosen to handle it and offering a criticism or judgment of this method.
5. What two-valued situations do you find on the TV screen? How true are these of life itself?
6. On the international scene two-valued orientation is rife. Here are two witnesses:

Hitler: "Of Marxism and the German people, only one can triumph, and it is Germany that will win."

Mussolini: "The struggle between two worlds can permit of no compromise. . . . either we or they! Either their ideals or ours!"

Find a similar example on the current scene in the words of a political leader. What effect may this attitude have on the solution of world problems?

ANALOGIES

Monroe C. Beardsley

The following quotation from the New Yorker *affords an illustration of analogy: "The living language is like a cowpath: it is the creation of the cows themselves, who, having created it, follow it or depart from it according to their whims and needs. From daily use, the path undergoes change. A cow is under no obligation to stay in the narrow path she helped to make, following the contour of the land, but she often profits by staying with it and she would be handicapped if she didn't know where it was and where it led to. . . ." Let us note three things here: this is a comparison, dissimilar things are compared, and they are compared in a number of respects. Such, roughly stated, is what constitutes an analogy. In the selection below, Monroe Beardsley defines analogy more precisely and shows both its desirable uses and the traps it holds for the unwary thinker. Professor Beardsley teaches logic at Swarthmore College.*

ANALOGIES: THEIR USE AND MISUSE

In a closed simile two things are compared in certain respects, which are specified by the simile.[1] Now, there are two different kinds of characteristics, or respects, in which things may be compared.

[1] E.g. "The international situation is *as tense as* a ball-game tied up in the ninth inning." [eds.]

They may be compared in terms of *qualities:* for example, they may both be hot, noisy, or angry. Or, they may be compared in terms of *relationships.* Any thing, considered as a *whole,* consists of parts that are arranged in certain ways, and this arrangement, or organization, of the parts is a web of relationships that each part has to the other parts. Now, if we compare, say, a brick building with a *papier-mâché* model of it, we can't make the comparison in terms of the qualities of the parts. For the parts are made of different materials. But we can make the comparison in terms of the relationships *between* the parts. For if the model is a good one, the positions of the floors and windows and doors, for example, will be related to each other in exactly the same way as in the building itself.

This notion of relationship is what marks an analogy. An analogy is simply a rather extensive closed simile in which the comparison is in terms of relationships.

Consider, for example, a map. The dots on the map (say, a map of the United States) are not very much like actual cities, and the lines on the map are not tall like mountains or wet like rivers, and the colors of the map are not at all like the colors of the earth in various states. But the structure of the map, if it is a good one, *corresponds to* the structure of the country it represents. That is, the shapes of the states are like the shapes on the map; the relative sizes of the states are like the relative sizes of the shapes; and the relative distances between actual cities are like the relative distances between the dots on the map. So the analogy between the map and the country is very close. When we can find such *strong* analogies as this, we can use one thing to represent the other.

The analogies we ordinarily use are not nearly so strong as in this example. But they can nevertheless be very useful. In particular, there are *two* ways in which analogies are a help to effective thinking, and there is a *third* way in which they are harmful to effective thinking.

First, we often use analogies to illustrate and clarify general principles. If you are trying to explain the way a steam engine or a gasoline motor works, it may be helpful to find something simpler that works on a similar principle. Popular science is full of ingenious, and often extremely illuminating, analogies of this sort. They act as small-scale models of the real thing, and they make an easy first step toward complete understanding.

But, of course, all such analogies break down at some point. Comparison with ocean waves will take the beginner a little way in a study of sound waves, and comparison with sound waves will take him a little way in a study of radio waves. But the comparison can be pushed to a point where the two things are so unlike that the analogy becomes misleading. The "ether" is not an ocean.

Second, analogies are fruitful for suggesting ideas that may lead to important discoveries—*working hypotheses* that can be put to experimental test. Suppose you are studying one thing—say, lightning—for the first time. And suppose you notice that it has many characteristics in common with electric sparks. You know that electricity can produce a current, and you wonder whether lightning may be like electricity in this way, too. Of course *you* know it is. But Benjamin Franklin did not know the answer until he tried his famous experiment. The analogy between the growth of the embryo and the course of evolution, between electro-magnetic fields and gravitational fields, between the solar system and the structure of the atom—all these, and many others, have been very useful in the history of science.

But, again, these are only analogies. An analogy doesn't *prove* anything; it merely calls to mind a *possibility* that might not have been thought of without the analogy. It's the experiment that counts in the end. Bohr's classic model of the atom is *only* a picture. It has clarified some points about the atom, it has hinted at some good hypotheses; but if you take it as *proving* anything about the atom, you are misusing the analogy. You can be fooled just as much by it as were those early inventors who tried to construct airplanes that flapped their wings, on the analogy with birds. Analogies *illustrate*, and they lead to *hypotheses*, but thinking in terms of analogy becomes fallacious when the analogy is used as a *reason for* a principle. This fallacy is called the "**argument from analogy.**"

The makers of a patented drug to relieve headaches used to advertise their product over the radio with this patter: "It is like a doctor's prescription, since it contains not one, but many, proven ingredients." One interesting thing about this argument—apart from its imbecility—is that the conclusion is merely *suggested* by the context, and not very definitely at that. You gather that the advertiser is suggesting that the drug is safe to take, is designed for your specific illness, is scientifically prepared by a pharmacist. You think: This must be all right for me, if the doctors say so. Of course, the advertisers were careful not to come out and *state* these claims, since there is a

Federal Bureau which keeps a watchful eye on false advertising claims.

Probably this argument has actually convinced many people that the drug is better than aspirin for a headache. In any case, the form of the argument from analogy is pretty clear from this simple example:

> X has certain characteristics *a, b, c* . . . . .
> Y has the characteristics *a, b, c* . . . . .
> But Y also has other characteristics *x, y, z*.
> *Therefore:* X has the characteristics *x, y, z*.

The argument begins with two things, X (the drug) and Y (a doctor's prescription). It proceeds from certain *assumed resemblances* (they both contain many "proven ingredients") to certain *inferred resemblances* (they are both recommended by doctors, for example). The underlying principle is: If X and Y have a number of characteristics in common, then it is likely that any *further* characteristics found in Y will *also* be found in X.

We have said that if two things have a good deal in common, we may guess that they may have even more in common. The likeness may justify a further investigation to see whether they actually *do* have more in common. But it does *not* justify our believing that they have more in common *without* the further investigation. It remains a guess. This is so because, no matter how many characteristics a pair of things have in common, there may be any number of other ways in which they are different. You can't even say that the more known resemblances there are between X and Y, the more likely it is that X will have any further characteristic found in Y.

The above argument is not a good one, but it could be the *beginning* of a good one. When we see what it would take to make a good argument, it will be easier to see why the argument from analogy is unsound. Suppose you analyzed a number of things, each of which contains several "proven" ingredients (*a*) but which is very different from the rest in other ways (a sponge cake, a plastic toy, blood, an Old Fashioned). And suppose that in every case you found that these things were recommended by doctors (*z*). Then you might make a generalization: "Everything that has *a* also has *z*." You might say: "Here is this drug. It has many proven ingredients. If my generalization is true, this drug will also be recommended by doctors." This is the way you would ordinarily extend a generalization to a new case where it can be applied. But, of course, in this case the generalization would obviously be untrue.

. . . The important point here is that it takes at least a *fairly large number* of *different kinds* of cases to make a good generalization. The argument from analogy is an attempt to short-circuit this rule without appearing too implausible. If the relevant generalization about the drug is already proved, then the argument is *not* an argument from analogy any more: it is a legitimate extension of a known generalization to a new case. If the relevant generalization has *not* been proved, there is no basis whatever for the argument.

ANSWERING AN ANALOGY

The argument from analogy turns up constantly in ordinary discourse; it is one of the commonest fallacies. When you find such an argument trying to impose upon your thinking, the first thing to do is get the argument straight by analyzing the assumed resemblances and the inferred resemblances. Then you know exactly what the argument is, and you are ready to answer it. There are *three* different ways of showing what is wrong with an argument from analogy.

(1) To begin with, the assumed resemblances may *not* be actual resemblances at all. If this is so, the simplest answer to the argument is to point out succinctly the weakness of the analogy. Suppose someone argues for a world federal government by analogy with the American colonies. There will be *some* resemblances, but there may be also important differences that have been overlooked. Of course, if the arguer stacks up a number of historical examples—the unification of Germany, Italy, Switzerland, Greek city-states—then he may be trying to establish a generalization. But if he merely gives *one* example, he is arguing by analogy, and the first question is: how *strong* is the analogy?

If the analogy is weak, then, you can answer it by *attacking the assumed resemblances:*

A: "We shouldn't blame the movie-makers for the cultural level of their pictures. Movies are simply manufactured goods. They are just like washing machines; therefore, producers are justified in selling whatever pictures the public will buy."	*Statement of Analogy*

B: "I admit movies are manufactured, but they are not much like washing machines. A poor washing machine is merely a waste of money; a poor movie is bad for the mind." *Attack on Assumed Resemblances*

(2) The assumed resemblances may really *be* resemblances, as far as they go. Nevertheless, even if X and Y are both red, and Y is round, it doesn't follow that X is round—unless there is some reason for believing that probably everything that is red is also round. In short, only the generalization would justify the inference. To answer the argument from analogy it is enough to show that the generalization is untrue. To do this, give examples that tell against it.

The second answer, then, consists in *attacking the underlying generalization:*

A: "Fellow temperance-workers, we know that the delicate membranes of the stomach are like the delicate membranes of the eye, and if you want to see what alcohol does to the stomach, just pour some gin in your eye." *Statement of Analogy*

B: "This is no argument at all, unless the speaker is suggesting that anything that hurts the eye will also hurt the stomach, which is absurd. If it were true, lemonade would not be good to drink." *Attack on Underlying Generalization*

(3) But even if the required generalization is true, a person who argues from analogy lays himself open, frequently, to a simple but effective retort. If he says, "We should not change horses in midstream," it's easy to reply, "Oh, but when the horse has bogged down, and the flood-waters are rising, you have to change horses or drown."

This answer consists in *extending the analogy* to the point where it boomerangs. Of most of the loose and confused analogies that figure in political argument, especially the old one comparing the state with a ship, it may be said that, if they proved anything (which they don't), they would prove *too much.* Almost any such analogy can be extended to include points that the original user would find embarrassing. This third way of answering the analogy is, of course, *not* an argument against the truth of the other person's conclusion.

It merely uses the analogy to show that the original argument was fallacious, which is a legitimate refutation.

Sometimes it is also the most convincing refutation. Notice how B, in the passage below, turns A's analogy against him. B uses the analogy as an *illustration* to show that the principle of the argument from analogy cannot be defended.

Statement of Analogy

A: "If we want to find out who is the best 100-yard sprinter, we have to have a race and let everyone compete in it; and we must not interfere with the race by holding up some runners and helping others. Now, economic competition is just like a race, and if we want the most efficient industries to come out on top, we must leave them alone."

Extension of Analogy

B: "Your analogy is an excellent one, only you don't carry it far enough. For we can't run a fair race without *rules*, to keep the runners from jumping the gun and tripping each other up. That's the only way you can be sure that the winner really is the best runner, not merely the best tripper. Thus your analogy implies that we must have strong rules to keep down monopoly, and price-fixing conspiracies, to make the economic race a fair one. Moreover, your analogy implies that, to ensure fairness, we should start everyone off at the same place, with an equal amount of money."

SUGGESTED ASSIGNMENTS

1. Put yourself in this situation. You have a three-record album of Verdi's *Aïda* and you accidentally break one of the records. You therefore write to the record manufacturer ordering a replacement. The company replies, expressing regret that they do not sell single records of this album and that you must buy the entire album to get the record you want. This gets your dander up, and you answer hotly that they are in the same position as an automobile manufacturer, who feels himself obligated to furnish parts for the cars he sells. But the company has a neat riposte for you. "No," they say, "we are really like a book

publisher" and defend themselves with a counter-analogy. See if you can finish their analogy. Which one of you is right?

2. At a poorly marked railroad crossing, a loaded passenger car is demolished by a passenger train. As a result, the newspapers are filled with agitation for gates and an automatic signal. But the company objects. "Why," they ask, "should we put up a signal and gates now? That's just like locking the barn door after the horse is stolen." Point out the fallacy in this analogy.
3. In the American Association of University Professors *Bulletin* for Autumn, 1951, page 514, Edwin H. Reeder points out that the average professor and the average layman accept what John Dewey once called the "cold storage" idea of learning, which he explains in this way: "They visualize the mind as a sort of cold storage warehouse, which is empty at birth. The process of learning consists in hanging on the walls of the warehouse chunks of fact and information. Teaching consists in superintending this process, in assuring that the correct chunks are carried into the warehouse and hung on its walls. The chunks hang there in the same condition in which they were first stored until some day the student needs one or more of them; then he can go to the warehouse, unhook the right chunk, and use it for some mature purpose which he could not have conceived in the immature condition of his mind when he first acquired the material." Write a theme in which you explode this analogy by (1) attacking the assumed resemblances and (2) extending the analogy to the point where it boomerangs.
4. Analogy is often used not to convince or persuade but to clarify a description or illustrate an explanation. You will find analogies frequently in your college reading. Here is an example from Mortimer Adler's *How to Read a Book*. Professor Adler is clarifying the point that the reader should set forth the major parts of the book and see how these are organized into a whole by being related to one another and to the whole. His analogy is as follows:

> You know the difference between a heap of bricks, on the one hand, and the single house they constitute, on the other. You know the difference between one house and a collection of houses. A book is like a single house. It is a mansion of many rooms, rooms on different levels, of different sizes and shapes, with different outlooks, rooms with different functions to perform. These rooms are independent, in part. Each has its own structure and interior decoration. But they are not absolutely independent and separate. They are connected by doors and arches, by corridors and stairways. Because they are connected, the partial function which each performs contributes its share to the usefulness of the whole house. Otherwise the house would not be genuinely livable.
>
> The architectural analogy is almost perfect. A good book, like a good house, is an orderly arrangement of parts. Each major part has a certain

amount of independence. As we shall see, it may have an interior structure of its own. But it must also be connected with the other parts—that is, related to them functionally—for otherwise it could not contribute its share to the intelligibility of the whole.

As houses are more or less livable, so books are more or less readable. The most readable book is an architectural achievement on the part of the author. The best books are those that have the most intelligible structure and, I might add, the most apparent. Pages 163-164.

Write an analogy to clarify or illustrate, carrying it as far as it can legitimately go. You might use such subjects as these:

a. My roommate's study habits remind me of a fisherman.
b. Going on a blind date is like reading an unfamiliar book.
c. Human life is like a highway (a game of chess or poker, a bridge, a river).
d. College life resembles a trackmeet.

5. Analogies are frequently used to convince or persuade and can be very successful among the unthoughtful. They tend to appear when controversy or self-interest is strong, as in political campaigns and in labor-management disputes. Here is the complete advertisement of a chiropractor. Analyze it for its soundness.

The nervous system is very much the same as a telephone system. The central office is the brain, the nerves are the wires, and each cell in the body is a telephone user. If all the wires from the central office came out at one point as a cable, it would be as the spinal cord which is made up of billions of nerves which serve the same purpose as wires carrying messages to and from the brain.

The brain controls all the activities of the cells through this network of wires. Irritation of these nerves by pressure from vertabrae slipping out of place would produce somewhat the same results in the body as a short or 'crossed wires' in a telephone system.

A person with such a condition would be known as a highly nervous wreck with symptoms far and many, such as tired feeling, sleeplessness, loss of appetite, highly irritable [*sic*], fidgety [*sic*], hallucinations, digestive disturbances etc., and might lead to a nervous breakdown.

Chiropractors are as highly specialized linemen who ferret out these 'shorts' and adjust them with the result that normal service is resumed.

6. Write an analogy to convince your readers of a proposition you wish to uphold. Here is the kind of analogy you might try:
   a. A writer should understand grammar for the same reasons that a doctor should know his anatomy.
   b. One grading system for all students is unfair. Instead, students should be graded in relation to their aptitude and ability as shown by reliable tests. The student body can fairly be compared to a large garden with a wide variety of growth.

c. In a liberal arts curriculum all students should take the same courses if we are to produce liberally educated graduates. Do engineering schools offer electives in the training of engineers?

AMBIGUITY

Lionel Ruby

A college freshman once wrote, "During my twelve years in school I have had about thirty odd teachers." This remark is an example of ambiguity, an expression that has more than one meaning in the context in which it appears. The writer faces an ever-constant struggle as he chooses and arranges words so that his message will be free from ambiguity. The difficulty may be gauged by the fact that it is easier for the perceptive reader to find examples of ambiguity than of almost any other writing blunder. Yet in a world deluged with both spoken and written communications, what can be more important than precision and clearness of statement? Lionel Ruby, Professor of Philosophy at Roosevelt University, here offers a survey of the pitfalls of ambiguity.

THE MEANING OF AMBIGUITY

THERE ARE many obstacles in the path of successful communication, but ambiguity is undoubtedly the worst offender. An ambiguous word is one that may be understood in more than one sense. Thus a symbol may be interpreted differently by speaker and hearer; communicators and communicatees are at cross-purposes and there is no meeting of minds.

Most of the words in any language have more than one referent. This is in many ways a boon rather than an evil, for the range of possible meanings in any limited number of words is greatly increased. Our vocabularies are enlarged when one word has different meanings in different contexts; the single word then becomes the equivalent of many different words. In many cases the differences in referents may be on a "large" scale, as when the word "secretary" refers in turn to "a person who attends to correspondence," "an executive officer in the government," "a writing desk," and "a South African bird with long legs." There are many other words in which the differences in the referents are of a more subtle nature, the shifts in meaning being less obvious, as in the different ways in which the word "man" is used in the following contexts:

All *men* are mortal.
The child is father to the *man*.
Those were the days when *men* were *men*.
What a piece of work is *man!* How infinite in capacity!
The football team is under*manned*.

Successful communication occurs only when the reader correctly interprets the symbols used by the writer. . . . When the communication is successful then the communicator and the communicatee have their minds referred to the same referents; they have the same *terms* in mind. They have "come to terms." But ambiguous words are obstacles to such happy consummations; communication is frustrated. . . . When such failures of communication occur, the speaker and the hearer have different referents in mind.

But note that ambiguity is an evil only when it results in these frustrations of communication. In scientific discourse, where the aim is to achieve clear and precise reference, ambiguity is an unmitigated evil. But there are other fields of thought in which ambiguity may have certain desirable effects. This is the case in poetry, where ambiguity may sometimes contribute to the poetic effect by suggesting a rich aura of implied meanings: "Life is a tale told by an idiot, full of sound and fury, signifying nothing"; "Faith is the substance of things hoped for; the evidence of things not seen." In this manner poetry approximates the effects produced by music, which, among all of the arts, is certainly the most expressively ambiguous. One of the great charms of music lies in the ambiguity with which it expresses moods, so that each hearer may interpret the musical score in his own way. Ambiguity also has more mundane uses. Diplomatic language has developed the art of saying things ambiguously so that failure to agree will be masked by "face-saving" language. Finally, the ambiguous aspects of words are exploited as a rich source of humor. Gagsters and punsters thrive on the double-meanings of words. Our primary interest, of course, is to learn how to avoid ambiguity in scientific discourse.

Ambiguity is the direct opposite of synonymity (the use of synonymous words). An ambiguous word refers to several referents; in synonymity a single referent is referred to by several different words. "Spade" refers to at least two referents: a playing card and a garden implement. Fool, lout, simpleton, oaf, dunderhead, ninny, nincompoop, addle-pate, and dope, all refer to the same referent, or to substantially the same referent, since few synonymous words are absolutely identical in meaning. . . .

THE ANALYSIS OF AMBIGUITY

Though many words have more than one meaning, the context of surrounding circumstances will usually clarify the sense in which the word is used. The initial ambiguity is often completely eliminated by the context. We shall be primarily concerned with examples in which the ambiguity is not eliminated by the context, with a resulting blockage of communication. . . .

When two or more interpretations of an author's language are possible, the reader does not know what is in the author's mind. We should be clear as to the task of the logician in analyzing instances of ambiguity. The logician cannot eliminate ambiguity; his primary task is to call attention to the fact that ambiguity occurs and to show the different ways in which it occurs. The logician can also help to make the reader sensitive to ambiguities in places where ambiguity might be unsuspected. The logician can also advise the reader to find out what was in the author's mind before the reader interprets ambiguous language. The reader's task here may be likened to that of a judge whose task is to decide what the legislature meant by the ambiguous language in a law. The court will investigate the circumstances in which the law was passed, the remarks of legislators concerning the intent of the law, and so on. In other words, the context will be studied for light on the probable meaning of the words.

We shall examine the manner in which ambiguity occurs in the use of words, phrases, and sentences. Ambiguity, as we know, is a fruitful source of humor, and we shall note some of the entertaining aspects of its various forms. Humorists deliberately use the ambiguities of language in various kinds of jokes and "gags." Finally, we shall examine some of the "fallacies" of ambiguity. This aspect of ambiguity is of greatest interest to the logician. The failure to recognize ambiguity often results in misinterpretations of meanings and in erroneous inferences.

THE TYPES OF AMBIGUITY

1. SIMPLE AMBIGUITY

By *simple* ambiguity we shall mean the fact that single words or phrases may refer to more than one referent, even after we have examined their contexts. Verbal disagreements are based upon this type of ambiguity. Any statement containing a word which is ambiguous in its context exemplifies this vice: "The early Christians were communists." Since the word "communist" has more than one referent in this context, ambiguity exists. "Communist_1" means one who favors a system of social organization in which goods are held in common; "communist_2" means an advocate of "the dictatorship of the proletariat." Before we affirm or deny the truth of a statement we should find out what the writer means. Questions may also involve simple ambiguity, as in "Do you believe in God?" "God" means different things to different persons, and a yes-or-no answer is inappropriate until we learn what referent the questioner has in mind. Spinoza, for example, defined God as "everything which exists." Spinoza was a deeply religious man whose pantheistic philosophy was permeated with devotion to God. The Catholic Church, however, has condemned his pantheism as equivalent to atheism.

Simple ambiguity is closely related to "vagueness," but should be distinguished from it. An ambiguous word has several distinct referents; a vague word lacks precision and definiteness in its reference. Thus, the question, "Has there been any progress during the past 2,000 years?" involves the use of the vague word "progress." The reader spontaneously responds to such a question with his own questions: "Progress in what sense? In spiritual growth? In the advancement of the common man? In a material sense?" The word "progress" is vague rather than ambiguous, for in each case it means "advancement toward a definite goal," but the question does not specify the goal involved.

Vagueness, rather than ambiguity, will also be found in the following incident. In the summer of 1947 General Eisenhower was reported to have said that "the United States Army is a 'poor second' to that of Russia." Congressman Short asked, "In what sense?" In quantity? In quality? The United States Army has never been equal to the Russian army in size either in war or peace. Here too, "poor second" is not ambiguous, since it means "far behind the first," but its meaning is not precise.

Questions containing vague words cannot be answered without further clarification of their meaning. We should also note how careful thinking may result in the discovery that "clear" words are actually vague. Thus, the question "Is this building moving?" may appear to be clear. But we must ask: "In relation to which frame of reference?" In relation to the sun, this building is moving at a speed of eighteen miles per second. In relation to the earth, however, it is stationary.

Simple ambiguity has two forms, written and oral. The phonetic sound "teers" may stand for two different words: "tiers" and "tears." An amusing example of oral ambiguity based on this sound is found in the following:

> A reporter was describing a scene at the House of Commons to another reporter. "There, on the floor of the house, stood the Prime Minister speaking," he said, "back of him were the members of the Cabinet, in front of him sat the members of the Opposition, and in tiers around him sat the other members of the House."
>
> The second reporter was very young and very earnest. "Not really *tears*," he exclaimed. "Poor chaps!" (Albert Levi and Albert Frye, *Rational Belief*, Harcourt, Brace, 1941, p. 108.)

Simple ambiguity lies at the basis of much humor, especially in puns, as in Wordsworth's remark, "If I had a mind to, I could write like Shakespeare."

2. AMPHIBOLY

"I shall lose no time in reading your manuscript," the noted critic wrote to the aspiring young author. Should the author have been pleased with this message? Would the critic read his manuscript soon or never?

The critic's remark is an example of an amphibolous sentence. Its meaning is ambiguous though no *word* in the sentence is ambiguous. The ambiguity results from the way in which the words are put together in the sentence.

Amphiboly refers to the fact that the meaning of a sentence may be ambiguous, not because any of its words are ambiguous, but because the grammatical construction of the sentence permits several interpretations as to its meaning. The amphibolous sentence is capable of being understood in more than one sense. This may result in a failure in communication. A sentence combines words in order to express a thought. The referents have a certain relationship in the mind of the speaker. The grammatical construction of the sentence may fail to direct the hearer's mind to the relationship referred to by the speaker. The logician calls the reader's attention to these factors. The grammarian seeks to teach writers how to make themselves clear.

Vivid examples of amphiboly are found in humorous exaggerations of this fault. Thus, the following account was reportedly given by a newspaper reporter, with reference to the departure of the famous prewar dirigible from the Lakehurst airport: "The Graf Zeppelin was leaving the Lakehurst airport. Among the last to enter was Mrs. Smith, lone woman passenger. Slowly her huge nose was turned into the wind. Then, like some huge beast, she crawled along the grass . . ."

Grammarians have noted a type of error similar to amphiboly in the error called "the dangling participle," as in "Zooming along under her own power, Jane was fascinated by the spectacle of the glider before her." The participle "zooming" seems to refer to Jane. The words are unambiguous, but ambiguity results from the manner in which they are put together.

A famous historical source of amphiboly is found in the Delphic oracle, in ancient Greece. The oracle was certainly the most astute diplomat who ever lived and also the Nostradamus of its time, except that, unlike Nostradamus, the oracular pronouncements were right 100 per cent of the time. This success was due to the use of amphiboly. The oracle was consulted on the eve of great undertakings, in order to obtain its "inspired" predictions as to success or failure. The oracle always retained its reputation for infallibility because of the manner in which it made its pronouncements: "Apollo says that the Greeks the Persians shall subdue." Cyrus, the Persian King, sent messengers to the oracle for a prophecy concerning a projected war. The messengers were informed that "the King yet lives that Cyrus shall depose." The variant interpretations of these statements are obvious.

Amphibolous sentences of the type just noted may be called *completely* amphibolous in that the reader does not know how to interpret them correctly. In most cases, though two or more interpretations are possible, it will generally appear that one interpretation is more reasonable than the others, either from the context or the customs of speech. Thus, when a law court is presented with an amphibolous document, the "reasonable" interpretation will be applied. For example, a licensing agreement between the holder of a patent and the manufacturer provided that the manufacturer would pay the patentee "50¢ a unit for producing 5,000 units or less, and 30¢ a unit for all units of an output of over 5,000 units." The manufacturer claimed that when the output exceeded 5,000 units he was obligated to pay 30¢ per unit for *all* units produced. The court ruled that the agreement meant "50¢ for the first 5,000 units and 30¢ for all units in excess of 5,000." Otherwise the patentee would receive less royalties for a production of 6,000 units than he would receive for 4,000.

It is impossible to state whether a sentence is true or false until we understand its meaning. An amphibolous sentence must be given a definite interpretation before we can judge it as true or false. For example, a man says, "All women are not fickle." By this he may mean either that "some women are not fickle" or that "no women are fickle." If the speaker is available we should question him to determine what he meant. If he is not available, how shall we interpret the statement?

Note that the sentence takes the "All . . . are not . . ." formation. The logician adopts a rule of interpretation here, stating that all such statements shall be read as if they meant "*Not all* women are fickle" or "Some women are not fickle," unless he has clear evidence from the context or elsewhere that the speaker meant "No women are fickle." In the sentence "All human beings are not perfect" the speaker probably means "No human beings are perfect," but in "All Russians are not communists" he probably means "Some Russians are not communists."

Other types of amphiboly that require interpretation are such sentences as "All agree with me who are not ignorant of the facts."

This may mean either "All who agree with me are persons who are not ignorant of the facts" or it may mean "All who are not ignorant of the facts agree with me." The speaker may mean either one, but in the absence of further evidence, the grammarian will adopt the latter interpretation as the more likely one.

3. AMBIGUITY IN EMPHASIS

A unit of discourse may make different kinds of sense depending upon which of its parts we accent or emphasize. We should always seek to give writings the emphasis which the author intended them to have, but when the writing is ambiguous in this respect, the reader may be unable to determine where the proper emphasis lies. The full and complete meaning of a sentence may even require that we hear it spoken. Thus the invitation "I hope that you will come to dinner" may accent "I," "you," or "dinner" when it is spoken. When you leave, you say, "The dinner was very good." You may accent "dinner." It is for this reason that classroom instruction is superior to mere reading for most students, since the instructor gives oral emphasis to the most important words.

Ambiguity of emphasis occurs when a reader does not know which parts of a writing deserve chief emphasis. Troublesome cases of this sort occur when a writer presents somewhat conflicting points of view, as in Book V of Plato's *Republic*, concerning the nature and status of women in his ideal state. The reader will find "equalitarian" remarks such as, "The only difference between men and women consists in the fact that women bear and that men beget children," and "The differences between men and women do not justify different types of education for the two sexes. Women as well as men, should be trained to qualify as rulers of the state." But elsewhere Plato says that "women are inferior to men in all pursuits followed by each." Again, that "men and women possess the same qualities and differ only in their comparative strength and weakness." Does Plato believe that women are essentially the same as men, or does he hold that the weaker sex is the inferior sex? No one can answer this question with certainty.

When summaries are made of writings, ambiguity of emphasis may create similar difficulties. The summarizer should emphasize the most important elements. When excerpts and quotes are given they should be truly representative of the author's meaning. Summaries, however, open the door to many errors of carelessness or deliberate misinterpretation, to be discussed further under the "fallacies of ambiguity." Book reviewers are often accused of "not having read the whole book" when the author thinks that his position has been misinterpreted. The reviewer's misinterpretation, however, may be due in whole or in part to the author's failure to make his points clear. Or the author may state somewhat conflicting positions, as in the selections from Plato's *Republic.*

A different type of problem concerning emphasis or "accent" occurs in problems of punctuation. Literary scholars seek to interpret Shakespeare's meanings accurately, but there are variant readings of many of the plays. The Folio and the Second Quarto editions, the oldest sources, differ in many important respects. Consider the different possible readings of Hamlet's speech to Guildenstern (II, 2, 315). The Neilson and Hill version of the speech, based upon the Quarto version, is stated as follows:

> What a piece of work is a man! How noble in reason! How infinite in faculty! in form and moving! How express and admirable in action! How like an angel in apprehension! How like a god!

The Everyman's edition, following the Folio version, prints the lines as follows:

> What a piece of work is man! How noble in reason! how infinite in faculty! In form and moving how express and admirable! in action how like an angel! in apprehension how like a god!

4. THE AMBIGUITY OF SIGNIFICANCE

By this type we refer to statements whose semantical meaning may be clear, but whose factual significance is not. A statement may contain no ambiguous words, its sentence structure may convey an unambiguous meaning, and it may contain no ambiguities of emphasis. But its significance may be "ambiguous." As an illustration, consider the statement that there were 454 deaths due to traffic accidents in the United States during the Thanksgiving holiday weekend last year. The significance of such a statement is ambiguous in many respects. An isolated fact means something, of course. We all deplore the large number of deaths reported. But its full significance would require knowing whether the number was higher or lower than the number killed during the previous year's holiday weekend, and whether the figures for a non-holiday weekend are higher or lower.

It should be apparent that alertness to this kind of "ambiguity" is almost synonymous with the scientific attitude. Every statement whatsoever will have different kinds of significance depending upon its context or surrounding circumstances. It should also be obvious that this kind of "ambiguity" is not a genuinely semantical problem. We deal with it here only because it concerns a kind of uncertainty to which readers should be alerted, and because ambiguity in its broadest sense refers to doubtfulness or uncertainty.

Many other examples of such ambiguous isolated statements come to mind. "There are 3 million unemployed in the United States." Up or down since last month? In comparison with last year? What is the normal number of unemployed even in periods of "full employment"? Many statements are ambiguous to the uninitiated though not to the well-informed. "You have 5 billion germs in your mouth." What is the significance of that fact to a non-physiologist? In all the examples cited we find statements whose referential meaning is unambiguous, but whose significance is subject to varying interpretations.

The significance of many statements is ambiguous until we answer the questions: "Who said it?" and "under what circumstances?" In the fall of 1947 a United States Congressman said, "We will be at war with Russia in one month." Who was the speaker? A responsible or an irresponsible talker? When we listen to criticism of the foreign or domestic policies of the federal administration, we should of course judge these criticisms on their own merits, but we should also be concerned with the background of the critic. Is he a member of the opposition party? Is he blindly partisan? In the absence of coercive evidence we will give greater or lesser weight to criticism depending upon the stature of the critic. If the speaker is thought to be impartial, greater weight will be given to his criticism. In a law court great weight is given to statements which are called "admissions against one's own interest."

Another important distinction concerns the question as to whether a statement is being made in jest or in earnest. "Smile when you call me that" is a type of comment which emphasizes the ambiguity of significance. Persons whose humor is "dry" often make ironical or sarcastic statements that should not be interpreted literally.

An amusing example of the ambiguity of significance occurred when the late Heywood Broun, a wit among drama critics, once wrote that a certain actor, *J*, was "the world's worst 'actor.' " Broun was sued for libel and acquitted. Sometime later, *J* appeared in another play, and Broun, reporting the performance, wrote: "Mr. *J* was not up to his usual standard last night."

THE FALLACIES OF AMBIGUITY

Thus far we have noted four different types of ambiguity. When confronted with ambiguities we are not certain as to how we should interpret (1) single words or phrases, (2) the sense of a sentence, (3) the emphases or accents desired by the writer or speaker, or (4) the significance of a statement. The careful reader will be alert to the presence of these uncertainties. He will ask the appropriate questions in order to get information that will help to interpret the statements correctly.

A *fallacy* of ambiguity is a distortion of meaning or an error of reasoning based upon an incorrect interpretation of an ambiguous word or phrase. These errors of reasoning usually occur in *use* (by the writer). Distortions of meaning, on the other hand, occur in *interpretation* (by the reader).

Note that the presence of ambiguity is not, in itself, an "error." If a friend tells us that he shot a secretary (meaning a bird) on his last safari to Africa, we may or may not be aware of the ambiguity of the word "secretary." If we jump to the conclusion that he shot a beautiful female of the human species, this would be an error resulting from our faulty interpretation of the ambiguous word. We shall now examine two major fallacies arising from the various types of ambiguity: equivocation and accent.

1. EQUIVOCATION

The fallacy of equivocation is an error of use, rather than of interpretation, i.e., it is committed by writers and speakers rather than readers and listeners. It occurs when a writer (or speaker) uses an ambiguous word (or root or phrase) in more than one sense in a given unit of discourse, such equivocal use resulting in an unjustified inference. Some examples: A speaker says: "I am sure that communists really believe in God. It is generally agreed that for its followers communism is a religion, and religious people believe in God." The term "religion" is used in two different senses. Communism is a religion in the sense that its followers show an ardent devotion and fidelity to its tenets, but it is not a religion in the traditional sense of "conviction of the existence of a Supreme Being." The failure to distinguish these meanings resulted in an unjustified inference.

Our second example involves the ambiguous term "law." In its legal sense law means a rule regulating human conduct established by an appropriate governing body. In science, a law refers to the uniform behavior of natural events, i.e., to an order or pattern in nature that is regarded as unvarying under the given conditions. An example is the law of gravitation. It is impossible to "violate" such a law, nor can it have exceptions, for if there is an exception the behavior is not uniform and there is no law. A convenient way of distinguishing the two senses of law is to say that a law of nature is a *description* (of nature); a legal or civil law is a *prescription,* a command. Now suppose one were to argue as follows:

Science has discovered many laws of nature. This is proof that there is a God, for a law implies the existence of a lawgiver, and God is the great Lawgiver of the universe.

The term "law" is used equivocally in this argument. Law in the sense of an order or command implies the existence of a lawgiver or commander, but law in the sense of a description does not.

Equivocation may of course be used deliberately for the purposes of wit and humor. "Your argument is sound, nothing but sound." Thus Benjamin Franklin's pun, "If we don't hang together, we'll hang separately." Or the absurd syllogism, "Some dogs have shaggy ears. My dog has shaggy ears. Therefore, my dog is *some* dog."

Note that equivocation can occur only if the ambiguous term is used at least twice in the same unit of discourse. When an ambiguous word is used only once, this is simple ambiguity. It goes without saying that equivocation should be avoided in our discussions. A word should be used in the same sense throughout a unit of discourse. If we do not use our words consistently there can be no communication or reasoning.

2. ACCENT

The fallacy of "accent" is an error which results from giving an obviously improper accent or emphasis to the words in a sentence or to the ideas in a unit of discourse.

Such improper accenting or distortion of meaning may be done deliberately, in order to deceive, but usually occurs where there is ambiguity of emphasis. Misinterpretations may then occur because of careless writing or careless interpretation. We shall note three typical ways in which the fallacy occurs:

a. The incorrect emphasis of the words in a sentence

The commandment says, "Thou shalt not bear false witness against thy neighbor."

If one were to stress the word "neighbor," implying that it is permissible to bear false witness against those who are not our neighbors, this would be an obvious misinterpretation.

b. The incorrect interpretation of amphibolous sentences

If one were to interpret the example given earlier (p. 477) as meaning that *Jane* was zooming along under her own power, the amphibolous sentence would be misinterpreted.

c. Incorrect summaries

When a summary is made of an author's statements, it should represent his most important thoughts. When a unit of discourse is improperly summarized, the fault may lie, of course, with the author, whose meaning was not clear. On the other hand, the summarizer may distort the author's meaning either carelessly or with the intent to deceive. We shall now examine some of the forms in which this type of accent occurs.

The reader should always be on the alert when excerpts from a writing are presented. Dishonest examples of "excerpt-lifting" abound. A dramatic critic writes that he "liked all of the play except the lines, the acting, and the scenery." He is quoted as having said that "he liked all of it." Ironical remarks are open to this kind of misinterpretation. A schoolteacher tells her civics class that "communism is the best type of government if you care nothing for your liberty or your material welfare." She is quoted as having said that "communism is the best type of government." Unwitting errors of the same sort occur when a student fails to distinguish between a lecturer's own views and those which he quotes, or even between a speaker's own views and those which he attacks.

The careful thinker will always be on his guard against quotations taken out of their context and he will ask, "Let's have the whole of that quotation." This does not mean that quotations are improper, but only that quotations should be fair and accurate representations of the meaning of the author.

Newspaper headlines purportedly summarize the news, but may distort the meaning by improper emphasis. The "headline reader" is thereby misled. "Let me write the headlines," an editor once said, "and I care not who writes the news." Advertisements may achieve similar results by the use of large case type in bold letters. The "come-on" elements will be presented in large letters, and the less attractive ones will be minimized by the use of small type. A famous example is one that was used by Barnum to advertise the first Canadian concert of the Belgian violinist, Ysaye. It read,

THEIR EXCELLENCIES,
THE PRINCE AND PRINCESS OF BELGIUM
have been asked whether they
WILL ATTEND THE CONCERT OF YSAYE,
WORLD'S GREATEST VIOLINIST

A form of summary called "special pleading" or "stacking the cards" is perhaps of greatest importance in this connection. Speakers emphasize only those elements in a report which suit their purposes and omit the rest. This may be permissible practice for debaters and lawyers who seek to win a case, but it is not in the spirit of the seeker after truth. Thus, in the days when India was struggling for its independence, rioting was frequent. A pro-Indian spokesman on a radio panel was denouncing the British for their callous disregard of elementary decency and reported an incident in the House of Commons in which the Conservative members of parliament "stood up and cheered" when informed that the British Army in India had killed 500 Indians. His audience was profoundly shocked by this report. But another speaker on the same program then read from the full Parliamentary report of the incident. This report stated that many British soldiers had been killed during the rioting, that about 500 Indians had been killed, and the report ended with the Prime Minister's declaration that the government intended to preserve law and order at all costs. (Cheers from Conservative benches.)

Accent, of course, is sometimes a fruitful source of humor when the incorrect interpretation of accent or emphasis is deliberate. Thus, Humpty-Dumpty says to Alice: "They gave it me—for an unbirthday present." "I beg your pardon?" Alice said with a puzzled air. "I'm not offended," said Humpty-Dumpty.

Another: "Would you—be good enough"—Alice panted out, after running a little farther, "to stop a minute—just to get one's breath again?" "I'm *good* enough," the King said, "only I'm not strong enough. You see, a minute goes by so fearfully quick. You might as well try to catch a bandersnatch!"

SUGGESTED ASSIGNMENTS

1. The following items may be considered examples of simple ambiguity, although the line between simple ambiguity and amphiboly is sometimes hard to distinguish. Revise each one so that it will be clear in writing.
   a. Paul beat the man around the corner.
   b. How will he find his dog when he returns?
   c. Davidson ordered another drink and sat tight.
   d. At 10 a.m. today, the anchor will be carried out into Lake Ontario aboard a naval craft and consigned to the waters. The three chaplains will accompany it.
   e. I don't know what kind of car you have to sell.
   f. Here is the box you used to pack your books in years ago.
   g. In their old age they lived in a poor house.
   h. Rev. Keith Hammond was congratulated on being able to get his parish plastered. Soon it will be the finest social center in Tujunga-Sunland.
   i. Our business is growing (nursery advertisement).
   j. Persons who find that they cannot use their seats at any performance are requested to notify the committee.
   k. Your answers to the questions were all right.
   l. Mary didn't care for the pigeons.
   m. Use more realistic details.
   n. Nothing is too good for you.
   o. He rented the house for $80.00 a month.
   p. The local weather bureaus are not permitted to dispute the predictions of the central bureau, regardless of whether they are right or not.
2. The *New Yorker* magazine often prints short news items which contain amusing ambiguities. Here are a few. Point out how the ambiguities could have been avoided.

   a. In the evening he will speak on "How to Keep Sane in the First Methodist Church under the direction of Rev. David Young."

   b. Headline: FRENCH DAM SITE BETTER OFF WITH U. S. AID FUNDS

   c. Peanut-Butter Grilled Corn

   Husk fresh corn; spread ears lightly with peanut butter. Wrap each ear with bacon slice; fasten with toothpick. Place on grill; grill over glowing coals, turning, until done—about ten minutes. Or, let everyone grill his own ears, using long skewers to do so.

d. Whatever her thoughts, they were interrupted as the hotel lobby door swung open and a young woman carrying her baby and her husband entered.

3. Revise the following examples of amphiboly:
   a. Newspapers always print the bad things that teenagers do on the front page.
   b. Everything $.50 (Sign on table with articles for sale).
   c. . . . Win Bruner, wife of the doctor, who grew up in Rochester.
   d. I like Joe as well as George.
   e. Zola was able to describe the characters, the places they went, and the things they did very well.
   f. I spent most of the afternoon talking about the books I had read with the librarian.
   g. This easy, longer waist line . . . lets you step into the fashion light looking and feeling elegantly relaxed.
   h. What we believe profoundly influences our ability to listen fairly to any subject.
   i. There is a theater located in the business district which is crowded every night.
   j. All the conditions were not bad.
   k. The club will be open to members only from Monday to Thursday.
   l. Jigger was taken to a small animal hospital.
   m. Give me a piece of fresh apple pie.
4. An informative and interesting book on the difficulties of framing unambiguous and serviceable questions is Stanley L. Payne's *The Art of Asking Questions*. Mr. Stanley writes from the point of view of one who prepares public-opinion polls. Read Chapter 10, pages 158-176, and report to the class on simple words that produce ambiguity.
5. Such words as prepositions, conjunctions, and articles can be ambiguous. Margaret Bryant has written a book on the part that these words play in legal decisions. It is called *English in the Law Courts*. Look up the cases on pages 101-105 involving the preposition *between* and report how the ambiguity of this word has been legally resolved.
6. A list of twenty grammatical situations that are open to amphiboly is given in an article entitled *Some Structural Ambiguities* in the *English Journal*, November, 1958, pages 479-486. Write one example for each situation listed and bring the examples to class for discussion and revision.
7. Go to the library, choose a newspaper at random, read all the headlines, copy down any ambiguous headlines that you find, and bring them to class for discussion.

FURTHER READINGS

1. Black, Max. *Critical Thinking*. Englewood Cliffs, New Jersey: Prentice-Hall, Inc., 1952. On ambiguity, see pp. 183-202.
2. Castell, Alburey. *A College Logic*. New York: The Macmillan Company, 1935. On analogy, see pp. 58-66.
3. Frye, Albert M. and Albert W. Levi. *Rational Belief*. New York: Harcourt, Brace & World, Inc., 1941. On ambiguity, see pp. 103-129.
4. Hayakawa, S. I. *Language in Thought and Action*. New York: Harcourt, Brace & World, Inc., 1949. On either-or, see pp. 221-247.
5. Mander, A. E. *Logic for the Millions*. New York: Philosophical Library, Inc., 1947. On generalization, see Chapter 5; on evidence, Ch. 3 and 4; on *post-hoc*, pp. 130-133.
6. Stebbing, L. Susan. *Thinking to Some Purpose*. Baltimore: Penguin Books, Inc., 1939. On generalization, see pp. 205-236; on analogy, pp. 106-126.
7. Thouless, Robert H. *How to Think Straight*. New York: Simon and Schuster, Inc., 1950. On generalization, see pp. 20-30; on analogy, pp. 103-118; on ambiguity and vagueness, pp. 132-146.

Index to Authors and Titles

INDEX TO AUTHORS AND TITLES